Contributors

DIETER BRUNNSCHWEILER
Michigan State University

JOHN F. DAVIS
University of London

W. GORDON EAST
University of London

ERIC FISCHER
George Washington University

F. KENNETH HARE
McGill University

GEORGE W. HOFFMAN
University of Texas

VINCENT H. MALMSTRÖM
Middlebury College

THEODORE SHABAD
The New York Times

GUIDO G. WEIGEND
Rutgers University

A GEOGRAPHY

of

EUROPE

Including Asiatic U.S.S.R.

Edited by

GEORGE W. HOFFMAN

DEPARTMENT OF GEOGRAPHY
UNIVERSITY OF TEXAS

SECOND EDITION

THE RONALD PRESS COMPANY · NEW YORK

Library of Congress Catalog Card Number: 61–7732
PRINTED IN THE UNITED STATES OF AMERICA

Preface

This book presents an authoritative description of the physical and cultural landscape characteristic of each of Europe's major regions. Organized around seven basic regions, its emphasis is on economic and political geography within the physical and historical context of each major area.

The organization of the book is the outgrowth of the teaching experience of the authors and those who have used the first edition. In the Introduction the reader is given an idea of what the term "Europe" implies, and the cogent reasons for including in this edition all of Turkey and the Asiatic U.S.S.R. Chapters 1 and 2 provide an essential grounding in the continent's complex physical, biogeographical, and historical background.

The presentation of an integrated picture of the European scene requires the use of subdivisions derived from political boundaries, from the boundaries of recognized natural regions, and from the boundaries of broad cultural areas. All are used by the specialists who have contributed the seven regional chapters. The order of their chapters follows the logic of beginning with the British Isles, in many ways peripheral to the rest of Europe, and of closing with the Soviet Union, which is also peripheral to the rest of the continent.

The summary chapter gives the reader an opportunity to assess the importance of the various regional problems and the efforts to solve some of these problems by cooperation between Europe's many nations. Even more important, the chapter brings into perspective both the great struggle of Western Europe to retain its place in the world's economy and the rapid economic development of Eastern Europe and the Soviet Union.

This second edition has been extensively revised, resulting essentially in a new book. To insure the closest possible integration and to prevent the end product from becoming a collection of individual essays, the complete manuscript has been critically reviewed by each contributor. The chapters on Physical and Biogeographical

Background, Western Europe, Eastern Europe (East Central Europe in the first edition), the Soviet Union, and Europe's Place in the World (formerly Europe in the World's Economy) have been completely rewritten, most of them by new authors. The remaining chapters have been carefully reworked, and several were reorganized.

The text of each chapter is closely integrated with its maps, nearly all of them especially prepared for this book. The illustrations have also been carefully revised for this edition, and the latest available data have been brought into the statistical tables in the Appendix.

Place names in the text and on the maps generally conform to the accepted usage which is found in English-language atlases and the National Geographic maps. The most important publications are listed at the end of every chapter. References considered essential by each coauthor have been marked with asterisks. Suggested readings in foreign languages may provide a stimulus for those students with language proficiency.

To each of his associates go the Editor's thanks for his scholarly contribution, for his reading of the other chapters, for the suggestions he made concerning them, and for his patience. Many professional colleagues have also reviewed one or more chapters, and many users of the first edition have been kind enough to pass on specific suggestions. Grateful acknowledgment is made of the invaluable help received from various government agencies in the United States and in Europe, from the embassies of nearly every European nation, and from the United Nations. Mr. Vaughn Gray has again been responsible for the cartography. Lastly, the Editor makes public acknowledgment to his wife, Viola, for her invaluable help during the many months of manuscript preparation.

GEORGE W. HOFFMAN

Austin, Texas
  February, 1961

Contents

APPENDIX

Maps

EUROPE'S PLACE IN THE WORLD

A GEOGRAPHY

of

EUROPE

Introduction

Europe—A Geographical Expression

It is by no means self-evident why Europe has so long been recognized as a continent in its own right, since in physical geography it might appear as merely a large peninsular extension of Asia, which is four times its size. The Greek historian Herodotus could not see why his contemporaries of the fifth century B.C. distinguished three continents—Europa, Asia, and Libya—in what was to him one continuous land area. The eminent German scientist Alexander von Humboldt regarded Europe as part of one land mass (*Erdteil*) which he called Eurasia. Hugo Hassinger in Germany and Sir Halford Mackinder in Britain both emphasized the idea of a single land mass, which the latter called the World-Island—this was Europe, together with Asia and Africa. It is thus of some interest to inquire how a small part of Eurasia came to be regarded as a separate continent. It is further desirable to consider just what are the limits of Europe. This is indeed necessary if confusion is to be avoided, since four or more Europes [1] are presently known and referred to in the writings of geographers, statesmen, journalists, and others.

THE IDEA OF EUROPE AS A CONTINENT

The concept of Europe as a separate continent derives from the ancient Greeks of the fifth century B.C., who viewed the world they knew as tripartite. Although the Pythagoreans, a century earlier, rightly imagined that the world was a sphere, the idea long persisted

[1] Thus there are (1) the Europe which stretches eastward to the Ural Mountains, (2) the Europe which lies west of the Iron Curtain, (3) the Europe made up of the 18 countries which are members of the Organization for European Economic Co-operation, and (4) Little Europe—the six countries of the European Iron and Steel Community and of the Common Market. See Chapter 10.

3

of the earth as a disk encircled by the ocean and divided into three continents. It was thus represented in the so-called T/O maps (Fig. 1) of the Middle Ages. In such maps, Europe and Libya each made up a quarter of the world and were marked off from the remaining

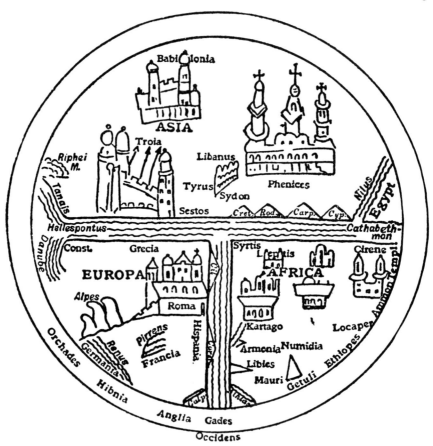

Fig. 1. A medieval T/O map of the world. The T-shaped Mediterranean Sea divides the world into one half (occupied by Asia) and two quarters (one of which is Europe and the other Africa). The representation of the three continents, the Mediterranean, and the encircling ocean is, of course, diagrammatic. Cadiz ("Gades") lies at the approach to the Mediterranean from the Atlantic. The Nile is shown entering the Mediterranean, and the Don ("Tanais") and the Danube are shown flowing into the Dardanelles ("Hellespontus").

half, Asia, by the Mediterranean Sea. The word "Europe" was long thought to derive from the Semitic word *erib* and thus to mean "the land of the sunset," or of the west. It was contrasted with "Asia," which lay beyond the Aegean and Mediterranean seas, and which meant "the land of the sunrise," or of the east. More recently a Greek derivation of Europe has been advanced.[2] This suggests that Europe means broad-faced. Such a term may fittingly have been applied by the classical Greeks to the territories of greater scale which lay to the north of their insular and peninsular homelands in and around the Aegean Sea.

Knowledge of the geography of Europe was inevitably very sketchy in the days of classical Greece. The Greeks were above all seamen, as Plato (fourth century B.C.) put it, "living round the sea like ants or frogs round a pool."[3] Herodotus, for example, who was well traveled and otherwise well informed, knew of the Black and Azov seas, of at least the lower courses of the great rivers Danube, Dnieper, and Don, something of the interior of the Southeastern Peninsula, and more of the Mediterranean coastlands. The interior of Europe was largely shut off from the Mediterranean lands by mountains and forests and by the extensive grass steppe of southern Russia, where already pastoralists roamed. The colder winters of Europe north of the Mediterranean Sea, which Greek writers exaggerated, were an added deterrent. Not much was known about the remote west and north of Europe— the British Isles and Scandinavia—before the remarkable voyages of Pytheas of Massilia (Marseille) around 300 B.C. It was the Romans, themselves primarily landsmen, who, in the course of their conquests, explored and opened up not only Britain but also large inner parts of the continent, up to and beyond the Rhine and Danube rivers. Even as late as the second century A.D. Ptolemy depicted on his famous world map the larger Scandinavian peninsula (i.e., Norway and Sweden) as an island (Fig. 2).

Thus vaguely conceived, Europe was only an idea for the learned few, philosophers, writers, and map makers. The Jews adopted the pagan Greek concept of the tripartite world, of which Europe was allegedly colonized by the descendants of Japheth, son of Noah. Roman trade penetrated beyond the imperial frontiers, as coin finds show, as far east as the river Neman and as far north as southern Sweden.[4] For the Romans, however, Europe had less significance than the sharply contrasted world around them which was either Roman and thus civilized, or extra-Roman and thus barbarian. During the medieval period which followed, Europe was conceived of not

[2] Denys Hay, *Europe: The Emergence of an Idea* (Edinburgh: The University Press, 1957), p. 1.
[3] E. H. Warmington, *Greek Geography* (London & Toronto: J. M. Dent & Sons, Ltd., 1934), p. 22. This work provides, with a commentary, numerous translated extracts from ancient Greek texts.
[4] See Sir R. E. M. Wheeler, *Rome Beyond the Imperial Frontiers* (London: G. Bell & Sons, Ltd., 1954).

as part of the surface of a spherical world (as Ptolemy had shown) but as part of a disk-shaped surface surrounded by ocean. The special cartographic advance made in the later Middle Ages was the so-called portolan charts, which sketched the seas and coasts of Europe with some precision. Europeans were, however, more concerned by then with the concept of Christendom than with that of Europe which formed only a part of this broader concept. The view of Europe as

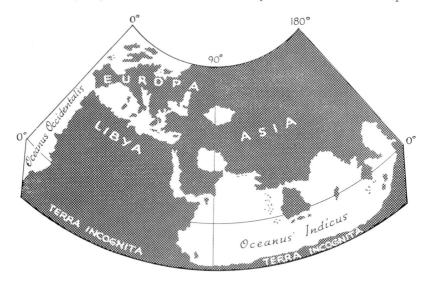

Fig. 2. The world according to Ptolemy.

a distinct territorial unit was underlined, however, when Christian peoples there found themselves hemmed in to the east and to the south by non-Christian intruders. These were, in the south, Moors and others who had been won to Islam by the Arab conquests; in eastern Europe the Mongols of the Golden Horde, Shamans at first and Moslems only later (after *ca.* 1300); and in Asia Minor the Moslem Seljuk Turks. The crusading wars, to which went warriors from many countries of Europe to fight Moslems in the Holy Land, also lent some distinctness to the idea of Europe as a Christian citadel. It thus acquired a certain emotive significance in addition to its coldly territorial connotation.

There was a time, then, when the term Europe symbolized a loose cultural unit framed by more or less effective physical barriers. Before the great voyages of discovery which opened up the whole world in modern times, Europe was shut off by the Arctic and Atlantic oceans and by the deserts of northern Africa and Arabia. To the east where the continent broadens, forest and marsh, then more widespread than now, discouraged human settlement, while the steppe zone, which extends from eastern Hungary across the Ukraine and into Asia, invited continually the advance of enemies—nomadic horsemen.

It would be easy to exaggerate the degree of cultural unity achieved by medieval Christendom, for clearly race, language, religion, economy, and history divided it in many ways. Yet the Europe of today cannot claim the community of interest which was then fostered by a widely current language—Latin, known at least by the educated. As sundering forces emerged—the Reformation, nationalism, Fascism, and Communism—the political and ideological community of Europe disintegrated. The last hundred years or so, although they witnessed in Europe the political unification of both Italy and the German *Reich*, witnessed also the dissolution of old empires and a decline in the concept of Europe's underlying unity (see Chapter 10). Europe has become, more so than in the past, a geographical expression.

Viewed from the outside, however, Europe may appear to have more significance than when viewed from within. We are all aware that in world affairs Europe, and in particular western Europe, has played an outstanding part in the creation of Western civilization— by geographical discoveries, overseas colonization and economic development, and widely ranging achievements in the fields of science, technology, and the arts. In this sense Europe stands distinctly in the world, even though the contributions from the several parts of the continent are different and unequal. After all, Europe, like Asia, is an old continent. It has exploited its opportunities and, for a long time, largely dominated the world. But its status is changing as other lands, notably the United States and the Soviet Union, the latter in part European, have become settled, developed, and strong.

THE LIMITS OF EUROPE

Europe, then, clearly does not now signify either a cultural or, still less, a political entity. What reality it possesses is geographical, and, this being so, we may well ask what its limits are. Curiously perhaps, in view of its age-long settlement, Europe's limits appear always to have been, as they remain, partially uncertain. It has been wisely argued, for example, that Europe should include geographically those marginal lands of North Africa and the eastern Mediterranean Basin which share a common physical (including climatic) environment. These lands were for a long time politically as well as economically oriented toward Europe. Even the western limit of Europe raises problems. "Europe's domain," wrote the distinguished British Foreign Minister George Canning,[5] "extends to the shores of the Atlantic,

---

[5] H. W. V. Temperley, *The Foreign Policy of Canning* (London: G. Bell & Sons, Ltd., 1925), p. 471.

England's begins there." This view reminds us that, although the United Kingdom is geographically part of Europe, it is also the senior partner of a world-wide commonwealth. Iceland stands even further detached from continental Europe but, because of its long cultural links with Scandinavia, is rightly regarded as European. Greenland, in contrast, is now usually reckoned part of North America, with which it has increasing contacts, although historically and culturally it looks to Denmark, of which it is in fact a part.

On its eastern flank the limits of Europe are least defined, except where the waters of the Dardanelles, Sea of Marmara, and Bosporus divide the Southeastern Peninsula from Asia Minor. Farther north, beyond the Black Sea, a variety of limits have been proposed at different times to divide what the Western world has chosen arbitrarily to distinguish as Europe and Asia. The limit given by Herodotus was the lower course of the river Phasis, now called the Rion, which descends from the Caucasus Mountains to enter the Black Sea north of Batumi. For this limit the classical Greeks later substituted that of the river Don and the Azov Sea, and this limit long persisted. The Don, in crossing first the wooded steppe and then the grass steppe in its southward course, bisects the Great Russian Lowland, so that this large physical unit lay both inside and outside Europe as it was first conceived. The Russian state, when it emerged, thus also lay astride the continental divide. It has always stood both inside and outside Europe. Dostoevski held the view that Russia should form a unit not in Europe but in face of Europe.[6]

Figure 3 shows some of the limits assigned to Europe in the east. In modern times the tendency has been to shift these to the east of the Don but not directly to the east of the Sea of Azov. Use has been made of visible geographic features—the Manych Depression, the middle Volga, the Kama and Ural rivers, and, lastly, a line at the eastern foot of the Ural Mountains. Somewhat in contrast to these various proposed lines is another, well to the west and related to the obstacle (formerly very considerable) of the Pripet Marshes which now lie in the Belorussian S.S.R. (Fig. 2–1). The French geographer Jacques Ancel, in suggesting this as the eastern limit of the continent, argued that east of these marshes reigned the climate, broadly uniform landscapes, and immensities of Asia. For H. J. Mackinder,[7] writing in 1918, the "real" or "populous" Europe, before this century at least, extended eastward to a straight line drawn from Petrograd (now

[6] Cited by A. Mousset, *Le Monde Slave* (Paris: Société d'Éditions Françaises et Internationales, 1946), p. 42.

[7] H. J. Mackinder, *Democratic Ideals and Reality* (New York: Henry Holt & Co., 1919), pp. 144–145. Since Mackinder wrote, much settlement and economic development have taken place east of this line, notably in the Ural area.

Leningrad) to Kazan, and then to the curved line from Kazan along the Volga and Don rivers to the Black Sea. Beyond these limits, he wrote, began "the vacancies of Central Asia." In short, geographers

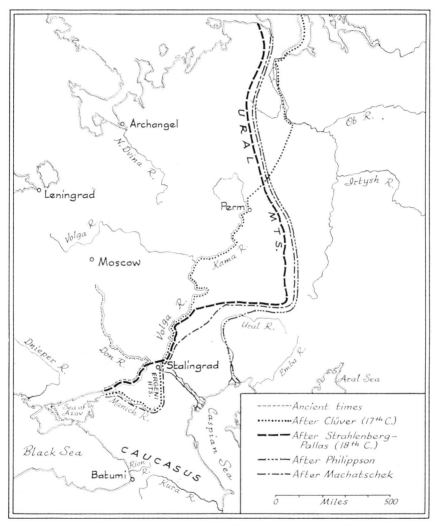

Fig. 3. Eastern limits of Europe (data from E. von Seydlitz).

have come to accept a conventional eastern limit of Europe, such as that used by the German geographer Machatschek. This limit pays no attention to the internal or external boundaries of the U.S.S.R.

In this book no rigid and limiting definition of Europe has been assumed. Indeed, its scope has been enlarged to include the two countries—the U.S.S.R. and Turkey—whose territories lie both within and outside Europe.

The question of limits apart—and such a discussion could well become profitless—the reality of Europe remains. While it is important that we should know what we mean when we read or talk about Europe, we should have no doubt that Europe's existence as a continent is a valid fact. It is a permanent regional division of the habitable world, which, together with the Far East, the Indian sub-continent, and northeastern North America, has proved to be one of the four outstandingly favored settlement areas of the world. Enclosed between the Arctic Ocean and the great North African deserts, between the Atlantic Ocean and the steppes and forests of the Great Russian Lowland, Europe presented a relatively small peninsular framework, accessible at many points from the Mediterranean Basin where civilized life developed by a process of diffusion from the riverine lands of Egypt and southwest Asia.

While the richly variegated physical background and historical development of Europe are themes of the two succeeding chapters of this book, it will help to allude here, in general terms, to two of Europe's special characteristics, namely, its geographical position and its main divisions.

THE GEOGRAPHICAL POSITION OF EUROPE

The geographical position of Europe can be conceived of in two distinct ways—as absolute and as relative. What is striking about the absolute position of Europe, as determined by the latitudes and longitudes within which it lies, is first its centrality in the Northern Hemisphere and second the absence of hot and cold desert. Since the Northern Hemisphere contains the greater part of the earth's land surface and also those parts which have been longest developed, Europe's position is a strikingly good one for world-wide contacts by sea and by air. In the small proportion of its area which is economically useless because of extremes of cold or heat, it compares favorably with both North America and the Asiatic U.S.S.R., which include the same latitudes as Europe but extend farther both to the north and to the south.

Europe's relative position, in contrast, is not stable and has greatly improved in the course of world history. In prehistory Europe occupied a remote and terminal position in the world, aloof from the cradle areas of civilized life, yet accessible enough to receive civilizing currents from them, especially by sea. Although the Mediterranean-Red Sea waterway, and other routes by land, gave Mediterranean

Europe slender links with the populous and civilized lands of monsoon Asia from Greco-Roman times onward, the Atlantic—the "green sea of darkness," as the Arabs called it—was impassable, and western and northern Europe in particular occupied only marginal locations in the known world. This position changed radically when the Atlantic's sea routes to the Americas and to southern Asia were opened up in the late fifteenth century and improved still further as the newly discovered American lands and the later-discovered Australasian lands were colonized and developed. Thus Europe, especially those parts which had oceanic fronts, enjoyed greater opportunities, which it in fact exploited to conquer and settle overseas and to play the leading part in world commerce and the economic development of the other continents. In this last respect western Europe, and Britain in particular, took the lead in that expansion of manufactures associated with the Industrial Revolution. This was marked by the effective use of available resources of coal and other minerals, of capital, of transport facilities—especially by water, and not least of an inventive and skilled labor force. Thus as new lands grew in economic and demographic strength, Europe came to stand less and less on the edge of the oecumene but nearer its center: the term "Midland Ocean" for the North Atlantic in part expresses this idea. Moreover, in this age of air navigation, even the formerly forbidding Arctic flank of Europe is now crossed by convenient polar air routes to North America and monsoon Asia.

THE MAJOR GEOGRAPHICAL DIVISIONS OF EUROPE

Geographers are continually at pains to divide Europe into significant parts, the better to understand the diversity of its human environments, large and small. The task of dividing it into major regions, suited to discussion in this book, is a task of some difficulty. Various criteria may be employed, and each will produce a different set of regions. It is clear that, if divisions are made according to each of the environmental factors in turn, the continent will be divided into many different units which will little correspond. A map of Europe's major structural units or of its major climatic types will show little correspondence with those of either linguistic or political divisions. Accordingly, large-scale geographical units are selected for study in this book, broadly on ground of their relative positions (Fig. 4). We distinguish Western Europe,[8] Northern Europe, Southern Europe, Eastern Europe, and, beyond this, the U.S.S.R., which strides from the confines of Europe across Asia to the Pacific. To these is

[8] The British Isles, part of Western Europe, are separately discussed in Chapter 3.

Fig. 4. The major geographical divisions of Europe, as presented in this book.

added Central Europe, the extent and implications of which have given rise to much discussion.[9] It must suffice to note that Central Europe comprises here Germany, Austria, and Switzerland—countries which must find their place in any geographical interpretation of Central Europe. It will be noted that each of these major divisions is a group of states. This needs little justification in view of the importance of the political factor in the geography of Europe. Indeed, its political organization gives expression to the main national, linguistic, and other cultural aspects of the human geography. It will be evident that any scheme of division such as that adopted here can be criticized in detail. While, for example, we have assigned Norway to Northern Europe and Portugal to Southern Europe, both occupy a western location and might be regarded also as parts of Western Europe. So also may Denmark be regarded geographically not only as part of Northern Europe but also as part of Central Europe. The attentive reader may consider such points as he reads. But divide Europe we must in our efforts to describe and account for the remarkable variety of its physical and human geography, mindful too of the outstanding role of this small but populous continent as the homeland of both Western civilization and Communism.

[9] See, for example, K. A. Sinnhuber, "Central Europe–Mitteleuropa–Europe Centrale: An Analysis of a Geographical Term," *Transactions and Papers, The Institute of British Geographers* 20 (1954): 15–39.

1

The Physical and Biogeographical Background

The main purpose of this chapter is to introduce the reader to the European landscape from the standpoint of physical geography. Even though it is recognized that the natural environment is not a set of factors which forces man into a particular type of occupancy in any particular area, its influence upon human pursuits has played and still plays a role hardly to be underestimated. It is, therefore, necessary to establish a solid framework of Europe's physical geography in order to evaluate the impact of these physical factors upon human activities. It is emphasized, however, that the approach in this chapter is strictly systematic in the sense that each physical and biogeographical element is discussed per se and not as a possible environmental factor in the human drama. This is left almost entirely to the discussions in the individual regional chapters, where more space is provided for analysis of the interplay between physical and cultural factors.

It should be stated clearly that the focus is always on Europe as a whole. We are here using a reducing glass to recognize the basic physical patterns of Europe, thereby intentionally refraining from going into details within individual areas. If regions of physical homogeneity, such as physiographic or climatic regions, are described and delimited, they are mainly intended to serve as a kind of physical framework for the ensuing regional discussions. This will enable the student to see the relationship of any region to its surroundings and to realize the magnitude of areal variations of the individual physical factors of Europe.

An attempt has been made to put equal weight on both descriptive and genetic analysis of the physical landscape. Although the genetic treatment of landforms and climate might handicap students with limited training in physical geography, it should lead all to an understanding, rather than just a superficial knowledge, of the European landscape.

THE RELIEF OF EUROPE

Horizontal Surface Configuration

General Characteristics. One of the outstanding characteristics of the map of Europe is the interpenetration of land and sea. Strabo [1] spoke very aptly of the "very irregular shape" of Europe. We should not overlook, however, that this description applies only to the western half of Europe. East of the Finnish shore of the Baltic Sea and the Vistula-Prut line, the character of the land mass is quite different. We have to differentiate clearly between a peninsular and insular Europe west of the line mentioned, and a massive and compact one east of it. If we want to speak of a "European peninsula," as has frequently been done, it would begin at this line from which, in a westward direction, the width of the land mass decreases more or less continuously, the land opens toward the Atlantic, and the peninsular and insular coastal configuration becomes increasingly evident. The western Soviet Union, in contrast, forms an unarticulated body, decidedly different in its compactness, its landlockedness, and its openness toward the continental interior.

The degree of horizontal articulation of a continent can be expressed by several methods. If we compare the area of the main body of a land mass with that of its peninsular and insular members, a relatively good index of its compactness or brokenness can be obtained. Europe is easily the least compact of the earth's land masses. More than one-third of Europe consists of peninsulas and islands.

Another good measure is the mean distance from the coast.[2] In Europe the mean distance is 210 miles with 62 per cent of the land below and 38 per cent above this value. The small size of Europe would, of course, give a relatively small figure for mean coastal distance, but in comparison with Australia, the only continent smaller than Europe (by some 900,000 square miles), a considerably higher proportion of Europe can be considered as coastal fringe land.

[1] Loeb Classical Library, *The Geography of Strabo* (New York: Putnam's Sons, 1917), Vol. II, p. 467.

[2] The mean distance from the coast is obtained by drawing zones of equal distance from the sea, computing the sum of the products of area and coastal distance of each zone, and dividing it by the total area of all zones.

	Total Area (million square miles)	Area of Islands and Peninsulas (million square miles)	Area of Islands and Peninsulas (per cent of total area)
Europe	3.85	1.33	34.6
North America	8.92	2.33	25.5
Asia	17.06	4.11	24.0
Australia	2.97	0.66	22.0
Africa	11.51	0.24	2.1
South America	6.86	0.71	1.1

The Coast of Europe. A closer examination of the coastal configuration reveals that the ground plan of Europe is determined to a great extent by the main structural units of the land mass. Size, shape, and relief of the coastal areas; the type of shore lines; and the submarine topography, all reflect the complex geological history of the land. A tripartition with respect to major coastal types clearly manifests itself. There are wide expanses of flatland along many coastal stretches, particularly along the Atlantic and Baltic shores of mainland northwestern Europe and north of the Black Sea. Offshore, the coastal lowland continues onto a broad submarine platform, the continental shelf (Fig. 1–4). Shallow seas, rarely more than 600 feet deep, and often less than 100 feet deep, have inundated this presently invisible but inherent part of the continent. The continental slope, a marked declivity indicating the continental margin in a geological sense and the edge of the shelf, often lies several hundred miles offshore. Many islands rise from these submarine platforms. They are called shelf islands or continental islands, indicative of the fact that only a slight drop of sea level would join them to the continent with which they were very often connected through geological time.

The second coastal type is found in southern Europe. Most shore lines are characterized by steep ascent from the deep sea to the coastal hinterland. Coastal plains are narrow or missing except where the larger rivers have built deltas and alluvial plains into a sea little affected by tidal differences. The shelf is well expressed in a few areas only. Peninsulas and islands rise sharply from the sea bottom. We deal here with a coast line the major characteristics of which are determined by a complete reorganization of land and water in a major and not yet completed geological revolution. The formation of the Alpine mountain range made the Mediterranean and adjacent inland seas as by-products, so to speak. In the south of Europe upheavals and breakdowns of the earth's crust, rather than fluctuations in sea level, were responsible for the coastal configuration. We speak of "ingressional" coasts, as compared to the "transgressional" character of the flatland coasts in the north.

Intermediate between the lowland and the steep coasts, a third littoral type can be differentiated. Cliffs are conspicuous along portions of the Atlantic coast, but they owe their origin to processes quite different from those mentioned in the case of the Mediterranean. The sharp break of the land in southern England and northwestern France is a result of incessant marine erosion, while the steep and strongly articulated (fjord) coasts of western Scandinavia, Scotland, and Iceland were produced mainly by glacial erosion and subsequent oceanic inundation. The land, in both the cliffed and the fjord coast stretches, was comparatively stable, but the forces of marine and terrestrial erosion were still able to carve deeply into the continental margin.

The individual sections of the European coast line will now be briefly discussed. The northern coast of European Russia is separated by the White Sea into two parts: the flat and ill-drained Timan coast in the east and the Murmansk coast in the west, with a much less extensive lowland fringing the block of the Kola Peninsula. The character of the coast changes abruptly west of Murmansk with the northern end of the Scandinavian mountain system abutting the Arctic Ocean with long and relatively wide fjords extending in a northerly (Porsanger) or easterly (Varanger) direction. The Barents Sea, extending from Novaya Zemlya to the longitude of the North Cape (26° E.), is a typical shelf sea and most of the Arctic islands (Novaya Zemlya, Svalbard, Franz Josef Land—"Zemlya Frantsa Iosifa") are therefore geologically outlying parts of the mainland. The northernmost point of Europe lies on Mageröy (island) at latitude 71° N.[3] The shelf narrows into a submarine coastal platform of a few miles width around the northern end of Scandinavia.

In contrast to the Barents Sea, the Norwegian Sea overlies a deep basin with a maximum depth of over 10,000 feet. The Norwegian west coast is one of the most strongly articulated coasts of Europe, with a multitude of deep and long fjords separating peninsulas and promontories, and a great number of islands and island groups (e.g., Lofoten, Vesterålen) lying close to the mainland. The land rises sharply from the sea except where marine erosion, in combination with a subsequent upheaval of the land, has produced a conspicuous coastal platform ("strandflat" in Norwegian) slightly above present sea level (Fig. 1–1). Scandinavia is set off from central and eastern Europe by a chain of straits (Skagerrak, Kattegat, Sund, Belts) and the Baltic Sea, all shallow transgressional water bodies, with the ex-

---

[3] This is exactly the same latitude as the northernmost point of Alaska.

ception of the entrance to the Skagerrak, where a deep and old trench separates Norway from the shelf platform north of Jutland. The Baltic Sea, the "Mediterranean" of northern Europe, with its three extensions (gulfs of Bothnia, Finland, and Riga), divides the area into the Scandinavian, Finnish, and Baltic peninsulas. All islands rise from the shelf (the Danish group, Öland, Gotland, Dagö, and Ösel, and the Åland group). A lowering of the water level by 400 feet would leave the Baltic Sea almost completely dry.

Fig. 1–1. The innermost portion of a fjord near Tromsö (Norway), at latitude 70° N. Note the near-vertical wall (left) and the "fjell" plateau above the timber line here formed by stunted birch.

The largest marginal sea of Europe is the North Sea, rarely exceeding a depth of 300 feet until the continental slope is reached west of the British Isles. In the areas of the "banks" (Dogger, Great Banks) and south into the Strait of Dover the depth of the North Sea averages less than 100 feet. Thus, the British Isles are shelf islands par excellence, structurally clearly a part of the European mainland. A submarine ridge (Wyville Thompson Ridge and Iceland Plateau) extends northwestward from the North Sea shelf, linking the Faeroe Islands and even Iceland to Europe. Iceland, however, even though showing affinities to northwestern Europe with its strongly fjorded shore line, had an entirely independent geologic evolution. It is mainly of volcanic origin, and, like the Azores Islands, was built on the submarine Atlantic Ridge. The British Isles, with Great

Britain [4] and Ireland as the two dominating land bodies, rise in many places quite abruptly from the shelf base. Marine erosion and tectonic readjustments during the formation of the Alps were mainly responsible for the separation of these islands from the continent. The affinities of the northern part of Great Britain and Ireland with the Scandinavian mountains and those of the southern portions of Great Britain with northwestern France are obvious if a map showing trends of mountain ranges, or age and type of rock material, is consulted (Fig. 1–4). The coasts themselves are very similar on opposite sides of the North Sea and the English Channel—the fjords of the North Sea become the "sea lochs" of western Scotland; the *falaises* of France become the cliffs of England (Fig. 3–3).

In contrast to these sharp breaks between land and sea, however, stand the "flat" coasts of the Netherlands, Denmark, northern Germany, Poland, and the Baltic provinces of the Soviet Union. Here, because of the postglacial rise of the sea level on one side and the low relief of the coastal plains on the other, the marginal portions of the latter were inundated and the lower courses of the larger rivers became estuaries. Extensive stretches of the shore line are occupied by belts of unstable sand dunes. Strings of offshore islands are separated from the mainland by tidal flats (the Dutch *Wadden* and the German *Marschen*), flooded at high tide only. Curving sand pits (*Nehrungen* in German) with shallow lagoons (*Haffe*) on their landward side are conspicuous along the southeastern Baltic (Figs. 6–2, 6–3). All these features attest the recent formation and the unfixed position of the shore line. It needed the work of many generations to stabilize the land against the attack of marine erosion (Fig. 1–2).[5]

The North Channel, the Irish Sea, and St. George's Channel lie between Great Britain and Ireland, all of these water bodies being shelf seas containing numerous banks which, however, lie at greater depth than their counterparts in the North Sea. The westernmost point of Europe, shelf islands included, is located at Dunmore Head, a promontory in southwestern Ireland, at longitude 10° 30′ W. just one degree longitude farther west than the western extremity of the mainland (Cabo de Roca, 20 miles west of Lisbon).[6]

[4] Great Britain with her 89,000 square miles is the eighth largest island of the world. Great Britain and Ireland together are 4,000 square miles smaller than Norway, but 4,000 square miles larger than Italy.

[5] The area of the Netherlands has been almost doubled since medieval times through the construction of many hundred miles of dikes. The catastrophic inundations of February, 1953, nevertheless, are a grim reminder of the never-ending battle against the sea.

[6] Land's End, the westernmost point of England but not of Great Britain, lies at longitude 5° 50′ W. 170 miles east of the Spanish "Land's End," Cape Finisterre. It

South of the latitude of Brittany, the largest peninsula, after Jutland, on the west coast of the mainland, the Atlantic re-enters toward the continent and forms the Bay of Biscay in the right angle between the southwest coast of France and the north coast of Spain. The straightness of the shore line is remarkable, but is of completely different origin on the two sides of the bay. The flat coast of France with

Fig. 1–2. The Dutch coast near the village of West Kapelle on the island of Walcheren. The entire village was destroyed when the old dike was breached during the liberation campaign in 1944. A new dike has since been constructed (upper right, along the short side of the pool, which is a not-yet-drained remnant of the inundation). (Photo: Netherlands Information Service.)

long stretches of dunes and lagoons, *étangs* in French, especially south of the Gironde estuary, is fringed by a broad shelf, whereas the ocean bottom drops to a depth of over 10,000 feet within fifty miles in the Cantabrian Sea along the north coast of Spain. Here the shelf coast of western Europe, with its almost accidental location of the waterland boundary, comes to an abrupt end.

is often overlooked that most of Spain lies in the Western Hemisphere and that all of Portugal is west of Great Britain. If we consider outlying islands in the Atlantic as part of Europe the westernmost extremities of Europe are northwestern Iceland (latitude 65° 30′ N. and longitude 24° 30′ W., i.e., some five degrees longitude farther west than the northeast coast of Greenland) and the island of Flores in the Azores archipelago (latitude 40° N., longitude 31° W.).

The coast of the massive Iberian Peninsula shows all evidences of being conditioned by comparatively recent geologic events. Its stable interior has withstood major deformations during the period of the formation of the Alpine mountain system, but its marginal areas were strongly affected by them. The straight shore lines are the result of foundering along faults, zones of vertical and horizontal shear within the earth's crust. The coast along the northwest corner of Spain has been recognized as one of recent submergence, with drowned valleys (*rias*) reminiscent of, but differing in their origin from, fjords. Seismic activity is strong (e.g., the catastrophic earthquake of Lisbon, 1755), and volcanic effusives are found along the fault cracks. All this is indicative of the fact that the shape of the land is conditioned by recent crustal instability.

At the Strait of Gibraltar, 10 miles wide at the constriction between Piedra Marroqui [7] and the Moroccan coast, we enter the Mediterranean Basin. Coastal configuration and submarine topography bear ample evidence of the intensive geologic activity which has occurred in connection with the formation of the mountain systems of southern Europe (see also the discussion on tectonic evolution, pp. 30–37). In spite of its relatively small size the Mediterranean is a deep sea, or rather a series of deep sea basins separated by islands, peninsulas, and submarine swells. Shelf flats are restricted to narrow sills; only offshore from the conspicuous deltas of the major rivers are they more extensive. A typical Mediterranean shore is characterized by steep slopes and cliffs rising sharply from the sea (Figs. 1–18, 7–6). Small nichelike identations are frequent, but deep embayments which would offer sheltered harbor sites are rare. Widespread, however, are coastal terraces, sometimes several miles in width, created by recent upheavals of the land, somewhat alleviating the generally adverse character of the coast.

The western Mediterranean consists of two major basins separated from each other by the bastions of Corsica and Sardinia. The Balearic Islands rise from the western basin as remnants of a once unbroken mountain chain connecting the Pyrenees with the Sierra Nevada. The eastern basin (Tyrrhenian Sea) represents a typical kettle-like ingression (downwarp of the sea floor) which reaches to a depth of well over 12,000 feet in spite of its small size. Instability is further indicated by the many volcanic structures in its southern portion and

---

[7] Piedra Marroqui, latitude 36° N., is the southernmost point of the European mainland. Note that the 36th parallel crosses the United States from Cape Hatteras to Oklahoma and between Los Angeles and San Francisco, leaving the southern tier of the United States south of the southernmost point of Europe. Tokyo also has the same latitude as Piedra Marroqui.

adjacent land stretches (e.g., Vulcano and Stromboli islands in the Lipari group, Vesuvius, and Etna).

The eastern Mediterranean, east of the Apennine peninsula, Sicily, Malta, and Pantelleria, all of which are parts of a formerly uninterrupted mountain chain connecting the Atlas Range of North Africa with the Alps, exhibits a most pronounced coastal articulation in its northern part. In the Ionian and Aegean seas a former land bridge has foundered, leaving Crete and Cyprus as its largest remnants above sea level and a great number of closely spaced islands in the Aegean Sea as further evidence of a once continuous land mass (Cyclades, Sporades). Volcanic eruptions [8] and the most devastating earthquakes of recent times attest to the instability of the land. Deep troughs and basins are found close to the land. The Ionian Sea exceeds a depth of 15,000 feet fifty miles south of Cape Matapan, the southernmost point of the Peloponnesos, which with its three peninsulas represents the southern end of the Dinaric branch of the Alpine mountain system.[9] North of the Strait of Otranto extends the shallowest of all Mediterranean water bodies, the Adriatic Sea. Its Dalmatian shore is much more articulated than the Italian. Longitudinal islands and bays, both parallel to the coastal trend, are typical.

The straits of the Dardanelles, the Sea of Marmara, and the Bosporus (all three together called the Turkish Straits) form a geologically recent connection between the Aegean Sea and the Black Sea. The latter is deep in its southern part only, whereas the Bay of Odessa and the Sea of Azov are shelf seas. Lagoons and sand bars mark their shore line, and marshy tracts are widely distributed, particularly in the lowest portions of the large river valleys. West of Odessa there are peculiar long, narrow, and stagnant water bodies (locally called *limans*) representing former embayments, now separated from the sea by sand bars.

Vertical Surface Configuration

General Characteristics. The great variety of landforms is obvious from a quick glance at any map showing all or part of Europe. We might even speak of a "physiographic chaos" which it undoubtedly is if looked at one section after another without recognition of the relationship between the individual units. Once the continuance of the plains, the mountains, and the valleys is established on the basis of

[8] The central lava cone in the sea-filled crater of the island of Santorin (Thera) appeared above sea level in 1925.

[9] The Peloponnesos was not an island in Pelops' time (*nesos*, Greek for island), but it is now a man-made island owing to the Canal of Corinth, connecting the Gulf of Corinth with the Gulf of Aegina, not quite 4 miles apart.

the geologic evolution, the confusion resolves into a still complex, but intelligible, pattern.

From a strictly topographical point of view Europe may be divided into four physiographic units (Fig. 1–3):

1. *Coastal Lowlands and Interior Plains.* The low-lying terrain of Europe forms an almost continuous belt along the Atlantic and Baltic coasts and widens into the vast Russian plains. Elevations rarely exceed 500 feet above sea level. Local differences in elevation lie within 100 feet.

2. *The Central Uplands and Plateaus.* The northwestern lowlands end rather abruptly along a continuous highland of hilly, plateau-like, or mountainous character, which stretches from south central France to northern Czechoslovakia. Altitudes are between 500 and 2,000 feet with isolated areas protruding well above 4,000 feet. The terrain in the lower portions of the upland is not exceedingly rough, but the higher lands are steep and heavily forested.[10]

3. *The Northwestern Highlands.* The mountainous terrain of Scandinavia, the north of the British Isles, and Iceland constitutes a special type of highlands. Even though often higher than the central uplands (above 8,000 feet in southern Norway), the surface configuration is more plateau-like than truly mountainous. Only in the steep descent to the shore do we find considerable differences in elevation within short distances. Really flat land, however, occurs only along larger rivers. All these highland areas were affected by pronounced glacial erosion.

4. *The Southern Mountain Ranges.* This heading is a broad generalization for a variety of landform units all of which have in common genuinely mountainous aspects. We will later refer to them as the Alpine system of mountains. It is here that we find the highest mountain ranges and peaks of Europe attaining crest altitudes well above 10,000 feet. The mountain ranges often are continuous over long stretches separating deeply incised valleys or extensive basins (e.g., Po, Danube basins) and plateaus (Spanish tableland, Anatolian plateau). The complexity of the relief in southern Europe will receive special attention in the following section in which the origin and evolution of the European landforms are explained.

Tectonic Evolution and Structural Units. Both the horizontal and vertical surface configuration of Europe owe their complexity to a geologic evolution which time and again furnishes evidence that the greater part of the continent lies in an unstable zone of the earth's crust. The contrasts in present-day relief characteristics are strong—

---

[10] Note that the forested nature of the mountains is reflected in mountain names, such as Black Forest, Bohemian Forest, etc.

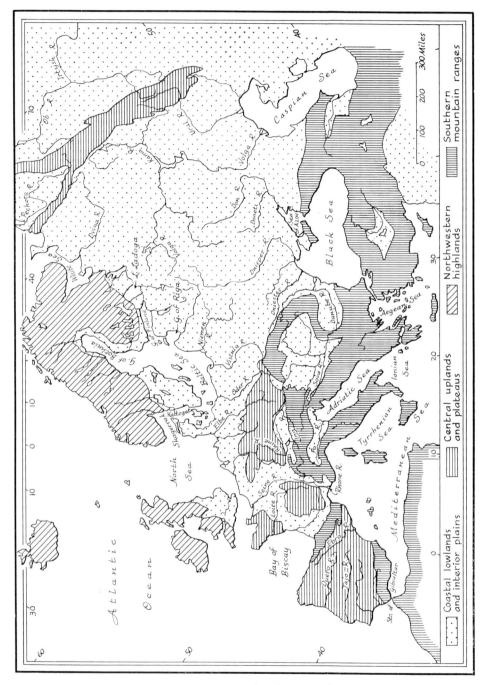

Fig. 1–3. Major physiographic divisions of Europe.

stronger really than in most other parts of the world of comparable size.

The fact that northern Europe has a subdued relief as compared to southern Europe does not mean that in the north mountain-building processes were absent. They only lie further back in geological time than those which built the Alps. The mountain systems which evolved in earlier geological periods in the northern and central parts of Europe once probably rose to as majestic heights as do the present Alps. Through the subsequent periods, however, they were worn down by the uninterruptedly working forces of weathering and erosion, and today only roots or stumps of the original structure remain. In great contrast, the young mountain system in southern Europe shows all evidence of geologically recent folding, thrusting, and faulting of rock layers. Form and structure still conform to a considerable extent, but the forces of erosion have long since begun their work, and have already cut down to the very roots of the structure in some places. The sequence of events which led to the present relief can be best summarized in graphic form (see Appendix I). Europe has experienced four orogenies (mountain-building periods). Geologically, they are referred to as the (1) Pre-Cambrian, (2) Caledonian, (3) Hercynian, and (4) Alpine orogenies.[11]

1. THE PRE-CAMBRIAN OROGENY. The Pre-Cambrian orogeny lies so far back (an estimated one billion years) that it is difficult to recognize any trend in the present terrain. The area affected by it lies around the Baltic Sea. Extensive masses of granites and metamorphic rocks build up a land surface of low relief, geologically referred to as the Fenno-Scandian or the Baltic Shield.[12] The Shield continues, mostly buried by younger sediments, underneath most of the Great Russian Lowland. Together with the Central Siberian (Angara) Shield, the Canadian Shield, and large parts of Greenland, the Baltic Shield probably represents a remnant of an old northern continent (Laurasia). It is truly the core of the European land mass, acting as a rigid block along and around which younger mountain systems were thrust up. Once the primeval European orogeny had ended, the Shield experienced only isostatic movements such as upheavals and subsidences en bloc. Periods of erosion alternated with transgressions of the sea. During the latter the crystalline foundation

---

[11] "Cambrian" after the Cambrian Mountains in Wales, "Caledonian" after the Latin *Caledonia* for Scotland, "Hercynian" after the Latinized word for the Harz Mountains in central Germany, "Alpine" after the Alps.

[12] The term "shield" is used in reference to the shieldlike shape of the Fenno-Scandian terrain, with the Baltic Sea filling the concavity of the inverted side of the shield. Note the similarity with the Canadian Shield, with Hudson Bay in the center. Note also that Finland is part of the Baltic Shield.

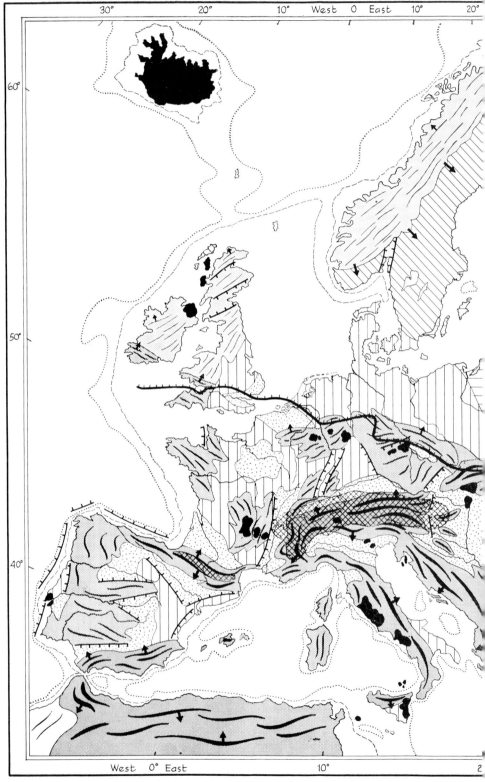

Fig. 1–4. Structural units

urope (see p. 28 for legend).

became covered with sediments increasing in thickness toward the east. With the land mass finally rising above sea level in late Tertiary time the sedimentary plateaus of western Russia emerged and now form the Great Russian Lowland—plains and tablelands. In some parts of the covered section of the Shield late uplifts have exposed the crystalline bedrock or its oldest sedimentary cover (Azov-Podolian Massif, Voronezh Block, Timan Swell). The Baltic Sea is a recent transgression over the Baltic Shield following the depression of the land by the Scandinavian ice sheet.

2. THE CALEDONIAN OROGENY. The beginning of the Paleozoic era was characterized by widespread marine transgressions over most of Europe, but in the Silurian period the Caledonian orogeny began to affect large sections of northwestern Europe. Structure, trend, and rock material of the Irish, Scottish, and Norwegian mountains are very similar and mainly due to the Caledonian orogenic period, during which early Paleozoic marine sediments were folded and overthrust, and at the same time highly metamorphosed. The thrust was directed northwestward in the British Isles against the then still existing portion of the "old north continent," the gneisses of the Hebrides and the Lofoten being interpreted as the easternmost edge of it (Fig. 1–4). On the other hand, the rock layers are overthrown toward the east against the Fenno-Scandian Shield in the Scandinavian mountains. The Caledonian system [13] can be followed northward into Svalbard and northern Greenland. It has since been under continuous erosion, and, during later orogenies, large sections of it have either foundered or were uplifted, arched, or tilted. One of the most conspicuous geologic formations of northwestern Europe, the Old Red Sandstone

[13] There are no Caledonian mountains on any map of Europe, but structurally one can refer to Caledonian mountains, Caledonian trend, Caledonian overthrust, etc.

Legend for Fig. 1–4.

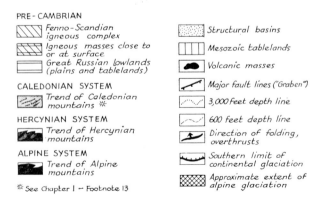

PRE-CAMBRIAN

Fenno-Scandian igneous complex

Igneous masses close to or at surface

Great Russian lowlands (plains and tablelands)

CALEDONIAN SYSTEM

Trend of Caledonian mountains *

HERCYNIAN SYSTEM

Trend of Hercynian mountains

ALPINE SYSTEM

Trend of Alpine mountains

* See Chapter I – Footnote 13

Structural basins

Mesozoic tablelands

Volcanic masses

Major fault lines ("Graben")

3,000 feet depth line

600 feet depth line

Direction of folding, overthrusts

Southern limit of continental glaciation

Approximate extent of alpine glaciation

of Devonian age, represents the continental waste products of the Caledonian mountains.

3. THE HERCYNIAN OROGENY. Subsequent to the existence of this "Great Northern Red Land" the sea again began to cover much of Europe. For the Baltic Shield and the greater part of the Caledonian system this was the ultimate marine transgression, whereas the west Russian crystalline shield experienced further inundations by the sea. The Carboniferous period began with a widespread submergence. The floor of the early Carboniferous sea, however, was already affected by the first spasms of the Hercynian revolution in so far as the "coal measures" must have been forming in slowly emergent swells with widespread coastal lowlands and marshes. The main axes of the Hercynian uplift were developing farther south, with the coal deposits being retained in large structural depressions or smaller basins along the northern flank of, or within, the Hercynian mountains (Wales, Namur, Ruhr, Upper Silesia, Donets basins).

To a remarkable extent, the remains of the Hercynian system dominate the relief of western and central Europe north of the Alps. Some of them are still topographically, and all of them are structurally, reminiscent of their original grandeur. The trend of the Hercynian mountains is clearly recognizable in many parts of Europe, in others only a detailed analysis of the structure will give clues as to their original direction. In some sections these folded mountains stand out sharply. Selective erosion has produced parallel ridges which give a strongly linear grain to the landscape.[14] This is particularly true in the central section of the system, where the mountain chains sharply separate the lowlands. These highlands are definitely mountainous with rock outcrops frequently visible through the dense forest.[15] The Ardennes in Belgium, the chains across the Rhine between Mainz and Bonn (Rhenish Slate Mountains, Hunsrueck, and Taunus), the ridges of the Harz in central Germany, the Rhoen, the Thuringian, and the Frankish forests all are distinct segments of the Hercynian system (see Chapter 6, pp. 371–76). At the Fichtelgebirge the chain splits into a northern (Ore Mountains, Sudeten Mountains) and a southern branch (Bohemian Forest), enclosing the Bohemian Basin. Other topographically outstanding Hercynian remnants are the backbones of the Brittany and Normandy penin-

[14] This landform pattern is comparable to the Ridge and Valley Zone in the Appalachians of eastern North America. The Appalachians also owe their original folding to the late Paleozoic revolution, called the Appalachian orogeny in North America. In central Asia the Altai orogeny corresponds to the Hercynian.

[15] In German the term *Mittelgebirge* is used for the central uplands. The *Mittel* or "middle" refers to their intermediate character, topographically speaking, between hill lands and mountains.

sulas (geologically referred to as the Armorican Massif[16]), Cornwall, and the Kerry Mountains in south Ireland, as well as the Urals in the extreme east of Europe, at the edge of the buried part of the Baltic Shield. The western and eastern branches of the Hercynian system converge in the Central Massif in southern France. There are other massifs,[17] particularly in the southern portions of the Hercynian belt: the Vosges and the Black Forest, two granitic blocks separated by the trough of the Upper Rhine Plain, the Bohemian Massif, and the Rhodope Massif, to mention only the largest ones.

Hercynian structures are found within the Alpine body, where they now represent the granitic massifs of the Alps. The Iberian Peninsula—with the exception of the Pyrenees, the Cantabrian Mountains, and the Sierra Nevada—is also of Hercynian structure. Here, some of the Hercynian chains stand out sharply above the Spanish tableland, owing to their igneous cores (Sierra de Guadarrama) or to "horst and graben" tectonics (Sierra Morena).

The discontinuity of the Hercynian mountains as we see them today is attributable to three major post-Hercynian developments: First, the mountains were exposed to long periods of erosion. Second, marine transgressions repeatedly inundated the European continent during the Mesozoic era; their sediments, lying unconformably over the eroded Hercynian structures, are proof that intensive planation had taken place before the transgressions. Finally, the Hercynian mountains were profoundly affected during the Alpine orogeny, which produced most drastic results in southern Europe but has influenced all of Europe in a more or less intense manner.

4. THE ALPINE OROGENY. When we direct our attention to southern Europe, it becomes immediately obvious how the previous geological events on the Eurasian continent bear upon the Alpine orogeny. The great arch of the Alps projects northward between the two largest resistant old blocks of the Hercynian foreland, the French Massif Central in the west and the Bohemian Massif in the east. In eastern Europe the crescent of the Carpathians bulges northeastward between the Bohemian Massif and a buried spur of the Russian Shield in Rumania. The bend of the Jura Mountains is anchored on both ends at the Massif Central of France and the Vosges, respec-

---

[16] Armorica was the Roman name for Bittany, Latinized after a Celtic word for the peninsula.

[17] Massifs are blocks, rather than ranges, of old mountains which consist mainly of igneous and metamorphic material, projecting through the sedimentary cover of their surroundings. They are uplands either because of their greater resistance to erosion or because they were uplifted during the Alpine orogeny.

tively. The Mediterranean mountain chains are squeezed in between the Iberian, Tyrrhenian (exposed in Corsica and Sardinia), and Rhodope massifs. This complex, garland-like pattern of mountain chains (Fig. 1–4) has led students of tectonics to assume that the earth's crust has a high degree of mobility, and that its upper layers must have experienced vertical and horizontal dislocations of great magnitude. Whoever has seen the structure in the rock walls of Alpine valleys, with the layers of sedimentary rock crenulated in

Fig. 1–5. The folded limestone mountains of the "Grande Chartreuse," between Grenoble and Chambéry, looking northward. In the extreme upper left the first anticlines of the Jura Mountains are visible, which here branch off from the Alps. Note the dense cover of coniferous forest, which contrasts with the vegetation of the drier southern portions of the French Alps. (Photo: Swissair.)

miniature meanders, or lying in sweeping folds several miles long, must be convinced that the present rigidity of rocks has only been reached after a long series of plastic deformations (Fig. 1–5).

The evolution of the Alpine mountain system may be briefly summarized as follows: Through most of the Mesozoic era southern Europe was covered by a primeval "Mediterranean Sea" (Tethys)[18]

[18] The name applied by geologists to this ancient sea, after the wife of Oceanos in Greek mythology.

into which a very great amount of sedimentary material of mostly calcareous nature was deposited. An ancient sea lay between two large land masses, the Laurasian continent with all its Pre-Cambrian, Caledonian, and Hercynian elements in the north, and Gondwana Land, a southern continent, remnants of which can be discovered in the present land masses of Africa, India, and Australia. The accumu-

Fig. 1–6. The front range of the northern limestone Alps in northeastern Switzerland, culminating in Mt. Säntis (upper left center). The alternation of the light-colored limestone and layers of darker shale produces the "banded" effect. To the left are the first "molasse" hills of the Swiss midlands; in the background is the trough of the Rhine. (Photo: Swissair.)

lation of thousands of feet of sediment in the Tethys can be explained only if a continuous subsidence of its floor through most of the Mesozoic era is assumed. To a basin of such long persistence and of such large areal extent the name "geosyncline" has been applied. This "Alpine geosyncline," however, lying in a weak zone between the stable masses of two continents, could not retain its subsidence indefinitely. According to the theory of continental drift,[19] the

[19] Even though the concept of a one-sided thrust due to a large latitudinal displacement of the Gondwana block is still adhered to by many European geologists, others have postulated a more or less *in situ* development of the Alps with the geosyncline being underthrust from both the north and the south. Cf. Leopold Kober, *Bau und Entstehung der Alpen* (Structure and Origin of the Alps) (Berlin: Borntraeger, 1923).

African land mass began to push northward, steadily encroaching upon the vast sedimentary trough. Since the Hercynian massifs acted as rigid blocks against the movement from the south, the weaker sedimentary layers had to yield to the tremendous tangential pressure exerted upon them. Already in mid-Mesozoic times ridges began to form in them which soon appeared as island arcs above sea level. All through the Cretaceous period the deformation continued and reached its peak in the mid-Tertiary (Oligocene and Miocene). By this time the sedimentary layers and even the igneous substructures were lifted miles above sea level and thrown into gigantic folds (anticlines and synclines), many of them overturned toward the north. In the late phases of the orogeny, higher portions of the folds overrode lower ones or were dragged along by thrust sheets gliding above the previously built mountain structures.

The movement came to an end along what is now the impressive "Alpine front" in the French, Swiss, and Austrian Alps, often forming sheer cliffs several thousand feet in height above the Alpine foreland (Fig. 1–6). Intrusions, volcanic eruptions, upheavals, and subsidences on a large scale accompanied and followed the orogeny. Even though the Alps are of geologically recent origin, they still are but a torso, the original continuity being retained merely in downfolded areas, while the upper thrust sheets and the vertices of the anticlines have been partially or completely destroyed by erosional forces affecting the mountain mass from the very moment it rose out of the sea.

As can be best seen on the structural map of Europe (Fig. 1–4), the Alpine orogeny involved the greater portion of the southern half of Europe. The major branches of the Alpine mountain system [20] in the Mediterranean realm are the Pyrenees, Sierra Nevada, Atlas, Apennines, Dinarides (collective name for the mountain chains in Yugoslavia and Greece), Taurus, and Anatolian chains. The Alps proper extend from Genoa to Vienna, with an outlier in the Jura Mountains and an eastern European extension in the Carpathians, the Transylvanian Alps, and the Balkan Range. Six major structural units are commonly differentiated:

1. *The igneous cores, or massifs.* They occur along the axis of the western and central Alps, but are buried beneath the sedimentary folds in the eastern Alps. Owing to the absence of stratified rocks, some of the most rugged mountains and peaks are found within this unit [21] (Fig. 1–8).

[20] The Tertiary orogeny affected all continents of the earth simultaneously, geologically speaking. The continuous mountain chains along the southern rim of Asia and along the west coast of the Americas are all part of the Tertiary orogen.

[21] The concentration of names indicative of jagged peak forms in this area is striking: *aiguille* (needle), *dent* (tooth), Horn, *fuorcla* (fork), etc.

2. *The northern limestone Alps* (Helvetides, after the Latin name for Switzerland, Helvetia). They form the frontal ranges throughout the system, including the Jura Mountains. In a most complicated structure, several folds lie above one another, plunging northward immediately beyond the massifs and ascending toward the Alpine

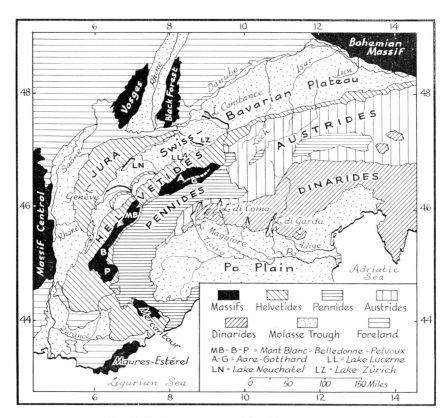

Fig. 1–7. Tectonic map of the Alpine system.

front. The "roots" of the Helvetides lie within or south of the massifs, often separated from the northern fold sheets (*nappes*) by erosion. The mountains are much more massive than those in the igneous zone, the banked sedimentary layers being conducive to the formation of summit plateaus, ledges, and steplike valley profiles. Again, local designations are illustrative: *Kasten* (chest), *dos* (back), etc.

3. *The eastern Alps* (Austrides, after Austria). Along the Swiss-Austrian boundary the nature of the rock material and the tectonic character of folds and thrust sheets change. The Austrides, in the process of folding, were pushed over all other tectonic units and for-

merly covered a much larger area than today. Evidence for this lies in the remains of east-Alpine rocks on top of the Helvetian folds (the so-called *Klippen*, or isolated outliers of the Austrides in Switzerland and Savoy), and the "windows" of west-Alpine formations within the eastern Alps, exposed by erosion ("Engadine" valley in

Fig. 1–8. View of the Aare Massif, one of the granite cores of the Alps, from above the Grimsel Pass, Canton of Berne, Switzerland. At their highest stage during the Ice Age, glaciers covered all but the jagged crests along the divides. Finstaarhorn (left center) reaches above 14,000 feet. The lakes are artificial and part of the impressive hydroelectric development of the Aare River headwaters. (Photo: Swissair.)

Switzerland, the "Hohe Tauern" in Austria). The Austrian Alps are characterized in their northern and southern portions by a series of structurally simple, east-west trending limestone ranges, while their central zone consists of complex igneous and metamorphic masses. Owing to an eastward divergence of the major mountain ranges, the Alpine body here has its greatest width (170 miles, as compared to less than 100 miles across the southern French-Italian Alps).

4. *The western Alps* (Pennides after the Latin *Alpes Pennini*). The fronts of the Pennine *nappes* advanced against the massifs and were unable to override them, thus becoming involved in the most complex plications anywhere in the Alps. The rock material is highly

metamorphosed, the gneisses of the fold cores enveloped by enormous schist series. The Pennides root along the southern margin of the Alps, where the rock layers stand vertical before becoming recumbent northward and westward. It will be seen on the tectonic map that the Pennides underlie the Austrides in the eastern Alps whereas the French and western Swiss Pennides actually represent structural units homologous to the Austrides.

5. *The southern Alps* (Dinarides, from the Latin *Dinaria*, for northwestern Yugoslavia). The separation of the southern Alps from the Austrides and Pennides is based mainly upon differences in rock material and the different lie of the folds: their fronts face southward, owing to underpushing of the sedimentary formations by the African land mass. Calcareous rock types are particularly well developed in the southern Austrian Alps (*Karawanken*), in northeastern Italy (dolomites), and in northern Yugoslavia, the last are famous for many solutional phenomena of the "karst" type. This section of the Alpine system is often referred to as the southern limestone Alps.

6. *The Molasse troughs.* The Swiss-Bavarian plateau (also called foreland, plains, or *Mittelland*), the Po Plain, and the Saône-Rhone depression contain the sediments which accumulated throughout the orogeny in the longitudinal troughs adjacent to the rising mountain mass. Close to the Alps conglomerate and sandstone formations represent the layers of deltas built by the primeval Alpine rivers into a Tertiary sea. The Molasse was overridden and tilted southward by the last advances of the Alpine front. By tracing the origin of the rock materials in the Molasse (as the Tertiary sediments are collectively called in French and German from Latin "ground stone") and by analyzing their tectonic relationship to the individual thrust sheets much has been learned about the sequence of orogenic phases in the Alps. At greater distances from the Alps the Molasse, including marine shale and limestone layers, lies practically horizontal.

The majestic mountains and the deeply incised valleys of the Alps which we observe today are, of course, much younger than the tectonic events which brought them into position. However, the pattern and arrangement of the major ranges and valleys convincingly lead to the conclusion that the present drainage system had its birth in a period when the Alps were still growing in height and extent. The longitudinal valleys, that is, the valleys parallel to the trend of the system in any particular section, often represent original depressions in, or separations between, the major thrust sheets (e.g., the upper courses of the Rhone and the Rhine between the Helvetides and Pennides, and in the root zones of the Helvetides). The much steeper, narrower, and shorter transverse valleys more often than not follow primary axial depressions or are located in re-entrants of the north fronts of the *nappes*. After the last en bloc upheaval of the Alpine body in a very late stage, however, the rivers tended to be increasingly less dependent upon structure and rock hardness. They often take the shortest routes to the foreland, regardless of obstacles in their way.

The formation of the Alpine system had far-reaching effects upon the areas of Europe not directly involved in the orogeny. The Hercynian massifs seem to have translated the tectonic forces to the sedimentary basins between them. They, themselves, were affected in so far as the majority of them were strongly uplifted and faulted. These vertical displacements produced the sharply linear features along coasts (e.g., west and north coast of Iberia, fjord of Oslo), or inland along the margins of most massifs. The Rhone-Saône valley, the Upper Rhine Valley between Basel and Mainz, the depression between the Slate Mountains and the Harz all belong to one big fault (*graben*) system. Volcanic eruptions of various types occurred practically throughout the period of tectonic unrest (Auvergne in the Central Massif, Kaiserstuhl in the Upper Rhine Plain, Eifel and Vogelsberg in the German Uplands, Colli Euganei in the Po Plain). Parts of the ancient shield also were affected. They adjusted themselves to the new conditions by tilting (Scandinavian peninsula), subsidence (Caspian depression), uplifts (blocks of Voronezh, Podolia, Donets), or even faulting (Kola Peninsula, Ladoga and Onega lakes shore lines, to mention but a few examples). If we take into consideration subsequent changes brought about by the glaciations, to be discussed in the following section, it becomes obvious that the surface configuration of Europe owes its present characteristics to events connected with the Alpine orogeny and the subsequent geomorphic evolution. Geologically old in many parts, Europe, in a morphological sense, is not an old, but a new world.

Europe During the Ice Age

The last one million years, the time span usually allotted to the Quaternary period, in which we still live, affected the European land in quite a different, but locally no less drastic, manner as compared to the transformations which occurred during the periods of tectonic action. The Pleistocene was characterized in the northern and Alpine areas by repeated advances of ice sheets which, during their maximum extension, covered about half of Europe (Fig. 1–4). There is evidence of four glaciation periods and three interglacial periods, not counting postglacial time (see Appendix I for subdivisions of the Pleistocene). In each of the glacial periods the ice began to accumulate during a climatic deterioration (assumed decrease of mean annual temperature by some 15° F.) in the Scandinavian mountains, the Alps, and various isolated areas even in southernmost Europe (Sierra Nevada). Ice streams began to form in the higher portions of those areas and flowed out into the adjacent lowlands, often coalescing in the foreland into a widespread piedmont glacier. The Scandinavian ice sheet advanced over the North Sea and joined the local ice cap over the British Isles. It also extended as far south as the present mouth of the Rhine River and came to a halt along the northern front of the Hercynian chains in central Europe. In eastern Europe it overrode the shield and its sedimentary cover southeastward to the Volga River, projecting deeply southward into the Ukraine, following the preglacial valley trains of the Dnieper and the Don. The Alpine valleys were filled by a network of glacial streams which, in their northernmost advance, reached into southern Germany and into the Jura Mountains, forming a continuous piedmont glacier in the northern foreland, while just reaching the margin of the Po Plain in the south.

In both the northern and Alpine realms as well as in the nonglaciated areas, the glacial regime had a most profound effect upon the preglacial terrain. Four basic changes brought about by the Pleistocene glaciations must be differentiated:

1. *Glacial erosion.* Close to the center of the glaciated areas, evidence of erosional activity prevails clearly in the present landform characteristics. The Alpine valleys received their typical U-shaped cross-sections [22] (Figs. 6–10 and 6–11), sharp crest lines and peaks were sculptured, and the bedrock surfaces were widely exposed, polished, and grooved (Fig. 1–8). In the Scandinavian highlands the wide expanse of naked rock surfaces of the *fjell* [23] plateau contrasts sharply with the deep fjords on the Atlantic slope (Fig. 1–1). In the fjords the ice tongues extended oceanward a considerable distance over the present end of the fjords. With sea level some 400 feet lower than at the present time, terminal moraines were deposited which can still be recognized in the present submarine topography.

2. *Glacial accumulation.* While these central portions of the glaciated areas are today characterized by the absence of a soil mantle, the terrain in the marginal reaches of the ice sheets received the

---

[22] Recent investigations support the belief that the deep troughs of the Alpine valleys, formerly considered almost exclusively the work of the glaciers, had already existed in preglacial times and that only part of the total excavation of the valleys is due to glacial erosion. Cf. Hans Annaheim, "Studies on the Geomorphogenesis of the South Alps," *Geographica Helvetica* (Bern, 1946): 65–149.

[23] Norwegian for mountainous terrain.

debris suspended in, and dragged along by, the ice in the form of moraines. These moraines, if deposited during a longer stagnation, such as during the maximum stage of the last glaciation, form an almost continuous belt of hill lands and are practically the only outstanding topographic features in the North European Plain. Areally more extensive are the "till plains," unsorted morainic material of a mixed lithological nature (sand, clay, boulders). Sheets of sand and gravel were deposited in valleys and basins beyond the moraines, often to a depth of several hundred feet, by the mighty streams forming in front of, and along, the ice margin during the melting phase of glaciation. In northern Germany and Poland these wide valleys are called the "primeval valleys of the streams." These outwash valleys and plains are extremely important in the north European area as well as in the Alps and their forelands, since they contain some of the best soils. Except for the steep slopes separating the numerous river terraces, and its flood-subject portions, this level land has been almost completely put into cultivation.

3. *Eolian deposits.* Closely related to the glacial regime is the deflation of silt from the outwash plains and its deposition as so-called loess.[24] In a band of considerable width south of, and partly within, the morainic territory, the virtual absence of vegetation close to the ice enabled the strong west winds to pick up the fine-grained material and to transport it over great distances. Southeastern Europe, particularly the Ukraine, the lower Danube Basin, and the non-glaciated zone between the Scandinavian and Alpine ice sheets, became the major areas of loess accumulation. In these regions, the loess cover often assumes the importance of a major landform element, in so far as its thickness is great enough to build up veritable plateaus in which sharp gullies or even gorges (*ovragi* of the Ukraine) have developed because of its unconsolidated structure. Loess is also found in many valleys of the Alps and the Alpine foreland (Rhone, Rhine, Danube). It is an excellent parent material for soils, and its distribution shows a close relationship to the most intensively used agricultural land of Europe.

4. *Postglacial upwarping.* The fourth transformation brought about by the advance of the ice is of a tectonic nature. The tremendous weight of the northern ice mass depressed the earth's crust to such an extent that in the retreating phase of the ice marine conditions prevailed over wide areas of the formerly ice-covered terrain. This is evidenced by marine fossils and wave-cut beaches, now lying

[24] The term "loess" is used locally in central Germany meaning fine, dusty soil, easily picked up by winds. The English word "loose" is related to the German word *Loess.*

several hundred feet above the level of the Baltic Sea owing to the postglacial emergence of Scandinavia. There are indications that this upheaval of the land has not yet been completed. In the Alps, it is difficult to separate the movements which might have been caused by the weight of the ice from those which occurred in the latest phases of the Alpine orogeny.

The effects of the Ice Age upon the relief of Europe, then, are of great importance not only locally, but regionally as well. Most local surface features are either directly or indirectly influenced by the morphologic processes active during the Pleistocene. Europe obtained its present outline only in the very latest period of geological time, since sea level returned to present normal barely more than 10,000 years ago.

Drainage Pattern

As a result of the morphological complexity and the strong articulation of the western part of Europe, the drainage pattern consists of a great number of units.[25] Even the east European plains, in spite of their homogeneous relief, drain into four different seas. Europe, in contrast to all other continents, does not have great collecting rivers. The divide between the Atlantic-Baltic-North Sea drainage system and that of the Mediterranean and Black seas, both of about equal area, generally trends southwest-northeast, but rarely follows the highest Alpine ranges. The sources of the Rhine and Rhone rivers in Switzerland, for instance, lie only 15 miles apart. These two rivers are confined in longitudinal valleys in their upper courses only, while those of the eastern Alps follow the trend of the Alps much longer before breaking out into the piedmont. The Danube, by far the largest river of non-Russian Europe, marks the boundary between the older and younger mountain systems in its upper course and then finds its way to the Black Sea by twice breaching the Alpine system, first between the eastern Alps and the Carpathians at Vienna, and then between the Transylvanian Alps and the Balkan range at the "Iron Gate." The Danube has encroached deeply into the Atlantic drainage system. Its source is now in the Black Forest, and once originated even farther west in the Jura Mountains. What it lost due to a "decapitation," as a consequence of the breakdown of the Rhine graben, it has made up in its lower course where its mouth followed the eastward shrinking of the Tertiary Black Sea, successively collecting rivers which were formerly independent drainage

[25] Readers are advised to make use of a good physical or physical-political map of Europe and carefully follow the courses of the various rivers mentioned in this section.

systems (Tisza, Sava, Morava, the rivers from the Transylvanian Alps, and finally even Seret and Prut).

The Rhine is the only river which managed to keep its course between the Alps and the Atlantic against all tectonic dislocations in the area traversed by it. Its lower course once extended over the floor of the North Sea as far as latitude 57° N., as is evident from a submarine channel beginning at the present Rhine mouth and ending northeast of the Firth of Forth. Most other rivers flowing into the Atlantic, the North Sea, and the Baltic rise in the Hercynian chains (Loire, Seine, Meuse, Weser, Elbe, Oder, Vistula). The rivers of the Iberian Peninsula either follow long-established courses over the less resistant parts of the Meseta tablelands (Duero, Tagus, and Guadiana) or their courses are determined by faults along the younger mountain systems (Ebro and Guadalquivir). The rivers of the Baltic slope of Scandinavia show a remarkably parallel pattern in their courses over the inclined shield surface. Along the boundary between the Caledonian ranges and the shield, as well as farther downstream, the rivers have developed a series of rapids caused by lithological differences, or by the unequal rate of uplift in different parts of Scandinavia during the postglacial emergence of the Scandinavian peninsula.

The divide between Atlantic or Arctic drainage on one side and Black Sea-Caspian on the other has been pushed far northward by the Russian rivers west of the Urals (Chapter 9, pp. 657–61). Here the separation between river systems is often indistinct with large swamp tracts communicating between two opposite watersheds. Many artificial canals now connect adjacent rivers, replacing former portages. The Volga is by far the largest river of Europe. Its source lies in the moraines of the Valdai Hills at an altitude of only slightly above 800 feet. In its upper course the Volga follows an easterly direction over an extensive outwash plain marginal to the terminal moraines. The gradients of the southwest Russian rivers are extremely small, except where they are forced to cross swells of the crystalline fundament, forming rapids, often the sites of hydroelectric developments (e.g., Kuibyshev on the Volga, Dnepropetrovsk on the Dnieper). These resistant rocks also have an influence upon the direction of flow in so far as the generally southeastern trend of the middle courses of these rivers is reversed toward the southwest in the lower courses. The "elbows" of the Don, Donets, and Dnieper are especially noteworthy. The Ural Range represents quite a sharp separation between the European and Asiatic river systems, with all the Siberian rivers draining into the Arctic Sea. (For details see Chapter 9, pp. 657–61.)

In concluding this short discussion of the major aspects of the European drainage systems it should be said that the time-honored concept of the rivers eroding in their upper courses, alternating between erosion and accumulation in their middle courses, and accumulating only near their mouths is an extreme oversimplification of their actual behavior. The tectonic movement, continuing into recent time, and the complete resculpturing of the terrain during the Ice Age brought with them transformations of such magnitude that rivers have only locally reached graded conditions.

As far as standing water bodies are concerned, the distribution of European lakes mirrors, for all practical purposes, the extent of the formerly ice-covered areas. Of the total area of fresh-water lakes in Europe (52,700 square miles),[26] well over 80 per cent lies within the realm of the northern glaciation. Finland has close to one-fifth of its total area covered by lakes. The Alpine valleys are rich in small lakes, but their combined area amounts to only 1,300 square miles. Most of the Scandinavian and Alpine lakes owe their origin either to glacial excavation of weaker rock materials or to the fact that they were dammed up by moraines or that they lie in tectonic depressions. Ice-scoured lake basins prevail in the Norwegian, Swedish, and Scottish highlands (in the latter area they are called "lochs") as well as in the high Alps (cirque lakes); moraine-dammed lakes are typical in the ground and end moraine districts of both the Scandinavian and Alpine ice sheets. Central Finland has been called a lake platform, and the same could be said for the lake-dotted moraine belts in northeastern Germany and northern Poland. Very typical are the long, finger-like lakes at the threshold of many Alpine valleys (Lake Geneva, Lake of the Four Cantons, Lake Zurich, Lake Maggiore, Lake Como, and Lake Garda). For the formation of some of the larger lakes such as Lake Ladoga and Lake Onega[27] in Karelia (U.S.S.R.), Venern and Vettern in southern Sweden, and Lake Constance between Germany and Switzerland, tectonic as well as glacial action were contributing factors. The largest lake of non-glaciated Europe is Lake Balaton in southeastern Hungary (240 square miles, greatest depth 36 feet), a remnant of a much larger Pleistocene lake. Small lakes in quite impressive numbers are found in volcanic terrain in the form of crater lakes (Auvergne, Eifel, Apennine peninsula), or in the solutional depressions (dolinas and *poljas*) of the karst areas of Slovenia.

[26] This figure approximates the combined areas of Lake Superior and Lake Michigan.
[27] These are the two largest European lakes, with an area of 7,100 square miles and 3,850 square miles, respectively.

THE CLIMATES OF EUROPE

In order to understand the climate of any portion of the earth's surface two basic sets of influences have to be considered. First, there are the terrestrial factors, in particular the absolute location on the globe and the position relative to water and land masses, and the surface configuration. Second, one has to deal with the atmospheric influences themselves, which can be studied in terms of the individual climatic elements.

In the case of Europe the terrestrial factors can be summarized as follows:

1. Europe is the only continent lying almost completely within the so-called temperate latitudes. Its south coast is well north of the Tropic of Cancer (latitude 23½° N.), and only its extreme north extends beyond the Arctic Circle (latitude 66½° N.). We may refer to the extreme northern and southern zones of Europe as subarctic and subtropical, respectively, but they are really much more closely related to the atmospheric circulation of the mid-latitudes than to that of either the arctic or the tropics.

2. Europe lies in the western portion of the largest land mass of the earth and along the eastern margin of a large oceanic water body.

3. There is no continuous mountain range across Europe which would interfere with the free movement of air in a longitudinal direction. This means that the land is open to both oceanic and continental air masses.

4. There is a practically unbroken chain of high mountains from northwestern Iberia through south-central Europe into southeastern Europe, which effectively prevents large-scale latitudinal interchange of tropical and polar air masses. The Alpine mountain system, therefore, represents, especially in its central and western portions, a very sharp divide of weather and climate.

5. Europe is surrounded on three sides by large water bodies, parts of which intrude deeply into the land. Of paramount importance is the fact that the water temperature off the European west coast in the cold season is considerably higher than that measured on the adjacent land. The northeastern Atlantic receives a steady supply of warm surface water through the North Atlantic Drift, driven toward the northeast by the prevailing southwest winds over the eastern Atlantic. The importance of this North Atlantic Drift as a climate factor, however, has been and will probably continue to be greatly exaggerated. It is true that it keeps the harbors of western and

northern Scandinavia ice-free as far east as Murmansk, but its influence on the temperatures of mainland Europe is not direct, and there is no such thing as a warming of Europe by the "Gulf Stream." Indirectly, to be sure, the influence of the warm northeastern Atlantic upon the European winter climate should not be underestimated. Cold air masses approaching Europe from the northwest are quickly warmed in the lower layers while traversing the Norwegian and North seas and arrive over Europe as relatively warm air masses. But far more relevant for the mildness of the climate of western Europe is the atmospheric circulation itself.

Atmospheric Circulation, Air Masses, and Fronts

The weather over Europe is controlled by five barometric-pressure systems, all of which are centered outside the European land mass most of the time. They are called "centers of action" because they are responsible for steering air masses of different character over the continent and for establishing the direction and velocity of winds. These five pressure systems are:

1. The low-pressure area permanently lying over the North Atlantic between Scandinavia and Greenland, commonly called the Icelandic Low.
2. The high-pressure ridge constantly centered southwest of the Iberian Peninsula, usually called the Azores High.
3. The low-pressure system located over the Mediterranean in winter, or the Mediterranean Low.
4. The high-pressure center located over Lake Baikal in northeastern Asia in winter, usually called the Siberian High.
5. The low-pressure system over southwestern Asia in summer, or the Monsoon Low.

It should be stated that these surface pressure centers are themselves influenced by the pressure field and the circulation in higher layers of the troposphere. At an altitude of 10,000 feet the surface pressure centers are replaced by quite a different pressure pattern: above this level there is a continuous trough of low pressure across northern Europe and a high-pressure ridge over southern Europe. These pressure features are, respectively, part of a circumpolar low-pressure trough and a subtropical high-pressure ridge, both of which are responsible for creating an uninterrupted band of high-altitude westerlies over the mid-latitudes of the Northern Hemisphere.[28]

[28] Included in the upper westerlies is a zone of particularly high wind speeds, to which the name "jet stream" has been applied. The location of the jet stream is highly significant in so far as it seems to have a direct influence on the weather pattern below. It lies over central Europe in summer, over the Mediterranean in winter, and usually is connected with poor weather conditions in these areas.

In the average situation the surface pressure gradient also induces a west-wind drift over Europe. However, it depends a great deal on the weather type on the one hand, on the location of the weather station on the other, to what extent west winds are recorded more often than any other winds. The maps of winter and summer circulation (Fig. 1–9) demonstrate clearly the generalization of the statement that Europe "lies within the westerlies." With the shift of the pressure centers toward the north in summer and toward the south in winter, the wind belts shift accordingly. It is for this reason that the winter and summer conditions are treated separately in later paragraphs.

While the pressure distribution governs atmospheric circulation, air masses and fronts are actually the direct causes of weather conditions. Since five major air masses are continuously or seasonally influencing the weather in Europe, there are a great variety of weather types during the year. Fronts between air masses are particularly well developed during winter, when temperature contrasts over different parts of Europe and the adjacent areas are most pronounced. The following scheme lists the air masses which influence the weather of Europe.

Air Mass	Source Region	Characteristics	Season of Occurrence
Arctic (A)	Arctic Sea	Very cold, dry	Winter
Maritime polar (mP)	North Atlantic	Cold, moist	Entire year
Continental polar (cP)	Eastern Europe and Asia	Cold and dry / Warm and dry	Winter / Summer
Maritime tropical (mT)	Central Atlantic	Warm and moist	Entire year
Continental tropical (cT)	Southwest Asia	Hot and dry	Summer

The main frontal system between the warm and cold air masses is the Polar Front. It is formed by mP and mT over the Atlantic, by either mP or mT, and cP over the continent. It usually lies diagonally (southwest-northeast) across northern Europe in summer, and extends into Mediterranean Europe in winter only. The front is usually connected with the barometric depressions over the North Atlantic or with migrating "lows." The trajectories of these lows, therefore, are indicative of the location of the Polar Front at any particular time.

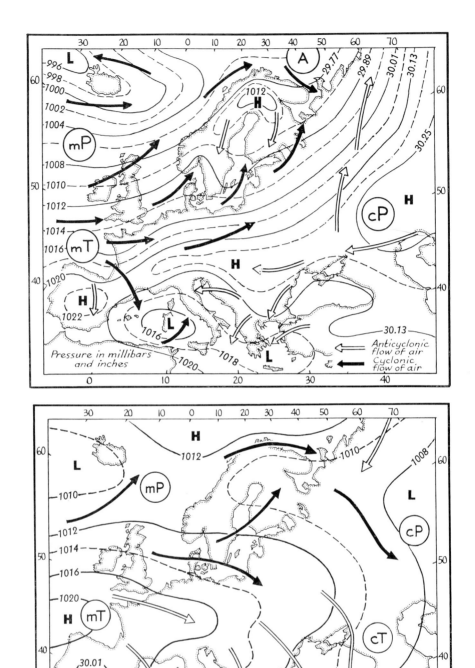

Fig. 1–9. Pressure distribution, prevailing circulation, and air masses. *Above,* in winter (January); *below,* in summer (July).

46

The Arctic Front affects the northernmost part of Europe during winter. The cold sector of lows along the Arctic Front is filled with very cold air emerging from the Arctic, while the warm sector contains mP or cP air. The absence of a truly arctic air mass in summer over the Arctic Ocean usually prevents the formation of an Arctic Front in summer.

Both frontal systems are mainly responsible for poor weather conditions in the areas occupied by them. Frontal precipitation, increased by orographic effects, accounts for a very high percentage of total precipitation in Europe.

Weather Conditions in Winter. The two maps of Fig. 1–9 show the atmospheric conditions over Europe in the extreme seasons. The greater contrasts and complexity of the winter situation are at once obvious. The pressure difference between southeastern and northwestern Europe activates a strong southwesterly wind drift within which cyclonic storms travel toward and into the continent. An advance of the continental anticyclone westward often shuts off or diverts northward maritime air masses and brings even westernmost Europe under the influence of frigid continental air with cold easterly winds. It is not at all unusual that with such weather types central Europe is 30–40° F. colder than coastal areas in northern Norway. On the other hand, there often exists an uninterrupted westerly drift from the Atlantic coast deep into the continent, thus bringing most of Europe a period of stormy, often rainy, weather in midwinter. The effect of the southern mountain ranges upon circulation is noticeable even on the mean map, but more so on daily weather maps. If the Alps in early winter are snowed in, an Alpine High is likely to develop, which often joins the high-pressure area in the interior of the continent. In such situations, cyclonic weather is confined to northern Europe. It is obvious, also, that the Scandinavian mountains and the high-pressure system often developed about them prevent cyclonic storms from crossing the peninsula. The Swedish side is frequently under prolonged anticyclonic control with subzero temperatures, while the Atlantic coast is subject to cyclonic weather with temperatures well above freezing.

The warm Mediterranean Sea acts as a meteorologic "magnet" to low-pressure systems approaching the mainland south of the British Isles in winter. The lows often "jump" over from the Bay of Biscay into the Tyrrhenian Basin, remaining there for days, stationary or traveling eastward and northeastward over the energy-supplying sea route. When cold air breaks into the Mediterranean area through gaps in the Alpine range (Rhone Valley, Slovenian depression, Vardar Valley), the temperature contrasts induce very strong cyclonic activity. Heavy rainfall or snowfall occurs in areas traversed by the cyclones. Local high-pressure centers frequently develop over the Mediterranean peninsulas, so the inland areas are less influenced by cyclonic storms than are the coasts.

Under prolonged anticyclonic regime a peculiar weather type develops in the central and southern uplands of Europe. After cold continental air masses have penetrated into the valleys and basins in the wake of an easterly cold wave, they become stationary and have little chance to escape unless cyclonic conditions are re-established to suck the cold, heavy air out of these depressions. Owing to the inflow of warm upper air in combination with the accumulation of combustion products (condensation nuclei) in the calm air above the densely settled and industrialized lowlands, a cloud layer soon begins to form along the boundary between the cold and warm air. This "high fog," as it is often called, absorbs and reflects the sun's rays, which gives the terrain above 2,000–3,000 feet warm, sunny weather with cloudless skies above and a "sea of fog" lying below (Fig. 1–10). Instead of a normal decrease of temperature with altitude, one therefore observes a strong temperature increase (a condition called "temperature inversion"). The Alpine resort areas may then have temperatures in the fifties during midwinter days, with very cold nights because of the nocturnal loss of heat into the cloudless sky. In contrast, the lowlanders may not see the sun for days or even one or two weeks, looking up at a grey, structureless cloud mass and measuring temperatures below the freezing point by day and night.[29]

Another Alpine weather type, most frequent in the transitional seasons, is the "föhn" situation. A föhn is a very warm and extremely dry wind falling down into those valleys of the Alps which are oriented north-south, as a consequence of strong pressure differences on opposite sides of the Alps. Föhn winds are particularly well developed in the northern Swiss and Austrian Alps when a deep low approaches the Alps from southern France and high pressure over the Balkans blocks the advance of the low. A strong southerly flow is then initiated between the two pressure systems and is forced to cross the Alps at right angles. While the southern slopes of the mountains receive intense rains owing to the forced uplift of the moist air masses uninterruptedly flowing northward, the north-Alpine slopes are under the regime of the föhn, which subsides and dries

---

[29] It is interesting to note in this connection that air traffic comes to a practical standstill if radiation fogs over central Europe combine with advection fogs over western Europe. On one memorable occasion British winter tourists headed for Switzerland landed safely on the frozen lake of St. Moritz—the only alternative was London!

Fig. 1–10. View from above the Jura Mountains over the stratus-covered Swiss midlands toward the central Swiss Alps. (Photo: Friedli, Swissair.)

out the moist air as it bursts into the transverse valleys. One sees from the Alpine foreland a wall of clouds hovering high above the Alps which, owing to the purity of the atmosphere, seem to be at an almost touchable distance (Fig. 1–11).

The dry, warm föhn is particularly dangerous as a fire hazard; the wooden structures of Alpine villages have repeatedly been consumed in holocausts. It also affects many people psychically, more because of the low pressure and low ozone content of the atmosphere than because of the high winds.

Winter Climate. The most characteristic feature of the temperature map is the meridional trend of the isotherms over most of non-Mediterranean Europe (Fig. 1–12). Mean January temperatures decrease as one goes east along any degree of latitude, while the temperature drop is very slight as one goes northward along a meridian. Bergen and Lyons, both at longitude 5° E. and 1,000 miles apart, have almost the same average January temperature (34° and 35° F., respectively), while Leningrad, at the same latitude as Bergen and not quite 1,000 miles farther east, is 16° F. colder in January. The temperature gradient from coast to interior is particularly strong between the west coast and the highlands of Scandinavia. Here winter temperatures drop by as much as 30° F. within a distance of 100

Fig. 1–11. Föhn weather in the Alps. Note the lenticular cloud sheets being driven northward by the föhn. (Photo: Swissair.)

miles, an effect of both altitude and anticyclonic weather control over the highlands.

The decrease of winter temperatures across central Europe is much more gradual, indicative of the transport of warm air masses into the inland areas.

The Mediterranean Basin is characterized by mean winter temperatures betwen 32° and 50° F., with daily maxima often in the seventies in its southern portion. However, it should be emphasized that the winter weather in this region is by no means warm. Periods of subfreezing weather occur each winter whenever cold continental air is able to cross the Alps. Only isolated spots in the extreme southern portions of the peninsulas and islands have not yet recorded temperatures below freezing at sea level.

The coldest area of Europe is the northeast, where the cold is rarely alleviated by invasions of maritime air. Normal daily means here are around 0° F. Temperatures below —40° F. have been measured in Moscow, and subzero temperatures occur regularly in all parts of eastern Europe. In severe winters, subfreezing weather may affect the continent as far west as the British Isles.

Winter precipitation is almost entirely connected with cyclonic storms intruding into Europe. As for temperature, there is a gradual

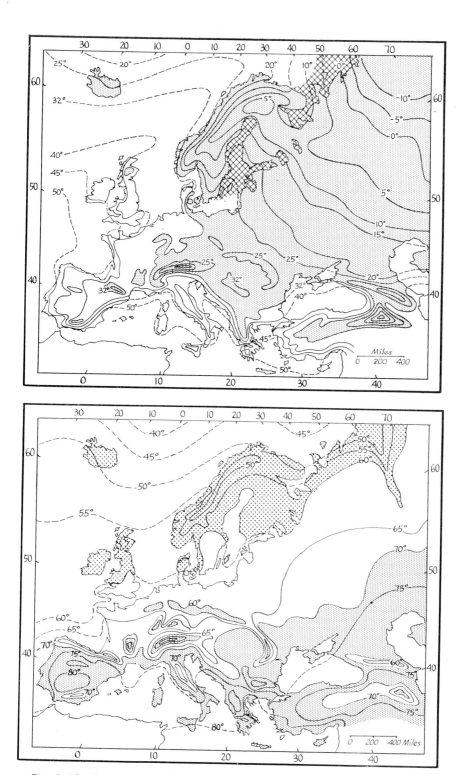

Fig. 1-12. Temperature distribution. *Above,* in winter; *below,* in summer.

decrease in the amount of precipitation eastward over the lowland area, a sharp decrease across the Scandinavian peninsula. The proportion of precipitation falling in the form of snow increases in the same direction. However, most of the eastern-European lowlands, including the Great Russian Lowland, have a characteristically low snow accumulation in winter. Rarely does a station receive more than 10 inches of snow (recorded as 1 inch water equivalent) in any of the winter months. Ample amounts of winter precipitation are recorded along the west coasts of the British Isles, Scandinavia, and the Mediterranean peninsulas, and in the Alps. In the western and northern portions of the Mediterranean, the winter rains usually begin rather abruptly in October with the first cyclonic storms appearing over the area. A majority of places along the northern shore of the Mediterranean have a fall and spring peak of rainfall and a noticeable lull in midwinter, the time when the rains are strongest farther south. This difference in the occurrence of the precipitation maximum between the southern and northern portion of the Mediterranean is closely related to the cyclonic weather along the Polar Front, which affects the northern Mediterranean twice (in fall and spring), the southern but once (during its southernmost position in midwinter). More than three-fourths of the total annual rainfall is usually recorded between October and April at most Mediterranean localities. Both the duration of the wet season and the total amount of precipitation generally decrease from west to east. Precipitation is much more evenly distributed throughout the year in non-Mediterranean Europe. However, the winter months are still the rainiest in the Atlantic borderland. Only at a considerable distance inland can we recognize the shift to summer as the wettest time of the year.

Weather Conditions in Summer. The main pressure feature in summer is the Azores High, then located some 5 to 10 degrees latitude farther north than in winter. It often forms an extension eastward far into the continent and prevents cyclonic storms from penetrating the Mediterranean. Pressure is also higher over the northeastern Atlantic with the Icelandic Low very much less in evidence than in winter. Thus, the north-south pressure gradient is smaller in summer, and as a consequence the westerlies are weakened. In certain synoptic types, however, particularly in spring and early summer in the central part of Europe, and in midsummer in the northern part, invasions of maritime air masses, pushing deep into the interior in the wake of cyclones, are accompanied by strong west or northwest winds. In three out of four Junes, Europe experiences a period of persistent rains, and one authority has spoken of a monsoonal tendency reminiscent in type, if not in intensity, of the summer monsoon rains along the Pacific coast of Eurasia. Low pressure prevails over most of non-Mediterranean Europe at this time of the year, and most stations east of a line North Cape-Oslo-Paris-Toulouse, therefore, record summer maxima of precipitation.

The most drastic change from winter to summer is observed south of the Alpine mountains where anticyclonic pressure controls the weather practically uninterruptedly from May to September. While the winds over the western Mediterranean are variable, a conspicuous wind system with northerly components has established itself over the eastern half. These dry northerly or northwesterly winds are called *etesians* (Greek for "yearly returning winds"). They are particularly strong and persistent over the Aegean Sea and the Adriatic. Cyclonic development in summer is rare and restricted to the extreme northern and western portions of the Mediterranean lands over which local heating produces convective showers and thunderstorms of high intensity and short duration.

Air-mass differences over Europe in summer are not as sharp as in winter. The dominating air masses are still those from the Atlantic. Maritime tropical air is most frequently found over southwestern and central Europe. If it arrives in connection with an advance of the Azores High, a spell of fine weather results. If, however, it drifts northeastward in the warm sector of cyclones and comes into contact with either maritime polar or continental polar air it brings poor weather. In these situations, the Alps have a strong lifting effect and heavy rainfall occurs on their northern slopes. In the transitional seasons waves of maritime polar air often bring snowy setbacks in spring or early snowfalls in fall in mountain locations. Along the northwest and north coasts of Europe, maritime polar air with high cloudiness, fog, and drizzle rules the weather most of the summer. Continental polar air, covering western Russia, is must drier and often warmer than maritime air. It forms in relatively shallow summer anticyclones over central Asia or originates from altered maritime tropical air. The driest and hottest air mass is found over southeastern Europe. It is either altered maritime tropical air, desiccated and heated due to subsidence along the east flank of the subtropical high, or it arrives as true continental tropical air from the hot interior of Asia on the north side of the southwest-Asiatic Monsoon Low.

Summer Climate. The arrangement of the summer isotherms (Fig. 1–12) is more nearly normal in the sense that it indicates a more or less regular decrease in mean temperatures from the Mediterranean to the Arctic Sea. Interior stations at low elevations are always warmer than stations adjacent to the ocean. Therefore, with

increasing distance from the coast, the temperature range between
the coldest and the warmest month increases. The isotherms of
80° F. enclose the hottest regions of Europe (the interiors of southern Spain, southern Italy, most of southeastern Europe, and the
Volga lowland). Occasionally extremes above 100° F. are recorded
as far north as the shores of the North Sea and the Baltic Sea.

For the bulk of non-Mediterranean Europe, summer is the rainy
season. Most precipitation is of frontal origin connected with invasions of maritime air, or falls in thunderstorms. Convectional
rains, however, contribute less than 20 per cent of the total summer
precipitation in any part of Europe. The coastal fringe along the
Atlantic, while still rainy and continuously cloudy, receives less rainfall in the summer half-year than in the six cold months, but, as far
as total annual precipitation is concerned, stations in this coastal strip
stand out with much higher yearly sums than the low-lying inland
stations. If we consider the three summer months only, there is no
general decrease of rainfall eastward: Moscow receives more rain
than Berlin, Paris, or even London.[30] Poland, the Danubian countries, and southern Russia are more often affected by droughts than
any other European area. Since agriculture in these areas is carried
on in dry farming operations, it repeatedly suffers severe losses, quite
in contrast to the Mediterranean land, where man centuries ago
turned to irrigation to overcome the summer drought. In the latter
area, the main climatic handicaps are actually the high rain intensity
in autumn, its variability from year to year, and frosts.

As can be seen on the map of annual precipitation (Fig. 1–13),
the annual total of precipitation is above 20 inches in all areas of
Europe except the southern Mediterranean, the extreme southeast,
the basins and valleys of the Alps, and the extreme north. It should
be emphasized, however, that these 20 inches represent a mean
amount which will not be received each year. With a succession of
dry years, even west-European areas face water shortages. Irrigation
has become a necessity over much of Europe in order to secure reliable crop returns.[31]

By way of summarizing the seasonal regime of precipitation, it
can be said that there is a conspicuous variety of types within the
relatively small area of Europe. From the autumn maximum along
the west coast to the winter maximum in the Mediterranean, and
over the spring peak in the Southeastern Peninsula and along the

---

[30] For comparisons, see the climatic diagrams in Appendix II.

[31] Even in some of the fjords of Norway, irrigation practices are followed. Within
10 miles of one of the wettest points of Switzerland irrigation or fallowing is necessary
on the slopes of the deeply entrenched upper Rhone Valley and its tributaries.

Black Sea shore to the summer maximum in the continental interior, any season may be the rainiest in some part of Europe.

Climatic Types and Regions

Having discussed the characteristics of individual climatic elements, we have now the task of integrating them into a climatic system. There are various ways of classifying climates. The one fol-

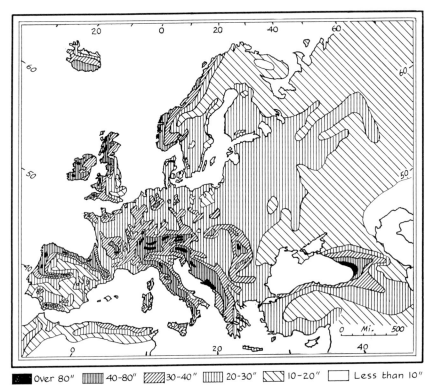

Fig. 1–13. Annual precipitation.

■ Over 80″   ▦ 40-80″   ▨ 30-40″   ▥ 20-30″   ◩ 10-20″   ☐ Less than 10″

lowed here is consistent with the approach chosen in the section on landforms. Emphasis is put upon the genesis rather than on the description of climates. The types of climate selected should therefore reflect the genetic factors responsible for them. As far as the areal extent of individual types is concerned, it should be remembered that climatic regions are rarely separated by sharp boundaries. Only the higher mountain ranges of Europe, such as the Alps, the Pyrenees, and the Scandinavian mountains, are sharp climatic divides. In the extensive central and eastern lowland of Europe, changes from one climatic type to another are very gradual. That is to say, the climate of western Europe differs from that of eastern Europe more in grade than in type. Another problem connected with delimiting climatic boundaries is the effect of altitude. Increasing altitude produces much sharper climatic gradients than does either increasing latitude or increasing continentality. Genetically, however, mountain climates are affected by the same weather types as the surrounding lowlands, but they have a different effect upon individual climatic elements (lower temperature, higher precipitation).

In relation to the major controls of atmospheric circulation (pressure and wind systems, air masses, and fronts) there exist four basic climatic types in Europe. They are:

1. maritime type (also called marine or oceanic type)
2. transitional type
3. continental type
4. Mediterranean (or subtropical) type

As can be seen from the map of climatic regions (Fig. 1–14), the first type occurs in westernmost Europe, the second in the eastern portions. Each of these two regions is characterized by the dominance of one air mass throughout the year: maritime air in the west, continental air in the east. These are the prime causes for the types of climate developed under their regime and bearing their names. The boundary between maritime and continental air masses is constantly fluctuating with the migrations of the Polar Front. Between the two extreme regimes in the west and the east, therefore, there must exist a broad zone of transition from a maritime to a continental character of climate. Central and eastern Europe lie in this zone. Its changeable weather bears ample evidence of the conflict of air masses of different character.

The climate of the extreme western portions of Europe is typically maritime. Its basic characteristics are ample and evenly distributed rainfall, prevailing westerly winds, high humidity and cloudiness, a small annual range of temperature, and rarely subfreezing weather. The climate of the eastern region is a moderate form of the true continental type of climate. The annual range of temperature in the extreme east of the European U.S.S.R. is large, but still only less than 60° F. as compared to more than 120° F. in eastern Siberia. The corresponding values are around 40° F. for central Europe and some 20° F. along the west coast. We might say that the climate in eastern Europe (i.e., the European U.S.S.R.) is only half as continental as it could be, but three times more so than the maritime type. The type referred to as the "Mediterranean" is found over the peninsulas, islands, and waters of the Mediterranean and Black seas. Its dry summers make it distinctly different from the aforementioned types. In winter, the maritime influence is as great as in western and central Europe.

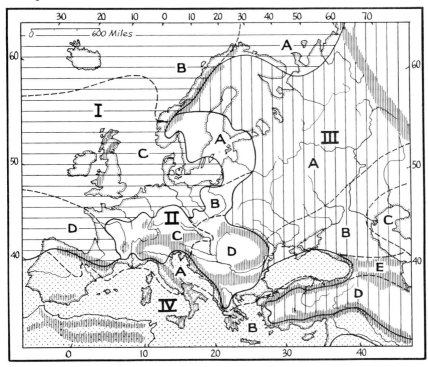

I. Atlantic Seaboard Region:
   Maritime Type
   Provinces:
      A. Arctic
      B. Norwegian
      C. North Sea
      D. Biscay

II. Central Region: Transitional
    Type
    Provinces:
      A. Baltic
      B. Polish
      C. Alpine
      D. Danubian

III. Eastern Region: Continental
     Type
     Provinces:
       A. Northern
       B. Southern
       C. Caspian
       D. Anatolian
       E. Caucasian

IV. Mediterranean Region: Subtropical
    Type
    Provinces:
       A. Northern
       B. Southern

Fig. 1–14. Climatic types, regions, and provinces. Highland modifications within each region are indicated by shading.

1. The Maritime Type. Each of the main types can be subdivided into subtypes (see summary, pp. 62–63). The areas in which they occur may be called provinces within the climatic regions of the major types. The maritime region contains four provinces: (1) the Arctic Sea coast, (2) the west coast of the Scandinavian peninsula, (3) the North Sea coastal lands, and (4) the extreme southwest of non-Mediterranean Europe. In addition, highland subtypes can be differentiated in all regions. The Arctic province lies north of the tree limit, and also extends above it, since it projects southward into the Scandinavian mountain land. The province is characterized by very cold winters which, however, are still considerably warmer than those at intracontinental stations toward the southeast (compare type stations Kola and Vorkuta in Appendix II). The major difference between the other three maritime provinces lies in their thermal regime. Thorshavn (Faeroe Islands), one of the most typically maritime stations anywhere in the world, has the extremely small annual range of temperature of 13° F. (February 38° F., July 51° F.). Copenhagen is 10° F. colder in winter and 10° F. warmer in summer, and Biarritz in southwestern France (not shown in Appendix II), almost 20° F. warmer than Thorshavn in summer and winter. All these maritime stations receive the highest amount of rainfall in the months of the cold season, with the maximum months delayed from autumn to early winter the farther south the station lies. The month with the highest rainfall is normally September in Bergen, October in London, and November in Bilbao, clearly revealing the southward migration of the rain belt along the Polar Front during the fall months.[32] On the west coast of the British Isles and on the outlying islands a midwinter maximum is recorded, a consequence of strongest air-mass contrasts and highest frequency of cyclonic storms at that time of the year (see diagrams of Thorshavn, Glasgow, Plymouth, Valentia, and Reykjavík).

2. The Transitional Type. The transition zone between the maritime and the continental climatic region, called the Central Region in Fig. 1–14, can be divided into northern (Baltic), central (Polish), southern (Alpine), and southeastern (Danubian) provinces. In the Baltic and Polish provinces winters are much colder than in the southern provinces, while the boundary between the two is based upon the cooler and drier summers of the northern province. The Alpine province, especially its higher parts, receives a much higher amount of precipitation than any other transitional province. In total amount, but not in seasonal regime, precipitation in the higher Alps is comparable to that of the rainiest sections of the maritime region (annual total above 80 inches [Fig. 1–13]). The Appendix II diagrams of Stockholm, Kraków, and the three Swiss stations (Basel,

---

[32] A secondary maximum of rainfall is recorded at some stations along the Atlantic coast in spring at the time when the Polar Front returns to the north.

Lucerne, and Säntis)[33] are representative of the temperature and precipitation regimes in the provinces of the central climatic region. All these stations show a marked summer maximum of precipitation. With the exception of Kraków, which already indicates the dry continental winter, they also receive at least 1 inch of precipitation in the driest month, usually January. The Danubian province is under the influence of continental air in summer (cT) and winter (cP), with maritime air intruding mainly in the transitional seasons. It generally receives less rainfall than the other four transitional provinces. Quite characteristic is the early summer maximum of precipitation at most of the interior stations (type stations Budapest, Dej, Prague), while those close to the Adriatic, Aegean, and Black seas have not only the convection rainfall peak of summer but also a secondary maximum in early and late winter (see type station Kragujevac). Since they are at the same time located in highland areas, they are much wetter than the basin stations.[34]

3. The Continental Type. The Eastern Region has five provinces. The only climatic trait common to this large area is the severe cold in winter, caused by the constant dominance of continental polar air. The subdivision is based on wide variations in both total amount and seasonal regime of precipitation. The northern province "A" of this Eastern Region shows definite affinities to the neighboring provinces of the central climatic region (compare the similar total and regime of precipitation of type stations Moscow and Helsinki, Appendix II). Winter temperatures in the central Russian plains, however, are 10–20° F. lower than in the central region, the summers slightly warmer. With the increased influence of continental tropical air in summer, rainfall diminishes and the critical 20-inch isohyet is reached in the Ukraine. This is the semiarid province "B" of the continental region, an area often afflicted by severe drought due to the unreliability of the summer rains and to the scorching winds from the trans-Caspian source region of dry, hot continental air. Still closer to the Caspian, truly arid conditions prevail in province "C" (see also type station Astrakhan, Appendix II). The interior of Anatolia ("D") is in a transitional area between the continental and Mediterranean types of climate. The thermal regime is similar to that in the afore-

[33] Lying in the northeasternmost chain of the Swiss Alps, the Säntis observatory (Fig. 1–6) records an extremely high precipitation (110 inches). It is fully exposed to maritime air masses and has a high thunderstorm frequency. The station also shows the effect of altitude in thermal respects.

[34] The combination of intensive winter and summer rains produces the largest total amount of precipitation of southern Europe in the Dinaric mountains close to the Gulf of Kotor (160 inches). The absolute maximum of precipitation in Europe occurs in southwestern Norway at the Jostedal Glacier (230 inches).

Summary of Climatic

Type	Region and Provinces	Pressure and Winds	Air Masses and Fronts
Maritime	Atlantic seaboard region Provinces: Arctic Norwegian North Sea Biscay (Highlands)	Stationary Icelandic Low in winter. Stationary Azores High in summer. Migrating lows. SW to W.	mP, mT (A, cP)* Polar Front active all year (except in Biscay province). Arctic Front in extreme north in winter.
Transitional	Central Europe region Provinces: Baltic Polish Alpine Danubian (Highlands)	Migrating lows throughout year. Extensions of Icelandic Low, Continental High in winter. Azores High often dominant in summer. NW to SW.	mT, mP, cP (cT) Polar Front activity throughout the year.
Continental	Eastern Europe region Provinces: Northern Southern Caspian Anatolian Caucasian (Highlands)	Stationary Continental High and migrating lows in winter. Moderate cyclonic activity in summer. SW in winter. NW in summer.	cP, cT (mP, mT) Polar Front activity pronounced in winter, weak in summer.
Subtropical	Mediterranean region Provinces: Northern Southern (Highlands)	Stationary Mediterranean High in summer. Migrating lows in winter. Variable in winter. NW–NE in summer.	mT, cT (cP, mP) Polar Front active in winter only.

*Less frequent or only locally significant.

Types and Regions

Type	Precipitation	Temperature	Miscellaneous	Other Type Designations
Maritime	Even distribution through year, strongest in winter. Annual total above 30 inches. Snow rare at sea level.	Small annual range (20° F.). Rarely below 32° and above 86°. Coldest month often February	High cloudiness and humidity, and fog frequency. Arctic province much colder than other provinces.	Oceanic, marine west coast. Cf, ET (tundra) according to Koeppen system.
Transitional	Even distribution, but well-defined summer maximum, particularly in eastern provinces and highlands. Annual total increasing with altitude.	Moderate annual range (30°– 50° F.). Abs. maxima > 100° F., minima < 0° F.	Mountain areas much colder and moister than lowlands, except during inversion weather in winter.	Humid continental, mesothermal. Cf, Df, ET according to Koeppen system.
Continental	Marked summer maximum, permanent snow cover in winter.	Large annual range (50°– 70° F.). Minima < 0°, maxima > 90°.	Rapid change from winter to summer and vice versa.	Short-summer humid or semiarid continental, microthermal. Df, BS according to Koeppen system.
Subtropical	Marked winter rainy season. Summers dry, except in highlands and marginal areas.	Summers hot (means above 80° F.). Winters cool to cold, but above 32° F. Annual range 20° – 40° F.	East coasts much drier than west coasts. Interiors much hotter than coastal areas in summer.	Mediterranean, etesian, dry summer subtropical. Cs, BS according to Koeppen system.

mentioned provinces, but the annual distribution of precipitation is entirely different, the pronounced summer dryness being the outstanding characteristic. The sources of moisture lie in the Mediterranean and Black seas, but due to the marginal mountain ranges little precipitation is received over the interior plateau. What there is comes in form of cyclonic rains before or after the anticyclonic control of midwinter (see type station Ankara). Due to convectional activity in spring, many Anatolian stations exhibit a pronounced April or May maximum of rainfall. Finally, the Caucasian region ("E") forms a distinct climatic province characterized by ample precipitation throughout the year. In the coastal areas, influenced by Black Sea and Caspian cyclones, more rain falls in winter than in summer; in the interior, the reverse is true.

4. The Mediterranean Type. The climatic region designated as the Mediterranean is unique in so far as dry, hot summers are coupled with rainy, cool winters. Rainfall generally decreases toward the south and the east, with a simultaneously growing number of dry months in these directions. The boundary between the two provinces delimited in the Mediterranean climatic region follows approximately the 1-inch isohyet of the driest summer month. North of this line, especially in the mountain areas, thunderstorm activity persists throughout the summer. Even though they are not treated as special provinces, reference should be made to certain areas which deviate from the normal type described above. The interior of Spain has a more "continental" version of the Mediterranean climate, with considerably colder winters and hotter summers than the coastal districts.[35] The Ebro Basin, in the rain shadow of the Pyrenees, is the driest area of southern Europe, and, together with the extreme north and southeast, of all Europe (Zaragoza 11.5 inches). Marked local contrasts, particularly between west and east coasts of islands and peninsulas, are typical, such as between the Adriatic and the Aegean side of Greece (Corfu 49 inches annual rainfall, Athens 16 inches) or along the shores of the Black Sea (the lowest temperature ever observed at Samsun, on the Black Sea coast of Turkey, was 20° F.; at Taganrog, on the north coast of the Sea of Azov, it was —22° F.!). The Po Plain has been included with the Alpine province of the central climatic region, because cyclonic developments may occur at any time of the year. Thus, both the cyclonic winter rains of Mediterranean Europe and those of central Europe in summer contribute to the large total rainfall figures in this area. Milan (see type station, Appendix II), in the center of the Po Plain, is 11° F. colder in winter

[35] As the adage goes in Madrid, "*seis meses invierno, seis meses infierno*" (six months of winter, six months of hell).

than Genoa, from which it is separated by the Apennines and only 80 miles distance.

By way of a summary the climatic regions and provinces are listed on pp. 60–61, with the corresponding meteorological and climatological characteristics.

BIOGEOGRAPHIC AND PEDOLOGIC ASPECTS OF EUROPE

Evolution of Biota and Soils

The present distribution of flora and fauna, as well as that of soils, is the result of three sets of influences: topographic, climatic, and anthropogenic. First, the evolution of the European land was not a regionally independent process which could have produced specifically European types of plants and animals. This is to say that Europe is as much a part of Eurasia biogeographically as it is structurally. The only boundary separating clearly different biotic areas in Europe follows the Alpine range and its western and eastern continuations. The zone north of the Alps is a part of the "Boreal" biotic realm, which also includes the higher latitudes of Asia and North America. South of the Alps, the Mediterranean biota are closely related to those of southwestern Asia and northern Africa.

Second, of paramount importance for the present floristic, faunistic, and pedologic associations were the climatic changes which affected Europe during and after the Ice Age. The ice sheets forced the biota into the unglaciated areas of central and southern Europe. The climatic zones shifted southward, and with them plants and animals. Most of Scandinavia was still covered by the ice some 10,000 years ago. Since then, with various interruptions during postglacial climatic fluctuations, flora and fauna, as well as soils and even landforms, have adjusted themselves to the present climatic conditions. The main biotic associations, therefore, have reached their present locations only recently, geologically speaking. Central Europe became an area of immigration of plants and animals from all sides, particularly from the east. It is questionable whether these migrations have really come to an end in the short span of postglacial time.

A third influence on biota and soils is man himself. "Natural vegetation" in Europe is only rarely natural in the sense of representing the original vegetation untouched by man. It has been established that well over 80 per cent of the European land was originally forested. Today only one-third of Europe is covered by trees, and much of this is either a cultivated second-growth woodland or, particularly

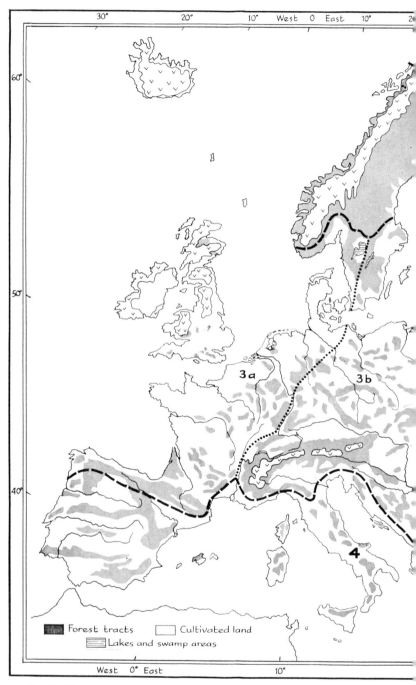

Fig. 1–15. Vegetation zones and actual distribution of forests. (1) tundr
fjell, Alpine meadows, heath and moorlands; (2) boreal forest: a, open;
closed; (3) mixed forest: a, Atlantic association; b, central association; c, easte

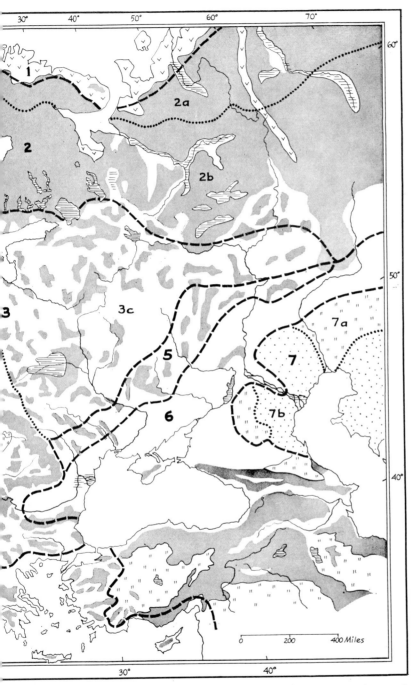

sociation; (4) Mediterranean hardleaf forest, excluding large areas of second-
y "maqui" associations; (5) forest steppe; (6) steppe; (7) desert: a, semidesert,
cluding grass and scrub steppe in Turkey; b, desert.

65

in the Mediterranean area, degenerated scrub forest. The long occupancy of the land and the high density of population had the effect of pushing the forest back to the non-arable areas of Europe. The same has happened in the grass steppes of southern Russia and the Ukraine, where little of the original grassland has been left undisturbed after centuries of intensive cultivation.

Plant Cover: Types and Distribution

Even though large stands of native vegetation are rare and widely scattered, over much of Europe it is possible to reconstruct the original plant cover by analyzing the species composition of these refugial sites. We can assume that without the interference of man the European forests would have the same aspects as those which appear relatively undisturbed in the midst of the deforested land. Figure 1–15 attempts to take into consideration both the actual and potential distribution by showing the boundaries between the major plant formations as they would exist had man not interfered, as well as the actual location of larger tracts of native vegetation. Due to the small scale of the map the pattern is, of course, highly generalized, but it allows one to recognize the relationship of vegetation to climatic and topographic factors. The fact that subtropical and arctic types of vegetation occur gives a first indication of the thermal conditions controlling the distribution of plants. The same evolves from the vertical zonation of vegetation. Increasing altitude has a similar effect on temperatures to that of increasing latitude, so that one crosses identical plant associations going northward and upward. In other words, the sequence: hardleaf forest – mixed forest – boreal forest – tundra from southern to northern Europe is repeated in the Alps, where these associations lie above one another. The forest reaches its northern limit just short of the Arctic Sea, while in the Alps the upper timber limit lies between 5,000 and 6,000 feet. In both areas sufficient summer heat is the critical climatic factor. A mean temperature of 50° F. in the warmest month seems to be the minimum requirement for sufficient wood growth in trees in the northern and Alpine forests. Other associations or individual species are limited in their distribution by excessive winter cold. This is particularly obvious with many Mediterranean plants which do not survive north of the Alps. Here it is the mean temperature of the coldest month which sets the limits for warmth-loving plants. Another important climatic boundary, clearly evident in the distribution of vegetation, is the limit of aridity. Tree growth is no longer possible, because of deficient precipitation, excessive evaporation, or both.

The natural plant formation in a semiarid climate is a treeless grass cover. Within Europe it is most typically developed in the extreme southeast, forming the vast steppes in the plains of southern Russia. The combined effect of climatic and topographic factors upon distribution of vegetation is one of zonation, in both a latitudinal and an altitudinal sense. A comparison between the map of climatic regions (Fig. 1–14) and that of vegetation zones (Fig. 1–15) reveals the close relationship between climatic and vegetational boundaries.

Soil Groups

Although the major soil groups (Fig. 1–16) again show the typical zonal arrangement the pattern is quite complex, owing to the fact that the soil-forming factors are more heterogeneous than those responsible for the plant cover. In addition to climate, the type of the underlying rock material, topography, drainage conditions, vegetation, micro-organisms, and the time factor all play a role in the formation of soils. The great variety of soils in Europe is at once obvious from an inspection of the map of major soil groups, which represents only a strongly simplified version of the complex mosaic actually existing. Most zonal soils (i.e., mature soils having developed a profile corresponding to the ambient climate) which can form in mid-latitudes are found in Europe. Azonal soils (i.e., soils without normally developed profiles) occupy large tracts of the land, particularly in the mountainous portions of southern Europe. By far the most widely distributed soils belong to the group of the forest soils, while the grassland soils of southeastern Europe are next in areal extent. The individual soil groups and their characteristics will be discussed in the following paragraphs, together with the biotic zones with which they are associated.

Tundra and *Fjell*. The Arctic zone, restricted in Europe to a narrow strip of "tundra" [36] along the Arctic Sea, is characterized by a rather luxuriant growth of low forms of vegetation. Lichen (symbiotic union of algae and fungi) prevail on drier sites, mosses and sedges in poorly drained areas. The tundra is not absolutely treeless in so far as tree genera occur. In the most favorable sites shrubs of birch and willow may form. Most of these wooden plants, however, creep along the ground. There is so little wood development in them that 100-year-old specimens may have less than 1 inch stem diameter. The tundra is quite rich in blossoming plants in midsummer, one of the pleasant surprises awaiting the traveler in the

[36] The word "tundra" is a derivation from the Finnish word *tunturi*, a mountain in Finland which projects above the timber line.

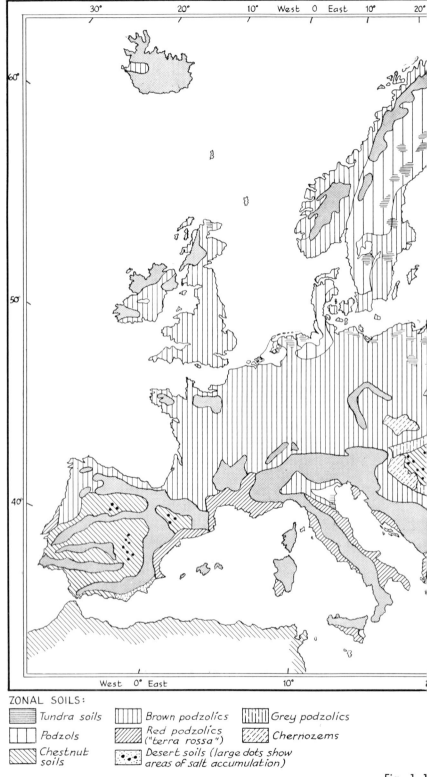

ZONAL SOILS:

☰	Tundra soils	⫴	Brown podzolics	▦	Grey podzolics
⊞	Podzols	▨	Red podzolics ("terra rossa")	▨	Chernozems
▧	Chestnut soils	⣿	Desert soils (large dots show areas of salt accumulation)		

Fig. 1–1

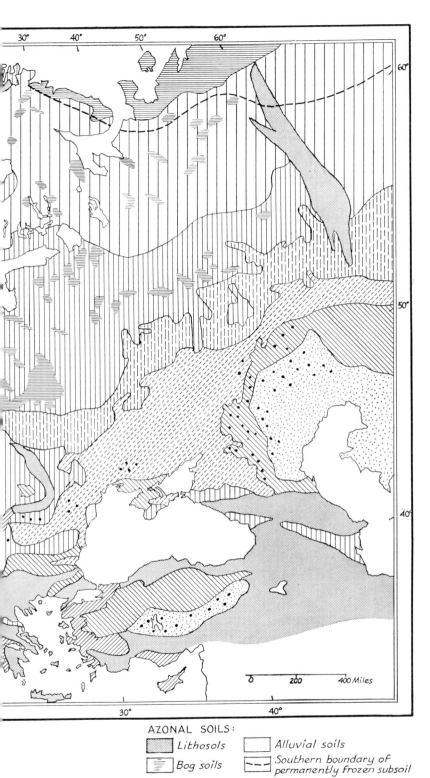

30° 40° 50° 60°

60°

50°

40°

0   200   400 Miles

30° 40°

AZONAL SOILS:

Lithosols

Bog soils

Alluvial soils

Southern boundary of
permanently frozen subsoil

groups.

subarctic. The yellowish lichen carpet, formed by the reindeer "moss" (botanically a lichen), the silver green of the arctic willow, the darker green of the mosses and sedges, and the multicolored flowers (*Ranunculus, Saxifraga, Dryas, Silene, Erica*—to name some of the most abundant genera) give quite a vivid coloring to the tundra landscape (Fig. 1–17).

Fig. 1–17. At the boundary between tundra and boreal forest in Swedish Lappland. The tundra with its moss, lichen, and sedge carpet is seen in the foreground; the coniferous forest occupies the lower levels in the center; and the Scandinavian mountains, with permanent ice fields, form the backdrop.

One can barely speak of tundra soils since a true soil development does not take place in the subarctic climate. In ill-drained depressions azonal "bog soils," actually slowly decomposing organic matter, black and extremely acid, are found to a considerable depth. A conspicuous feature in the highest and northernmost portions of the tundra is the perennially frozen soil, called "permafrost." [37] It may be from a few feet to a few hundred feet thick, with only the uppermost feet or even inches thawing in summer. Seasonal thawing and freezing keep the surface layer in constant motion, making it very difficult for plants to gain a foothold. Permafrost action produces a peculiar sorting of the frost-shattered rock debris which is often arranged in circular, polygonal, or mounded fashion. Occupying only isolated

[37] This ground ice is called *tele* in Norwegian, *tjaele* in Swedish, and *merzlota* in Russian. Permafrost is much more widely distributed in Asiatic Russia than in European Russia.

tracts in the Scandinavian tundra (bogs, high mountains), permafrost becomes areally very extensive in the extreme north of European Russia, where it even penetrates the boreal forest (Fig. 1–16).

The tundra fauna is limited in species but not in number. The arctic hare, the fox, and the lemming are representative of the circumpolar land fauna; the polar bear, the seal, and the walrus (the latter close to extinction) inhabit the arctic seas, rarely visiting the mainland. For uncounted numbers of migratory birds, the tundra and the shore and island cliffs along the arctic seas are the summer breeding grounds. Astounding are the swarms of flies and mosquitoes. The reindeer is only a summer resident of the tundra, migrating into the open woodlands farther south in winter.

The type of vegetation in the Scandinavian highlands, locally called the *"fjell,"* is closely related to that of the tundra. Dwarf shrubs (particularly the dwarf birch, the stunted birch, and various willows and heather shrubs) are more numerous, however (Fig. 1–1). Above the tree limit, here mostly formed by birches, and below the lichen-moss tundra, there is often an extensive zone of meadows. Their herbs, grasses, sedges, and flowering plants are floristically and ecologically very similar to the association of the Alpine meadows. The tundra animals are also found in the northern portions of the *fjell*, supplemented by the elk (related to the American moose). Wolves and bears are occasionally found above the timber limit.

The Boreal Forest. The boundary between the tundra and the boreal forest has to be conceived of as a zone, several degrees of latitude in width (Fig. 1–15). It has been referred to as lichen woodland, with the open stands of conifers and the willow and birch thickets on the lichen carpet giving the landscape a parklike appearance. In places open tundra intermingles with the "closed" forest, forming a forest tundra.[38] The open boreal forest then grades into the closed boreal forest, a spruce-fir association with a solid undergrowth of mosses and herbs rather than lichens (the Russian *taiga*).[39] The closed boreal forest is the largest biotic unit of Europe, covering some one million square miles, much of it still in natural conditions. In its western portions many of the stands are second growth, this area being one of the richest timber regions of Europe. Only a handful of species account for practically all coniferous trees (the Siberian-Uralian and European species of the spruce, the pine, the larch or

[38] Extensive bogs and forest marshland are also typical in the transitional zone between tundra and boreal forest.

[39] *Taiga* is a Tannu-Tuvan word also used by northern Mongols. It means the bald summit of a forested mountain, but its original meaning has been corrupted by the Russians and accepted by modern English to refer to the forest zone.

tamarack, and the fir, listed in order of abundance). In the boreal forest the cleared areas, rather than the woodlots as in central and western Europe, are "islands" in the landscape (Fig. 1–15).

The fauna is much richer than in the tundra. The fur-bearing carnivores (bear, fox, wolf, lynx, weasel, skunks, badger) and herbivores (beaver, squirrel, hare, marmot, muskrat) are typical forest dwellers. In addition, a great variety of birds, attached to the conifers in their eating habits, and deer live in the boreal forest. Many of the animals were formerly found farther west and south but have since retreated into the boreal forest with the disappearance of contiguous woodlands in the mixed-forest zone.

The relatively large amount of precipitation, little of which is lost by evaporation in the relatively cool summers, poor drainage conditions, and profusion of organic material decaying on the forest floor further the development of a specific soil profile under the boreal forest. Beneath the humus layer, excessive leaching takes place which removes all carbonates and other soluble substances except silicates and accumulates them in a clay-rich and often indurated lower soil layer. The leached horizon, left extremely acid, has a characteristically grey, bleached appearance. The Russian term *pod zola*, meaning "ash soil," implies the color of the leached layer. Podzols are inherently unproductive soils and at the same time often poorly drained either because of the hardpan or the thawing of snow and ground ice.

The Mixed Forest. South of approximately 60° N., the boreal forest becomes intermixed with broadleaf (deciduous) trees, the more so the farther west and south one goes. Only in the higher territory of central and southern Europe are conifers still found in pure stands. The zone of the mixed forest extends from the British Isles to the Urals; the Atlantic front of the zone stretches from southern Norway to northwestern Spain, while its eastern end comes to an apex in the Ural foreland. The triangular shape of the mixed-forest zone is indicative of the limiting climatic factors along its boundaries: excessive winter cold in the north, excessive dryness in the south; positively expressed, its range seems to be related to the area of year-round maritime influence. Within the mixed forest three subtypes can be distinguished (Fig. 1–15).

In the extreme west deciduous trees such as beech, elm, maple, and oak are more abundant than conifers, and there is an admixture of Mediterranean floral elements as far north as southern England. The chestnut advances to the Garonne, the grape to the Loire, and hardleaf evergreens are found in sheltered places of the British south coast. In higher tracts of land or on sandy soils the pine is the characteristic conifer. In the central European section of the mixed forest the beech is the character tree, but it no longer forms pure stands except in a few isolated spots (e.g., island of Rügen, Carpathians). Most of the second-growth stands have a large proportion of softwoods (spruce and fir). In the lower stories of the mountain forests beech-spruce associations are typical. At altitudes above 2,000 feet there exists a zonation within coniferous associations, the pine and the larch climbing higher than the spruce, the first two forming the timber line between 5,000 and 6,500 feet in the Alps, the last arriving at its upper limits between 3,000 and 5,000 feet in the non-Alpine mountains. In the morainic terrain along the North Sea and the Baltic swamp, moor and heath associations are widespread.

As on its Atlantic side, the mixed forest of central Europe grades into an association of somewhat different composition toward the east. The beech no longer occurs, and the oak now often dominates the forest, intermixed with conifers toward the north, and with grassland toward the south. With the southern boundary of the boreal forest trending southeast and the steppe extending much farther north in the Volga lowland than in the Ukraine, these two formations form a common boundary near the Volga elbow at Kazan, thus preventing the deciduous forest from reaching the Urals.

The rich fauna originally inhabiting the mixed forest has been greatly reduced, particularly in the western and central sections, during the long occupancy of man in this most densely settled area of Europe. The wild horse and the European wild ox have long been exterminated, the bison more recently. The elk has retreated into the boreal forest, the bear northward and eastward, and into the southeast-European mountains. The fur animals are less numerous than in the boreal forest. Deer, fox, badger, and wild boar have the widest range. Restricted to mountain areas are the chamois, the wild goat, the marmot, and the Alpine eagle. The main domain of the wolf is eastern Europe, but sporadically he appears as far west as eastern France or even northern Spain.

The soils in the mixed-forest zone, even though the majority belong to the podzolized group, exhibit an intricate mosaic on the soil map, which is the result of the physiographic variety as well as of climatic or biological factors. Differences in bedrock, drainage conditions, and time available for soil development virtually conceal the existing relationship of soils to the other pedogenetic factors. Excluding the azonal soils (lithosols of mountains, regosols in recent sand deposits of dunes and volcanic areas, and bog soils in areas with high ground-water table), a zonal pattern is still recognizable. Podzolization has taken place in most soils developed under the original mixed forest, but with decreasing intensity in a southward direction. Clay accumulation is still strong and the acidity is quite high, but leaching has been much less severe and hardpans have rarely developed. It is customary to call these soils "podzolics" and to classify them according to the color of the surface layer. Immediately south of the true podzols and in the higher terrain of southern Europe, the brown podzolic soil has developed, which grades into a grey-brown relative westward and into a grey podzolic southeastward, the latter being a transitional type to the black earth of the Russian steppes. In Europe they are referred to as "brown or grey forest soils." The relatively large amount of organic and nutrient matter, their loamy texture and well-drained condition make the podzolics better than average soils. Many areas occupied by these soils have been under cultivation for centuries and are still highly productive. This is, of course, also a consequence of heavy fertilization and careful management of the soil by the European farmer.

Within the podzolic soil group are some special types which deviate from the normal podzolic because of certain characteristics of the parent material. Thus, the extensive areas covered by loess (Fig. 1–16) carry deep, loamy soils of extremely high inherent fertility whereas shallow, stony, and excessively drained soils of low agricultural value have developed where limestone was the parent rock.

The Steppe and the Desert. South of the forest belt in Russia and in the basins of the lower Danube the surface cover was originally and still is in part characterized by wide expanses of grassland, or steppes (from the Russian word *step* for this grassland). There is a distinct transition zone between the forests and the steppe, extending diagonally across the southern European U.S.S.R., which is called the "forest steppe." This zone is characterized by an intermingling of oak forests and open grassland, the former dominating in the northern portions, the latter in the southern. The encroachment of the forest upon the steppe has had a distinct and negative influence on the soils of this zone in so far as the former grassland soils were subjected to podzolization. On the soil map these soils are designated as grey podzolics; they have also been called degraded black earths.

The absence of forests, except along rivers, and the almost continuous carpet of grasses, together with the black soils, or "chernozems" (Russian for black earths), are typical of the virgin steppe. Most of the steppe land in the south of the Soviet Union and in the southeast European basins represents today what might be called a "cultural steppe," since hybrid grains have long since replaced the original wheat grass. In the drier southeastern sections of the Russian steppes, however, where pasturage plays a greater role than grain cultivation, the steppe still is like a rolling sea of grass.

The steppe is the result of climatic conditions which are intermediate between those responsible for the growth of forests toward the north and those which produce the desert toward the southeast. As far as the available moisture is concerned, the climate of the steppes is subhumid or semiarid. The combined effect of temperature, precipitation, and evaporation seems to allow a vigorous growth of herbaceous plants, but to preclude forest development. The fact that most of the steppe land is mantled by loess has undoubtedly had a bearing upon the evolution of the deep soil profile and, indirectly, upon the plant cover itself. The conspicuously black surface layer of the soils in the subhumid portions of the steppe is the result of the accumulation of plant material which became incorporated with the mineral matter of the subsoil. The upper layer of the chernozem has undergone little leaching so that the nutrient minerals are available to the plants. Of particular importance is the high content of calcium carbonate, in great contrast to the soils of the forest zone. Additional assets of the black earths are their granular structure as well as their good drainage and aeration characteristics. All this in conjunction with the often perfectly level surface of the land makes the chernozem one of the most productive soils of Europe. It must be said, however, that overcultivation of these soils has created serious problems of soil erosion and deflation in many areas. Natural enemies of soil productivity are podzolization in the north, already mentioned above, and the formation of lime hardpans (*caliche*) in the drier portions to the south.

In the extreme southeast of the European U.S.S.R., with precipitation falling below 10 inches and with increasing summer heat, the steppe grades into a semidesert. The steppe grasses no longer completely cover the ground, and little organic matter can be taken up by the soils. Their color is now chestnut brown; they are extremely shallow and often contain lime or salt encrustations just below or at the surface. Due to the slowness of the soil-forming processes the type of surface material plays an increasingly greater role toward the Caspian and Transcaspian desert. Here, beyond the boundary of Europe as delimited in this text, soil development is at a minimum and is determined by surface deposits (clay flats, salt pans, sandy and stony desert).

The virgin steppe was the home of large herds of herbivores, but most of them have become extinct with hunting and the progressive cultivation of the steppe lands. Most of the wild horses (tarpans), antelopes, deer, roebucks, and wild boars did not survive the last century. The same is true for the many birds which originally inhabited the steppe. Only the bustard, the ptarmigan, and waterfowl are left in larger numbers. The typical steppe animals today are the rodents: hamster, ground squirrel, ground hare, and various species of mice and rats, and a few reptile species. Migratory locusts hatch in the delta thickets of the rivers and have occasionally devastated cropland in widely scattered steppe tracts.

The Mediterranean Zone. The Mediterranean lands are as unique from a biogeographical and pedological point of view as they are climatically. Although little is left of the original plant cover in the area, there is enough evidence to be gathered from its remainders, and from secondary and cultural vegetation, to establish the existence of a unique type of Mediterranean vegetation to which the generic name "maqui" has been applied. The people of Corsica refer to the shrubby, thorny, and aromatic thickets of their island as *maki* from which the French *maquis* [40] and the Italian *macchie* are derived.

Most native Mediterranean plants have developed similar protective measures against the water deficiency and the high evaporation rate in summer. Their leaves are small, leathery, often spiny, and are glazed with a coating of waxy substances. The trees are evergreens and of small size; in a few places such as the southern French Alps or along the east coast of the Adriatic they still have the aspect of the original Mediterranean evergreen hardwood forest. Macchie or cultivated trees and crops have practically everywhere succeeded the former forest associations. The macchie can be best described as a dense scrub forest, the tree crowns rarely reaching higher than 20 feet (Fig. 1–18). Floristically, it consists mainly of oaks (live oak ubiquitous, cork oak in western part only), shrubs of the heather family (laurels, oleanders), legumes, and junipers. In sites of extreme dryness and over the lithosols of limestone outcrops, the shrubs are more widely spaced. Droughty grasses and thorny flowering plants, most of them bulb perennials, then form a "steppe maqui" [41] association.

Myrrh, myrtle, lavender, mint, and many other strongly aromatic species are typical representatives of the Mediterranean flora. All these plants blossom profusely in spring, while in summer they are little more than strawlike, thorny stalks. The change in the appear-

[40] It will be recalled that the French resistance movement against German occupation forces during World War II used the name *le maquis*, with the implication that anybody going into the maqui thickets would be safe.

[41] There are a variety of local terms for this open type of maqui such as *garigue* in southern France, *phrygana* in Greece, *tomillares* and *monte* in southeastern Spain.

ance of the plant cover between the two seasons is most impressive indeed.

The altitudinal zonation of the Mediterranean plant formations was originally in the sequence: macchie – chestnut trees – beeches – conifers, the last establishing the timber line close to 6,000 feet. It should be clearly stated, however, that one rarely sees a continuously forested mountain slope in the Mediterranean realm. Deforestation

Fig. 1–18. View over the Gulf of Porto on the west coast of Corsica. The steeply sloping granitic mountainsides are covered by dense "maqui" vegetation. The remains of a Genoese watchtower stand above the harbor cove. (Photo: Miramont, Bastia.)

here has been much more thorough than in any other part of Europe. Overgrazing, clearing for cultivation, and the use of wood for charcoal burning have practically annihilated the forest, and a poor second-growth macchie has now replaced it. The long summer drought, the denuded nature of the soil, and the continuous use of potential forest sites as pasture land are making reforestation extremely difficult.

With the forest a good many animal species have disappeared. Still found are the wild goat, the mountain sheep (the muflon of Corsica and Sardinia), the wildcat, and the wild boar. The variety of reptiles (snakes, vipers, lizards, and turtles), insects, and mollusks is great. Birds are conspicuously few in number.

The soils of the Mediterranean lands are characterized by a distinct red color of the surface layer, particularly when developed on calcareous parent material. Genetically, these red earths are probably red podzolics, transitional in their characteristics between the mid-latitude podzolics and the red tropical soils. The group name "terra rossa" (red earth in Italian) has often been used to include soils of the Mediterranean lands with red surface color, but these soils vary greatly in other characteristics such as calcium or silica content, texture, and drainage. If deeper profiles are developed, which is the exception, terra rossa is quite a productive soil. In their shallow and eroded phases they are difficult to manage. On steeply sloping terrain the only practical measure against erosion is the construction of terraces. In the alluvial lowlands and basins, however, the situation is entirely different. Deep and fertile soils are encountered the productive capacity of which, particularly under irrigation, is as high as that of any other European soil. The Po Plain, the *huertas* (gardens) in Spain, and the *concha d'oro* (the golden bowl) near Catania in Sicily are but a few examples of intensively cropped Mediterranean lands.

It is this intensity of land use throughout the Mediterranean area which makes us wonder whether the people really have not made the best use of a not too favorable environment. Wherever there is a pocket of soil, a little piece of flat land, it has been transformed into a tiny garden. Many native plants have been cultivated into varieties which have much higher yields than their wild ancestors. The olive tree, above all, this sturdy and at the same time gracile senior of the Mediterranean plants, still grows wild throughout the area, but it is most conspicuous in the neatly set rows of the olive plantations. The same has happened to the grapevine, the citrus, fig, and stone-fruit trees, and even the date palms, all of which are natives of the Mediterranean borderlands and have been hybridized from wild into cultural varieties. They all make up the "fruits of the south," as the northerners lovingly refer to the products of the Mediterranean garden.

CONCLUSION

The intention of the preceding pages has been to outline in brief the physical and biogeographic components of the European landscape. At the same time an attempt was made to give the reader an insight into the variety of factors responsible for the physical character of the European lands. The physical environment, then, has been sketched as the background to the human occupancy to be examined in the ensuing chapters. Only at the end of the book might one expect to find the answer to the question which could logically be posed at this point: To what extent did the natural setting determine what man did with this portion of the earth? But the answer to this question is not given; rather, it may be read between the lines throughout the text. It will become very obvious that the many contrasts of the European landscape are the result of an uninterrupted interplay between physical and human forces from the Stone Age to the present day. We only can say here that man found Europe offering both favorable and unfavorable environments and that he has learned to take advantage of friendly surroundings and to cope successfully with harsher environments. Both the fertile lowlands and the steep Alpine slopes are the homes of European people. What man did is visible in his works, what the environment did is concealed within them.

BIBLIOGRAPHY

(Major references are asterisked.)

Books in English

ANNAHEIM, HANS (ed.). *Across the Alps: Aerial Views Between Nice and Vienna*. Bern: Kümmerly & Frey, 1959.

COLLET, LEON WILLIAM. *The Structure of the Alps*. London: E. Arnold & Co., 1935.

*DAVIS, WILLIAM M. *Geographical Essays*. New York: Dover Publications, Inc., 1954.

*DE BEAUFORT, LIEVEN FERDINAND. *Zoogeography of the Lands and Inland Waters*. London: Sidgwick & Jackson, Ltd., 1951.

*FLINT, FOSTER R. *Glacial and Pleistocene Geology*. New York: John Wiley & Sons, Inc., 1957.

*HARE, F. KENNETH. *The Restless Atmosphere*. London: Hutchinson's University Library, 1953.

*KENDREW, WILFRID G. *The Climates of the Continents*. 4th ed. London: Clarendon Press, 1953.

LOBECK, A. K. *Physiographic Diagram of Europe* (with text). New York: Columbia University Press, 1951.

*UMBGROVE, JOHANNES HERMAN FREDERIC. *Symphony of the Earth*. The Hague: M. Nijhoff, 1950.

Books in Foreign Languages

FIRBAS, FRANZ. *Spät- und nacheiszeitliche Waldgeschichte Mitteleuropas Nördlich der Alpen* (Late- and Postglacial Forest History of Central Europe North of the Alps). 2 vols. Jena: O. Fischer, 1949–52.

*GANSSEN, ROBERT. *Bodengeographie* (Geography of Soils). Stuttgart: Verlag Kohler, 1957.

*KOEPPEN, WLADIMIR, and GEIGER, RUDOLF (eds.). *Handbuch der Klimatologie* (Handbook of Climatology). Vol. III. Berlin: Gebrüder Bornträger, 1932–36.

*MACHATSCHEK, FRITZ. *Das Relief der Erde* (The Relief of the Earth). 2 vols. Berlin: Gebrüder Bornträger, 1955.

PENCK, ALBRECHT, and BRÜCKNER, EDWARD. *Die Alpen im Eiszeitalter* (The Alps in the Ice Age). 2 vols. Leipzig: Tauchnitz, 1909.

*RIKLI, MARTIN. *Das Pflanzenkleid der Mittelmeerländer* (The Vegetation Cover of the Mediterranean Countries). 3 vols. Bern: H. Huber, 1943–48.

*STAUB, RUDOLF. *Der Bau der Alpen* (The Structure of the Alps). Bern: Beiträge zur geologischen Karte der Schweiz, No. 52, 1924.

Articles

ANNAHEIM, HANS. "The Chronological Correlation of the Morphological Development in the Eastern and the Western Alps," *Experientia* 6 (1950): 121–25.

BIEL, ERWIN, "Die Niederschlagsverhältnisse der Alpen" (The Precipitation Regime of the Alps), *Mitteilungen der Geographischen Gesellschaft* 73–74 (Vienna, 1931): 188–94.

CONRAD, VICTOR, "The Climate of the Mediterranean Region," *Bulletin of the American Meteorological Society* 24 (1943): 127–45.

FLOHN, HERMANN, "Witterung und Klima in Mitteleuropa" (Weather and Climate in Central Europe), *Forschungen zur Deutschen Landeskunde* 78 (1953).

GARNETT, ALICE, "Insolation, Topography, and Settlement in the Alps," *Geographical Review* 25 (1935): 601–17.

GREGORY, STANLEY, "Climatic Classification and Climatic Change in Europe," *Erdkunde* 8 (1954): 246–56.

GUILCHER, ANDRÉ, "La Formation de la mer du Nord, du Pas de Calais, et des plaines maritimes environantes" (The Formation of the North Sea, the English Channel, and the Surrounding Coastal Plains), *Revue de Géographie de Lyon* 3 (1951): 311–30.

LOMBARD, AUGUSTIN, "Appalachian and Alpine Structures: A Comparative Study," *Bulletin of the American Association of Petroleum Geologists* 32 (1948): 709–44.

RÜBEL, EDWARD, "Heath and Steppe, Macchia and Garigue," *Ecology* 2 (1914): 231–37.

SAURAMO, MATTI, "On the Nature of Quaternary Crustal Upwarping in Fennoscandia," *Acta Geografica* 14 (1955): 334–48.

SION, JULES, "Le rôle des articulations littorales en Méditerranée" (The Role of Coastal Articulation in the Mediterranean), *Annales de Géographie* 43 (Paris, 1934): 372–79.

ZOLLER, HANS, "Die natürliche Grossgliederung der fennoskandischen Vegetation und Flora" (The Natural Division of Fenno-Scandian Vegetation and Flora), *Veröffentlichungen des Geobotanischen Institutes Rübel* (1955): 74–98.

2

The Historical Background

Any attempt merely to glance at the many sharply distinguishable cultural landscapes of Europe, or to consider the many elements compounded in any one such landscape, emphasizes how clearly the handwriting of history appears on its map. Dissected plateaus of wooded and pastoral aspect have become populous regions of coal mining and of heavy industry. Wide areas of steppe, which linked like areas of Siberia and central Asia with south Russia and the Danube Basin, have passed from the control of the nomad horseman to that of the settled agriculturist and of the town-dwelling industrialist. The geographical values attaching to different parts of the continent show continual change throughout history: the Mediterranean lands, for example, no longer dominate in population numbers, in political energy, and in civilization generally. One-fifth of the world's population has found its home in Europe, and distributed itself there in a very unequal manner: here densely concentrated in specialized industrial or intensively developed agricultural areas, there thinly spread over a rural landscape of mountain valleys, widespread forests, heath, moor, or marsh.

The countryside of Europe reveals the many varieties of rural settlement and of urban forms. It contains some metropolitan giants which mask with their buildings and their transport lines the nature and form of the underlying rocks, yet which they dare not wholly ignore. The landscape of the "conurbation," a term used to describe those continuously urban areas which have arisen through the coalescence of two or more towns mainly during the last hundred years, must also engage attention. And away from the towns of whatsoever size and function, villages, hamlets, and single farms scatter all over the continent, their distribution posing intricate problems to the solution of which agrarian history, related as it is to the variety of physical environments, can contribute much.

Many other features of the human geography have also grown out of the past; for instance, the ports and resorts of the coastlands, and the patterns of inland transport by rail, road, and water. And, if attention is turned to the inhabitants of Europe themselves, these are still separable into ethnic, linguistic, national, and state groups, the locations of which were first sketched long ago.

Confronted by the wealth of Europe's history, the student of human geography may well wonder what is his precise task in turning back to the past for the light which it can throw on the present. In essence, he is concerned with the study of groups of people and their settlements, of their forms of economy, and of their means of travel and of transport. Under each of these three main heads—settlement, economy, and "circulation"—a set of problems arises for separate discussion. Thus consideration of the peoples of Europe will refer to the growth and distribution of population, to rural and urban settlement, and to the ethnic types, languages, nations, and states as they are distributed over the continent. Similarly, attention will be turned to the variant patterns of agriculture, industry, and commerce, and to the patterns of transport on which they depend: all these will be noted in relation to their physical background and to their development through time.

THE PEOPLES OF EUROPE

Prehistoric Settlement. Geography need concern itself little with the Paleolithic period,[1] which, despite its long duration of perhaps 500,000 years, has left virtually no mark on the landscape of the continent. Paleolithic man inhabited those parts of the continent which were not invaded by the Fenno-Scandian and Alpine glaciers,[2] where probably a tundra-like climate prevailed or, at best, humid oceanic conditions, as in the Mediterranean peninsulas. An archaeologist has estimated for the earlier or Lower Paleolithic period that the total energy at man's disposal in Europe—and all of it was human—did not exceed that of a four-engined plane: as an agent of geographical change, therefore, Paleolithic man can be ignored.

That transitional phase between the Upper Paleolithic and Neolithic cultures which has been termed "Mesolithic" deserves passing

---

[1] The terms Paleolithic, Mesolithic, and Neolithic periods are used to describe settlement periods of prehistoric Europe.

[2] For geological terms, see Appendix I.

notice. When the north-German plain and the Baltic area had been abandoned by the glaciers and were being colonized by trees, some immigrants from the south, Mesolithic in culture, settled along its seacoasts and along the banks of its numerous lakes and rivers. From about 8000 B.C. until about 3000 B.C. these prehistoric tribes still lived by hunting, fishing, and food collecting, and were presumably ignorant of cultivation and of metals, and had no domesticated animals except the dog. Their tools and weapons were still fashioned of unpolished stone, flint, and bone; they had not yet learned to polish stone but only to flake and chip it; nor, with few exceptions, were they familiar with pot making. And this way of life lingered on, especially in northwest Europe, long after the Neolithic culture, based on agriculture and pastoral husbandry, had become established in Egypt, Mesopotamia, and northwest India.

The climatic and vegetational background to the Mesolithic period and the succeeding cultures of postglacial Europe is now being revealed in clear outline, thanks above all to the microscopic study of pollen grains preserved in datable layers of peat and other organic or semiorganic sediments.[3] It is now possible to envisage in relationship not only the main fluctuations of climate since the final retreat of the Fenno-Scandian and Alpine glaciers but also the various stages in the spread of forest-forming trees and the corresponding culture periods of the archaeologist. Four successive climatic phases have been distinguished: the Boreal, Atlantic, sub-Boreal, and sub-Atlantic, although the third of these is less clear. Compared with the cold pre-Boreal period which preceded it, the Boreal period was dry and increasingly warm; the Atlantic wet and warm; the sub-Boreal was cool but perhaps not so dry as was formerly believed, while the sub-Atlantic, which lasted into the historical period of the Roman Empire, was marked by cold and moist conditions. Precise calendar dates for these periods are as yet difficult to determine. Nor is it clear that the specified climates apply farther afield than Northern, Western, and Central Europe. But the succession of climatic changes is by now broadly established, and so also is that of the corresponding changes of the vegetation cover.

In contrast to North America, Europe has relatively few indigenous tree species and even fewer today than it had during the Tertiary period. This scarcity is not the result of its present climate nor of the adverse conditions of the Great Ice Age. It is due to the two

---

[3] On pollen analysis see H. Godwin, "Pollen Analysis: An Outline of the Problems and Potentialities of the Method," *New Phytologist* 33 (October, 1934): 278–305, and Stanley A. Cain, *Foundations of Plant Geography* (New York: Harper & Bros., 1944), especially Chapter X.

barriers aligned west-east: the middle mountain ranges and the Mediterranean Sea, which checked the retreat of tree species as climate worsened with the onset of the Great Ice Age. Fewer species were therefore able to immigrate into the continent from the southwest and southeast as the climate improved in the postglacial period. In the Boreal phase spruce, fir, pine, birch, and hazel established themselves as far north as central Sweden and Finland. In the succeeding Atlantic phase, these gave pride of place to mixed forests of oak, elm, linden, and common alder. The beech, especially sensitive to temperature and traveling fastest by way of river valleys, spread into Western and Central Europe from the Danube Basin during the sub-Boreal and sub-Atlantic periods./ Both Mesolithic Europe, which may be dated to the late Boreal and Atlantic phases, and Neolithic Europe, which falls within the late Atlantic and the sub-Boreal phases, must be thought of as thickly clad with trees and undergrowth, excepting only those areas where tree growth was precluded by high altitude, bad drainage, or exposure to persistent gales./ Even the considerable areas stretching from south Russia across the continent to the English Channel, where layer upon layer of loess had been deposited by wind during the Great Ice Age, are now known, thanks to pollen analysis, to have been covered, not with a steppe-heath flora, but with beech, hawthorn, juniper, yew, box, and ash. Also, the Mediterranean peninsulas had then an abundance of forest and scrub, rooted in an ample soil which, as a result of forest destruction by man and beast, has since been largely lost./

Attention can be paid here to only three particular aspects of the Neolithic and Bronze ages: the routeways (i.e., natural routes) used, the areas occupied, and the mineral sources exploited—since these are directly connected with the development of Europe as a home of man. It was by the diffusion of men and techniques from certain primary centers of progressive culture in Egypt and southwest Asia that Europe learned in turn, and adapted to its very different environment, the Neolithic and Bronze Age ways of life. The Neolithic culture, as it developed between 6000 and 3000 B.C. in its original homes, marked a major revolutionary change in man's use of his habitat. Its economic basis was food production by cultivation and stock rearing, and its social expression was, at first, the village and, later, the town. It brought technical inventions and new crafts: wheel-turned pottery, kiln-fired bricks, spinning and weaving, building, writing, trade, social organization, and the fashioning of works of art. All these new triumphs of human ingenuity, to which the beginnings of metallurgy were later added, characterized the Neolithic culture or civilization. Given the original location of the homelands of the Neolithic culture, it is not surprising to find that the new culture was first to appear within the European realm in Crete and the other islands and coastlands of the Aegean Sea, whence it spread by sea and by overland routes. The area which, chiefly on climatic ground, Ellsworth Huntington found most favored for civilization in Europe—the Northwest, including the British Isles—was the last to receive it.

Figure 2–1 illustrates the land and water routes by which, on the basis of the distribution of known prehistoric sites and artifacts, men and ideas seem to have spread into and throughout the continent. Prehistoric peoples were thus outlining the main areas of human settlement and linking them by sea and land channels of communication which have since then tended to remain in continual use.

It is doubtless highly dangerous to generalize about the areas occupied by European peoples in the various stages of the Neolithic and Bronze cultures, for several millennia are involved and the evidence cannot claim to be complete. There is, however, a striking correspondence between the areas settled by Neolithic peasants and certain areas of porous or pervious rocks. This applies particularly to the loess lands, but also to areas of sand, gravel, loam, limestone, and sandstone, all of which not only were well drained, but developed light-textured soils, easy to work with simple stone or wooden hoes.

The relative facility of cultivating such soils would seem to have been their main attraction; the absence of forest cover and its replacement by a steppe-heath type of flora under an allegedly dry sub-Boreal climate can no longer be offered as the explanation. Rather, it is now clear that the Neolithic peasants often settled in village groups at the wooded margin of the steppe, and made the first big clearance of forests by firing, in order to win land for agriculture and pasture. It is remarkable, too, that the lowlands and plateaus, once conquered in this way, have continued to be defended for the plow against a reinvasion of forests by a historical succession of colonists. Thus the Neolithic men of Europe and their livestock of the third millennium B.C. played a part in fashioning European downlands, steppes, and heaths from original woodlands. It is believed, for instance, that the great extent of heath in northwest Germany owes its origin to the agency of men and their grazing animals which, in the course of the sub-Boreal period (i.e., during the later Neolithic and Bronze Age), entirely destroyed the former forests.

The Bronze Age in Europe, which may be dated from about 1800 B.C., called attention for the first time to the mineral wealth of the continent, principally in those places where rocks of Hercynian folding were exposed. Among the regions which were then important for their minerals were Transylvania with silver, gold, and salt; Bohemia

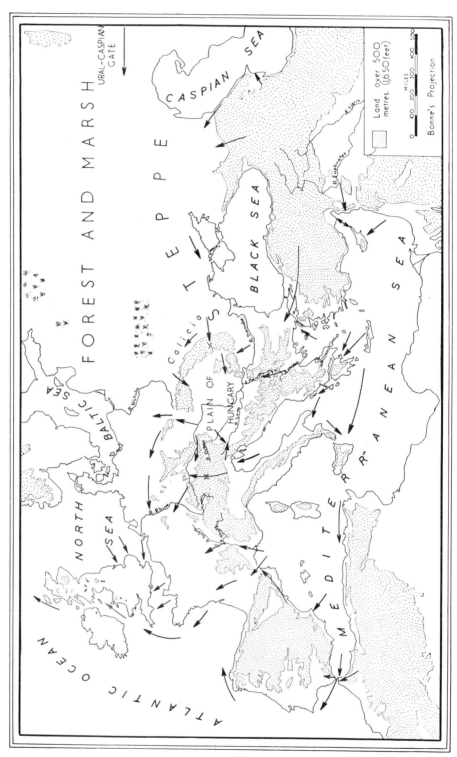

Fig. 2-1. The natural routes of prehistoric Europe. (This and the other maps in this chapter were prepared by the author.)

with tin and copper from the Erz Gebirge (Ore Mountains); Spain with tin and copper; Ireland with copper and gold; and Brittany and Cornwall, the mineral resources of which included the scarce metal tin necessary, with copper, for bronze making. The knowledge of bronze first reached Bohemia and Hungary to be diffused therefrom by nomad intruders from south Russia. New trade routes by land and sea were then opened up, including those along which amber was brought overland to north Italy from the Baltic. Ireland, then remotely placed, assumed for a time a leading role in metallurgical industry and European commerce. The sea route from the Mediterranean through the Irish Sea to the Orkney Islands and Scandinavia, which is inferred from a study of tomb plans and vases to have been in use in the third millennium B.C., was clearly an established trade route by about 1500 B.C., as is shown by the finds of traded products of known origin. The development of agriculture continued during the Bronze Age with a few local changes, some of which are known with surprising accuracy. Thus, in Denmark, expert studies of the impressions of grain still detectable on the prehistoric pottery and of carbonized cereals found in peat reveal that barley was by far the most important crop there in the late Bronze Age, although several varieties of wheat were no less prominent in the earlier Neolithic period.

It was during the Bronze Age that immigrants from the steppe lands north of the Black and Caspian seas brought to the rest of Europe the domesticated horse, which was used for pulling war chariots and only later for riding. These immigrants spoke the Indo-European language, and it would seem that for a time, during the latter part of the second millennium B.C., a single speech prevailed in Europe. If for no other reason than this, the European Bronze Age is geographically memorable, as it is from the language introduced then that, by a process of regional differentiation, most of the present languages of Europe have developed.

Our sketch of the prehistoric settlement in Europe should conclude with a reference to the expansion of Iron Age peoples into western Europe during the last thousand years before the birth of Christ. The knowledge of the working of iron had penetrated into the Danube Basin from the East, and once again it was from a Danubian area that a new technique was rediffused. From the upper Danube Valley between Bavaria and the middle Rhine in Alsace, Iron Age culture was carried into France, Iberia, Scandinavia, and the British Isles. Several waves of migration ensued. In Britain, for example, three can be distinguished and broadly dated, and these appear to have consisted of Celtic-speaking peoples who were bringing

with them successive Iron Age cultures. These immigrant "Celts"—
this term has only a linguistic meaning—were the ancestors of the
many peoples established in north Italy, Iberia, Gaul, Bohemia, and
Britain with whom the Romans later fought when, leaving peninsular
Italy, they launched their career of conquest. Numerous Celtic river
names in Europe, such as Rhine, Danube, and Thames, still attest
their former presence.

As its climate improved and fluctuated with the retreat of the
glaciers of the Great Ice Age, Europe, we have seen, became a
"pioneer" or "colonial" field, occupied and exploited by a succession
of immigrants of different cultural attainments. The temperate
forested lands of Europe owed this initial development to the inflow
of men and ideas from the precociously civilized countries situated
in lower latitudes, above all Mesopotamia, Egypt, and even Turkestan.
In these movements we may note the important roles played by the
island of Crete, the steppe of south Russia, and parts of the Danube
Basin. In the course of the first millennium B.C., the prehistoric period
in Europe gave place to the historical period, which is illuminated by
literary records. They reveal, as is known also from archaeological
evidence, that the Mediterranean lands of Europe reached the highest
degree of social and political organization, of commercial activity,
and of civilization in general: the Phoenicians, the Greeks, the
Etruscans, and the Romans of classical antiquity focus the attention
of the historian, while in Europe beyond the Mediterranean lake-land
world more primitive conditions of life prevailed.

The Nations and States. Even though present-day Europe still
shows traces of its prehistoric past, the main features of its human
geography are explained above all by processes operative during the
historical period. The peculiar patterns of "nations" and "states" in
Europe, to which we now turn our attention, are clearly the results
of such processes. It is a remarkable fact that Europe, occupying only
one-twelfth of the habitable earth, contains about a quarter of its
independent states. No less does Europe house a high proportion of
the self-conscious and articulate nations of the world. Time has
served only to intensify the trend toward the creation of more and
more so-called "nation states," and to produce what must appear to
Americans, familiar with larger and simpler state-and-nation patterns,
a parochially organized continent. This appears particularly true of
Central and Eastern Europe since nations and states are much more
simply arranged peripherally to these regions, in Western and Northern Europe.

As a glance through the pages of a historical atlas shows, state
territories and the boundaries of states have changed continually. In

contrast, the distribution of national groups shows marked stability. To define what constitutes a "nation" is not easy: like the concepts of "space" and "electricity" in physical science, it resists exact definition. But it is something more fundamental than the state, which, as twentieth-century history has shown, can be made and unmade. Social groups, bound together by common traditions and culture, have tended to become acutely conscious of their own individuality

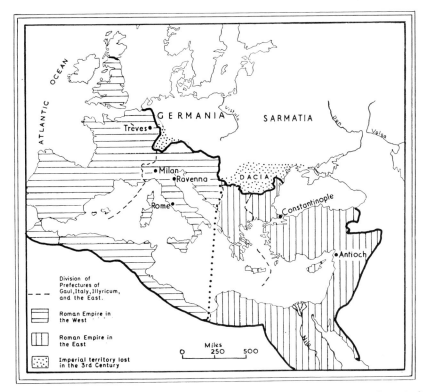

Fig. 2–2. The division of the Roman Empire in 395 A.D. Imperial capitals are named.

and have often, but not invariably, sought separate statehood, whether or not they possessed a single common language. But national self-consciousness and the idea of the "nation state" are relatively modern developments. Let us look back in time to see where and how the nationalities of Europe first appeared. It will be convenient to start this discussion by reference to the foundation and fortunes of the Roman Empire in the early centuries of the Christian era.

At its maximum extent in the second century A.D. (Fig. 2–2) the Roman Empire extended northward from the shores of the Mediterranean Basin to the Rhine and Danube and bestrode these rivers along parts of their courses—in the upper Rhine and in both the upper and lower Danube. Within this large part of the continent, Rome established centralized political organization and maintained the peace, security, and ordered life of her provinces by fortifying the imperial frontiers and by building a system of well-engineered roads. The Roman Empire achieved remarkable success as a multinational state: its citizenship provided a common bond to many different peoples—Gauls, Iberians, Illyrians, Greeks, Britons, and others—and its language, the Latin of the hillmen of Latium, was widely adopted except in less accessible areas, and in the eastern basin of the Mediterranean where Greek speech maintained its cultural ascendancy. While there were many distinct peoples or nations and many forms of native speech, the several nation-groups had not, nor did they seek, separate statehood. Indeed, the political pattern of Europe in the second century was one of greater simplicity than any other of later time: there was the extensive, well-organized, and highly civilized Empire, and beyond it, in regions which were only loosely and lightly occupied, the "barbarian" world, so-called by the Greeks, not to express loathing or contempt, but because its inhabitants made in their speech "bar bar" noises unintelligible to them.

The cultural gradient between these two worlds was steep, yet they did not fail to react on each other. Finds of Roman coins, as far east as the Vistula and as far north as central Sweden, point to trade relations. There were military engagements on both sides of the frontier. Barbarian peoples were, moreover, permitted at times to settle as colonists within the Empire, as were Germans, for example, in the plain of Alsace.

From the third century onward, the Empire weakened and for military and administrative convenience was divided in 395 A.D. into two parts, the eastern part being ruled by an emperor at Byzantium, renamed Constantinople (now called Istanbul), and the western by another emperor ruling from Rome or elsewhere as defense needs dictated (Fig. 2–2). The Eastern Empire, in which Greek or Hellenistic culture prevailed widely, succeeded in absorbing Slavic and other immigrants and in maintaining some semblance of imperial organization for another thousand years; known as the Byzantine Empire, it was overthrown only by the Ottoman Turks in 1453. The western half, which included Italy, Iberia, Gaul, Britain, and North Africa, collapsed under barbarian pressure in the fifth century. It was then that the more vigorous peoples from the barbarian world took the future of Europe in their hands, and among them can be seen the forerunners of the principal nations of present Europe—notably those of the German (or Teutonic) and of the Slavic groups.

The collapse of Roman power in Western Europe opened wide the floodgates to conquering barbarian peoples who sought new homes within the Empire, in lands richer, because more effectively exploited, than their own. These movements, not just of armies but of whole peoples, are known as "the barbarian invasions of Europe" or the *Völkerwanderung*. Peoples of Germanic stock were the protagonists; in their wake pressed the Slavs, while there were also some intruding peoples from Asia and North Africa.

The earliest known homeland of the German people, where they had been established since the second millennium B.C., lay in the glaciated lowlands and hills between the lower Rhine and the lower Oder, the Danish peninsula and islands, and southern Sweden. For a long time stock-rearers and fishermen rather than tillers of the soil, they increased in numbers and pressed southward from their difficult environments of forest, marsh, and heath, and in the course of time comprised a number of distinct nations, more or less settled and attached to the soil by their practice of stock-rearing and shifting agriculture. One branch, the East Germans, migrated from the lower Oder across the basin of the Vistula to establish themselves on the steppe to the north of the Black Sea, whence some were allowed to settle in the lower Danubian lands of the Eastern Roman Empire and others moved westward to Italy, southern Gaul, and Spain. The other branch, the West Germans, more civilized through closer contact with the Western Roman Empire, included the Angles, Saxons, and Jutes, who colonized the English Lowlands, and the Franks, who, under Charlemagne, re-created for a time the Roman Empire in the west and have left their name in the state of France.

⁄The long-term effects of the barbarian invasions, conquests, and settlements were to replace the Western Roman Empire by a number of smaller states in Italy, Gaul, Iberia, Britain, and the Rhineland, while political patterns began to appear too in the broad area of Central Europe, between the Rhine and Vistula and the Baltic and Danube, which the Romans had labeled *Germania* on their maps. The history of the Franks from the fourth to the ninth century explains how, by no means inevitably, the kingdoms of the West Franks and the East Franks—to become respectively France and Germany—originated within particular territorial frames. Charlemagne's empire, formally created in 800 A.D., did not last long. In extent, it was both more and less comprehensive than the Western Roman Empire of earlier days; more because it included considerable areas beyond the

Rhine, less because most of Spain and Britain and part of Italy were not included. The partition of Charlemagne's empire among three of his grandsons, by the Treaty of Verdun in 843 A.D. (Fig. 2–3), was the most important of many such divisions of the period because it had permanent effects. It outlined a kingdom, much smaller than

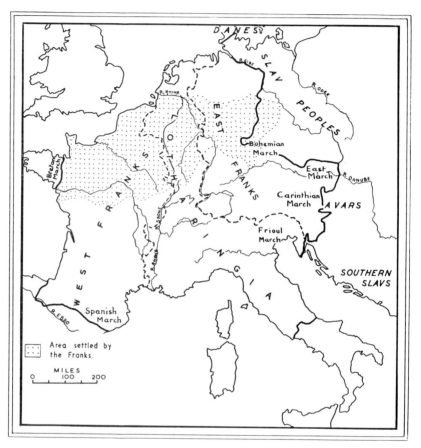

Fig. 2–3. The partition of the Carolingian Empire in 843 A.D.

Gaul, which was to become France; another, east of the Rhine, became Germany and grew greatly by eastward expansion. Between these two, a third, elongated middle kingdom, based mainly on the Rhine and extending from the North Sea to the Apennines, lacked the possibilities of political unity apart from surviving Roman roads. It could not survive troubled times. This territory proved indeed a bone of contention between its two neighbors right down to the present century; it contained, too, the "nuclear" or "core" areas for the states now known as Switzerland, Luxembourg, the Netherlands, and Belgium.

In the British Isles, the conquests and settlement of the Germanic Anglo-Saxons, Danes, and Norwegians brought political subdivisions which, in west Britain and Ireland, included those of Celtic-speaking peoples. The newcomers established their speech in the English Lowlands, thus effacing the Latinized speech which developed and persisted in most of the former imperial territories of the West. Only after yet another conquest, by the Normans—French in speech but Germanic in blood—was political unity re-established at least in the most settled and productive part of the British Isles, namely England, the wealth of which William the Conqueror astutely investigated by his famous Domesday Survey of 1086 A.D.

Italy suffered a succession of barbarian invaders. As in earlier and in later times, the Alps proved defensively useless, a "splendid traitor"; their passes served not to prevent but only to canalize ingress into the land which offered glittering prizes to the conqueror. Italy became a mosaic of states, including city-states, and so it still appeared in the mid-nineteenth century, on the eve of its unification as a kingdom under the House of Savoy, with its base in Piedmont. In the centuries which preceded this unification, north Italy was largely bound politically to trans-Alpine powers, notably the Holy Roman Empire and the Austro-Hungarian Empire; the Papal States stretched across peninsular Italy; south Italy and Sicily, caught in the stream of Mediterranean sea power, passed in part or as a whole first into Arab and then in turn into Norman and Spanish hands. But political disunity did not preclude the reflowering of city life—at Venice (Venezia), Genoa (Genova), Siena, Milan (Milano), Pisa, Florence (Firenze), Palermo, and elsewhere—nor high attainment in the industrial arts and in trade by land and by sea.

The Iberian Peninsula, "Spain" as the Romans conceived it, was occupied also by Germanic intruders: Suevi, Vandals, and Visigoths from across the Pyrenees—and Moslem Moors and Arabs, the former the more numerous, from North Africa. In their revival of classical learning, in their successful application of irrigation to agriculture, and, above all, in their architectural legacy at Cordoba, Granada, and Seville (Sevilla), the Arabs have left memorials of their conquest. But they never held permanently the northern provinces of Iberia, from which was waged against them the Christian Crusade which led to the establishment of the kingdom of Portugal in the thirteenth century and that of united Spain in the fifteenth century.

During the thousand years which followed the fall of Rome (476 A.D.), new nations and states emerged within the peninsular and formerly Roman territories of Western Europe. Farther afield, in the broad lowlands of Eastern Europe and European Russia, the contemporaneous movements of the Slavs have left their imprint on the map of the nations and states of the continent. The Slav peoples of Europe, who are conveniently classified into eastern, western, and southern groups, make up one-third of Europe's population and one-twelfth of mankind. The Slavs in no sense constitute biologically a "race," nor indeed do they conform to a single "ethnic type." They remain divided in religion, a result of geographical location and orientation in medieval times. Russians, Serbs, and Bulgarians belonged to the Greek or Eastern Orthodox Church; Poles, Czechs, Croats, Slovenes, and Dalmatian Slavs fell within the orbit of the Roman Catholic Church. Similarly, although it is language which provides the main bond between all the Slav peoples, the Russians, Serbs, and Bulgars have adopted the Greek Cyrillic alphabet, while others, notably the Poles, Czechs, Croats, Slovenes, and Dalmatian Slavs, use the Roman alphabet.

The original homeland of the Slavs cannot be precisely located. Tacitus, writing in 98 A.D., locates the Venedi (or certain Slavs) east of the Vistula and refers to their habit of wandering far and fast on foot, in the course of plundering forays, between East Prussia in the north and the Galician plateau in the south. As the Germans vacated Central Europe during the *Völkerwanderung* the Slavs pressed as far westward in their wake as the lower Elbe and its tributary the Saale. They also moved eastward into the mixed-forest region of the Great Russian Lowland, then lightly occupied by Finnic peoples, and southward into the Danubian and Balkan lands of the Byzantine Empire.

The economy of the early Slavs was primitive and their political organization weak. Swine-rearers, hunters, and fishermen, they grew flax and hemp for clothing and for oil and gathered honey from the wild bees of the forest and made intoxicating mead from it. They had no horses or cattle, no heavy plow, no vines or grain fields. Already in the ninth century, however, they had a variety of musical instruments, including those made from marsh-grown reeds. Indeed the Slavs in their way of life clearly owed much to environmental influences; they suffered too from their geographical position in the eastern marches of Europe. Like a "soft anvil," they were exposed to the blows of two hammers which were as hard as steel: one the recurrent waves of mounted nomads from the east, and the other the German pioneers and colonists from the west.

We can only briefly indicate here the shape of the present patterns of Slavic Europe and how they were formed. The Slavs long remained an inland people, cut off from the seas by the Balts (Old Prussians),

Lithuanians, Germans, and Swedes in the north; and by steppe nomads and the Byzantine Empire in the south. A broad wedge of non-Slav peoples remained within the Danube Basin: the Germans in Charlemagne's Ostmark (East March), which was to become Austria and the coreland of an empire; the Magyars, a mixed people, mounted horsemen from Asia, Finno-Ugrian in speech, who occupied the basin of Hungary toward the year 900 A.D.; and the Rumanians, who developed their Latinized speech in the aloofness of their habitats in the Transylvanian Alps.

The eastward colonial movement of the Germans after the year 1000 A.D. into the lands between the Elbe and the Oder largely effaced or at least obscured the Slavs, but they have held their own in Bohemia and Moravia. Within the forested basin of the Vistula the Poles found and maintained their homeland, although the boundaries of Poland have fluctuated widely during the last thousand years. In the south, Slovenes, Serbs, and Croats have preserved their identity, now recognized in the federal structure of the Yugoslav state. Greece, although it was overrun more than once by the Slavs, resisted Slavic influences. Slavs, however, form the major element in the Bulgarian nationality, which takes its name from the Finno-Ugrian Bulgars, nomadic intruders from the steppe in the seventh century.

From the Russian forests, other Slavs—the Great Russians—ranged far afield to the White Sea, the Caspian, and, beyond the Ural Mountains, to the distant Pacific. But it was the invading Scandinavians (Varangians) of the ninth century who forged the earliest Russian states, and it was only in the fourteenth century that Muscovy, shaking off the Mongol tutelage, launched the expanding Russia which we know now as the federated Soviet Union or U.S.S.R.

Many of the patterns of the nations and states of Europe thus begin to emerge from the conquests and settlements which followed the fall of Rome. The student of particular nations and states will direct his attention to their original "nuclear" areas which are often geographically significant: the Elbe Plain of the Czechs in Bohemia, the Paris Basin of the French, and the upland plains (*polja*) of the Serbs, to cite three examples. Minor shifts of national groups and changes in the territorial content of states have been continual, and many European state patterns are of twentieth-century origin. We may note that the populations of these states are seldom strictly homogeneous; everywhere there were or are still "inliers" or "outliers" of other nationalities. These two geological terms can be usefully applied to such minority groups—the former to indicate that the groups were established before, and the latter after, the nationalities by which they are at present surrounded. Thus the Basques and Bretons form "inliers" in France, just as the Volga Germans formed an "outlier" in the U.S.S.R. In the so-called "Shatter Belt" of Eastern Europe (see Chapter 8), the distribution of nationalities is more complicated, and was much more so before World War II than now.

For many centuries before the French Revolution, when it was exceptional to believe or assert that each nation should seek separate statehood, imperial regimes attempted, not always with success, to subject different nations to a common rule. But this twentieth century, notably during World War I, witnessed the eclipse of several empires established on European soil: the Ottoman Turkish, which once reached west to include most of Hungary; the Russian; the Austro-Hungarian, which tried not ineffectively to hold together Austrians, Hungarians, Czechs, and other Slav groups of the Danube Basin; and the German, created only in 1871 by Prussian arms and statecraft. Out of the fallen empires and in pursuance of the principle of national self-determination, Poland, Czechoslovakia, Yugoslavia, Austria, Hungary, and Finland were either created or re-created. The Baltic states of Estonia, Latvia, and Lithuania won their independence for a short time but now find themselves constituent republics of the U.S.S.R. Rumania, Bulgaria, and Greece have maintained the statehood which they won from the Turks with foreign aid in the nineteenth century, although there, as elsewhere in the politically unstable and ethnographically complex "Shatter Belt," boundaries have undergone much change. From one angle, the political pattern of Europe in 1961 shows a certain simplicity broadly similar to that of Roman times, with the Soviet Union and its satellites on the one hand and the "Western" states on the other.

Races and Ethnic Types. The European has yet to be born; European peoples abound. "A great multitude, which no man could number of all nations, and kindreds, and peoples and tongues. . . .": these words from the Book of Revelation may fittingly be applied to a continent whose human complexity is as great as its area is small. The peoples of Europe can be allocated to distinct groups on the basis of ethnic type, language, political allegiance, and in other ways. The findings of physical anthropology, archaeology, history, and linguistics help substantially to explain the present patterns, but part of the story of Europe's peoples, who during four or five millennia fashioned the habitat we now know, remains obscure.

Much has been lightly if feelingly written about the "races" of Europe, yet very little that is strictly scientific can as yet be said. "Race" implies biological relationships, especially genetic ones. If the existing peoples of Europe could be classified into clearly marked racial groups, could these groups be shown to be derived from early historical or prehistoric races? The idea of originally pure races from which present Europeans are descended has no authority in known fact. Since all the existing varieties of mankind belong to one species, and since man has always been the most adaptable and the most mobile of all animals, the quest for the geographical habitats of originally separate racial groups is a false trail. Certainly the anthropometric study of present Europeans has thrown no clear light on their genetic relationships, although physiological studies of blood groups may achieve more success.

It is wise therefore to turn to other aspects of the European peoples—to their ethnic types and their linguistic and national groupings—which can be discussed with more assurance and, indeed, are matters of everyday significance. For it must be confessed that, while racial theories have been potent destructive agencies, the racial history of Europeans, were it ever fully revealed, would be a matter of purely academic interest. We have no grounds for believing that "race" divides the population of Europe into socially significant groups, as do languages and, above all, states.

Although the racial history and racial classification of Europeans remain obscure, it is possible to describe their ethnic characters and even to speak of specific ethnic types. The existing populations are studied as they appear, in respect to physical characteristics, such as head and nose forms, stature, hair texture and color, and eye color. Using such criteria, Deniker [4] postulated the existence and showed the broad geographical distribution of six principal ethnic groups and four subgroups. The six principal ones he called "Northern," "Eastern," "Ibero-insular," "Cevenole or Western," "Littoral," and "Adriatic or Dinaric." Later writers emphasized the prevalence of three distinct types called "Nordic," "Alpine," and "Mediterranean."

The following broad ethnic divisions have been recognized:

	Stature			
	Long Head		Broad Head	
	Tall	Short	Tall	Short
Brunette		Mediterranean	Dinaric	Alpine
Blond	Nordic			Eastern European

Such a classification is clearly too simple to cover the numerous varieties present even in small areas of the continent, although it

[4] J. Deniker, *The Races of Man: An Outline of Anthropology and Ethnography* (New York: Charles Scribner's Sons, 1900), pp. 325–34.

points to some major contrasts of types and distributions. Indeed it is clear that the humble task of merely describing (let alone accounting for) the physical variety of Europeans has not yet been accomplished. Within any area, besides individuals of the main types, there are many others of variant subtypes, for the main types are determined in part by the personal judgment of the anthropologist and in part on the basis of average figures for the ethnic characters used as criteria; average figures in this context are no more significant than they are, for example, in climatology. The task of adequately describing the European peoples, to achieve precision, should involve estimates of the frequency with which the various types occur. Negatively, at least, it can be stated that no correlations appear between the distribution of ethnic groups and those of languages and nations.

The Languages of Europe. Certainly today Europe is, for its size, the most polyglot area in the world. Although advances in the means of transportation have virtually erased physical obstacles to the intercourse of the peoples of Europe, very long periods in the past, when movement was difficult, witnessed the sharp differentiation of languages which presents today so formidable an obstacle to European unity. Philological study has established, as a generally accepted hypothesis, that most of the languages spoken from northern India to the extreme west of Europe derive from a single original language called Indo-European. Languages unrelated to this parent speech are spoken by only a small number of Europeans and have not always been established in written form. In fact, these languages occur rather as survivals or as intrusions within a land of Indo-European linguistic parentage. But the family relationship between the tongues has now no practical significance. All the languages of Europe differ to such an extent that it is rare for any two distinct languages to be mutually intelligible. This being so, and in default of any single common language—such as Latin provided for educated Europeans during the Middle Ages and the Renaissance—it is not surprising that language has served more than anything else to foster national consciousness and thus to play a great part in the political subdivision of the continent.

The languages of Europe, most of which fall within the two classifications Indo-European and Ural-Altaic, are listed below:

Classification of the Languages of Europe (see Fig. 2–4)

A. *Indo-European*

    1. Celtic (now confined to the Atlantic coastlands of the British Isles and Brittany): Irish and Scottish Gaelic, Welsh, and Breton. Also includes Cornish (now dead) and Manx (almost dead).

2. Romance (descended from Latin): Italian, French, Walloon, Provençal, Spanish, Portuguese and Galician, Catalan, Rumanian, and various Alpine languages, including Romansch and Ladin. Also the Sardinian and Dalmatian dialects of Italian.
3. Germanic (Teutonic north-European group): German (High and Low), Dutch and Flemish, Frisian, English, Danish, Norwegian, Swedish, Icelandic, and Faeroese.
4. Baltic: Latvian and Lithuanian.
5. Slavic: Great Russian, White Russian (Belorussian), Little Russian or Ukrainian (including Ruthenian), Bulgarian, Serbo-Croat and Dalmatian, Slovene, Czech (including Moravian), Slovak, Polish, Sorbian (or Lusatian).
6. Hellenic: Greek.
7. Thraco-Illyrian (formerly widespread in the Balkans): Albanian.

B. *Ural-Altaic*

1. Finno-Ugrian (which includes also many languages spoken in the Asiatic U.S.S.R.): Magyar, Finnish and Karelian, Estonian, Lapp, Mordvinian, Komi, Komi-Permyak, Udmurt, Mari, Vogul, Ostyak, Nentsy.
2. Turkic or Turki-Tatar (mainly in Asia): Turkish (numerous outliers in the Balkan Peninsula), Kazan, Tatar, Crimean Tatar, Bashkir, Chuvash, Kalmyk, Kazakh.

C. *Semitic*

Maltese (many Maltese also speak either English or Italian).

D. *Basque*

In Europe, as elsewhere, language is a mark of social contact and not of race. Peoples have either adopted the language of their conquerors or imposed their own language on their conquerors. The language that tended to prevail belonged to the higher material culture. The adopted tongue developed in turn regional characteristics which often became sharp enough to define a recognized language. Thus Latin, the speech of the first Romans of Latium, being the expression of the superior Roman civilization, was adopted in Western Europe, North Africa, and Danubian Europe. In the eastern Mediterranean countries, however, Greek held its own despite Roman conquests, by virtue of its high cultural tradition. In western Europe provincial Latin conditioned the growth during the Middle Ages of languages of the Romance group (Fig. 2–4): French, Provençal, Italian, Catalan, Spanish, and Portuguese. In the Swiss Alps there are still some small "islands" of Ladin and Romansch, while an "inlier" of Romance speech, containing though it does some Slavic elements, occurs in Rumania, the territory of which once formed the Roman province of Dacia.

ROMANCE LANGUAGES. The distribution of Romance languages in Europe falls far short of the extent of Roman territories at their maximum. The areas from which Latin speech disappeared in favor of non-Romance languages were either frontier lands where Roman culture was less firmly established or lands where later invaders succeeded in imposing their language. Thus North Africa lost the Latin speech of its cities with the Arab conquest of the seventh to eleventh cen-

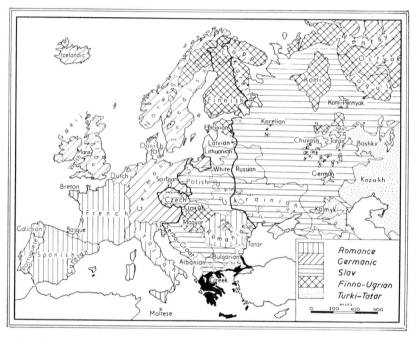

Fig. 2–4. Major linguistic patterns of Europe before World War II. Some subsequent adjustments of this pattern are referred to in the text. (After A. Meillet, modified.)

turies, as Egypt lost its former Greek speech. Similarly, southern Britain, where Latin was widely spoken by the Romano-British population, assumed, except in Celtic-speaking Cornwall and Wales, the Germanic speech of its Anglo-Saxon conquerors. In the Balkan Peninsula, Slavic languages developed, except where Greek, Vlach, and Albanian maintained their hold. Finally, within the frontier regions of the Roman Empire, along or astride the Rhine and Danube as well as in Switzerland, the present limits of Romance speech lie well behind the former imperial limits.

GERMANIC LANGUAGES. The second large linguistic group, the Germanic, includes several distinct languages, together with others that are clearly akin. When Old German was first recorded (in some inscriptions of the third and fourth centuries A.D.), three distinct forms existed: Gothic, which has died out; Western German, which includes present-day German, Dutch, Flemish, and English; and Northern German, of which Danish, Swedish, Norwegian, and Icelandic are the chief subdivisions. The widely distributed High German dialect has become the basis of a literary language current throughout Germany, Austria, and the greater part of Switzerland, but locally there can be found variations in pronunciation and vocabulary.

English has moved far from the original Anglo-Saxon speech and has undergone much admixture, notably from Norman French, so that its relationship with modern German appears distant. More unity is apparent between the written and spoken languages of the Scandinavian world. There is still enough in common between the spoken languages of Denmark, Norway, and Sweden to permit the nationals of these countries to understand one another. Both Sweden and Denmark have written forms, different in grammar and pronunciation, which go back to the Middle Ages, while Norway employs two literary languages; one is based on Danish and the other derived from old rural Norwegian dialects (Old West Norse) very different in pronunciation from Danish. In Belgium and the Netherlands, Dutch and Flemish are two forms of Low German speech which have a common literary form: Netherlandish, more usually called Dutch.

SLAVIC LANGUAGES. The Slavic languages, which constitute the third group within the Indo-European family, still preserve more in common than do languages of the Romance and Germanic groups, since they developed slowly and retain archaic features. They began to diverge notably from the ninth century onward, and present today three major varieties. The eastern (or Russian) variety includes Great Russian, White Russian, and Little Russian. Each of these has a literary and a spoken form. Little Russian has a wide currency over an area now equated with the Ukrainian S.S.R. It has held the status of a literary language only since 1905 and is the official language of the second most important republic of the Soviet Union. Whether spoken or written, Little Russian does not present much difficulty to compatriots of Great Russian speech. White Russian (Belorussian), spoken in the Soviet republic of that name, has little ground for separate status apart from Great Russian, which is by far the most widely used Slavic language in Europe and constitutes virtually the lingua franca of the whole U.S.S.R. The literary form of Great Russian was established in the eighteenth century, on the basis of the speech of the Moscow region.

The western Slavic languages, now represented by Polish, Czech, and Slovak, were once spoken as far west as the Elbe and its tributary the Saale. The so-called "Sorbian" or "Wendish" spoken, together with German, by over 100,000 people in Lusatia (the hill country southeast of Berlin) survives as a reminder of this former distribution. Polish and Czech are surrounded by other Slavic languages and German, Magyar, and Lithuanian speech, but have resisted effacement; indeed, both have literatures dating back to the later Middle Ages. Czech and Slovak show spoken and written differences, although some claim they form only one language and not two.

The southern Slavic languages, separated from the western and eastern groups by peoples of German, Hungarian, and Rumanian speech, are found in the broad northern part of the Balkan Peninsula between the Adriatic and the Black seas and north of the area in which Albanian, Greek, and even Turkish are spoken. Bulgarian and Serbo-Croat are the two chief languages of the southern group. Both had late medieval forms but were formalized as written languages only in the nineteenth century. In northwest Yugoslavia, Slovene is spoken by about two million people. Like Serbo-Croat, from which it does not differ greatly, it has been a written language since the later Middle Ages. In the Dalmatian coastlands, Slavic speech replaced a form of Romance speech related to Italian. So much variation occurs in Serbo-Croat and Bulgarian speech that in certain areas it is difficult to determine on any scientific principle which of these languages is being spoken; this is well illustrated in Macedonia, a frontier region of languages, where forms of Greek speech are also found.

To the Indo-European languages of the Romance, Germanic, and Slavic groups must be added Greek, Albanian, Celtic, and certain Baltic languages. The first has a limited range in the Aegean islands, the Peloponnesos, and the Greek peninsula as far north as Epirus and the coastlands of Macedonia and Thrace; modern Greek, be it noted, has changed so much since the days of ancient Greece that foreign students of classical Greek cannot take modern Greek in their stride! Albanian, the literary form of which was established only in the second half of the nineteenth century, is the sole survivor of Thraco-Illyrian languages once widely spoken in the Balkan Peninsula. It has borrowed much from neighboring languages in the past, especially from Latin. Two forms of Celtic survive in the west of Europe, where, at the dawn of history, this language was widely spoken. Gaelic survives in the lightly populated Scottish Highlands and Isles and provides the official language of Eire; Brythonic survives in Wales and Brittany. Welsh and Gaelic possess literatures and owe their survival not a little to national sentiment and stimulus. In the east-Baltic lowlands, Lithuanian and Lettish (in Latvia) are the two languages of the "Baltic" group, a third, Old Prussian, having been replaced by German in East Prussia by the sixteenth century. Lithuanian and Lettish are spoken by only a few million people. Although Lithuanian preserves the most archaic features of all the Indo-European languages of Europe, its literature dates only from the eighteenth century. Whereas Lithuanian has lost much ground over the centuries, Lettish has spread among Livonians who formerly spoke a Finnic language.

NON-INDO-EUROPEAN LANGUAGES. For the rest, the non-Indo-European languages of Europe can be noted briefly. Maltese represents a survival of Semitic speech from the days of the Arab conquest. Basque is believed, on the other hand, to have survived from the days before the settlement of peoples of Indo-European speech, for its relationship with other languages remains obscure. Before the Roman period, it was used widely in Iberia and in France south of the Garonne and west of the lower Rhone. Today it is confined to a small area athwart and west of the western Pyrenees, and even there educated people speak also either French or Spanish. Today, Basque is a factor in regional consciousness, as witnessed by the formation of a Basque republic during the Spanish civil war of 1936–38, and the provincial organization of Spain recognizes the distinctness of the Basques, the majority of whom occupy the province of Vizcaya.

FINNO-UGRIAN AND TURKIC LANGUAGES. There remain the numerous languages of the Finno-Ugrian and Turkic families, which are spoken by relatively small numbers in Europe, although over a considerable area. Finno-Ugrian is mainly represented by Magyar, which is spoken inside and outside the limits of the Hungarian republic, notably in the towns of eastern Transylvania, once a part of the Hungarian kingdom and now a part of Rumania. The languages of the Finns, Karelians, and Lapps also fall within this group, as do several others still spoken in the northeast of the European U.S.S.R.: Nentsy, Ostyak, Komi, Vogul, and the rest. Indeed, as river names still testify, Finno-Ugrian speech once prevailed widely in the European area now dominated by Russian speech. Finally, the Estonian tongue, spoken by only about one million people, is Finno-Ugrian and closely related to Finnish.

The Turkic languages are spoken in European areas of the Soviet Union which are now organized as autonomous Soviet Socialist Republics, i.e., the Bashkir, Tatar (or Kazan), Chuvash, and Kalmyk. Turkic speech extends also to Eastern Thrace (European Turkey) and to the Crimean Peninsula but is spoken by only a minority of the population.

CONCLUSION. The language map of Europe thus depicts many frontiers or areas of transition through which it is possible to draw boundary lines, often only with much difficulty and rough accuracy. Although linguistic groups are often compactly located, they are seldom homogeneous, and in places appear widely scattered. In Western, Northern, and Mediterranean Europe they are relatively compact, but even there islands of other languages and marginal areas of mixed languages occur. In Central Europe, and above all in the "Shatter Belt," the distributions are much more complicated, although less so now than in 1938. Apart from "alien" minorities within the country and the mixture of language groups on the state margins, there are, or were until recently, many scattered "outliers." Moreover, areas of great complication occur where very many languages are spoken, and where, as a result, the mapping of the distribution of languages becomes well nigh impossible. Macedonia, now divided between Greece, Yugoslavia, and Bulgaria, represents the most striking illustration of this complexity, so that Gallic humor has coined the expression *Macédoine de fruits* to describe fruit salad.

The explanation of the language map of Europe cannot be found solely in the physical geography of the continent. It has been argued that "language areas . . . have been largely determined by the character of the surface and climate" and that "linguistic lines of cleavage . . . conform to a notable degree with physical features." [5] Only if men, like plants, had specific climatic and edaphic needs could one expect to find in physical geography a complete explanation of the language map.

Certain physical features or environments do, it is true, help to define the linguistic patterns in Europe. The lower Danube, flanked by a broad belt of marshes on its north bank, does divide Rumanian from Bulgarian-speaking peoples. The boundary between French and German passes along the wooded summits of the high Vosges. The area of the Pripet Marshes separates Ukrainian and Belorussian speech. And the Pyrenees effectively separate French and Spanish. Areas of scantily settled steppe and rivers which are unnavigable upstream characterize the frontier region between Portuguese and Spanish. But, in the main, peoples and languages have negotiated physical obstacles such as mountains, rivers, highlands, and marshes. The watershed of the Alps does not neatly divide French and German from Italian; within the Alpine valleys, distinctive languages have developed in semi-isolation; neither do the eastern Pyrenees sharply divide the areas of Catalan and Provençal. As to the navigable rivers

[5] L. Dominian, *The Frontiers of Language and Nationality in Europe* (New York: Henry Holt & Co., Inc., 1917), pp. 2–3.

of Europe, they commonly serve to unite rather than to divide, so that the Vistula Basin forms the homeland of Polish speech, while the Rhine Basin has become mainly Germanic, though invaded by French on its western flank. The Danube, in contrast, presents a succession of language areas astride its valley.

In lowlands and hilly country, the frontiers of language bear no obvious relationship to the relief and are clearly the expression of social forces operative long ago. Even so, former geographic features —now erased—may have been significant: thus the former Carbonnière Forest did in medieval times form a zone of separation between Flemish speech in the Scheldt Basin and French speech to the south.

In short, Europe's language map, like that of its nations and states, can be explained only in terms of historical geography, i.e., the movements of peoples, their initial settlements and subsequent colonization outward, and their mutual reactions when brought into contact with each other. By the end of the Middle Ages the language patterns were clearly outlined; one can point to specific linguistic frontiers, notably that of French and German in the Lorraine Plateau and that of Walloon and French on the Franco-Belgian border where the boundary has changed but little during the last thousand years. And, since the end of the Middle Ages, the many migrations, colonizing efforts, and compulsory and voluntary transfers of population, especially in the 1940's, have modified distributions fixed long ago.

DEMOGRAPHIC CONSIDERATIONS

Population Growth, Densities, and Distribution. The population of Europe is estimated at nearly 600 million, that is, one-fifth of mankind, and is very unevenly distributed. The outstanding areas of high density occur in Italy and in a diagonal zone from the British lowlands and the Low Countries, in the northwest, to the Ukrainian steppe, in the southeast. The highest figure reached in a state-area [6] is 900 persons per square mile in the Netherlands (year 1958). Notably low densities occur in northern Europe, including Fenno-Scandia and the northern lowlands of Germany, Poland, and the U.S.S.R.; in Iberia; and in the southeast-European peninsula. Apart from Iceland and the northeastern parts of the European U.S.S.R., Norway has the lowest density, 28 persons per square mile. Clearly the present densities and distribution of population, no less than the high degree of urbanization that characterizes Europe, are the result of historical changes, some of the last two centuries or less, and are the particular

[6] For England and Wales, part of the state territory of the United Kingdom, the 1951 census figure is approximately 750 per square mile,

product of those changes connected with the increasingly effective exploitation of natural resources and opportunities.

From the dawn of history, Europe has always been one of the most densely populated areas of the world. Historians estimate the population of the Roman Empire, in its heyday, at 70 million when that of China, on the basis of its census of 156 A.D., reached an estimated 50 million. Europe contained only some of these 70 million, for some of the most populous areas of the Roman Empire lay outside its European boundaries—in Egypt, North Africa, the west coast of Asia Minor, Syria, and Palestine. Outside the Roman frontiers in Europe dwelt Celts, Germans, and Slavs, organized at first into tribes and later into nations. Their economy was so rudimentary as to support only relatively small numbers. Thus in the early Christian era, as today, Europe stood second only to Asia in population numbers, for to the numbers of Chinese must be added tens of millions of Indians and other Asians.

The distribution of population in the early centuries of the Christian era reflected the historical circumstance that progress in material culture, on which increasing numbers depended, spread from cultural centers in the east and southeast, i.e., Egypt, the Levant, Greece, and Rome. Italy was relatively populous in the Roman Empire, but it was the peninsula rather than the northern plain which then held the greater density of population. Generally, southern Europe—Italy, Greece, southern Spain, and the Mediterranean islands—showed the highest densities, while population grew scantier further away from the Mediterranean axis of the Empire. Thus Britain, less populous than Gaul, had but an estimated one million people during its centuries as a Roman province (43 A.D. to about 400 A.D.), while Central and Eastern Europe—the so-called "barbarian" world beyond the Rhine-Danube frontiers—and still more Scandinavia, can scarcely have accounted for more than a few million.

It would appear that the population of medieval Europe doubled between 1100 and 1300 A.D., fell sharply during the following century and a half, partly as a result of the Black Death, and rose to its former high level by 1500. Central Italy appears to have had the densest population about the year 1300, when notable increases in density also occurred in France and the Low Countries, in northern Italy, in the English Lowlands, and, to a lesser degree, in the German-settled lands between the Rhine and the Neman (Niemen). In other words, the pattern of well-populated lands had extended to the northwest since Roman times. Farther east in Europe, in Bohemia, Moravia, the Vistula-Bug basin, and the forests of north and central Russia, colonization, principally by Slavs, must have led to greater though still scattered settlement and higher densities than those obtaining at the time of Rome. The Iberian Peninsula in the mid-fourteenth century appears not to have advanced in numbers since Roman times: warfare between Christian princes and Moslem conquerors, carried on in the south, may well have served to check the growth of population.

For the early eighteenth century, although official censuses were still lacking, it is possible to see rather more clearly the broad outlines of Europe's population map. For the whole continent the population is estimated to have been then about 100 or 110 million. France, the British Isles, the Low Countries, and Germany had still further increased their relative demographic standing. As compared with today, the continent was but sparsely settled, by populations for the most part rural, drawing their livelihood from agriculture but also in some areas from rural woolen industries. The highest densities reached, notably in the English Lowlands, central Lombardy, Westphalia, the Rhineland, and Saxony, were of the order of only 100 to 175 persons per square mile.

Soil fertility was one important physical factor behind population densities, but not the only one. Urban concentrations were evidently related to industrial, commercial, and administrative activities, while some of the potentially best arable soils of Europe, notably the black earths of the Ukraine, the steppe soils of eastern Hungary, and those developed on the loess of Lower Silesia and Galicia, were as yet virtually unexploited.

A significant feature of the early-eighteenth-century map of population distribution is the semivacant tract which extended across the continent from the Baltic to the area between the Danube Delta and the Don. Of this sharp break in the settlement pattern between Western Christendom and Russia there are many complementary explanations: the extensive Pripet Marshes discouraged and diverted settlement; the Tatar (Mongol) invasions of the fourteenth century and many other wars had caused much destruction; the steppe lands were still subject to the mastery of the nomad; the material culture lagged far behind that of Western and Central Europe. It was in this zone that, from as early as the fourteenth century, Jews escaping from persecution in Germany and Western Europe increasingly sought refuge. They created what became known as "the Jewish Pale." The Baltic coastlands, covered widely with boulder clay and studded with small lakes, remained in 1720 very scantily populated, while in Northern Europe only the Swedish midlands (but not Scania and Småland) and the southern littoral of Finland were really populated. The upper Volga-Oka basin, where lay the old province of Moscow, and the area southward to Kiev were clearly the demographic core of Russia, al-

though its density of population fell well below the highest figures
of the time reached in Saxony, the Rhineland, the Low Countries,
Italy, and England.

Attempts have been made to estimate roundly the populations of
European countries in the early eighteenth century; some estimates
for the years 1720, 1820, and 1930 are given below. Josef Haliczer's
figures [7] for the separate countries have been grouped here (1960 estimates have been added) to fit the major regions discussed later in this
book. The areas of the named states, totaled for the several regions,
are those of 1930.

Estimated Populations of the Major Divisions of Europe in 1720, 1820, 1930, and 1960

Regions	Areas (thousand square miles)	Estimated Population (millions)			
		1720	1820	1930	1960
SOUTHERN EUROPE (Spain, Portugal, Italy, San Marino, Greece, European Turkey)	411	25	41	79	99
WESTERN EUROPE (France, Low Countries, Luxembourg)	239	22	36	59	67
BRITISH ISLES (United Kingdom, Republic of Ireland)	121	8	21	49	55
NORTHERN EUROPE (Denmark, Norway, Sweden, Finland, Faeroes, Spitsbergen)	485	3.5	6	16	20
EUROPEAN U.S.S.R. (including Estonia, Latvia, Lithuania)	1,800	17	39	125	156
EASTERN EUROPE (Poland, Czechoslovakia, Hungary, Rumania, Bulgaria, Albania, Yugoslavia)	445	..	38	94	100
CENTRAL EUROPE (Germany, Switzerland, Austria, Liechtenstein)	176	18	28	75	86
EUROPE (estimates)	3,700	110	210	500	583

What do these round figures show? The British Isles, together
with Western and Central Europe as defined in this book, although
they occupy only one-seventh of the continent's area, accounted in
1720 for between two-fifths and one-half of its population. This
proportion, however, fell to 35 per cent in 1960. In contrast, the
European U.S.S.R. and Eastern Europe, which dominate in area
(about 60 per cent), were so retarded in exploitation and settlement

---

[7] Josef Haliczer, "The Populaton of Europe, 1720, 1820, 1930," *Geography*, part
4 (December, 1934): 261–73. This article contains generalized distribution (dot) maps
for the selected dates.

in 1720 as to contain less than one-third of Europe's population. This proportion markedly increased by 1960 to 44 per cent, thus exceeding that of the British Isles and Western and Central Europe, reflecting much higher fertility rates than those prevailing in the west. The least settled major division of the continent, Northern Europe maintained over the last three centuries its small proportion of the European population, namely about 3 per cent. Southern Europe's share has clearly decreased, from nearly one-quarter in 1720 to only about one-sixth in 1960.

In general, these estimates show the remarkable increase in Europe's numbers, notably during the period 1820–1960, even though net emigration was then very considerable. They also illustrate that, over the period 1720–1930, the rates of estimated increase were lowest in Western and Eastern Europe, higher in Central Europe, Northern Europe, and the "Shatter Belt," and highest in the British Isles and European U.S.S.R. Further, they draw attention to the tilting of the demographic balance toward east-Central and Eastern Europe, and the European U.S.S.R., where the long-delayed evaluation of natural resources has been and is still being increasingly achieved. The demographic race, it would seem, is being won—in Europe at least—by the late starters.

Emigration and Migration. Some reference must be made to these dynamic aspects of Europe's population, notably during the last hundred and fifty years. There was an unparalleled exodus of population from Europe to lands overseas during this period; and there were also numerous smaller shifts of population, not always voluntary, within state territories and between states. The effects of the great outflow of Europeans have, of course, been written indelibly into the geography of settlement and the economic development and nation-building in countries which not so long ago were either virtually empty or only scantily peopled, notably the Americas, Australia, southern Africa, and New Zealand. The internal redistributions of population within Europe after the end of the Middle Ages, although continual and numerous (and excepting those redistributions of the last 15 years), have produced only relatively minor changes in the distribution of population and of nationalities.

At least 60 million are estimated to have moved from Europe to North America and Australasia alone, during the hundred years preceding 1924. Others in smaller numbers migrated to South America, South Africa, and elsewhere.[8] Although probably more than one-third returned to Europe, the movements were clearly on

[8] For a short account see J. S. Huxley and A. C. Haddon, *We Europeans* (London: Jonathan Cape, Ltd., 1935), Chap. 8, "Europe Overseas," by A. M. Carr-Saunders.

a grand scale, stimulated as they were by the new steamship facilities and by the labor demands of agriculture as it expanded overseas in response to growing demands for imported foodstuffs in the populous and industrial countries of Western Europe. It was the peoples of northwestern Europe,[9] with their established interest in the sea routes as avenues of commerce and/or of imperialism, who made the greatest contribution to emigration in the nineteenth century as in earlier centuries, while those of Southern and Eastern Europe and Russia dominated only during the first 15 years of this century.

Certain countries, especially Great Britain, Ireland, Italy, Germany, Spain, and Austria-Hungary, sent large numbers overseas; this fact bears on the interpretation of the differential rates of increase inferred from the summary on page 108. So also does the fact that there was a substantial outflow of Russians into their Asiatic territories (over 6 million persons moved there during the period 1901–14), where they found new lands for colonization and exploitation.

Despite Europe's long tradition of political division, no period in the continent's history has been without some movement of national groups, voluntary or enforced, from one state territory to another. While such movements were healthy in fostering economic developments, for instance, when German ironworkers, Flemish weavers, Dutch dikers, and Jewish traders applied their skill in new areas, they produced innumerable local political problems. With the growth of acute national consciousness particularly evident in this century, the presence of minorities of alien population was more and more resented in some national states.

The migration of the Germans, which was the most remarkable dispersion of people in Europe, continued long after their major colonial effort of the later Middle Ages. Between the sixteenth and the nineteenth centuries, they pressed east and southeast of Germany into the lands where less effectively organized states either welcomed them or were unable to oppose their entry and settlement. Before World War II, German minority groups were to be found in Poland, the Baltic states, Hungary, Rumania, Yugoslavia, Czechoslovakia, north Italy, south Ukraine, and the middle Volga region. The problem of the alien groups within would-be national states, characteristic particularly of the countries of Eastern Europe, was not restricted to Germans, for there were, for example, large Russian populations in Poland; Hungarian minorities in Rumania, Yugoslavia, and Czechoslovakia; and Yugoslavs in the Istrian area of Italy. Wartime and postwar expedients have had marked success in effecting, either by

[9] The peoples of Northern and Western Europe contributed fully three-quarters to the ancestry of the population of the United States in 1920: *Ibid.*, pp. 245–46.

forcible means or by voluntary action sometimes based on international engagements, many transfers of minority populations. These transfers were usually but not invariably to their national homelands. Thus, in response to national sentiment and in furtherance of the idea of the "nation state," Europe west of the Soviet Union shows closer concordance between its boundaries of states and of nationalities.

Internal migration of a different kind, leading to new patterns of population density, has been active in Britain during the last two centuries, and in much of continental Europe during the last hundred years. The Industrial Revolution and all that it entailed in industrial expansion and in new transport facilities was the major cause. The main effects were the great growth of town populations, the concentration of population in the coal fields and in other industrial districts, and the depopulation of many rural areas and of some highlands and mountain valleys, such as the Massif Central and Swiss Alpine valleys. This depopulation has been offset, in some areas, by the seasonal invasion of the holiday-maker.

THE SETTLEMENTS

The Towns. The town, ranging between the extremes of the country market center and the outsize metropolitan city, characterizes as never before the settlement geography of Europe. The degree to which population is concentrated in towns shows marked regional differences. Europe contains, too, a large proportion of cities of the greatest scale: rather more than a quarter of the world's cities of more than one million inhabitants. While the traveler is impressed by the conspicuous antiquity of many European towns, he can scarcely fail to note many centers which have clearly arisen within the last hundred years as a result of the Industrial Revolution. The geographer's study of towns turns attention to many of their varied aspects: their sites, situations, and positions; their spatial growth and areal components; their population numbers; and not least their manifold functions: industrial, commercial, administrative, defensive, residential, and holiday-making—to cite only the chief ones. With these main topics in mind, let us glance at Europe's long urban history for what light it can throw on the geography of its towns today.

The town proper, in a form unambiguously urban, either as a specially organized community or as a built-up area, owed its firm establishment in Europe to ancient Greece and later to the Roman Empire. The town was indeed the hallmark of Romano-Greek culture. The Roman Empire took over many long-established towns—

such as Athens (Athenai), Alexandria, and Marseille—situated around
the shores of the Mediterranean; and to the Roman Empire is due
the first spread of towns in Europe beyond the confines of the Mediterranean world.

Roman towns, although laid out in accordance with a plan, were
very different in shape, this being largely determined by the local
topography. They had a checkerboard road pattern, and were often
but not invariably girdled by high walls. With only a few notable
exceptions, these towns were by our standards very small. Londinium,
which the Romans established as a port and bridging place at the
head of the Thames estuary, occupied only half a square mile although it was the largest town in Britain and the equivalent of large
continental cities such as Cologne (Köln) and Mainz. Most towns
were much smaller; only a few, notably the imperial capitals of Rome
(Roma), Constantinople (Istanbul), and Lyons (Lyon), the capital
of Gaul, stood well above the rest. Roman towns enjoyed amenities
such as piped water and heated houses; their industries and trade
were normally limited. Some urban settlements were roadside stations rather than producing centers, or watering places like Wiesbaden
in Germany and Bath in England. Others were ports such as Ostia,
the port for Rome, and Marseille, first founded by Greek colonists as
early as the sixth century B.C. There were also the prototypes of the
later Calais and Boulogne, controlling the passage of the English
Channel.

A number of historic towns in Western and Mediterranean Europe
occupy sites on or near former Roman towns: we may note here
Milan (Milano), Naples (Napoli), Lyon, Bordeaux, Coblenz, St.
Albans, Lincoln, Canterbury, Vienna (Wien), Belgrade (Beograd),
Sofia (Sofiya), Niš, Dubrovnik, Split, and Salonika (Thessalonike).
The continuity of such towns as organized societies from Roman
times onward cannot often be demonstrated, although this may fairly
be claimed for some at least of the cities of the Eastern Roman
Empire, Italy, and Gaul. Often, as in Britain, there was a marked
hiatus in urban life, due to the destruction and disorganization which
followed the collapse of Roman power in the west. Immigrant conquerors and settlers, either nomadic or essentially agricultural in their
economy and unable for some time to establish peace and security
over wide areas, had little use for towns, which were reborn later
under more favorable conditions and in response to specific social
needs. The newcomers were at first content to occupy but a small
corner of a Roman town site, plundering its ruined buildings for stone
and tiles with which to build their churches, as at Nîmes and Autun
in Gaul. At some particular cities, such as Vienna, Belgrade, and

Regensburg, it is of much interest to discover that Christian churches were built on the sites of Roman temples and that Roman street patterns survived into later times. In other cities, like London, the Roman street pattern did not survive and the Roman occupation level lies buried a few yards below the present surface.

As the Dark Ages passed into the later Middle Ages, and as growing populations won new areas for the plow, towns on new as well as old sites gradually have come clearly into view. Vigorous industrial and mercantile societies, striving to achieve legal privileges from the Crown or from lay or ecclesiastical lords, formed trade associations and established civic self-government. The distinguishing marks of these towns were a charter, a market, and a wall.

We can only hint here at the origin and rise of towns in the different parts of Europe and note that they greatly increased in economic stature, particularly in the thirteenth century. It was as places of industry and trade that they made their mark in an age when power was largely attached to the ownership of land. Site and positional factors help to explain why the urban settlement came into being and why it grew: towns commonly arose, for example, at bridging and navigable points on tidal rivers. An important social and economic factor in the siting and growth of cities was often provided by a royal residence, a monastic foundation, a bishop's palace, or a feudal castle.

A remarkable phase of town building is attested in Belgium and the Netherlands from the eleventh to the thirteenth century. Many towns, often laid out carefully to a plan, arose there for the first time under the protection of a seignorial castle or a religious foundation often, as at Brugge (Bruges), on a navigable river, or along a dike. In northern France a number of towns—Troyes on the Seine, Châlons-sur-Marne, Bar-sur-Aube—flourished during the twelfth and thirteenth centuries because their fairs drew foreign merchants by overland routes from as far afield as Italy, Egypt, Syria, and Persia. With the opening (in 1317) of the sea route from Italy to the English Channel, such fairs as those of Brugge, Ghent, and Antwerp in Flanders took over the functions of these French fairs as entrepôts for a wide range of commodities of diverse origin.

The deliberate foundation of towns by royal or seignorial authorities, often for defensive purposes, accounts for other settlements, many of which failed to survive as such through lack of economic sinews. Winchelsea and Kingston-upon-Hull in England were thus founded by King Edward I (about 1300 A.D.), while in south France the so-called *bastide* towns (Villeneuve-sur-Lot is one) were laid out on a geometric plan in the thirteenth and fourteenth centuries. In south Germany the important regional capital of Munich (München) was a twelfth-century addition to a number of towns, such as Augsburg, which were originally of Roman foundation. Farther away, on the Great Russian Lowland, many of the fortified centers (*goroda*) of the Slavs grew into towns in the tenth century thanks to the political and mercantile energy of intruding Scandinavians.

Although certain periods stand out in the urban history of Europe, notably the later Middle Ages and the last two centuries, new towns were arising here and there at all times: one may note, as examples, the Channel port of Le Havre and the ducal capital of Mannheim in the Rhineland, respectively of seventeenth- and eighteenth-century origin. Madrid was a creation of the sixteenth century, succeeding as capital of a united Spain the old Castilian capital of Toledo.

To the colonizing efforts of the Germans, notably in the four centuries after 900 A.D., was due the basic distribution of towns in central and even east-central Europe. Sites already occupied by Slavs as local regional (or *gau*) centers or as fishing settlements were often selected, and some German place names with Slav suffixes such as *in* and *zig* (e.g., Berlin and Leipzig) recall this association. The new German towns east of the Rhine were distributed differentially within the physically contrasted zones of north-central Europe. Some were established along the North Sea and Baltic coasts at estuary heads, as Hamburg and Bremen; at the heads of bays, as Lübeck and Danzig (Gdansk); or in the shelter of lagoons, as Königsberg (Kaliningrad). Inland there were relatively few towns within the desolate heaths, woods, and marshes of the Baltic heights, except where major rivers such as the Elbe and Oder cut gaps through the hills, on their way northward. In the depressed and ill-drained zone farther south, some towns grew up on west-east river routes—Brandenburg on the Havel, Berlin on the Spree, Poznan (Posen) on the Warta among them. It was within the loess-covered foothill belt where the northern plains approach the Hercynian mountains that town development (and settlement generally) was most marked in a zone of natural west-east communication: Dortmund, Magdeburg, Hanover (Hannover), Brunswick (Braunschweig), Leipzig, and Cracow (Kraków) were among the towns founded in this physically favored countryside.

Most of the towns of Central Europe in the later Middle Ages were in size comparable to the nucleated villages of today. Their function was to serve peasants making their way on foot, within a radius of 6–13 miles. But a small proportion of these towns, well placed on land and water routes, like some of the cities of the Hanseatic League, throve remarkably in the last centuries of the Middle Ages as ports and trading places with widespread relationships.

Early engraved plans of European towns have much to tell about the expansion of medieval towns as new areas were built up and enclosed by walls. Figures 2–5 to 2–8 show how four important towns of today appeared in the sixteenth century. They emphasize how small were even capital cities like Paris and Moscow (Moskva). And although the old town walls, elaborately strengthened in the sixteenth and seventeenth centuries to withstand cannon fire, have usually disappeared to provide space for boulevards and buildings, and few medieval buildings have survived, the old sites, as depicted in such plans, provided the nuclei around which European towns have so widely grown, especially during the last hundred years.

In present Europe the phenomenon of the "giant" city calls for explanation. This is essentially a modern development related to the increasing population numbers and transport facilities of the nineteenth and twentieth centuries. In 1700 Europe had only 13 or 14 large towns, nearly all capital cities. London, with a population of 959,000, was the largest city in Europe in 1801, and only some 19 others, with about 100,000 or more, could then be accounted as of first magnitude. Chief of these were Paris and Constantinople, each with a population of about a half million. Some of the largest cities of today are merely those of 1800 grown in size; London, Berlin, Paris, Moscow, Leningrad, Vienna, Istanbul, and Marseille are well-known examples. Other large cities owe their stature to a development, often hand in hand with that of industry, only during the last hundred years or less. Some examples will make this point clear:

Population of Some Selected Towns of Europe—1800–1958

	1800	1850	1880	1920	1958
Essen	4,000	9,000	57,000	439,000	726,000
Duisburg	–	–	41,000	244,000	499,000
Düsseldorf	10,000	27,000	95,000	407,000	685,000
Munich	30,000	110,000	230,000	631,000	1,034,000
Rotterdam	53,000	90,000	148,000	511,000	731,000
Budapest [1]	54,000	178,000	371,000	926,000	1,870,000
Odessa	6,000	90,000 [2]	194,000	421,000 [3]	669,000 [4]
Belfast	40,000	87,000	208,000	387,000	436,000
Cardiff	2,000	20,000	83,000	200,000	254,000 [4]
Birmingham	71,000	242,000	437,000	919,000	1,091,000 [4]

[1] Until 1880 Buda and Pest were separately organized cities. [2] 1858. [3] 1926. [4] 1959.

Clearly, behind the population figures for such towns lies an interesting chapter of civic history.

Fig. 2–5. Paris in the sixteenth century.

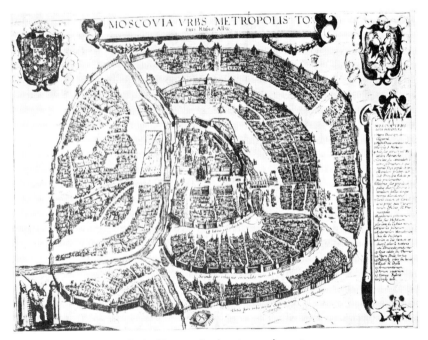

Fig. 2–6. Moscow in the sixteenth century.

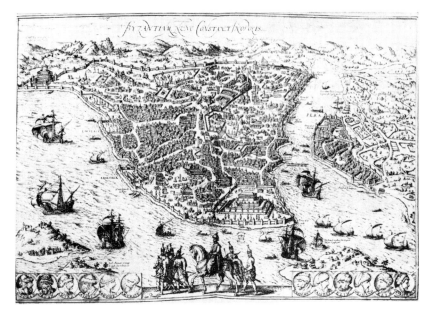

Fig. 2–7. Constantinople in the sixteenth century. The Golden Horn, between the city and Pera, provided a sheltered harbor.

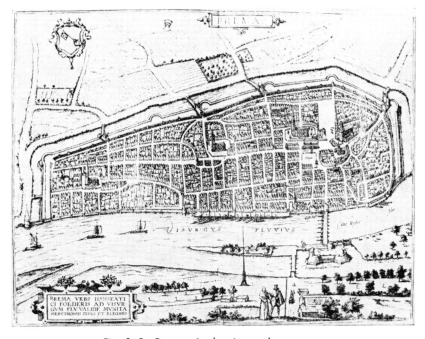

Fig. 2–8. Bremen in the sixteenth century.

The Rural Settlements. Not the least striking of the marks which social groups have written on the European landscape throughout history are the varieties of rural settlement which visibly symbolize man's appropriation, adaptation, and use of the land. Not merely have these elements of the European countryside their own intrinsic interest but, in their varying forms and with their associated economies, they also help to create different landscape patterns. Basically different patterns of settlement are found in "champaign" or *champagne* and "enclosed" or *bocage* countryside, as they were traditionally described in England and France. One is characterized by large nucleated villages surrounded by unhedged arable fields in a largely treeless plain; the other by numerous small settlements—homesteads and hamlets—with small fields enclosed by quick-set hedges or dikes, dispersed over a country generally wooded in aspect (Fig. 8–7).

Rural settlements today are the outcome of many successive phases of colonial activity and of changes in agricultural practice. Some settlements were spontaneous and some were planned; some of the stages are old and relatively obscure, while others, notably those since the Agricultural Revolution of the eighteenth century, can be more clearly seen. The geographer's main task is to show the broad distribution of the settlement types and, looking behind the existing patterns, to attempt to explain their origin. While it would seem that the principal explanation of Europe's rural-settlement map is to be sought in the agrarian technique and social organization of peoples at specific periods of history, it is evident that conditions of physical geography and biogeography are also relevant to the discussion.

Rural settlements appear in prehistory and may in some areas have fixed the sites of modern villages,[10] but it is to historical times that the student largely turns for the explanation of the contemporary map. Although the attribution of the communally organized open-field village with its surrounding unenclosed fields to Germanic influence cannot be accepted as generally and exclusively true, it is nevertheless clear that these features are revealed during the centuries which followed Germanic immigration and colonization in parts of northwestern Europe, notably in the English Lowlands, northern and northeastern France, southern Belgium, Lorraine, and the Rhineland. In other areas which were also subject to early Germanic settlement, such as Kent (England) and central and southern Gaul, as well as in countries not so affected, such as Wales and Brittany, settlements of the hamlet and homestead types, with early enclosed fields and *bocage* aspect, became prevalent. Indeed, in some places

---

[10] A. Demangeon draws attention to the existence of Celtic villages in Roman Gaul and claims for these villages a Neolithic origin. See his *Géographie Économique et Humaine de la France* (Paris: Armand Colin, 1946), Vol. I, p. 187.

either Roman or pre-Roman Celtic settlements and agrarian systems survived as an element in shaping the countryside, despite German conquest and settlement. Certain settlement patterns and field systems also developed independently of influence from outside, for example, the communally organized villages and fields of Sardinia.

But if the photographic plate of Europe's rural-settlement map begins to "develop" during the Dark Ages, which followed the barbarian invasions of Europe, it clarifies and sharpens as further colonization of the later Middle Ages and of the last two centuries goes on. New branches are grafted onto the trunk of primary settlement as population grows and mastery is won over hitherto undeveloped areas of forest, marsh, moor, and steppe. Numerous marsh and forest villages are created by freeholding peasants and commonly set out in linear form along a dike, a stream, or a road, with individual holdings running back at right angles to the village axis. At the same time colonization by single homesteads is also made, as in the drained polder lands of the Low Countries and in the woodlands of the English Weald. The increase in population in Western Europe, especially between the eleventh and thirteenth centuries, leads to the creation of many "daughter" settlements, i.e., homesteads or hamlets beyond the fields of the parent village. Some such settlements arise from "free lance" action, others—and this was the more usual reason—by the organized efforts of secular, ecclesiastical, and monastic landowners intent on the better exploitation of their lands. The new villages assumed many different forms.[11]

At a much later date, the Agricultural Revolution of the eighteenth century, which brought new possibilities of enhanced productivity from lands enclosed under individual ownership, became the cause of much new dispersed settlement, as tenants moved out from existing villages. The steppe lands of southeastern Europe, notably in the Ukraine and eastern Hungary, began in the second half of the eighteenth century to be transformed from an environment of semi-nomadic pastoral husbandry to one of settled villages, with cultivation as the basis of their mixed farming. As transportation facilities improved during the last two centuries, wealth won by urban dwellers in industry and commerce has also often been used to modify the rural landscape through building of large country houses and the creation of gardens and parks.

The student of rural settlement in Europe should thus be much concerned with the history behind geography. This is true whether he confines his attention to any one country or, indeed, to part of one

[11] See R. E. Dickinson, "Rural Settlements in the German Lands," *Annals of the Association of American Geographers* 39 (December, 1949), No. 4, pp. 239–63, for a discussion and illustrations.

country. France still shows striking contrasts, clearly observed by Arthur Young[12] during the years 1787–89, between the *champagne* of large hedgeless villages in the north, the *bocage* of smaller dispersed settlements of the west and center, and the mixed, once mainly nucleated, settlement of its Mediterranean south. Britain, too, shows such contrasts of landscape types and complicated patterns of settlement woven throughout history. The county of Pembroke in Wales, for example, as a result of Anglo-Norman colonization, contains old nucleated villages with fields now enclosed in its southern lowland, and the older dispersed Welsh settlements in its higher northern parts. Certainly many settlement types have established themselves without strict regard to physical geography. In the waterless limestone plateau of Causses as in neighboring well-watered parts of the Massif Central, dispersed settlements prevail alike; in the Pays de Caux, despite broadly uniform physical conditions, settlements are dispersed in the west and concentrated in the east. Yet in the more detailed study of the sites, distribution, and frequency of villages, correlations with physical conditions are often evident enough: for example, the alignment of villages along the scarp-foot and dip-slope edge of limestone plateaus, along the terraces of rivers, or on dry island sites in former fenland.

A workmanlike guide to the rural-settlement map of Europe is provided by Demangeon's genetic classification of settlement types.[13] This provides no easy key, since it assumes much knowledge of rural history. Settlements as they now appear may have changed drastically in form, even in recent times: witness how in Denmark, in the Channel Islands, and in many parts of Ireland[14] and Scotland present dispersed settlements replaced nucleated villages in the course of the nineteenth century.

Among nucleated villages Demangeon distinguishes three types on the basis of their origin. First, the communally organized "open-field village" which appears widely established in Western and Central Europe from the Dark Ages onward, although it is claimed that some originated in the clearings and settlements of Neolithic times. The dwellings of a nucleated village grew up around some or all of the following features: church, manor house, inn, bridge, spring or well, pond, and mill; only from this central area could the villagers have convenient access to their scattered holdings in the village fields.

[12] Arthur Young, *Travels in France During the Years 1787, 1788, 1789* (2 vols.; Bury St. Edmunds, 1794).

[13] Albert Demangeon, *Problèmes de Géographie Humaine* (3d ed.; Paris: Armand Colin, 1947), pp. 185–202.

[14] E. Estyn Evans, *Irish Heritage* (Dundalk, Eire: Dundalgan Press, 1942), p. 48.

These lay open around the village and were cut into strips; its meadow and pastoral waste were communally used. The communal organization lasted on into the nineteenth century; the scattered strips have been by now mostly consolidated into compact units, but only exceptionally, as in England, have they been fully enclosed. This farming was proudly acclaimed in the eighteenth century as *la grande culture*, for the open-field system was operated on some of the richest soils of the continent, notably those which overlie the loess, although it included, too, some mountain valleys and heavy-clay lands.

The second type is the "village with contiguous fields." To this category belong the linear villages created in forest clearings and drained marshes in the later Middle Ages; from their origin, the lands adjacent to the village were divided into individually owned holdings. Such villages are found in the Low Countries and northwest Germany and in many forest clearings of the Hercynian highlands, for example, in the Black Forest and the Bohemian Forest.

The third type, the "village with dissociated fields," is best represented in Mediterranean Europe, where very large compact settlements perched on high sites, originally chosen in part at least for reasons of defense, stand aloof and distant from their fields, as indeed from their supplies of water. This settlement type is found in association with large estates in south Italy.

Similarly, four kinds of dispersed settlement can be distinguished. The first kind, the so-called "primary dispersion," was effected long ago. It is believed that much of the dispersed settlement of the Massif Central, Cornwall, and Wales is of this type, as well as that of Norway, the language of which has no word for "village." The second is "intercalated dispersion," which refers to dispersed settlement made subsequently to nucleated settlement, by a process of "filiation" from existing villages as organized clearance of the waste took place. The fifteenth century witnessed much settlement of this kind in France as feudal lords and monastic houses conceded to peasants parts of their demesne. The third kind of dispersed settlement, "secondary dispersion," takes place when, for reasons of agricultural convenience, peasants move out from their village and settle by their lands; the *tanyas* of Hungary and the *bastides* of Provence resulted from such secondary dispersion. Much of the settlement pattern of England is of this type, following the enclosure of the common fields, between the fifteenth and nineteenth centuries. Lastly, the "primary dispersion of recent date" can often be easily noted. From the nineteenth century onward, better transport facilities and superior water control and water supply permitted widespread dispersion of dwellings.

THE ECONOMY, INCLUDING CIRCULATION

The economy of Europe in all its regional variations and in its diverse visible features has its roots in the distant past, although the effects of the last hundred years stand out with particular clarity. The student's interest in the economic geography of Europe is rightly directed to the maps of its agriculture, its forests, its mines, its industrial concentrations, its transport patterns, and its seaports, which together show the effects on the face of the land of a concerted effort to exploit what nature has provided.

The peculiar features of contemporary European economy—and notably its interregional and international trade relations—are discussed later in this book (Chapter 10). It is enough here to note its five broad characteristics. First, the industrial and commercial importance in the world of Western and Central Europe, based on the application of a large and skilled labor force to available natural resources in an area geographically well placed for, and historically conditioned to, oceanic commerce. Second, the continuing importance of agriculture throughout the whole continent and its higher relative importance in the broadening lowlands of Eastern Europe and the European U.S.S.R. Third, the well-developed railroad network, notably in Western and Central Europe, and the continent's many major seaports related to the routes of world trade. Fourth, the economic contrast between Western and Central Europe on one hand and the remaining greater part of the continent on the other, where industrialization in its modern forms came later and had a more restricted place. Lastly, the political dichotomy between East and West, which has sharpened since the end of World War II and clearly has its economic aspect. In the brief discussion which follows, the reader is invited to consider a little of the history which lies behind Europe's present economic map. For "what is" has sprung from "what was."

Agriculture. European agriculture was indeed, in Neolithic days, a very different thing from what it has now become. Long subordinate to stock raising, carried on in small temporary fields, on light shallow soils with the aid of a digging stick or hoe, and in a setting dominated by forest, the earliest agriculture lay technologically remote from modern forms with large permanent fields, tractors, selected seeds, fertilizers, and heavy farm machinery. Yet, technological progress apart, and despite regional specialization in manufacturing industry and in mineral exploitation, Europe remains almost everywhere an area of agricultural productivity. It absorbs in agriculture the greater part of its labor force. European agricultural economy shows little of that broad standardization which characterizes large areas of North America where terms like "cotton belt" and "corn belt" introduce the student gently into the complications of agricultural geography. On the contrary, Europe's agriculture presents great regional and local variety in response to physical conditions of climate, soil, slope, and other landform aspects, and to the differential energy and enterprise with which they have been used. In the size and organization of the farm unit, in the range and yield of crops, in the degree of "mixed farming," in the application of capital and mechanization, in the use of irrigation and of artificial fertilizers, in the emphasis on farming for subsistence or for "cash crops," in the manpower required per acre, and in the ouput per man-hour obtained —in all these and in other ways European agriculture is diversified. But thanks to this diversity and thanks, too, to much intensity of farming, especially in Western and Central Europe, the continent produces most of its food, leads the world in the production of wheat, and grows a wide range of other cereal crops including even rice. It also produces some specialized products like olive oil, wine, and essential oils; vegetable fibers like flax and hemp, though only a trifling amount of cotton; a wide range of fruits, including citrus; and much cattle fodder, sugar beet, and tobacco.

We may glance at two important background facts to the present-day agriculture in Europe. First, it represents the culmination of an age-long struggle to tame an environment little suited in its primitive state to large-scale agricultural development. The tillage of European soil results from prolonged and hard efforts which were devoted to forest clearance, marsh drainage, and soil improvement. Second, since it reflects the outcome of much scientific and technological progress, we should not ignore that outstanding phase of reorganization and improvement which is summed up as the Agricultural Revolution. This was effective at different times in different parts of the continent, between the seventeenth and the nineteenth centuries.

"The country . . . either bristles with woods or festers with swamps": this is how Tacitus described Central Europe in 98 A.D., through which, from the middle Rhine to the Carpathians, stretched the "Hercynian Forest," as Caesar named it. The German peoples at first had no inclination to destroy the forests which harbored their divinities and protected their settled islands of farmland. Nor were the Slav and Hungarian peoples to the east, and the Scandinavian peoples to the north, inclined to pit their strength against the vast permanent woods which encompassed them and were useful in providing them with game, timber, fuel, honey, wax, and some marginal rough grazing. When the Germanic peoples had possessed themselves of and settled in former imperial lands, their energies were turned first to the recovery of cultivated fields which had been wasted and abandoned. Only later was the pioneer clearing of forested land undertaken, although in England Anglo-Saxons and Danes were quick to launch fresh attacks on the woodlands.

The reign of Charlemagne (768–814 A.D.), however, witnessed the felling of great stretches of primeval woodland, notably on both sides of the middle and lower Rhine, in the Main Valley, and in Hesse. More land was needed for settlement, for stock raising, and for agriculture. In later centuries, as the Germans pushed eastward their conquests and colonization under the leadership of Church and State, forest clearance was made in scale and is recalled by many of the names of their settlements, notably those containing the elements -rode, -reud, -ried, -rath, -rade, -brand, -hain, -schwend, and -grün. The later centuries of the Middle Ages witnessed much forest clearance in France, and Germans and Flemings were called into Hungary to fell trees in Transylvania. Some woodlands disappeared by "assarting," i.e., by clearings made around existing settlements. But great stretches of hunting country, much of it wooded, were carefully preserved by law to gratify the hunting tastes of emperors, kings, and lords. Forest clearance was not wholly deliberate—witness the destructiveness of goats grazing the rugged hills of the Mediterranean countries; sometimes the first cutting led to soil erosion and further destruction of woods, as in the Dauphiné province of France in the western Alps. Nor was forest clearance wholly due to agriculture, a fact attested by the inroads made by seafaring peoples of the Mediterranean Basin and by iron smelters, using charcoal for fuel, in such areas as the Harz, the Weald of England, and the Ural Mountains of Russia.

The clearance of the forests, together with the reclamation of marshland, heath, and bog land, the drainage of lakes, and the plowing up of the steppe—all contributed to the increase of the agricultural area. The increase of the arable area in response to the growth of population must have been continual. Figures available in the nineteenth century show the rapid increase, from 364 to 546 million acres between 1820 and 1880.

These changes markedly altered the face of the country. They produced too, notably in Western and Central Europe, a shortage of timber, which in turn led to efforts to reforest suitable unused areas. By the Railway Age there were only a few countries, notably Norway, Sweden, and Russia, which could offer timber for export.

In Norway and Sweden, as in many other countries, forests are now "cropped," i.e., the annual cut is equated to annual replacement. Reforestation has meant much change in the character of such woodlands. Thus, in Germany, quickly growing conifers now dominate in forested areas where formerly deciduous species, useful for grazing as well as timber, held sway.

In addition to the clearing of woodlands, the reclamation of marshland and sea-invaded lowland, and the drainage of lakes have contributed to the agricultural area of Europe. Hollanders and Flemings, with the encouragement of their counts, lords, bishops, and monastic foundations, took the lead in the attempt to make profitable the lands lying near or just below the high-tide water level. In the late Roman period the sea invaded coastal Flanders (where a layer of marine silt covers the Roman occupation level) and submerged large parts of Roman-occupied Holland and Zeeland, where large artificial mounds—*terpen* or *werden*—had been previously built to provide dry points for settlements.

The drainage of parts of maritime Flanders, Zeeland, and Holland and their settlement by a free and independent peasantry began early and was going on vigorously in the eleventh century. Further invasions by the sea during periods of high tides or violent storms in the later Middle Ages only intensified the struggle of the Dutch against the sea. Hollanders and Flemings carried their skill into marshlands beyond their own countries—to the English Fenlands and to the estuarine lowlands of the Weser, Elbe, Oder, and Vistula. Cities and monastic houses in the north Italian plain similarly started in the twelfth century to drain the marshes which had formed largely through neglect of former Roman measures of water control. Nowadays, along the coasts and rivers of the Low Countries, the "polders," as the drained and diked lowlands are called, are held safe for dairy cattle and crops with the aid of steam and electric pumps, which have largely replaced the traditional windmills. In recent decades part of the Zuider Zee has been reclaimed, and its remainder, enclosed by a sea wall, has become the fresh-water IJsselmeer. The largest surviving ill-drained tract of the continent—a relic of the Great Ice Age—lies in the Pripet Marshes of the Belorussian S.S.R., but the Soviet government is by stages effecting their reclamation.

Present-day European agriculture owes to the past the expansion of its area of field, pasture, and meadow; it owes to the past, also, the major changes in agrarian organization and the applications of modern science and technique. The Mediterranean lands of the Roman Empire were the first to lead in the art of agriculture, and, despite the shrinking of the agricultural area and the falling off in agricultural practice during the Dark Ages, Roman traditions largely survived, supplemented by Arab innovations—themselves in part based on Roman models—to inform the farming of Western and Central Europe. Within the Roman Empire the "two-course rotation," that is, the autumn sowing of either wheat or barley followed by fallowing, was developed to meet the need, under the Mediterranean climate, of "dry farming." Great care was taken by successive plowings of the topsoil of the fallow field to retain moisture for the following crop. To supplement the hoe, the farmers of the Empire used the *aratrum*, a light, wheel-less plow, with or without a colter, although the *caruca*, a wheeled plow which was better adapted to heavy soils, appears to have been invented then in north Italy. Roman agriculture knew, and in some measure grew, fodder crops such as vetch, lucerne, alfalfa, and chick-pea, so valuable for winter feed, while the value of enriching land by the application of stable manure, pigeon dung, wood ash, and vegetable compost was also well understood. The practice of transhumance, effected by the seasonal movement of sheep between high- and low-level pastures was well established in the Mediterranean lands of the Empire. Nor should we forget the remarkable success achieved by the Romans in irrigation and in the cultivation of the vine, the olive, and other fruit-bearing trees.

Western and Central Europe largely inherited these legacies but made their own modifications to suit the very different conditions of climate and landforms. It was a striking advance when tillage for crops superseded cattle raising as the dominant feature of the economy of the Germanic settlers in the west. It was not less striking when regular crop rotations, adapted to two or three fields, took the place of the former temporary cropping of burnt-over ground. The Roman *aratrum* long prevailed in use, although the *caruca*, much better suited to the northern lowlands and drawn by horses instead of oxen, was increasingly used at the end of the Middle Ages. Marling (i.e., liming) of arable fields was an important northern practice, although limited by transport deficiencies to areas with easy access to supplies of chalk. But with all its success in expanding the agricultural area and the supply of food and raw materials (wool, flax, etc.), agriculture in Western Europe became in many respects inefficient and resistant to progressive change. What has been called "the Agricultural Revolution of the eighteenth century" was necessary to provide the possibility and means of advance. And, even then, Eastern and parts of Mediterranean Europe were little affected: organization and practice there have only changed substantially during the last hundred years.

It is not surprising, geographically, that many of the ideas of the new husbandry were derived from north Italy and the Low Countries. That these areas, and in particular Lombardy and Flanders, led in agricultural efficiency was due not so much to physical advantages—although soil and climate were broadly favorable—as to the economic stimulus long exerted on the surrounding countryside by numerous rich and populous cities. The Agricultural Revolution was most marked in England and parts of northern France. It largely brought to an end the old communally organized fields and pastures of the open-field system, and it led to some consolidation of the strip hold-ings in the fields and, notably in England, to much new enclosure of fields by hedgerows, walls, and ditches. Individual ownership or holding of farmland brought new initiatives and techniques. It be-came possible to abolish the fallow field by scientific rotations and, at the same time, to grow winter fodder (roots and clover) for live-stock. Especially in England, capital was increasingly applied to agri-culture for the production of more grain and meat. Transport by road, river, and canal was much improved. Poor soils were found to be not always useless: by heavy manuring, for example, the sands of central Belgium have become little distinguishable from the intrinsi-cally richer marine clays farther north. By scientific stock breeding cattle doubled and sheep trebled in weight in the course of a century. The pressure of population, much of which was engaged in industry, was the economic stimulus behind the Agricultural Revolution.

The Americas made their contribution of plants which have now become long-established staples in Europe. Chief among these were the potato, corn (maize), and tobacco. The potato was first grown in gardens and later became a field crop. Although at first regarded by peasants as fodder rather than as human food, it became also a foodstuff of great importance, above all in Ireland, and was well adapted to the north-European lowlands. The sugar beet is a nine-teenth-century innovation, the cultivation of which has been delib-erately favored by European governments in order to secure their independence of seaborne supplies of cane sugar in time of war. By the middle of the last century it was being grown in northern France, Belgium, and throughout the loess belt of Germany, Bohemia, Moravia, Hungary, and the southern-European U.S.S.R.

We may conclude this brief sketch of the antecedents of present European agriculture by noting how agrarian changes, designed above all to break up large estates for peasant holdings, occurred in Eastern Europe (except in Hungary) after World War I. The estab-lishment of "collective farming" in the U.S.S.R. brought radical changes, including mechanization, to the Soviet countryside. In some measure this system has been introduced into the Soviet satellite countries of Eastern Europe, following the breakup of surviving large estates.

Industry. The numerous industries of Europe may be distinguished into two groups: the extractive and the manufacturing. The extractive industries include mining and quarrying, fishing and whaling, and lumbering, the localization of all being determined by the facts of economic geology or geography. To this category of industries should doubtless be added industrial developments of this century, such as the generation of hydroelectric power and the extraction of nitrogen from the air. The manufacturing industries are legion, and, in so far as in most of them goods are made by machines rather than by hand, the term might appear literally misleading. On the one hand are a wide range of light industries, including luxury industries, where the skill of the craftsman is still all-important: French wines, Parisian gowns, Harris tweeds, Belgian lace, and German wooden toys, to name a few. On the other hand are those major industries on which modern industrialized states depend, where power-driven machinery is essential and large-scale plant usual—industries such as steel making, heavy chemicals, engineering, and shipbuilding.

Industry in Europe is no new phenomenon. In the Middle Ages there were already both urban and rural areas where industry played a dominant part in economy—for example Flanders, with its many cities engaged in making woolen and linen textiles, the Harz, the Thuringian Forest and Siegerland with their iron mines and smelters, and the English West Country, with its worsted manufacture based on the supply of water and of water power from its streams. The novelty resides in the fact that modern industry, using power-driven machinery, much capital, and a large labor force, is operated on a grand scale usually in and around towns and tends to group itself geographically within specific areas. In many parts of Europe today "industrial belts" must engage the interest of the student of geography.

The reasons for this localization spring from considerations of many kinds. The presence of local supplies of fuel and power—especially coal and hydroelectricity—is often the main explanation. The occurrence of either mineral ores or coal seams, in surface outcrops or at accessible levels below the surface, no less clearly explains the localization of mines and quarries and of related industries. The outsize towns like London, Berlin, Milan, Vienna, Paris, Moscow, and Leningrad are big industrial regions for quite different reasons. They provide ample labor, large markets, good transport facilities, and can with ease utilize electrical energy. Some industrial areas find their explanation in history, and their continued importance illustrates what can be best termed "historical momentum." Thus Lancashire, favored by the abundant soft water and supplies of wool from the Pennine moorlands, was traditionally engaged in the manufacture of linen and woolen textiles. But, following a start made in the seventeenth century, it has become a specialized area for cotton textiles, using American cotton imported via Liverpool, and steam-powered machinery. In contrast, other areas which were famous in the past for particular products failed to compete successfully when coal replaced water for motive power and charcoal for fuel. This happened, for example, to the English West Country, where the manufacture of Witney blankets survives to recall its more famous past, and to the English forests of Dean and the Weald, where iron was dug, smelted, and forged into implements and weapons of war down to the end of the eighteenth century.

We must allude here, also, to the Industrial Revolution, which, like that in agriculture, revitalized industry and gave it vastly enlarged scope. The Industrial Revolution had its home in Britain, where geographical, economic, political, and social conditions favored, indeed stimulated, industrial progress. In the eighteenth century Britain had built up overseas trade, based on sea power and imperial territories, and was amassing capital. The depletion of her forests focused attention on her resources of coal, of all the chief varieties, some of which were well located for shipment by sea and many of which contained seams of iron ore. Her labor supply was inadequate to keep pace with the growth of her trade in domestic staples, notably textiles, and this provided a stimulus to the invention of machines which could economize on labor. Certainly the application of the scientific ideas to industrial technique, together with the ingenuity of engineers and other craftsmen, was responsible for many remarkable inventions which transformed the organization, scale, and cost of industrial production. Among many triumphs of inventiveness were the steam engine, first used for pumping water from mines, the "spinning jenny" and new weaving looms, the use of coke for smelting iron ore, the Bessemer and Gilchrist-Thomas steel-making processes, which enormously increased the range of production and utilization of steel, and the more recent revolutionary developments in the chemical industries. On the basis of these and other technological innovations, notably in the field of transport, Britain became in the nineteenth century the "workshop of the world."

The geographical effects of this industrial activity are here relevant. First, it resulted in the rapid growth of Britain's industrial regions, marked by their high densities of population and high degree of urbanization, by their relation to coal fields—for, in the last century even more than today, coal was industrially king—and by their dependence on overseas trade. This overseas trade brought in essential raw materials such as cotton, flax, silk, and wool and, increasingly after 1870, foodstuffs (above all, wheat and meat). The second geographical effect was the spread of the new ideas to the continent, where, after an appreciable time lag and in suitable areas, especially on coal fields, the present industrial regions began to take shape.

The industrial map of Europe shows a highly populated belt extending from the Pennines and South Wales in Britain to the Ural Mountains and the Donets Basin in the U.S.S.R., where rocks of Hercynian folding are still exposed. These rocks were originally rich in economic minerals, although some of the former lodes are now worked out. With them are associated considerable coal deposits of the Carboniferous period, which helps to explain the location and character of industrial regions engaged mainly in mining, smelting, steel making, heavy chemicals, and engineering. Within this diagonal belt across the continent lie the British industrial areas, some of which were just mentioned, the Franco-Belgian coal field, the Luxembourg and German Westphalian industrial regions, that of western Bohemia in Czechoslovakia, the Upper Silesian coal field of Poland, the Donets coal field and industrial region (mainly in the Ukrainian S.S.R.), and lastly the industrial region which bestrides the central and southern Urals. In Iberia, too, where Hercynian structures also occur, a range of minerals—tungsten, copper, mercury, and iron, together with some coal in the north—testifies again to the link between geological history and economic geography, although these resources have not as yet become the basis of any considerable industrialization.

Other industrial regions of Europe are explained by considerations which differ from that of the Hercynian coal basins. For example, the extensive lignite and potash deposits of East Germany [15] have provided in recent decades an abundant low-grade fuel for many important industries, including chemicals, as in the middle Elbe region of Saxony. Another distinct category of industrial region includes large seaports such as Hamburg, Rotterdam, Marseille, and Glasgow, well placed for the economical import of raw materials and the distribution of their manufactured products. Shipbuilding and the many associated industries which it involves have established themselves at certain estuarine and seacoast sites near supplies of coal and steel: Clydeside below Glasgow in Scotland, Tyneside below Newcastle, and Hartlepool on the Wear in northeast England are

[15] Officially known as the German Democratic Republic.

outstanding centers. There remain, also, the newer industrial regions which draw their power resources from hydroelectricity.

Hydroelectric power in Europe is derived—to an estimated 86 per cent—from its glaciated lands. Thus metallurgical, chemical, engineering, and other industries of the continent are not confined to areas with accessible supplies of solid fuel. Hydroelectrical undertakings, of course, call for a substantial capital investment and usually a considerable engineering effort. The relief features of a landscape eroded by ice, such as steep valley slopes and high-level lake basins, coupled with an abundant supply of running water from rainfall and snow melt, have provided the means for a number of countries deficient in coal to play their part, if modestly, in modern industry. Italy, Sweden, Norway, Finland, Switzerland, Austria, and Spain owe their industrial activity largely to "white coal." The Soviet Union, which produces much coal, continues to exploit the very considerable hydroelectric potentialities of its glaciated northern lands, of the Caucasus Mountains, and of its rivers. Nevertheless, only 20 per cent of its electric-energy consumption is derived from hydroelectric power.

While hydroelectricity and petroleum are now increasingly used as sources of energy in Europe outside the U.S.S.R., coal is still the principal source of power. Even so, the use of "white coal" explains the growth of some of the industrial areas which are aloof from coal fields. It explains, also, the dispersion of industrial undertakings, since electricity can be cheaply distributed over short distances, and the avoidance of the landscape features of the "black country" which disfigure so many industrial areas located on coal fields. Witness as illustrations the semirural location of industries in the Swedish midlands, the specialized clock- and watchmaking in the Swiss Jura, and the metallurgical industries at Zaporozhe and Dnepropetrovsk on the lower Dnieper in the Ukrainian S.S.R. While "white coal" is mainly used in light industries, it is particularly useful in a group of industries which make very heavy demands on electric power: electrochemicals, electric smelting and refining, nitrate making by extraction of nitrogen from the air, and synthetic rubber. Thus Norway has been able to develop the manufacture of nitrates, the refining of copper, and an aluminum industry based on imported bauxite.

While the industries of Europe depend primarily on its generous endowment of coal and lignite, which are widely distributed though often difficult to obtain, to these must be added its hydroelectric capacity, and its petroleum supplies, in large part imported. Outside the U.S.S.R., which has many important fields, notably that of the Volga-Urals ("Second Baku"), Europe's oil production accounts for only a small part of its consumption.

Thanks to its wide command of mechanical energy and a long tradition of industrial skill, Europe has achieved, and has retained despite the destruction of World War II, a very high place in industrialization. It recovered rapidly from the damage and setbacks caused by World War II, and by 1955 Western Europe had raised its industrial production 70 per cent above its prewar (1938) level. Despite the recession in the United States during 1958, Western Europe continues steadily to increase this output. In the Soviet Union, where industrialization started later than in Western Europe, the rate of industrial growth has been higher. By 1955 the U.S.S.R. had virtually trebled its prewar (1940) industrial output. A high rate of increase is envisaged for the current seven-year-plan period, 1958–65, at the end of which the U.S.S.R. hopes to have achieved a level of industrial output equal to that of the United States in 1958. Broadly, it is true to say that industrialization has spread eastward in Europe during the last hundred years and that the most recent developments in basic industries, those of the U.S.S.R. in its Asiatic territories, give the greatest promise of continued expansion. While the U.S.S.R. is largely self-sufficient in metallic and non-metallic minerals and in other raw materials—natural rubber, wool, jute, and tin appear to be its chief deficiencies—the rest of Europe is very dependent on seaborne supplies.

Iron-ore supplies are as a whole insufficient, although France (from her Lorraine mines), Sweden, Spain, and Britain are big producers. The European countries command large supplies of bauxite (in France and Hungary) and appreciable amounts of copper, zinc, mercury, sulphur, ferroalloys, and salt, but variously depend on imports for many metals and other industrial raw materials: aluminum, tin, nickel, chrome, lead, copper, manganese, wool, cotton, jute, and natural rubber. Most of the industrialized countries west of the U.S.S.R. and south of Fenno-Scandia need also to import timber. Scientific and technological progress, however, continues to provide new industrial products, of which artificial fibers and plastics are two striking illustrations.

Commerce. Leaving aside a discussion of trade within state territories, which of course vividly reveals the regional differences of climate, terrain, and economy, we shall glance here at the historical geography of the interregional trade within Europe, and at Europe's overseas commerce.

During many centuries—until the Columbian era—Europe's trading activities were confined largely within its own limits. The chief traders of Europe were first to be found in cities of the coastlands of the Mediterranean Basin; Phoenicians, Greeks, and Romans did not venture very much outside this virtually tideless sea. So, during the Middle Ages, the Mediterranean "lake" proved the main trade route of Europe, with cities like Constantinople, Venice, Pisa, and Genoa taking the lead through importing by overland and sea routes valuable goods from the monsoon lands of Asia and exporting the high-grade manufactures from their own workshops.

The rise of northwestern Europe in the centuries which followed the creation of Charlemagne's empire was reflected in the activities of industrial and commercial cities in that area. It made the interconnecting Baltic and North seas another highway for shipping their local produce, i.e., fish, salt, timber, flax, wool, and finished textiles. Between the two parallel maritime axes of trade—the southern and the northern—overland routes carried traders and goods. In 1317, the Venetians, having built sailing ships with oars (galleys) strong and mobile enough to face the troubled tidal waters beyond the Strait of Gibraltar, opened up direct trade by sea to the ports of Southampton, London, and Brugge.

As the limits of the known world expanded during the Age of Discovery, the positional values of the two inland seas of Europe— the Baltic and the Mediterranean—decreased, for in the sixteenth century geographical knowledge, advances in shipbuilding, new navigation aids, and commercial enterprise broadened the theater of trade by use of the ocean highways and created an all-sea route via the Cape to India and the East Indies. The riches of Central and South America and of the Indies were the chief lure. Trade followed the flag, for the power of the state was fundamental for the protection of shipping as well as for the securing of territory, trade depots, and privileges in distant lands. In this oceanic phase, it was the nations fronting the open sea which were the first to exploit the new opportunities, not only in trade but also in conquest, settlement, and proselytization of the Christian faith; in turn, Portuguese, Spaniards, Dutch, English, and French turned to overseas commerce. The first two have long lost the leading position which they earned by their early achievements in sea-borne exploration. The Dutch, as the "waggoners of Europe," had their commercial heyday in the seventeenth century. Britain, which had played during the Middle Ages a mainly passive role in overseas trade, achieved, thanks to its naval strength and empire building, a leading position among the commercial states of the world. Others, like Norway (with a large merchant tonnage), Germany, and Italy, joined much more recently in large-scale maritime commerce.

The interregional trade in Europe naturally arose from the variety of products which were available in different parts of the continent, partly because of climatic contrasts; now it is much reduced by the divergent politico-economic policies of the Soviet Union and the West. It is enough here to recall some of the distinctive products of particular countries and areas: the iron ore of Sweden, Lorraine, and Spain; the timber and timber products, especially of Sweden and Finland; the olive oil, tobacco, and citrus and dried fruits of Mediterranean countries; the early vegetables and flowers of Italy, Brittany, and Mediterranean France; the wines of France, Spain, Italy, Portugal, and Yugoslavia; Swiss watches and watch parts; Swedish electrical equipment; British machinery, transport equipment, tin plate, and textiles; French, Dutch, and Swiss cheeses and the high-class dairy produce of Denmark; and German capital goods and chemicals. On purely geographical grounds, it might have been expected that Eastern and Western Europe, since the former is relatively well wooded and more agricultural in its economy and the latter is more emphatically industrial, would have engaged as in the past in a profitable trade in complementary products. But Soviet policy, which is now extended to cover its many satellite states in Europe, aims at diverting the trade of these areas from the West to itself and also at achieving, behind the "Iron Curtain," a high degree of economic self-sufficiency. This policy discourages interregional East-West trade in Europe. The attempt to link the trade of the U.S.S.R. and that of its satellites has achieved some success. The former commands many valuable commodities which it can make available to the latter, as it deems expedient: cotton, flax, hemp, manganese and chrome ores, apatites for phosphate fertilizers, petroleum, platinum, and gold. In exchange for these products it can obtain, for example, machinery and textiles from Czechoslovakia, coal from Poland, and bauxite from Hungary.

The overseas trade of Europe, which commands virtually one-half of the world's ocean-going merchant tonnage, is largely in the hands of the Western countries. One feature of this trade, which is worldwide, derives from the fact that many states, i.e., Britain, France, the Netherlands, Belgium, and Portugal, still have political dependencies overseas which afford sheltered markets for their metropolitan products. Another feature, especially since 1945, has been the increasing volume of trade with the United States. Of the European exports to the United States, Britain supplies over one-quarter, and Germany more than one-fifth. The American market is valuable for countries with certain surplus raw materials, ores, and semiprocessed goods. Such are wood pulp and furs from the Baltic countries, Greek and Turkish tobacco, and Yugoslavia's copper ore. But the American market receives, too, some highly reputed and specialized products from the industrial countries of Western Europe. Central and South

America also remain an important field for trade, but this particular trade has relatively decreased to the advantage of the United States.

Circulation. In this age of fast travel and speedy communication we are not likely to underrate the importance of routes of all kinds— by land, by sea, by inland waterways, and by air—"as a sustenance without which organized society would be impossible." [16] In the earliest days of human colonization in Europe, it is true, men used the route- ways left open by nature: the inner seas, the river valleys, the un- wooded or lightly wooded steppe. Travel by horse or horse-drawn coach and transport by pack horse, by sailing ship, and by river craft long provided the best means of movement, until the inventions of the last century brought the steamship and the locomotive. These were supplemented, in turn, through application of the internal com- bustion engine, by the motorcar and aircraft. Distinctive man-made elements of the countryside reflect social efforts to promote circulation and at the same time interpenetrate the region. The route patterns of European countries present today features etched on the surface of the land in many past and sometimes remote periods of history. And although the railroads, highways, and navigable waters are now the paramount means of travel and of shipment of goods, prehistoric ridge-way and stretches of Roman road (in some areas still in use) survive to remind us of earlier geographies of circulation.

Trade and travel do not depend merely on routes; they are sensitive to political conditions. Roman roads, built by legionary and auxiliary troops, gave Europe, south of the Danube and west of the Rhine, its first system of engineered roads, which, thanks to the efficiency of Roman government, served the needs of soldiers, merchants, officials, and others. These highways, firm and cambered though of course narrow, were less useful after the collapse of centralized imperial government. Even though they suffered from neglect, they largely survived to serve the varied needs of governments and of the two Christian Churches—the one organized from Rome and the other (after 395 A.D.) from Constantinople.

The seaways—and this meant chiefly the Mediterranean—suffered no less from the fall of Rome and the subsequent advance (in the seventh century) of the Arabs into the Mediterranean Basin. Al- though the Eastern Roman Empire, centered on Constantinople, maintained some show of sea power, it was not until the rise of the Italian trading cities that the Mediterranean came to flourish as a commercial thoroughfare. In the same way it was the political and naval strength of the northern cities of the Hanseatic League which

[16] J. H. Belloc, *The Road* (London: T. Fisher Unwin, 1924), Preface.

opened the Baltic and North seas to trade. Although Roman trade had spread into parts at least of the Baltic, Ptolemy (second century A.D.) had mapped Scandinavia as an island. The new importance of the Baltic Sea was marked when Adam of Bremen, in the eleventh century, described its maritime entries and the peninsular character of Scandinavia. A few centuries later, such was the stature of the Baltic in European commerce and politics that it was carefully portrayed in a semipictorial map by Olaus Magnus.

Already in the later Middle Ages a system of roads, aligned roughly east-west and north-south, brought into relationship the various parts of the continent and its neighboring seas. Naturally, the contemporaneous distribution of population, cities, ports, and economic activities defined the starting points and goals of routes, the volume of traffic which they carried, and their relative importance. We may note how many Alpine passes carried well-frequented thoroughfares and linked the ports and industrial cities of northern Italy (and also Rome, the seat of the Pope) with France, Germany, and southeastern Europe. In the western Alps, the Great St. Bernard and Mt. Cenis passes, approached via Turin, were preferred. The St. Gotthard Pass, its northern approach facilitated by the building of a bridge and valley road in the thirteenth century, joined Milan to the Rhine at Basel and to the Danube at Ulm. Farther east, the Brenner Pass became the principal link between the Italian and German lands of the Holy Roman Empire and for traders between northern Germany and northern Italy. In the eastern Alps, several passes carried roads from Venice toward the Drava and Sava rivers, along which passed roads leading to the Aegean Sea. The laden mule and ass afforded the means of transport. Thanks to modern engineering, the railroads, using long tunnels, can now ignore the passways, although they still must use the easiest gradients provided by the valleys.

Another interesting north-south route across the continent, which then served the needs of European commerce and now affords only internal circulation, was based on navigable rivers and portages. It was opened up in the ninth century across Russia from the Gulf of Finland to the Black and Caspian seas. In part, this route was an attempt to find an alternative to sea and land routes in the western basin of the Mediterranean which were obstructed by Moslem power. The importance of the new route lay in the fact that Constantinople was its chief southern terminal and that, as a result, Russia derived therefrom its Orthodox or Greek Christianity, its alphabet, some architectural influences, and perhaps some imperialistic notions too.

In some parts of the continent the medieval road system was largely that bequeathed by Rome, in others new routes were laid out in the course of conquest and colonization. Thus in the Balkan lands of the Byzantine Empire the major routes which made government possible were still those which linked Constantinople with Salonika and Durrës on the Adriatic coast and with Belgrade on the Danube via Sofia; another route led from Salonika to Belgrade via Niš. In each case the road was closely related to valley-ways and structural depressions. But in Central and Eastern Europe, largely as a result of German con-

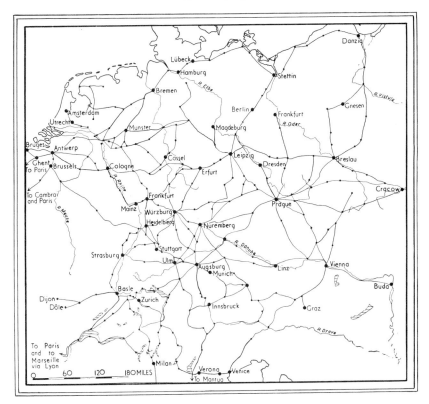

Fig. 2–9. The road system of Central Europe about 1570.

quests, new roads were built to give access from the Rhine and Danube cities. Figure 2–9, based on an early topographic map made about the year 1570, shows that an effective route system existed in this part of the continent. Among the roads there shown, that which led eastward from Brugge, Antwerp, and Cologne to Leipzig, Breslau (Wroclaw), and Cracow, the medieval capital of Poland, is of special interest. It follows one of the major lines of movement across the continent at all periods, and is aligned below the northern edge of the middle mountain zone.

The lack of west-east roads in the North German Plain, except for the Hamburg-Lübeck-Stettin-Danzig road, reflects the scantier settlement and lower value of these lands of glacial deposition. The route centers, too, arouse interest: Frankfurt and Würzburg (both on the Main), Nuremberg, Prague, Leipzig, Breslau, and Vienna. The principal rivers supplemented the land routes in no small measure: the Rhine, Elbe, Oder, Vistula, and Danube all played a part.

Figure 2–9 may be compared with Fig. 2–10, which depicts the principal highways of Europe in 1850, a time when the railroad network was at an early stage of its development. Paris was clearly *the* center of the French road system which had been re-created in the eighteenth century, although in the Roman period Lyon was the route center and Rheims, nearer the Rhine frontier, was the chief route focus of northern Gaul. London occupies a similar position as the chief focus of the routes of England. The closeness of the network of roads in Central Europe is very striking, testifying *inter alia* to its middle position within the continent. No less striking is the paucity and wide spacing of the roads in Southern, Eastern, and Northern Europe—which still obtain.

Waterways, too, contributed much to bulk transport within the continent. After the improvement of rivers by engineering works, the construction of canals, especially in the eighteenth century, was hailed as a triumph in man's control over nature. They provided water connections between navigable points on rivers and indeed could be built in watershed areas where no navigable rivers existed at all. Above all, they were designed to carry bulk cargoes—coal, stone, fertilizers, ore, timber—and, until the advent in turn of railroad and motor transport, proved indispensable, notably in the Netherlands and in Britain.

While the railroad and motor truck could and did efficiently usurp the functions of many canals, these have by no means lost importance. In countries like the Netherlands, canals serve more than one purpose. German canals provide not only routes (as in Westphalia) for ore and coal shipments to the Rhine and Ems, but also the means of internal distribution of goods (in north Germany). Moscow is known as "the Port of Five Seas" thanks to the waterways which link it to the Baltic, White, Black, Azov, and Caspian seas. In England, the Manchester Ship Canal makes inland Manchester a port for ocean-going shipping, while the commercial and strategical importance attached to the Kiel Canal needs no elaboration here.

Of the great rivers of the continent, the Rhine and Volga carry the largest tonnages of goods. The Rhine, which admits fleets of large barges far upstream, owes its importance primarily to its proximity to

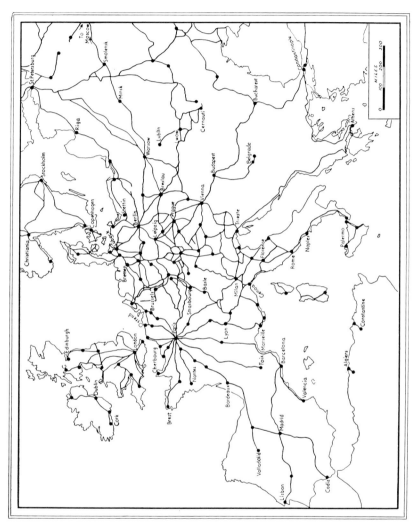

Fig. 2–10. The post roads of Europe in 1850.

the Rhine-Westphalian industrial region and to the Dutch commercial cities near its outlets. The Volga, which lies wholly within one state territory, that of the U.S.S.R., carries upstream heavy cargoes of oil, salt, fish, and grain, which can reach as far as Moscow with the aid of the Moscow Canal. The Danube, "the king of rivers," as Napoleon called it, today plays a humble role and has lost the legal status of "an international river" open to the navigation and trade of all nations.

Europe, owing to its central position in relation to the land areas of the earth, to its indented coastline, and to modern engineering works, boasts many of the great seaports of the world. One broad geographical contrast may be noted here—that between ports on navigable tidal rivers, such as London, Antwerp, and Hamburg, where docks must be provided with lock-gates because of the tidal range, and those of the almost tideless Mediterranean Sea, where modern docks offer access at all times and are not subject to the deltaic accretions of the rivers. Note, in particular, Marseille, Trieste, Genoa, Naples, Barcelona, and Salonika. The great international port of Rotterdam, related to the Rhine, has improved access by canalization.

Finally, we may allude to the beginnings of railroad building born of the Industrial Revolution and the need for faster bulk shipment of heavy freight. Figure 2–11 shows that, by 1850, Great Britain already had a network of railroads, closest in the English Lowlands. Across the English Channel, the Low Countries and northern France had already built many connected lines, but to the north and east of Germany and in Mediterranean Europe railroad construction had scarcely begun. In Russia, only the line from St. Petersburg (Leningrad) to the Tsar's summer palace at Tsarkoye Selo (opened in 1838) and the first stretch of the St. Petersburg-Moscow railroad had been constructed. Although many railroads must now be drawn on the blank spaces of this map, the network of lines remains relatively open outside Western and Central Europe.

CONCLUSION

The present is but the past flowing into the future. The geography of Europe has been fashioned during several millennia. Changes are presently in operation and will continue. There is no finality in the human value which attaches to the areas of Europe. The value attaching to land changes, as ideas and technology change. While we note the high densities of population and the high degree of industrialization and commerce which characterize the more peninsular and more physically varied western part of the continent, we should not

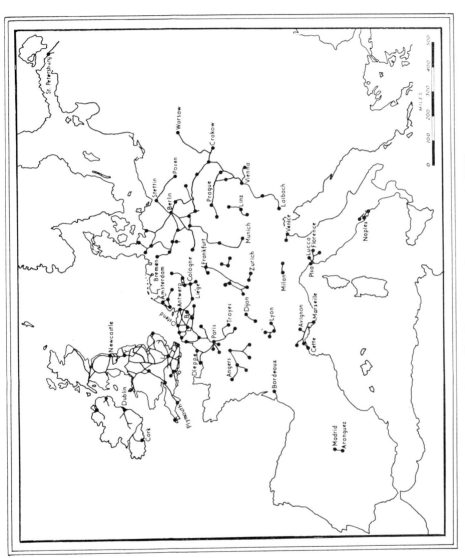

Fig. 2-11. The European railway pattern in 1850.

fail to recognize that the larger and physically more uniform eastern part of the continent has developed belatedly and will economically progress further. We should not fail to note, also, that, in the east, Europe merges with Asia and that in Siberia, Kazakhstan, and central Asia it has projected its culture in the guise of Soviet communism and modern technology.

Above all, the study of the history behind geography underlines how little unity, except in the formal sense of territorial continuity, the term "Europe" connotes. We have glanced at some of the past processes which explain the social and territorial divisions of the continent—its many tongues, nations, and states—which clearly reflect the earlier localism of human groups in days of slow and difficult travel and their close attachment to the soil. So far, political unity over large areas of Europe has been achieved only temporarily and by the coercive efforts of would-be master states. Soviet power and Soviet policy have produced, since 1945, some trend toward unity, if only within two opposed eastern and western segments of the continent. The unity of Europe is not yet.

BIBLIOGRAPHY

(Introductory references are asterisked.)

Books in English

Burke, G. L. *The Making of the Dutch Towns: A Study in Urban Development from the Tenth to the Seventeenth Centuries.* London: Cleaver-Hume Press Ltd., 1956.

Chadwick, Hector Munro. *The Nationalities of Europe and the Growth of National Ideologies.* London: Cambridge University Press, 1945.

Childe, Vere G. *Prehistoric Migrations in Europe.* Cambridge, Mass.: Harvard University Press, 1951.

Clapham, John H. *The Economic Development of France and Germany 1815–1914.* 4th ed. London: Cambridge University Press, 1948.

Clapham, John H., and Power, Eileen (eds.). *The Agrarian Life of the Middle Ages.* (*The Cambridge Economic History*, Vol. I.) London: Cambridge University Press, 1941.

Clark, J. G. D. *The Mesolithic Settlement of Northern Europe.* London: Cambridge University Press, 1936.

Coon, Carleton S. *The Races of Europe.* New York: The Macmillan Co., 1939.

Darby, Henry C. "The Clearing of the Woodland of Europe" in *Man's Role in Changing the Face of the Earth*, William L. Thomas, Jr. (ed.). Chicago: University of Chicago Press, 1956.

Darby, Henry C. "The Face of Europe on the Eve of the Great Discoveries" Vol. I, Chap. II of *The New Cambridge Modern History.* London: Cambridge University Press, 1957.

Dickinson, Robert E. *The West European City.* London. Routledge & Kegan Paul, Ltd., 1951.

Dominian, Leon. *The Frontiers of Nationality and Language in Europe.* New York: Henry Holt & Co., Inc., 1917.

Dopsch, Alfons. *The Economic and Social Foundations of European Civilization.* Condensed by E. Patzelt and translated by M. G Beard and N. Marshall. New York: Harcourt, Brace & Co., Inc., 1937.

*East, W. Gordon. *A Historical Geography of Europe.* 4th ed. New York: E. P. Dutton & Co., Inc., 1950.

Huxley, Julian S., and Haddon, Alfred C. (eds.). *We Europeans.* London: Jonathan Cape, Ltd., 1935.

Morant, G. M. *The Races of Central Europe: A Footnote to History.* New York: W. W. Norton & Co., Inc., 1940.

Pirenne, H. *Economic and Social History of Medieval Europe.* Translated by I. E. Clegg. London: Routledge & Kegan Paul, Ltd., 1949.

Postan, Michael M., and Habakkuk, H. J. (eds.). *Trade and Industry in the Middle Ages.* (*The Cambridge Economic History,* Vol. II, ed. by M. M. Postan and E. E. Rich.) London: Cambridge University Press, 1952.

Proudfoot, Malcolm J. *European Refugees: 1939–1952.* London: Faber & Faber, Ltd., 1957.

Sauer, Carl O. *Agricultural Origins and Dispersals.* New York: The American Geographical Society, 1952.

Wheeler, Sir R. E. M. *Rome Beyond the Imperial Frontiers.* London: G. G. Bell & Sons, Ltd., 1954.

*Whittlesey, Derwent. *Environmental Foundations of European History.* New York: Appleton-Century-Crofts, Inc., 1949.

*Wright, John K. *The Geographical Basis of European History.* New York: Henry Holt & Co., Inc., 1928.

Zeuner, Friedrich E. *Dating the Past: An Introduction to Geochronology.* 3rd ed. London: Methuen & Co., Ltd., 1952.

Books in Foreign Languages

Ancel, J. *Manuel Géographique de Politique Européenne* (Manual of the Political Geography of Europe). Paris: Librairie Delagrave, 1936–45.

Bloch, M. *Les Caractères Originaux de l'Histoire Rurale Française* (The Original Character of French Rural History). Cambridge, Mass.: Harvard University Press, 1931.

Braudel, Fernand. *Le Méditerranée et le Monde Méditerranéen à l'Époque de Philippe II* (The Mediterranean and the Mediterranean World in the Epoch of Philippe II). Paris: Armand Colin, 1949.

Demangeon, Albert. *Problèmes de Géographie Humaine* (Problems of Human Geography). 3d ed. Paris: Armand Colin, 1947.

Dion, R. *Essai sur la Formation du Paysage Rural Français* (Essay on the Formation of the French Countryside). Tours: Arrault et Cie, 1934.

Meillet, A. *Les Langues dans l'Europe Nouvelle* (The Languages of Modern Europe). 2d ed. rev. Paris: Payot, 1928.

Schmidt, P. W. *Die Sprachenfamilien und Sprachenkreise der Erde* (Language Families and Language Regions of the World). Heidelberg: C. Winter's Universitätsbuchhandlung, 1926.

3

The British Isles

Two main islands—Great Britain and Ireland—make up the British Isles. Set between the ports of Northern Europe and the trade route to the Americas, these islands have for long exerted a power disproportionate to their small size. On their 121,000 square miles there live an estimated 54,495,000 people, a population density of about 450 to the square mile. A vast colonial empire remains within the jurisdiction of the United Kingdom, and dominions many times her size owe allegiance to either the British Crown or the Commonwealth. The English language has become the most widely spoken lingua franca of the civilized world, as well as the mother tongue of millions non-British by birth.

Four peoples, three governments, and two states exist within the British Isles, and the succeeding account will be unintelligible to the student unless he has a clear notion of their political organization and mutual relations. Great Britain consists of the three national units of Scotland, Wales, and England, each conscious of its separate identity, but divided today by unmarked boundaries of very limited political significance. The United Kingdom includes these three units and the six counties of Northern Ireland—comprising most of the ancient province of Ulster. The Irish people is thus divided, for the remainder of the island is the Irish Republic (Eire), created as the Irish Free State in 1921, and now by its own vehement wish independent of the British Crown.

The United Kingdom is a parliamentary democracy (based on universal suffrage) with a limited constitutional monarchy. Paramount authority rests with Parliament, over which neither the Crown nor the Judiciary has any power; it has been well said of the British Queen that she reigns but does not rule. Parliament—seated in Westminster, on the bank of the Thames—governs England and Wales directly. In certain aspects of government: agriculture, health, planning, education, and home affairs, Scotland is governed through administrative departments responsible to the Secretary of State for Scotland; there is, however, no separate Scots parliament. Northern Ireland elects members to Westminster, but also has its own parliament in Belfast; this body legislates for most matters except foreign affairs, income tax, the post office, and the judiciary and fiscal policy, including customs and excise.

The Irish Republic is also a parliamentary democracy, with an elected President of limited constitutional powers not unlike those of the British monarchy. A long and harsh record of interference in Irish affairs has earned for the Protestant English the bitter anger of the Catholic population, a sentiment fanned and exploited by most political groups. The partition of Ireland into two units is vociferously denounced by the southern Irish and as stoutly defended by the Protestant Ulstermen, who precipitated the Civil War by their refusal to accept government, as they put it, from Rome via Dublin.

English is the first tongue of most members of all four nations. Three of the old Celtic tongues survive, however: Gaelic (in the western Scottish Highlands), Welsh (spoken as the first tongue in parts of northern and western Wales), and Irish Gaelic, the tongue of the densely populated Atlantic shore of Ireland, the Gaeltacht. Manx (on the Isle of Man) is virtually extinct, as is Cornish. The Celtic tongues and the ancient traditions with which they are associated are jealously preserved by nationalist sentiment. In Wales, this nationalism takes the benevolent form—as a rule—of a widespread interest in a national literature and in song. In the Irish Republic, however, efforts are being made to revive Gaelic as the national tongue, and access to public office is now confined to those who speak it.

The British Empire, one of the largest world-wide territorial organizations, is joined to the parent country by ties of widely varying closeness. The self-governing dominions, including Canada, Australia, South Africa, New Zealand, India, Ceylon, and Pakistan, are joined only by ties of sympathy and comradeship. Not even allegiance to the Crown can now be claimed for all of them; India, for example, is constitutionally a republic, though she accepts the Queen as the symbol of the free association of the independent member nations and as the head of the Commonwealth. All these self-governing states are politically independent of the United Kingdom and may withdraw from the Commonwealth if they so wish. The dependent territories (i.e., those lacking complete autonomy and the freedom to secede) are governed in several ways: some are colonies, others protectorates, still others federated states or groupings. Some, like Malta, have achieved complete self-government in home affairs. European territories having the status of British colonies are Malta and Gibraltar, both strategic naval bases vital to the defense of the Mediterranean.

To the parent nation, the colonial territories long ago ceased to serve purely as areas exploitable for raw materials and cheap labor. In all of them, the colonial authorities are committed to programs of education, better social services, improved technology, and scientific research. The aim of the British has been, in general, to raise the level of education, technical skill, and communal responsibility to the point at which each colony can attain self-government. This program has proved costly, and most of the colonies are liabilities rather than assets, in the financial sense. In certain areas, however, these territories produce exportable surpluses of goods having a high value on the world's markets: thus the rubber production of the plantations of Malaya is vital to the dollar earnings of the entire sterling area; and independence leaves this unchanged.

THE PHYSICAL LANDSCAPE

The land of the British Isles exhibits two strikingly contrasted aspects. The west and north, confronting the Atlantic, is hilly or mountainous, and has a wet, oceanic climate. The term "Highland Zone" is often applied to it. Southern and eastern England, by contrast, is the gently rolling "Lowland Zone," with a drier climate akin to that of the nearby European lowlands.[1]

The major divisions of the British landscape are structurally determined; each division has its characteristic types of rock and a distinct structural pattern (Fig. 3–1). The landscape also shows many traces of a complex erosional history, upon which we can barely touch in this chapter.[2] It falls readily into three provinces, each of which corresponds to one of the major divisions of the mainland of Europe:

1. *Caledonian Britain*, comprising a series of rugged uplands in the north and west, which continue the structural province of the Kjölen Range in Scandinavia.
2. *Hercynian Britain*, making up the rest of the Highland Zone, and including in addition the chief coal fields. As its name implies, this

[1] See, for example, H. J. Mackinder, *Britain and the British Seas* (London: Oxford University Press, 1902). Much of this geographical classic is written around the Highland-Lowland theme.

[2] For geological terms, see Appendix I.

province corresponds to the Hercynian belt of the continental mainland.

3. *Lowland Britain*, consisting of the gently folded Mesozoic and Tertiary rocks of the English plain, and very comparable in structure, for example, with the Paris and Münster basins.

Caledonian and Hercynian Britain together make up the Highland Zone already mentioned. They have much in common, and might be considered together but for the vital difference that only the Hercynian structures affect the distribution of coal fields.[3]

The Three Major Provinces

Caledonian Britain. In this province, the surface structures largely date from a mid-Paleozoic disturbance. The belt consists of (a) the Scottish Highlands and the hills of Donegal and Mayo, a unit composed largely of gneisses and schists, with large granite intrusions; (b) the Scottish Southern Uplands and the mountains of southeast Ulster, where the bedrock is chiefly of greywackes, slates, and intrusive granites; and (c) the plateaus of North Wales and Wicklow-Dexford in Eire, where the rocks are similar but contain the giant Wicklow granite. In all these separate uplands, the physiographic trend follows the NE-SW run of the folding, as it does in Norway. All three consist of bleak, rain-swept highlands, broken into Irish and British segments by the Irish Sea and its channels. To them may be added the small, compact mountain region of the English Lake District, with its nucleus of early Paleozoic volcanics. To this upland the later mountain-building episodes have contributed much, but its affinities are Caledonian.

Though the rocks of Caledonian Britain range in age from Silurian to early Pre-Cambrian, and in lithology from fine-grained slates to massive, coarse-grained granites, differentiation between rock types is not of major geographical significance. Everywhere the land is rolling, considerable in elevation (usually 1,500–3,000 feet), and generally rather impervious. The Caledonian highlands are par excellence the scene of that characteristic British landscape, the moorland. Since they are nowhere heavily mineralized and nowhere present extensive lowland areas, they have remained unattractive lands for settlement since the Bronze Age.

Hercynian Britain. The continuation and structural contemporary of the Hercynian hill country of Central Europe and France,

---

[3] Valuable additional material is given in Great Britain, Geological Survey, *British Regional Geology* (London: H. M. Stationery Office, various dates), a series of short memoirs covering all parts of Great Britain.

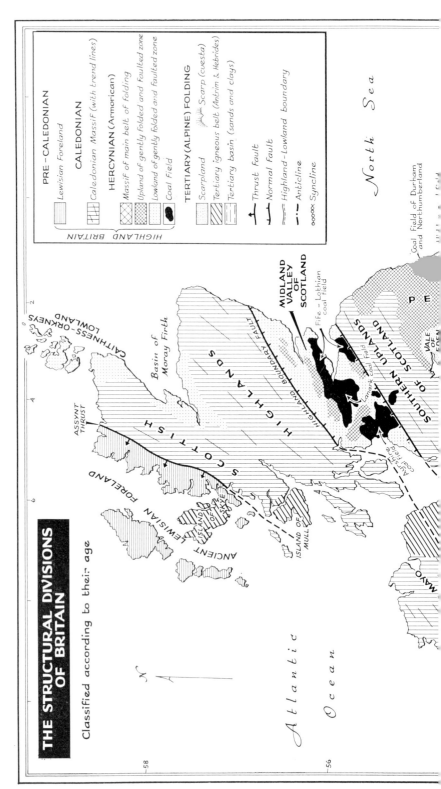

THE STRUCTURAL DIVISIONS
OF BRITAIN

Classified according to their age

Legend:

PRE-CALEDONIAN
Lewisian Foreland

CALEDONIAN
Caledonian Massif (with trend lines)

HERCYNIAN (Armorican)
Massif of main belt of folding
Upland of gently folded and faulted zone
Lowland of gently folded and faulted zone
Coal Field

TERTIARY (ALPINE) FOLDING
Scarpland — Scarp (cuesta)
Tertiary igneous belt (Antrim & Hebrides)
Tertiary basin (sands and clays)

Thrust Fault
Normal Fault
Highland–Lowland boundary
Anticline
Syncline

HIGHLAND BRITAIN

North Sea

Atlantic Ocean

ASSYNT THRUST
ANCIENT LEWISIAN FORELAND
CAITHNESS-ORKNEYS LOWLAND
Basin of Moray Firth
SCOTTISH HIGHLANDS
HIGHLAND BOUNDARY FAULT
MIDLAND VALLEY OF SCOTLAND
Fife–Lothian coal field
SOUTHERN UPLANDS OF SCOTLAND
Ayrshire coal field
VALE OF EDEN
ISLAND OF SKYE
ISLAND OF MULL

Coal Field of Durham and Northumberland
PE
MAYO

58
56
2
0
4
6

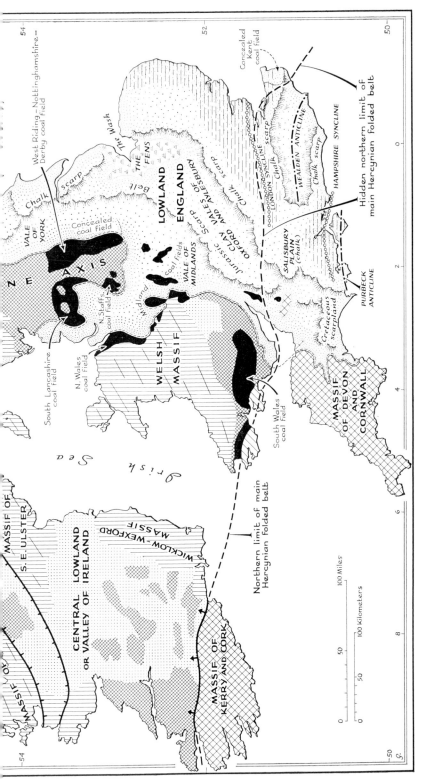

Fig. 3-1. The structural divisions of Britain.

149

this second province presents a striking contrast to the bleak, thinly populated landscapes of the Caledonian belt. Coming as they did at the close of Carboniferous time, the Hercynian earth movements were able to involve in their structures the precious Coal Measures that were to be the basis of the British Industrial Revolution. The largest concentrations of population now occur in the coal fields along the margin of the Highland Zone.

This second component of Highland Britain is divisible into two broad parts. Southernmost Britain, from southwest Ireland to Kent, lies within the main belt of Hercynian folding (continued in Brittany to the south). The mountains of Kerry, Cork, and Waterford belong to this belt. Here the chief ranges trend roughly east-west, parallel to the folding. The valleys between the ranges have been partially drowned to form the celebrated "ria" coast. The peninsulas of Devon and Cornwall, Pembroke, Gower, and the Vale of Glamorgan in South Wales make up the rest. Most of the rocks of these areas are limestones, sandstones, shales, or slates, but large granite bosses occur in Devon and Cornwall, forming the high ground of Bodmin Moor, Dartmoor, and smaller uplands. This southern division of Hercynian Britain resembles the Caledonian belt in landscapes. Coal-bearing rocks are rarely involved in the principal folded belt.

The second division lies north of the chief folded zone, and consists of an extensive series of gently folded and fractured basins or uplifts. The relief is varied, extensive lowlands alternating with some of the hilliest parts of Britain.

The Midland Valley of Scotland, the northernmost division, separates the Caledonian masses of the Highlands and Southern Uplands, from which it is divided by boundary faults, making it a true graben. Much of the floor of the Valley, the populous heart of Scotland, is underlain by sandstones, but certain areas of volcanic rocks have formed high hills, such as the Ochils and the Campsie Fells. There are three large basins containing coal-bearing sediments, in Ayrshire, Lanarkshire, and Fife-Midlothian. The boundary faults are continued into northern Ireland, where a similar graben (unfortunately coalless) separates the Donegal-Mayo Caledonian massif from that of southeast Ulster.

The Pennine axis forms the backbone of northern England, extending from the Southern Uplands of Scotland to the Trent Valley in the Midlands. The upland consists chiefly of an upfaulted block, whose western rim is a high fault-line scarp looking across the lowlands of the Eden Valley and the Lancashire basins (Fig. 3–2). The eastern slope is less abrupt, the Carboniferous sediments that make up the entire upland dipping gently eastward beneath the younger rocks of Yorkshire and Lincolnshire. The upland is floored chiefly by the Millstone Grit, an estuarine deposit whose name suggests its connection with the metallurgical industries of Sheffield. In places, however, limestones form the upland surface, which is there dry and riddled with potholes, caverns, and dry gorges. Most of the Pennines are wet moorlands with summits averaging 1,500 to 2,000 feet.

On either flank of the Pennines are basins containing Coal Measures, some of which form major coal fields. On the west flank there are three such basins. The northernmost borders the north slope of the Lake District massif. The central basin, the largest, is the South

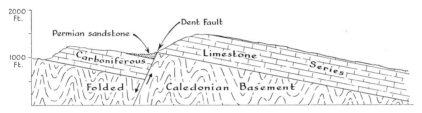

Fig. 3–2. Geological cross-section of the Northern Pennines, about latitude 54° 30′ N. The uplift is a tilted block of the Carboniferous Limestone Series (Mississippian period), bounded along its western margin by a fault scarp on the Dent Fault. Elsewhere in the Pennines, structure is more akin to a true upfold (anticline), but the western edge is usually faulted as above. (After D. A. Wray.)

Lancashire coal field, the home of the cotton textile industry. The third is the North Staffordshire coal field, around Stoke-on-Trent, forming the southwestern extremity of the Pennine upland. On the east flank there are two basins only, but both are large and important coal fields. In Durham and Northumberland the Coal Measures outcrop over a wide area of low moorland, and continue eastward beneath the sea and the younger rocks of the Lowland Zone. In West Riding, Nottinghamshire, and Derbyshire there is an even larger coal-bearing region, which is extended eastward as a "hidden" coal field beneath the younger rocks of the Trent Valley.

There is no Irish equivalent of the Pennine structures. The entire center of the island, the Central Valley, between the Caledonian and Hercynian massifs already discussed, is floored by gently folded sandstones, shales, and limestones, now largely obscured by glacial till and the great peat bogs. Though generally a lowland, central Ireland has several areas of considerable hills.

A large basin makes up much of South Wales and Herefordshire north of the main Hercynian folded belt. In Glamorganshire a large area of Coal Measures forms the South Wales coal field, a hilly country traversed by deep valleys in which the mining towns are clustered. In Herefordshire, by contrast, the Devonian Old Red Sandstone underlies a broad, fertile lowland famous for its brilliant red soils. Between the two contrasted landscapes is a line of formidable moorlands, the Brecon Beacons, Black Mountains, and other hills.

The remaining element in Hercynian Britain is the submerged floor of Lowland England, where the Paleozoic rocks are obscured by the younger cover. In many parts of the Midlands the buried landscape re-emerges; the small South Staffordshire coal field and the basins of Leicestershire are of this type. The entirely concealed East Kent coal field was first deduced by geologists, and then proved (in 1890) by a trial boring put down in connection with the Channel tunnel project.

Lowland Britain. This third province is a rolling countryside whose highest cuestas (escarpments) barely exceed 1,000 feet. Composed of Mesozoic and Cenozoic rocks much softer than those of Caledonian and Hercynian Britain, the Lowland Zone is essentially a cuestaform landscape with cuestas on the resistant limestones and sandstones, and broad lowlands ("vales" being the accepted local term) on the intervening clays and marls.[4]

In general, the beds dip gently southeastward toward the English Channel or southern North Sea. The oldest rocks outcrop in the Midlands, lapping like a sea against the limits of the Highland Zone, and the youngest occur in eastern East Anglia. But the simplicity of this picture is disturbed by the existence of four major east-west folds that dominate the outcrop pattern of southern England. These are (a) *the London basin* or *syncline*, roughly coincident with the lower and middle Thames basins; (b) *the Wealden anticline*, forming the peninsula of Kent, Surrey, and Sussex; (c) *the Hampshire basin* or *syncline*; and (d) *the Purbeck anticline*, delimiting that basin on the south. Much of the last system is drowned by the English Channel.

The two basins of London and Hampshire, respectively, form broad vales floored largely by Tertiary sands and clays (hence the common term "Tertiary basins"). The anticlines, however, bring to the surface the Mesozoic strata, and the cuesta-and-vale landscape of the east Midlands is renewed about their flanks.[5]

The Midlands of England are largely floored by bright red soils developed on the clays and sands of the Triassic outcrop. The Mid-

---

[4] A very detailed account is given in S. W. Wooldridge and D. L. Linton, *Structure, Surface and Drainage in South-East England* (London: Institute of British Geographers, Publication 10, 1939).

[5] *Ibid.,* pp. 52–56, 80–97.

land plain passes southeastward into a succession of cuestas and vales that makes up the whole of southeast England. Some of the cuestas are very significant in the life of the country. The Cotswolds, for example, developed on limestones of Jurassic age, have become a rich farming land famous for the beauty of its stone houses and rich villages. Elsewhere in the Jurassic outcrop are the iron-rich deposits of Northamptonshire, Lincolnshire, and East Riding. Scarcely less significant is the cuesta developed on the Chalk, an Upper Cretaceous limestone that provided the dry uplands on which early man preferred to live, as well as the flints from which he fashioned his tools (Fig. 3–3). None of these cuestas much exceeds 1,000 feet (the highest being the Hambleton-Cleveland Hills in the Yorkshire Wolds) and many are much less. The locations of the most significant are shown in Fig. 3–1.

The vales between the cuestas, being developed chiefly on heavy clays, remained for long under heavy forest. Today, however, they are mostly prosperous farmlands devoted to a pastoral husbandry.

The gentle folds that diversify the structure of the Lowland Zone were formed at the time when the great convulsion of the Alpine mountain-building period was in progress. The British Isles were in the groundswell of this disturbance. While the lowland of England was receiving the imprint of these movements, igneous activity broke out in the north of Ireland and in western Scotland. The islands of Mull and Skye, and the great basalt flows of Antrim were formed at this time.

The Effects of Glaciation

In common with most of Northern Europe, the British Isles succumbed to several glaciations during Pleistocene times, and the landscapes of both Highland and Lowland zones show many traces of this ordeal. The ultimate advance of the ice covered almost all of Britain north of a line from the Severn estuary to the coast of Essex. The ice sheets were local, deploying on to the plains from dispersal centers over the principal massifs of the Highland Zone. The main Scandinavian glacier did, however, reach eastern coastal districts during at least one of the glacial episodes.

In the Highland Zone, the erosive effects of the glaciation were considerable. The uplands are typically thin-soiled, and there are many *roches moutonnées*, crag-and-tail phenomena, and the like to confirm the effects of the ice. These are conspicuously absent from the hills of Devon, where deep residual soils are widely developed. Ireland owes much of its present-day landscape to the glaciations. Its

Fig. 3–3. The Chalk Cliffs of Dover. Much of England's coast line is "cliffed" by the recent marine submergence. (Photo: UKIO.)

Central Lowland is plastered with drift, much of it yielding soils of high fertility. The drainage is badly disturbed, and there are numerous ponds and lakes. Large areas of peat bog—a characteristic Irish landscape—overlie the till and provide the inhabitants with much of their fuel.

Lowland England contains considerable areas of drift-covered terrain. Much of the east is covered by thin sheets of calcareous till, largely derived from the Chalk or Jurassic oolites over which the ice was forced to pass. The Midland tills are made up chiefly of Triassic debris. The rivers of southern and eastern England are flanked by numerous gravel terraces, associated with the frequent shifts of base level in Pleistocene and recent times. The most recent movement of base level has been upward, and most of the rivers reach the sea through drowned estuaries, with wide areas of marshes and saltings. The Wash, with the Fens that surround it, is the best-known example. Drainage and careful containment of the sea, the patient work of English and Dutch engineers for three centuries, has converted the Fens into the richest arable land of England.

Climate

Little need be written of the general character of the British climate beyond what has been said in Chapter 1.[6] The country exhibits in a marked degree the oceanic characteristics typical of the whole northwest coast of Europe. Within Britain itself there are marked differences of climate, chiefly of rainfall and secondarily of temperature. The Highland Zone has in general a high rainfall and a small annual range of temperature, whereas the Lowland Zone is much drier and more extreme in its temperature cycle. Rainfall is lowest in the Thames estuary and in the Fenlands, but is nowhere so low as to create serious problems for the farmer except in drought years. The wettest parts of the Highland Zone—the Lake District and the Snowdon Massif—have stations with mean annual rainfall over 150 inches. At the opposite end of the scale are rainfalls of less than 20 inches in the Thames estuary.[7]

Winter is mild. Mildest conditions extend along the west coast, and even the Orkney Islands have mean temperatures of 40° F. in January (warmer than Paris). Coolest regions are the eastern coastal districts of Scotland and East Anglia and, of course, the high hills.

[6] The standard reference work is E. G. Bilham, *The Climate of the British Isles* (London: Macmillan & Co., Ltd., 1938). Note that temperature maps in this volume are reduced to sea level, a fact which deprives them of all value.

[7] See climatic graphs, Appendix II.

Very heavy rainfall deluges the uplands, and severe gales are frequent along the south, west, and north coasts as Atlantic cyclones pass to the north of Scotland. Snowfall is uncommon, and rarely lies long on the west coast or the lowlands. The southwest coast is exceptionally mild, and may escape frost during many winters. Subtropical plants are open-grown in many places along the Cornish Riviera, which is also the place of origin for early vegetables and flowers for the London market.

The summer is warm enough for most of the common cereal and root crops, though corn (maize) cannot be attempted except for silage. Over the southern half of Ireland and Britain, July temperatures slightly exceed 60° F., whereas in the coolest parts of Highland Scotland they barely attain 55° F. Wheat can be grown over most of Ireland, Wales, and England; it ripens as far north as the Moray Firth. Oats and barley are at home throughout the country.

Vegetation

The landscape of Neolithic Britain was very densely forested, like that of eastern North America before white settlement. Today, after several millennia of assaults by man, the forests have all but vanished, and Britain has the poorest forest cover in Europe. The landscape of the lowlands shows few traces of the vanished forests, though hedgerow trees and farm woodlots or game coverts give the distant prospect a wooded look. Ireland has the least area of forest—if St. Patrick banished the snake from Ireland, his people have been almost as successful in ousting the tree. British forests have vanished under the combined needs of farmers for cleared land, the early navy for ships and their masts, ironsmiths for charcoal, and the general populace for firewood.[8]

The climax forest appears to be dominated by the pedunculate oak [9] and the durmast oak, both of which extend right across peninsular Europe. Oakwoods occur in every part of the British Isles. The durmast oak seems dominant in the woodlands on the thin, acid soils of the wet hill lands of the Highland Zone, whereas the pedunculate oak is dominant in the drier east. The two species hybridize freely. The common ash is often a codominant, and may form extensive pure stands, especially in limestone country. The beech is also common as an associate of the oaks. Like the ash, it may occur in pure stands,

---

[8] This section owes much to A. G. Tansley, *The British Islands and Their Vegetation* (Cambridge: Cambridge University Press, 1939). This monumental work also contains long treatments of soil, a topic little regarded in much-plowed England, where soil profiles of a mature sort are hard to come by.

[9] Recent opinion suggests that this oak may have been introduced by man.

but it is largely confined to the south and southeast of England. Other hardwoods of common occurrence are the birches (discussed below), certain elms, willows, alder, aspen, lime, and the hornbeam.

This deciduous forest climax has been established in Britain since the climatic optimum some 7,000 years ago. Since it now survives only in patches, it is impossible to sketch the constitution of the climax cover in any detail. In particular, one cannot say for sure whether the cover extended without essential thinning over the lower hills of the Highland Zone or over the dry chalk Downs of England, which may have been grassy.

The forests that covered Britain in the Boreal and pre-Boreal climatic periods (roughly 9000–5000 B.C.) were very different in composition. The birches were the most widespread trees, but their dominance was challenged by the Scots pine. Today the birches are common all over Britain, especially in open heaths and sandy soils. The pine forms considerable forests in Highland Scotland, but finds its ideal home on the sandy soils of southern England, where it forms a distinctive and handsome landscape. The Bagshot plateaus in the London Basin and the New Forest in the Hampshire Basin have the largest stands. There is also much ornamental woodland planted by park designers, usually of hybrids or of exotic conifers. Indeed, over many parishes in southern England the number of foreign species probably exceeds considerably the roster of native ones. There are probably more cedars of Lebanon in some English counties than in Lebanon itself.

The hills of the Highland Zone of Britain are characteristically treeless, and present the landscape known throughout the country as "moorland." Much of this vegetation is today established on land that would certainly sustain forest, but for the work of domesticated animals, rabbits, and other beasts. Moorlike vegetation also occurs on sandy common land in the Lowland Zone, often as an early stage in the succession leading to pine forest. Characteristic species are the lowland gorse and various brambles.

THE PEOPLING OF BRITAIN

Prehistory. The peopling of the British Isles began at so early a date that its detailed story is forever lost. The earliest inhabitants have left us nothing but primitive flint tools and weapons with which to trace their homes and characteristics. Paleolithic man appears to have been scattered thinly around the coasts and in the hills of southern England, where he practiced in the second and third interglacial periods his crude economy of fruit gathering and hunting. The Riss-

Würm glacial advances may have driven him from Britain, or perhaps into the sea caves and limestone caverns of southern England; we have no means of ascertaining his movements. In any event the early dawn of man's occupancy, though it was probably spread over a period a hundred times as long as that which has elapsed since Paleolithic times, has left no trace on the British landscape, and contributes nothing to present-day geography.[10]

It is all otherwise with the primitive societies that spread across Britain in Neolithic, Bronze Age, and Iron Age times (2500 B.C.–100 A.D.). The peopling of the islands proceeded in these years from both western and eastern sources. Within the Lowland Zone, pre-Roman settlement appears to have preferred the high limestone plateaus or sandy plains with loamy soils. Here the forest (of beech and ash) was thinner and may have yielded more readily to the primitive axe of the pioneer. Much of the lighter land was brought under the plow, or was used to pasture stock, and the settlements themselves tended to be grouped along spring lines. Salisbury Plain, on which several of the drier ridges converged, was the most thickly and continuously settled area; the fields of the farm on which the author of this chapter was born still bear the impress of this early agricultural civilization. The clay vales, by contrast, resisted for long the efforts of early man to occupy them; the dense oakwood and the abundant surface water were both unwelcome to a people of limited technology. As Sir Cyril Fox put it,

> This forest was in a sense unbroken, for without emerging from its canopy a squirrel could traverse the country from end to end. . . . [The forests were] haunted by lynx, wolf and boar, bear and fighting ox; and were hostile in themselves to Man, his flocks and herds.[11]

Thus in pre-Roman times both Highland and Lowland zones were thinly occupied by Celtic-speaking Britons. As later, more-vigorous settlers invaded from the east, both the ways and the tongues of these primitive folk were banished into Ireland, Highland Scotland, Wales, and Cornubia. Vestiges of the old traditions linger in the ceremonial of the Welsh, the most tenaciously conservative of the Highland people. Such traditions find their expression in modern literature, as in the poetry of Dylan Thomas, and in local ritual (though not in the annual Eisteddfod, whose Druidic rites are charming but apocryphal). They also form the basis of resurgent Irish nationalism, whose disciples are striving doggedly to revive the moribund Gaelic tongue.

---

[10] A classic in the geographical literature of Britain is C. Fox, *The Personality of Britain: Its Influence on Inhabitant and Invader in Prehistoric and Early Historic Times* (Cardiff: National Museum of Wales, 1933).

[11] *Ibid.*, p. 82.

The Roman Interlude. Upon this simple culture the Roman Empire imposed four centuries (A.D. 43–400) of Mediterranean civilization and law. The Roman conquerors entirely subjugated the Lowland Zone of Britain, but made little attempt to penetrate the Highlands. Civil administration was established over the Lowlands, and the Celtic peasantry was in considerable measure knit into the structure of a Romanized state. Towns of typical Mediterranean plan were constructed, and trade, already active in Bronze and Iron Age times, was substantially increased, both internally and externally. Wales, northern England, and southern Scotland were constituted military zones, whence the Roman legionaries watched the tribesmen of the hills beyond.

The most significant modern legacy of the Roman interlude was the military road system. As in other parts of conquered western Europe, the Romans built straight, well-metalled highways which have in some areas survived into modern England as major routeways. Thus Watling Street, from Richborough (now defunct as a port, near modern Sandwich) to London (already the largest trading center) and across the Midlands to Wroxeter, today forms highways A2 and A5. Ermine Street (London-Lincoln-Humber) is still in several stretches a major north-south routeway. On the other hand Fosse Way, a route following roughly the belt of Jurassic scarps from Lincoln to Cirencester and Exeter, has for considerable distances lapsed to the status of a footpath (Fig. 3–4).

Of the cities that flourished under Roman rule, some (like Silchester—*Calleva Atrebatum*) have vanished as such, others have flourished. Since the Roman interlude London, for example, has remained the largest commercial center of the kingdom. The root "-chester" is a corruption of the Latin *castra*, a camp, and its abundance in English place names is proof enough of the capacity of the Roman overlords to select sites that would stand the test of time.

The Anglo-Saxon, Norse, and Danish Invasions. In the fifth century A.D. the Romanized Celtic civilization of Lowland England was eclipsed by renewed barbarian invasions from the east—the Angles, Jutes, and Saxons, whose Teutonic tongues and warlike philosophy swept the civilized culture of the Britons from the Lowlands into the Highland refuges of the west. In the Britain of the Dark Ages we lose sight of the progress of settlement and cannot regain our perspective until the Norman invasion. It is clear, however, that the Anglo-Saxons completely occupied the Lowland Zone and in several places penetrated deeply into the Highlands, as in southeast Scotland and Devon. They showed a marked preference for well-drained, loamy soils, though they did not shun the oakwoods of the clay vales as thoroughly as did their Celtic predecessors.[12]

In the eighth and ninth centuries A.D. the young English kingdoms so established were themselves overrun by the second wave of "Nordic" invaders, the Danish and Norse Vikings. The Norwegians followed the outer-sea route round Cape Wrath and established

Fig. 3–4. The Fosse Way, near Tetbury, on the Cotswold backslope. The large arable fields and the abundance of hedgerow trees should be noted. (Photo: Aero Pictorial, Ltd.)

scattered settlements all along the western seaboard; Caithness, Galloway, much of Ireland, the Isle of Man, the Lake District, and parts of South Wales were invaded. The Danes, in contrast, landed in great numbers in eastern England, establishing a broad belt of Danish settlement in the "Danelaw," essentially the lowland zone east of Watling Street. They also established a kingdom in Normandy, from which, two centuries later, the final invasion and conquest of Britain were to come.

[12] S. W. Wooldridge, "The Anglo-Saxon Settlement," chap. iii of H. C. Darby (ed.), *Historical Geography of England before 1800* (London: Cambridge University Press, 1936), p. 91. See also S. W. Wooldridge and D. L. Linton, "The Loam-Terrains of Southeast England in Their Relation to Its Early History," *Antiquity* 7 (September, 1933): 297–303.

Despite war and bloody rapine, ordinary events in pre-Norman Britain, it is clear that the Lowland Zone was fairly fully occupied at this time. Even the clay vales, with their damp oakwoods, had begun slowly to yield. We can attempt to reconstruct the process of settlement by the study of place names, a fascinating field of geographical research. Names ending in -ingas (now -ing) and -ingaham (now -ingham) are of early Anglo-Saxon origin, and -ton is of a later Saxon period. In the Danelaw, names ending in -by (Old Scandinavian -byr, i.e., village, town) and -thorp (Danish, hamlet) and those containing Danish proper names abound. Place-name research is an intricate and highly developed technique for which little space can be found here.[13]

The Norman Conquest. The Norman Conquest was the final episode in the peopling of Britain from without her shores. The Normans were few in numbers, but they extended their autocratic rule over most of Britain and introduced a Latin element into the English language. The English feudal system was largely their creation, and the rural settlements of both England and Ireland bear many traces of their rule. Once again, it was in the English Lowlands that Norman feudalism was most readily established; beneath its heel the English peasantry and its manorial overlords occupied all but the most intractable soils. The Norman castle on its mound survives in many places to remind us of this vital phase in the taking up of the land. Over all England there spread the Norman conception of statehood, of authoritarian government, of codified and enforceable law. In the cities arose the great cathedrals, Romanesque at first, derived from France, but expressing later a rising English genius in Gothic architecture. Through the teaching of Norman, French, and Italian clergy the mainstream of European civilization resumed its flow into Britain.

The Highland Zone was less tractable. Wales was subjected to conquest, but could not be assimilated into the English kingdom until the Tudors—a Welsh family—ascended to the throne. Scotland, a poor, lightly settled land in which Saxons and Celtic clansmen intermingled, was nevertheless not united with the British crown until 1707, and separation still exists as a political aspiration. Ireland was conquered by part-Welsh earls who established Norman feudalism only to see it absorbed by Irish tribalism.

Nevertheless, the Norman period marked the final stage in the emergence of the English state and in the initial occupancy of the

---

[13] The method is explained in E. Ekwall, *The Oxford Dictionary of English Place-Names* (London: Clarendon Press, 1936), pp. vii–xxxiv.

soil. By the time the Normans themselves had been absorbed into the English people, and the English tongue was once again the language of power and government, England and Wales had become a consolidated kingdom that has never since bowed to invasion. Scotland was as yet independent, but her days were numbered. Only Ireland stood beyond the pale, as she again stands. The peopling of Britain was thus complete, and the identity of her four subsidiary nations—Welsh, Scottish, Irish, and English—established.

Medieval Britain was a land of cities and trade on the one hand, and an entrenched, landed feudal aristocracy on the other; town and country were distinct in the landscape, at least to the Highland border.[14] They have remained distinct into modern Britain, whose geography can best be discussed in terms of the urban and rural landscapes.

The Rural Landscape

The British Isles as a whole are blessed with a climate that permits a varied and productive agriculture. Almost all the tillable land has been under the plow or improved grassland for generations and, in some areas, since Neolithic times. In the United Kingdom, 47,853,000 acres (about 79 per cent of the whole country) is in agricultural use, and about 4.3 per cent of the working population is employed upon it. In the Irish Republic, by contrast, 38.2 per cent of the labor force is engaged in agriculture. In highly industrialized Britain the gross agricultural output amounts to only about 4 per cent in value of the gross output of goods and services. In contrast, agricultural production and that of associated industries are the kernel of the national economy of the Irish Republic. Notwithstanding the apparently small contribution it makes to the national income, British agriculture is highly organized and productive.

The 12,441,000 acres of British land not in agricultural production is largely inaccessible mountain or moorland, much of it peat bog, of which most is in the Scottish Highlands. The Land Utilisation Survey of Britain has reported that in Britain itself (excluding Northern Ireland) about 3,000,000 acres are occupied by houses with gardens, cities, industrial or mining sites, and for other agriculturally unproductive uses. In short, Britain's urban economy, which contributes at least 90 per cent of the national income, and which has made her one of the world's largest industrial powers, is prosecuted on only 6 per cent of her land, which remains overwhelmingly rural.

British farming is highly mechanized. The number of tractors now exceeds the number of separate farms (444,000), an eightfold increase since 1939. Similar advances have occurred in the use of electric dairy

[14] H. C. Darby, "The Economic Geography of England, A.D. 1000–1250," chap. v of Darby, op. cit., pp. 165–229.

equipment and combine harvesters. Agriculturally, Britain now ranks among the world's most mechanized countries.

The Medieval Landscape and Its Legacy. The modern British countryside is largely the creation of the past two centuries, when most of the enclosed fields, compact farms, and ornamental parklands that personify it were created. Until the seventeenth century most of the land was occupied under a husbandry derived from the medieval manorial system, or the more primitive organization of Celtic Britain. Though the Agricultural Revolution has effaced the older landscape effectively, it has not fundamentally changed the distribution of settlement. Certain villages have been abandoned, and much secondary dispersal of settlement has followed the enclosures; nevertheless, enough of the older pattern survives to make it necessary for us to glance at the husbandry of medieval times.

The Lowland Zone was cultivated under variants of the open-field system, in which the tenantry (largely in a condition of serfdom in earlier days) plowed intermingled strips of from a quarter to a whole acre in extent, within two or three arable fields. Each field was sown with a single crop—usually rye, wheat, oats, barley, peas, or some other "green" crop. One field was left under fallow. Beyond the arable fields was a common pasture on which a small head of cattle or sheep was tended. There was also much-treasured hay meadow along the stream courses. A woodlot for communal grazing, timber, and firewood made up the rest of the land. None of the fields were enclosed, though growing crops and hay were protected by hurdles. The village's inhabitants were thus communally concerned with the management of all the land; the individual farm was a thing of the future.[15,16]

The two-field and three-field systems were widely distributed in the Midlands and the southwest. In East Anglia, the eastern London Basin, and Kent, however, the open-field system in its pure form never existed, and some measure of enclosure seems to have prevailed very early.

The Highland Zone was thinly settled, but was nevertheless agriculturally organized. The most widespread system of land use was the infield-outfield system. Here from two to fifteen tenant families operated (also communally) a looser form of husbandry. The infield was close to the settlement: it was plowed continuously, and upon it was spread all the available dung. The larger outfield was used for poor pasture, but strips of it were also plowed from time to time in a shifting fashion, so that in time all of it was cultivated and prevented from relapsing to rough grazing or moorland. This so-called "Celtic"

[15] *Ibid.*, pp. 189–207.
[16] A good summary of field systems is given in W. Smith, *An Economic Geography of Great Britain* (London: Methuen & Co., Ltd., 1949), pp. 3–23.

system—a bad misnomer—was widespread in Scotland, the Pennines, Wales, and Cornwall, but also occurred on poor soils and uplands in Lowland Britain.[17]

The older husbandry all over Britain was close to a subsistence economy. Regional differentiation of farming practice was kept to a minimum because the necessities of life had to be produced locally. Nevertheless, upon the richer lands of the Lowland Zone and the

Fig. 3–5. Wherwell, Hampshire, which exemplifies the traditional village architecture of southernmost England. Note the thatched roofs, the half-timbered walls, and the carefully tended hedges. (Central Office of Information, London.)

outer fringe of the Highlands there arose a considerable surplus which was ultimately to color Britain's modern economy. The first and foremost was wool, for which medieval Britain was famous. It made her, first, a large exporter of raw wool and, later, the home of a prosperous woolen and worsted textile industry which remains one of her industrial staples.

All over the Lowland Zone, the old economy tended to create nucleated settlement: each village, a little world in itself (Fig. 3–5), was located at or near a source of drinking water, usually a spring. The dry tablelands of limestone or sandstone, and the wet, marshy

[17] The crofting system of modern Highland Scotland has certain affinities with the older Celtic husbandry. See I. F. Grant, "The Highland Openfield System," *Geographical Teacher* 13 (1926), 480–82.

clays, were avoided. Favorite sites were along the spring lines flanking the cuestas (Fig. 3–6).

The breakdown of the medieval system was slow. It was marked
by enclosure of the old common pastures, as well as of the arable.
At first the enclosure movement derived from the desire to create vast
sheep runs, when wool was the most precious raw material in Europe.
Later, however, enclosure became the preliminary to improvement in

Fig. 3–6. The cuesta of the South Downs (Chalk) at Poynings, Sussex. The
beds dip toward the left, where the chalk forms a bold face about 600 feet high,
largely supporting poor, dry pasture land. At the foot of the scarp is a wide
shelf covered by fertile downwash; the shelf is under arable cultivation in large
fields. Poynings is on the spring line and is a typical nucleated village clustered
around its church. (Central Office of Information, London.)

farming, for the new techniques of the eighteenth and nineteenth
centuries could not be applied to open fields. The culmination of the
movement came with the General Enclosure Act of 1845. Hence-
forward Britain was a land, not of communal manors, but of farms
and farmers, each with his distinct plot of ground. The villages remained, but to them was added a disseminated farming population.[18]
The enclosure movement also established a fourfold division of the
rural population which persists to the present day in the Lowland
Zone, including

[18] W. G. East, "England in the Eighteenth Century," chap. xiii of Darby, *op. cit.*,
p. 471.

1. *Landed gentry*, owning much land and deriving income chiefly from agricultural rents.
2. *Owner-farmers*, owning their own farms and land and living off the sale of produce, or off the produce itself.
3. *Tenant farmers*, renting their farms from the gentry and making up the largest group in modern Britain.
4. *Laborers*, owning and renting no land but working for wages for the farmers. The farm laborer is the descendant of the villager displaced from his land by enclosure.

The tenant farmer is the characteristic countryman of Britain. Protected by legislation from arbitrary displacement, he no longer occupies a hazardous position. The FAO's world census of 1950 showed that about 36 per cent of the holdings in England and Wales were wholly owned by the occupier, 49 per cent were wholly rented, and 15 per cent were part owned and part rented. For Scotland the figures were 36, 60, and 4 per cent, respectively.[19]

The farm laborer is essentially an inhabitant of eastern and southern England. In Highland Britain, enclosure of the old "Celtic" townships did not displace so many landsmen, nor did it provide a market for agricultural hired labor. In Wales, Highland Scotland, the Pennines, and Ulster the typical unit is the family farm in which the farmer, his wife, and his family can work the land without assistance.

The Modern Farming System. Present-day land use in Great Britain is well known through the nationwide studies of the Land Utilisation Survey (directed by L. Dudley Stamp), whose maps of land use, on a scale of 1:63,360, cover the whole country, and whose nine-volume report, *The Land of Britain*, is unique in geographical literature.[20] Stamp's own *Land of Britain: Its Use and Misuse* is an appraisal of the results [21] and renders all other studies of the subject obsolete or incomplete. A similar survey exists for Northern Ireland (directed by D. A. Hills). These land-use studies have been supplemented by the publication of maps showing types of farming and land classification in terms of fertility. They show a complexity that makes nonsense of most attempts at a regional division of British rural life. The striking difference from the old patterns is the existence of local specialization and differentiation, in which the farming practice shows a high and increasing correlation with soil type and climate (Fig. 3–7).

[19] *Britain: An Official Handbook—1959* (London: H. M. Stationery Office), p. 253.
[20] L. Dudley Stamp (ed.), *The Land of Britain* (9 vols.; London: Geographical Publications, Ltd., 1943–46).
[21] L. Dudley Stamp, *The Land of Britain: Its Use and Misuse* (London: Geographical Publications, Ltd., and Longmans, Green & Co., Ltd., 1948).

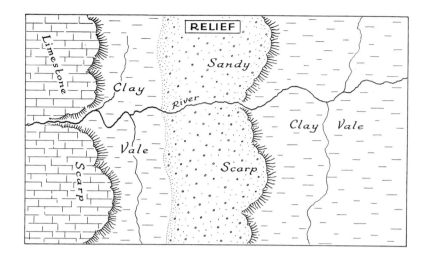

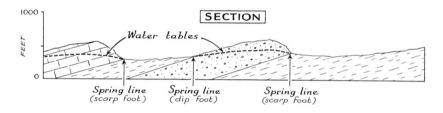

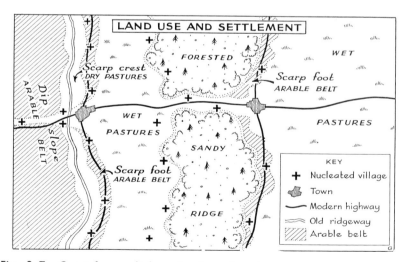

Fig. 3–7. Cuestaform relief, nucleation of settlement, and differentiated land use in Lowland England. The upper diagram shows a typical example of the relief, and the section diagram shows the location of spring lines. Upon these, many villages are sited. Large settlements tend to occur near the mouths of wind- or water-gaps at old bridging points.

167

England and Wales: Farming Types. In general it may be said that Anglo-Welsh farming tends toward two extremes:

1. An arable economy, in which most of the land is plowed regularly on an established rotation. Such land is largely confined to the drier east and is most widespread in East Anglia, the Fenlands, and much of Yorkshire.
2. A pastoral economy, in which the land is left unplowed. There are two distinct subtypes, the rough hill grazing of the moorlands of the Highland Zone and the richer pastures widespread on the heavier soils of the Midlands of England.

Between these extremes there is a broad range of intermediate economies, in which arable and permanent improved grass intermingle. The three types are mapped in Fig. 3–8.

Hill sheep farming is typical of the higher moorlands of the Highland Zone, both in Wales, Devon, and Cornwall and in northern England. The farms are large, partially enclosed tracts of heather and grassy upland on which flocks of hardy mountain breeds are maintained. The flocks are of ewes, and the economy depends on the sale of the annual lamb crop (Fig. 3–9).

Stock rearing is localized on the lower hill country of the three main parts of the Highland Zone: Devon-Cornwall (Fig. 3–10), Wales, and northern England. The land may either be improved pasture or arable. If the latter, however, it is usually under the specialized form of husbandry known as ley farming, in which the land is sown out to grass for two, three, or four years after each phase of cropping. The crops themselves are usually oats, turnips, swedes, or other animal foodstuffs. The economy turns on the rearing of young cattle (or sheep in some cases) for sale to the rich fattening lands to the south and east. In most cases the cattle are of famous beef breeds like the Hereford and Devon (which are now world-wide in distribution) or dual-purpose animals like the Shorthorn. The greater part of the world's beef production today comes from breeds fixed on these British hill farms.

Stock fattening, the complement of stock rearing, is widely dispersed among the Lowland pastoral and intermediate economies, but is especially noteworthy on the permanent grass of the clay plains of the English Midlands, particularly in Leicestershire.

Dairying is now the most widespread farming type of lowland Britain, where it attains its highest form on the permanent grass of the clay vales of the south and east. Concentration upon dairying was determined originally by the nearness of great local markets. Nowadays, however, improved access by road, the marketing services

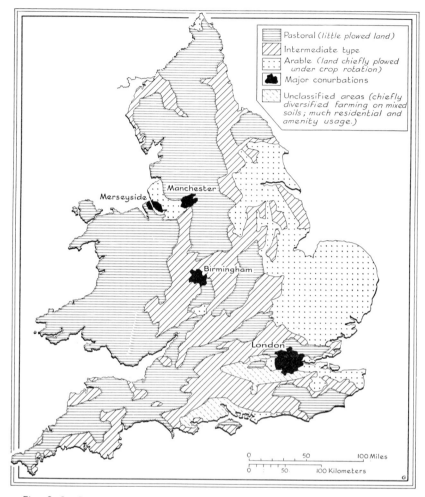

Fig. 3–8. Dominant farming economies of England and Wales. Note the concentration of pastoral types on western moors, and on the clay vales of the Midlands; intermediate types are most widespread on limestone soils and in the Midland Vale.

of the Milk Marketing Board, and the increased demands of the large creameries have made dairying profitable in most areas where soils are not excessively light. The characteristic breeds are the Dairy Short-horn and the Holstein, as well as the Jersey and Guernsey in the south.

Mixed farming is a collective term for the varied economies typical chiefly of the lighter soils of the Lowlands. Barley and wheat are common crops, and sheep are usually numerous, especially in the limestone belts. Much of this land now has an increasing interest in dairying.

Arable (crop) farming, in which the production of crops for sale off the farm is the preoccupation, is mainly an eastern type, being found on medium soils in the drier belts. The till-covered plains of East Anglia, the rich, organic or silty soils of the Fens and the Vale of York are the largest areas. Wheat and barley are the major cereals,

Fig. 3–9. A typical farm of the more rugged parts of the Highland Zone, Langdale Valley, Lake District Caledonian Massif. Oats are being harvested for winter fodder. Sheep moors in the background. (Fox Photos, London.)

sugar beets and potatoes the chief root crops. In the Fens crop farming is the only significant activity: the richest soils in England are here farmed in drained areas reminiscent of the Dutch polders. Elsewhere, however, the crop economy is added to by extensive sheep flocks, by dairying, and by stock fattening. The plain of southwest Lancashire, the only western representative of this type, is a region concentrating largely on poultry, potatoes, and green vegetables.

Market gardening, in which arable specialization reaches its ultimate form, is not extensive but raises much of the needs of the large cities in small fruit, fresh vegetables, and flowers. The largest areas are: (a) the brick-earth belt of the Thames terraces east and west of London; (b) a part of the clay vale of Evesham; and (c) areas of sandy soil in Bedfordshire and Cambridgeshire. Regions (a) and (c) serve the London market.

Fruit farming is of limited significance in cool, cloudy England. Two areas, however, stand out—the west Midlands (Worcestershire, Herefordshire, Gloucestershire, Somersetshire) and Kent. The latter county has been aptly named the garden of England. The Kentish orchards, nurseries, and hop gardens occur in two principal belts, the

Fig. 3–10. Stock-rearing country on a more tractable part of the Highland Zone, Vale of Widecombe, Devon. Note the small fields on the lower ground and the rough moors above the small village of St. Pancras. The farms are widely disseminated. (Photo: UKIO.)

loam-soil belt of north Kent, along the foot of the backslope of the North Downs, and the similar belt to the south along the backslope of a cuesta of calcareous sandstone. Apples, cherries, plums, and hops are the characteristic products.

Scotland: Farming Types. Scotland has less good land than England and has a shorter, cooler summer. Nevertheless its farming is technically superior, and follows in several ways a distinctive tradition.

As in England, one can distinguish arable, pastoral, and intermediate economies, but the distinction loses some of its significance. Much of the arable land is farmed on the ley principle—with several

years of unplowed rotation grass following each period of cropping.
On the other hand, purely pastoral economies are rare on the improved land; there is no Scottish equivalent for the great Lowland
permanent pastures of England. Only the moorlands present large

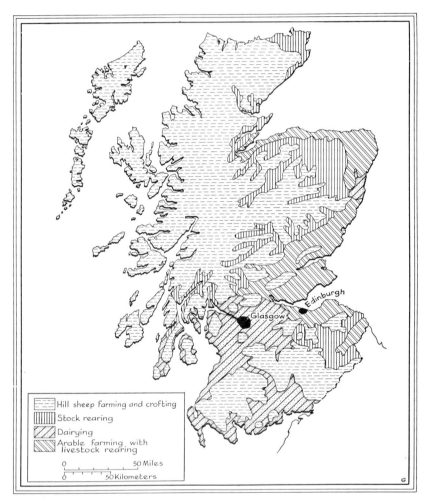

Fig. 3–11. Predominant farming types of Scotland. (After L. Dudley Stamp.)

areas of unplowed but productive land. Four distinct farming types
can be distinguished, and are outlined in Fig. 3–11.

Arable farming with livestock raising occurs on areas of level
ground and loamy soils along the drier east coast. The chief crops in
the arable rotation are oats, barley, wheat (chiefly south of Aber-

deen), potatoes, turnips, and other root crops designed for use as winter feed for livestock. There is also much rotation grass, the timothy-hay crop being especially valuable. A considerable volume of off-the-farm sales of crops is characteristic. Throughout the belt, however, there is a specialization in the feeding and fattening of livestock. In the Tweed Valley, sheep outnumber beef cattle; Cheviot, Border-Leicester, and their cross, the Half-bred, are the characteristic breeds of this spacious country. In the rest of the belt the fattening of store cattle from the nearby rearing lands is commoner than sheep farming. The eastern half of the Midland Valley has such an economy, and dairying is also considerable.

Stock rearing, as in England, is localized on the hilly margins of the main uplands, namely the Southern Uplands and the more accessible Highlands. Almost always the rearing is carried out on arable farms using long leys of rotation grass, and producing oats and turnips as the only significant crops. Famous beef breeds have characterized this country, the Aberdeen Angus in the northeast, the Highland in the west, and the Galloway in the western Southern Uplands. Sheep rearing, though widespread, is dominant only around the Tweed Valley.

Dairying is widespread, and is the dominant farming type in two principal regions, the western half of the Midland Valley (where it supplies the large markets of Clydeside) and around the western flanks of the Southern Uplands in Ayrshire, Wigtown, Kirkcudbright, and Dumfries, where the milk is sold wholesale to creameries or to the Scottish Milk Marketing Board. The Ayrshire cow is the characteristic dairy animal.

Hill sheep farming extends over the moorlands of the Southern Uplands and the Highlands; the Blackface ewes roam the bleak heather moors in thousands, with Cheviots on the grassy slopes. Crofting is a vanishing farming type, thinly scattered through the Highlands, and seen at its purest in the Hebrides and Shetland Islands. It involves the inherited tenure of tiny patches of cultivated lands on the raised beaches and coastal platforms or valley floors, with limited grazing rights on the nearby hillsides.

Planning. One of the most striking developments of the last fifteen years in the United Kingdom has been the emergence of town and country planning as a national policy and interest. The acute pressure on land, the necessity of protecting the food supply, the problems of rebuilding war-damaged cities, and the widespread desire to protect Great Britain's lovely countryside have combined to awaken the nation to the need for land-use planning. All parties agree on the need, though there is some difference between them in the emphasis laid upon specific problems. Space is lacking to recount here the immense body of work undertaken in this field. The most remarkable visible result of the planning movement is the construction of new towns, which are intended to rehouse the overcrowded population of the large cities and to achieve some measure of decentralization of light industry away from strategically vulnerable areas.

The Rural Life of Ireland. The Irish landscape in no way resembles that of Britain to the east. Behind the apparent peace of the white farmhouses and the emerald-green pastures there lies a troubled history. It has already been said that 38.2 per cent of Ireland's working population lives off the land and that even her industry is largely concerned with agricultural produce. The mild climate, with its cool, cloudy summers and largely frost-free winters, has encouraged the development of a pastoral economy that allows a large-scale export of farm produce.[22, 23]

In the early nineteenth century Ireland was a densely populated land of tenant farmers, occupying tiny farms rented, without security of tenure, from a land-owning class whose political and economic ambitions were best served by a minute subdivision of the land. Much of the land was arable, producing potatoes as the staple of the local diet and wheat for export to England. A progressive increase in population taxed the resources of the land beyond its limit, and in 1845 there began a famine that caused 750,000 country folk to die of starvation before they could escape to the ports. There ensued a drastic revolution in population and land tenure, of which three elements can be distinguished here:

1. Large-scale emigration to Britain, the dominions, and America has reduced the population from 8,175,000 in 1841 to 4,283,000 in 1936–37, since when population has slightly increased. Ireland is unique in Europe in showing a large decline in population over this period. There has also been—especially in Ulster—a migration from the country to the towns, notably to Londonderry, Belfast, Dublin, and Cork.[24]

2. The land has been transferred by governmental action from the landlord class to the farmers, who now largely own the land they farm, in both Northern Ireland and the Irish Republic. In the

---

[22] The best reference on the geography of Ireland is T. W. Freeman, *Ireland* (London: Methuen & Co., Ltd., 1950).

[23] E. Estyn Evans, *Irish Heritage* (Dundalk: Dundalgan Press, 1942) and S. O'Faolain, *The Irish* (Harmondsworth: Penguin Books, Ltd., 1947) give excellent accounts of the cultural and traditional background of modern Irish life.

[24] Cork is unique among the group in that its population has not markedly increased. Emigration from the town has offset the influx from rural districts.

latter, especially, attention has been given to the congested lands of the western Gaeltacht.

3. The economy has become mainly pastoral, devoting the land to the rearing or fattening of cattle (largely for the British market), or to dairying and poultry farming.

Acute land hunger still exists, and farms remain remarkably small. Population pressure in some areas continues severe. Seventy-nine per cent of the holdings of the Republic is in farms of 50 acres or less, and upon this minutely divided land dwells the greater part of the farming population: the smaller the farm size, the greater the rural population density. The record of individual holdings is even more striking; in 1946, for example, 60 per cent of all farm holdings in Northern Ireland were of less than 30 acres, and the equivalent figure for the Republic was also 60 per cent.

The greatest concentration of small farms—and hence of high population density—extends up the west coast from the Shannon through the hilly Caledonian country of Galway, Mayo, Sligo, and Donegal. This area contains a high proportion of those able to speak Gaelic.

Ulster is also a land of minute farms, but here there is a higher level of prosperity. The traditional crop is flax, grown for the production of linen, a famous specialization of the province. The acreage of flax sown fluctuates widely, and the remaining energies of the people are devoted to the raising (in the higher regions) or fattening of beef and young dairy cattle, of which there is some export to Britain. Dairying is also practiced, especially in Fermanagh.

The southern and eastern parts of the Republic present a happier picture than does the congested Gaeltacht. Farms are larger, and population densities lower. The land is mainly pastoral. Dairying predominates in the southwest, stock fattening in the eastern Central Plain. Sheep rearing and fattening is common in the Hercynian and Caledonian massifs. There is, however, a wide variety of local products, and specialization is nowhere excessive.

Ireland's agricultural surplus goes almost wholly to Britain, on whom she is dependent for imports of coal and many industrial products.

The Urban Landscape: Industrialization

Britain has been an industrialized nation since medieval times, when her woolen textiles began to figure largely in international and domestic trade. The Industrial Revolution began in Britain, a country rich in coal and mechanical skills. Well ahead of her nearest rivals, Britain became in the mid-nineteenth century the workshop of the world. She pioneered in the development of the locomotive, textile machinery, the iron ship, and the Bessemer and open-hearth steel processes. In a brief century, Britain changed from the peaceful, agrarian aristocracy depicted in the pages of Addison and Steele into an arrogant industrial empire whose ships carried the world's commerce, whose capital city was the financial center of the earth, and whose exports of manufactured goods poured forth in a steady stream to all the world's markets.

She remains a modern, industrialized society. Her early start, however, has had unfortunate repercussions. The men who captained the nineteenth-century industrial expansion had little thought for the well-being of the vast new proletariat that flocked into the cities. These cities became squalid, overcrowded, and gloomy, and today present abundant problems to the city planner. Much of Britain's industrial plant is old or obsolescent, and an endless program of modernization lies before her industrialists. Her markets dwindled as manufacturing industries sprang up overseas. Two wars have also disrupted her economy. Nevertheless, the United Kingdom remains a great industrial power, second only to the United States in the Western world's commerce.

The Irish Republic, in contrast, has virtually no heavy industry and only one industrial center of any size—Dublin. The Republic's poverty is traceable mainly to her shortage of power. She has practically no coal and too little hydroelectric power.

Coal. Coal lies at the root of Britain's industrial eminence. Her reserves and present fields lie distributed in several large and many smaller basins on the flanks of the Highland Zone in England and Wales, and in the Midland Valley of Scotland. Workable reserves will last for about 400 to 500 years at current rates of consumption. But certain types such as high-quality coking coal will be exhausted long before then unless they are eked out by blending with other types. The coal is mostly bituminous, though there is some anthracite in South Wales. Steam and coking coals are both available in quantity. The disposition of the individual basins has been indicated in Fig. 3–1.

In 1957, production was 227 million metric tons. The coal was raised by about 285,000 miners and 425,000 other colliery workers employed by the National Coal Board, the publicly owned monopoly established since World War II to operate the mines. In postwar years much difficulty was found in maintaining adequate levels of production. In 1938, 231 million metric tons were raised, of which 47 million metric tons were exported or used in foreign ships; the prewar economy was in fact adjusted to a large export of coal, chiefly to France, Eire, Argentina, and the Scandinavian countries. Production during the war declined seriously due to a variety of factors, of which the most significant were (1) an aging and diminishing labor force, it being difficult to persuade young men to enter the collieries; (2) the rapid exhaustion of the more accessible seams, especially of good coking coal, in great demand today; (3) poor techniques of extraction, including a low degree of mechanization; (4) poor pit-head conditions, wages, and housing for the miners; and (5) embittered labor relations. These and other factors, notably the folded or faulted character of the coal seams, which rendered mechanization difficult, had reduced productivity to a very low ebb. In 1947, during an unprecedented cold spell which disrupted transport, reserves were exhausted, and industry was paralyzed for two weeks.[25]

Successive investigating committees had recommended national ownership as the only solution of these difficulties, and in 1945 this advice was put into effect, when the policy was no longer politically controversial. Despite much-publicized differences and labor disputes, the industry has recovered remarkably, the 1957 production being 14 per cent greater than that of 1946. Exports have been resumed, amounting to over 6.7 million metric tons in 1957. These results are being achieved by a tremendous program of rehabilitation that still has far to go. Mechanization, recruitment of a larger labor force, better pit-head conditions, and better pay for the miners are some of the devices employed. Efforts are also being made to close old, uneconomical shafts and shift production to newer fields, like the concealed part of the Yorks-Derby-Nottingham field and the Fife and Lothian fields in Scotland. There has also been a large-scale development of open-pit mining.

The largest producing field is that of Yorks-Derby-Nottingham, on which is located the large concentration of industrial population associated with the textile industries of the West Riding, the heavy metallurgical industries of Sheffield and Rotherham, and many smaller activities. The concealed coal field east of the older area of mining is the most active area of recent development; deep shafts sunk through the overlying Mesozoic sediments reach the coal seams. The pit heads of many of these collieries are surrounded by the oaks of Sherwood Forest, famed as the home of Robin Hood.

South Wales and the Northumberland-Durham fields have much in common. Both are very near the coast, and both have contributed much in the past to the export trade. Each is famous for special types of coal—South Wales for steam coal and anthracite, Durham for

[25] For statistical tables, see Appendix III.

coking coal. Heavy metallurgical industries and a large industrial population characterize both areas.

The remaining fields are smaller, though several are associated with major concentrations of industry. Thus the Lanarkshire and Ayrshire fields (the latter being largely worked out) have long supplied Glasgow and Clydeside, the great centers of the shipbuilding industry; South Lancashire has begotten Manchester and the cotton-textile industry; the North Staffordshire field is the site of Stoke-on-Trent, which concentrates 75–80 per cent of the British pottery industry, including the celebrated Wedgwood plant; the multifarious metallurgical and engineering works of Birmingham lie near the Black Country field of South Staffordshire. It becomes clear, therefore, that the great bulk of British industry and nearly all the major centers of population lie on or near the coal fields. London, the national capital and greatest seaport, is the only striking exception in England, though in Ireland neither Belfast nor Dublin has nearby coal.

Coal, apart from imported oil and gasoline, is the only important fuel in Britain. Electricity, the demand for which is increasing rapidly, is 98 per cent coal-generated; hydroelectric installations (in Wales and Scotland) contribute only about 2.3 per cent. In recent years about a fifth of the national output has been converted to electricity, and more than a fourth consumed in coal-gas plants or coke ovens. Domestic consumers receive half of the present output of coal gas in Great Britain, almost all in Northern Ireland.

Steel. If coal is the motivating force of British industry, steel is its indispensable raw material. Iron manufacture has a long history in Britain; the local ores have been smelted since pre-Roman times, and the modern techniques of steel making had their origin here. Though she has since been eclipsed by the United States, Germany, and the Soviet Union, Britain has remained a major producer and is at present expanding her output rapidly. High-quality alloy steels and special finishes are a specialization. Until recently, production was largely in the hands of large, vertically integrated companies. Under the Iron and Steel Act of 1949 the industry passed into public ownership in 1951 and was administered by a public corporation. The Conservative government elected in October, 1951, returned the industry to private hands.

The raw materials of the industry—coal, ore, and limestone—are bulky, and their producing areas are highly localized. British ores are largely of low iron content, and of the bedded type. Most of them are extracted from the Jurassic cuestas of Yorkshire, Lincolnshire, and Northamptonshire. Much of the needed ore is imported, by far the largest port of entry being Middlesbrough. Most of the steel industry now carries on its operations with basic open-hearth converters.

The producing areas are mostly on or near coal fields, the cost of coal transportation being the determining factor. In many instances, the smelting of pig iron was originally based on Coal Measure iron ores (as in South Wales, the Black Country, and Clydeside). These are largely worked out, and nearly all blast furnaces use Jurassic or imported ores. The largest producing centers are Clydeside (Glasgow, Coatbridge, Motherwell, etc.), supplying the local shipbuilding and engineering industries; Teeside (Middlesbrough); South Yorkshire and Derbyshire (Rotherham, Sheffield, and Chesterfield); and South Staffordshire and South Wales (the Swansea area, Cardiff, and Ebbw Vale). The Scunthorpe (Lincolnshire) and Northamptonshire plants are unusual in being located on the ore body rather than on the coal field.

High cost, high quality, and local specialization characterize the industry. Thus the Swansea district is largely concerned with the needs of the local tin-plate industry, now undergoing expansion. Sheffield—a famous name among steelmen—is a steel-making town, having no blast furnaces. For centuries, it has specialized in quality work and has become the home of (among other types) high-grade alloy steels, Sheffield stainless being an example, based in part on imported pure iron. The nearby Coal Measure grit allowed a grinding industry, and the valleys behind Sheffield have long specialized in cutlery.

The Non-ferrous Metals. The non-ferrous metals, though less bulky and less central to the economy, are essential to the steel and engineering industries. Aluminum, copper, lead, tin, zinc, nickel, and many less common metals are produced largely from imported semi-refined concentrates rather than the crude ore. Birmingham is the chief center, concentrating especially on brass and aluminum ware; over 40 per cent of the labor engaged in these industries work in this city and the surrounding satellite towns. Birmingham is unique among the world's great cities (it has over 1,103,000 inhabitants) in being built on a drainage divide (which accounts, incidentally, for the early date on which it was served by canals). No one geographical factor can account for this specialization at Birmingham. Today the district has one of Britain's greatest concentrations of the engineering industries, and a ready market for semifinished and finished non-ferrous articles is close at hand.

Other major centers of this complex group of industries are the London district (where again there is an immense local market and an accessible port), South Lancashire, the West Riding of Yorkshire, and South Wales.

The Engineering Industries. The engineering industries represent the other end of the scale of heavy industry. Here again there is a long tradition of skill, and British engineers—especially the Scots— have penetrated every corner of the earth, as have their products. In recent years technical precedence and the greater part of the world's market have passed into American hands, but the British engineer was never busier than he is today. A very wide variety of finished metal goods is produced, and the industry is widely distributed. Nevertheless, certain marked concentrations are visible:

1. Shipbuilding is concentrated on a number of estuaries. Between 1945 and 1957, Britain has provided 1.4 million tons out of 8.5 million tons launched; in 1956 alone, 417,177 gross metric tons were launched at Clydeside (the Glasgow region), which in prewar days launched the "Queens" and many other liners. The Tyne (with 221,000 tons), the Wear (184,000), and the Tees (106,000) were the next group, launching chiefly colliers and tankers. Belfast (99,000) has long specialized in the smaller liners, motor ships, and refrigerated vessels. There are smaller yards at Merseyside and at Barrow-in-Furness. A large marine-engineering industry supports each of these regions, especially in the Glasgow district. The industry has recently suffered from West German and Japanese competition.

2. Textile machinery is a marked specialization of the South Lancashire and West Riding coal fields, where it feeds the large local textile industry.

3. The heavy constructional and automotive industries—bridges, locomotives, armaments, automobiles, etc.—are typical of the Scottish lowlands (especially near the great firths), Manchester and South Lancashire, Birmingham and the Black Country, and the Yorks-Derby-Nottingham coal field. Britain is a large exporter of automobiles, most of which come from Birmingham, Coventry, and Oxford. Bicycles, popular in Europe, come chiefly from the Midland area.

4. Specialized light engineering, though widely disseminated, is increasingly concentrated in the London district, which is also the center of the new "luxury" industries; London is surrounded by hundreds of new plants producing a thousand-and-one small products which reach the country's largest market with ease.

Textiles. These industries, the last for which we can offer details, are among Britain's oldest skills. Using her traditional and home-produced raw material, wool, her craftsmen had created for themselves a high reputation before the Industrial Revolution. It was in the textile industries that this Revolution really began, when successive inventions in the late eighteenth century made possible the use of power, first from water mills and then from James Watt's steam engine. The traditional industries were widely dispersed, in the southern Pennine valleys, in East Anglia (the early home of worsteds), in the Cotswolds, and in southwest England. With the advent of steam power and factory manufacture, however, the districts remote from coal either expired or specialized, and today production is concentrated overwhelmingly in South Lancashire (cottons) and the West Riding of Yorkshire (woolens and worsteds). Smaller areas of production are the Glasgow district (cottons) and Belfast (cottons, poplins, and linen). All the raw cotton and most of the wool and flax required are imported.

The specialization on cotton in South Lancashire dates from the early eighteenth century. Here there is soft water, a naturally high humidity, abundant coal for power (and, in earlier times, waterpower), and the largest concentration of the country's chemical industries, on the salt deposits of nearby Cheshire. From this center British cottons grew to great significance in the national economy, and were the largest export (by value) from the late nineteenth century until World War II. In recent years, however, stiff competition in the Asiatic markets from cheaper Japanese and Indian cottons has severely restricted this trade, and the industry has been chronically depressed. The plants are usually old and mechanically inefficient by comparison with those, for example, of the United States Piedmont. A large-scale program of rehabilitation is now proceeding, much of it concerned with the installation of automatic looms. The volume of exports in 1957 was only half of that of 1949 and only a fourth of the prewar level of 1935–38.

There are three distinct areas of specialization. Spinning of yarn from raw cotton is concentrated at the headwaters of the Mersey tributaries, north of Manchester, in and around the towns of Bolton and Oldham. Weaving of cloth takes place in the Colne and Ribble valleys, farther north, the largest centers being Burnley, Blackburn, Preston, Nelson, and Colne. Finishing—largely a chemical process—takes place in and around Manchester-Salford, the commercial and technological capital of the industry.

The concentration of woolen and worsted manufactures at the West Riding of Yorkshire is equally emphatic; the Aire and Calder valleys are the scenes of the largest production, which was originally based on local wool and an abundance of waterpower. More recently, soft water (from the outcrop of the Millstone Grit on the Pennines) and the local supply of coal have been the significant localizing influences; the inheritance of traditional skills and the absence of a competing metallurgical industry (which excludes the industry from the Sheffield-Rotherham district, equally suitable on most other counts) have also assisted. The largest producing center is Bradford, in many ways the Manchester of the wool trade. Halifax, Huddersfield, Dewsbury, Keighley, and Wakefield are other large centers. Leeds is in some degree the commercial capital of the West Riding, but plays little role in the woolen and worsted trades at the weaving stage; the city concentrates, however, a large fraction of the clothing trade.[26]

Like cottons, woolen goods have long figured very large in the British export trade. Stiff overseas competition has been experienced in recent years, but the high quality of British cloth has maintained her position. Stress is laid upon exclusive lines of pattern and color, but the range of types is wide, extending from tweeds—of which the Harris tweed is a well-known example—to tropical worsteds. In 1957, 103.8 million square yards (86.8 million square meters) of woven piece goods were exported, a figure much larger than that for 1938, the last prewar year. Considerable modernization of plant is in progress, and efforts are being made to compete vigorously in the cheap-cloth field.

Linen—the raw material of which is the field crop flax—is another textile in which the United Kingdom has long dominated the world market. Spinning and weaving of linen were formerly widespread in Britain, and some production is still active in the eastern part of the Midland Valley of Scotland. The industry has become concentrated, however, in Ulster and especially in Belfast. Flax grown locally normally supplies about 10 per cent of the demand, and the rest is imported. In 1957, linen amounted to about 13 per cent of Northern Ireland's exports, by value. Londonderry has a large production of finished linen and cotton goods, especially shirts.

It remains to be added that Great Britain, like most other countries, has witnessed the development in the past twenty years of large-scale artificial-fiber manufactures such as rayon and nylon. The largest producing areas tend to lie within the older textile provinces, notably for example, the North Lancashire district.

Communications

Overseas Shipping nd the Ports. The British merchant marine comprises almost a fifth of the world's shipping. A large fraction of the nation's overseas earnings has come during the past century from

---

[26] The West Riding landscape in many ways exemplifies industrial Britain. See S. H. Beaver, "The West Riding," part 46 of L. D. Stamp (ed.), *The Land of Britain, op. cit.*

carrying the commerce of other nations; the British tramp steamer carrying anything to and from anywhere has been an indispensable element in world transportation. The importance and heavy bulk of Britain's own overseas trade is a further guarantee of her maritime activity. Her losses in shipping during World War II amounted to no less than 12,000,000 metric tons, yet her merchant fleet today exceeds 19,857,000 gross registered tons, largely the result of rapid launching of new vessels.

Britain has numerous ports, as befits a trading nation. Many of them suffered considerable damage during the war from air raids, though in few cases was the damage serious enough to render the port inoperative even for a few days. Much-needed programs of renovation, especially of warehouse and transshipment facilities, have since been completed. Six ports—London, Liverpool, Hull, Manchester, Southampton, and Glasgow—now do 75 per cent of the total business in terms of value, 60 per cent of all foreign business in terms of tonnage.

London, discussed as a city below, is much the largest port, concentrating about a third of the overseas trade. The Thames estuary provides a deep, easy approach. The outer docks (for large shipping) are at Tilbury, in Essex, but most of the shipping comes right into the East End of the city. Though there are numerous wharves, much of the unloading is carried out by lighters and barges, which transfer the imported goods into warehouses that line the Thames for miles below (and even above) Tower Bridge. The commerce of the port is extremely varied, but especially noteworthy are the imports of perishable foodstuffs, for which London, with its warehouses and cold-storage facilities, is much the biggest port (Fig. 3–12).

Liverpool, the second port, handles over a fifth of the overseas trade in terms of value, ranks third in terms of tonnage, and is the principal transatlantic port. It is above all the Atlantic port of the industrialized north of England and the Midlands. The port is built at the mouth of the Mersey estuary (which has completely replaced Chester on the Dee as the main Irish Sea harbor); on the Lancashire shore is Liverpool itself, but there are also docks on the Cheshire shore in the large urban areas of Birkenhead and Wallasey.

Hull ranks eighth in terms of tonnage and fourth in terms of value. It stands on the north shore of the Humber estuary and has easy communications with the industrial north, especially the West Riding of Yorkshire. It has varied interests. Much of its connection has been with northern Europe, but it also has a large coastwise trade and an immense trawling fleet. The wool for the West Riding textile belt is largely landed at Hull, though surprisingly enough the greater part is transshipped coastwise from London, the main port of entry.

Manchester ranks seventh in terms of tonnage and third in terms of value. It is an inland city linked to the Mersey estuary by the 35-mile-long privately owned ship canal completed in 1894. The canal has 28 feet of water over the lock sills and allows ordinary cargo vessels to reach the port.

Fig. 3–12. The Royal Victoria, Royal Albert, and King George docks. The barges and lighters that form so pronounced a feature of cargo handling are much in evidence.

Southampton, fifth in the value of commerce and second in terms of tonnage, is the chief passenger port and the normal starting point of passenger ships to all western and southern destinations, including the important transatlantic traffic. Southampton Water is reached from the English Channel from either east or west by the Solent, a drowned river valley sheltered on the south by the Isle of Wight. The double entry is enhanced by a double high tide, a valuable adjunct in the handling of large ships, though even at low tide there is 35 feet of water.

Glasgow, the remaining large port, is approached by the beautiful Firth of Clyde. It is the great port of lowland Scotland and has an active export trade in heavy engineering goods. Other chief ports are Bristol, Newcastle, and Harwich.

Inland Communications. Land transportation in Great Britain is now under the administration of the British Transport Commission, set up on January 1, 1948, to integrate road, rail, and canal services. In Northern Ireland the Ulster Transport Authority, also established in 1948, has similar powers. In the Irish Republic, however, inland transportation has been under the merged *Coras Iompair Eireann* for a longer period.

Rail and road penetrate every corner of inhabited Britain, and traffic densities are very high. There is scarcely a point in the settled area of the country more than five miles from a railway. The railway system is now nationally owned and is known as "British Railways"; administration is carried on within regions that resemble both in name and extent the old independent systems. Nearly all the main-line trackage is two-, three-, or four-tracked, and both speeds and traffic densities are high. Most passenger movement is by rail for long hauls, and there is also an extraordinarily dense suburban traffic, especially in the London area. The motive power is still largely steam, though diesel power is rapidly replacing it. There is a large mileage of electric propulsion, chiefly in the south; London is linked to the coast at Portsmouth, Brighton, and Eastbourne by frequent electric services that have brought many of the beach resorts within commuter range, though they are 50 to 60 miles from London.

The Irish railways present a less satisfactory picture. Northern Ireland is well served from Belfast and Londonderry by the old Northern Counties Committee lines, which were owned and operated by the L.M.S.R., a British company. The Great Northern links Belfast and Dublin, and has a large mileage on both sides of the border. Formerly privately owned, it is now publicly owned. Main-line services in the rest of the Republic are over the tracks of the Great Southern, Midland Great Western, and other former lines; there have been many abandonments of minor trackage.

Roads throughout Great Britain are hard surfaced, and the network is astonishingly dense. Much the same is true of Ireland, though some western districts are less accessible. In both islands truck and bus transportation have made considerable headway, and have created serious competition for the railways.

The British canal systems (except for the Manchester Ship Canal) are old, narrow, and shallow. Though they carried over 10.5 million metric tons in 1950, most of them are little used, and many have been allowed to fall into disrepair. A limited program of rehabilitation is in progress.

The Four Capitals

It is fitting that we should glance finally at the four capital cities of the British Isles: London, Edinburgh, Belfast, and Dublin. Wales is remarkable in having no true capital and no focal point in its communications system; it has been truly said that a future Welsh parliament, if one is ever convened, would have to meet in some border town like Wrexham or Shrewsbury if the legislators were to get there with a minimum of fatigue! The grain of the country renders any internal site difficult of access; good Welsh routeways lead to England.

London, home of the Crown, seat of the United Kingdom government, and center of the sterling bloc, the Commonwealth, and a host of other organizations, is perhaps the world's greatest city. Today it is challenged by New York, both in function and in population, but it has no other peers. It is a vast, sprawling, but attractive city lacking any formal plan—unlike Paris and Berlin—but possessing an appeal that some others lack. Its status as a city arises not merely from its governmental functions but from its role as the nation's leading port; from the commercial, financial, and legal power of the City's institutions; from the vast new industries that have sprung up on its outskirts; and from the intangible appeal of its cultural and intellectual eminence, to say nothing of the power to entertain in theaters, cinemas, restaurants, and bars.

The old core of the town, on a gravel terrace which provided the lowest feasible bridging point over the Thames, is still identifiable as the "City," in whose half a square mile are concentrated most of the banks, the insurance houses—including Lloyds—the Royal Exchange, and St. Paul's Cathedral, as well as the headquarters of a large part of Britain's commercial and industrial empire. The shopping and entertainment districts lie two miles or more to the west, around Charing Cross, Trafalgar Square, Piccadilly Circus, and Oxford Street. Westminster, a mile upstream from Charing Cross, is the home of government. Around this differentiated center sprawls a densely populated ring of boroughs, residential and industrial, and still farther out a forest of new houses served by the electrified lines of London Transport and the southern lines of British Railways.

Edinburgh is the traditional capital of Scotland; today it houses many of the administrative branches of Scottish government, as well as the official seat of the Crown in Scotland. It is a handsome town on a striking site overlooking the Firth of Forth. The Castle and much of the old town lie on a steep, volcanic hill, whereas the chief shopping districts—of which Princes Street is renowned—lie on another ridge to the north. Between them is a deep valley unfortunately occupied by the partially concealed main line of the old London and North-Eastern Railway, and its Waverley Station. In spite of everything that the twentieth century has done to ruin it, the heart of Edinburgh remains one of the sights of Europe. In recent years, the town has been the site of an annual festival of music and drama that bids fair to outdo Salzburg.

Belfast is not so much a traditional capital as a modern industrial city. Nevertheless, it is the site of the Northern Ireland government and is closely identified with the Orange movement and the cause of Protestant Ireland. It is also the site of Queen's University.

Dublin dominates the life of the Irish Republic as Vienna does that of Austria. There are no competitors among the smaller towns of this rural country. Its harbor affords the natural gateway to the Central Lowland and was recognized as such by the Norsemen who established the town and by Normans who captured it in the twelfth century. Thenceforward it was the English capital of Ireland. They established its cathedrals, its old university (Trinity College), and the great castle that still dominates the city. In the eighteenth and nineteenth centuries the modern city was laid out by Georgian architects, whose broad streets, terraced houses, and formal squares gave the city an air of spacious dignity that it has never lost. Today it is the seat of the president and government of the Republic, and of the administrative machinery of both government and finance. The large industrialization it has undergone during the past century has created behind the Georgian terraces a welter of slums, and overcrowding is a perennial problem. Nevertheless, the city retains a real beauty and fascination.

*   *   *

In common with other west-European nations, the United Kingdom and the Irish Republic have seen a fairly steady recovery in the years since the end of World War II. Although there have been monetary difficulties, chiefly with the stability of the pound and anxiety about dollar resources, the British Isles are now enjoying the highest living standards in their history. The geographer can take some pride in this, since it has involved the rational and intelligent use of that most precious asset, the land, and in this process the professional geographer has played a considerable part.

There remains one uncertainty—the place of Britain in Europe. From most of the recent cooperative moves among European nations toward economic union, so vital to the maintenance of peace, Britain has stood aloof. Her economic links with her own overseas territories and with the nations of the Commonwealth have seemed more important to her statesmen. Common-market schemes inevitably prejudice these special links, and thus Britain stands today where she has stood so often in the past—on the brink of Europe, rather than wholeheartedly within it. This decision has exposed her industries to stiff competition in European markets, and it may ultimately be reversed through *force majeure*. Still, however, she remains a world power rather than a pan-European nation; and there is as yet no sign that she will relinquish this position unless compelled.

BIBLIOGRAPHY

(Major references are asterisked.)

Books in English

*Bilham, Ernest G. *The Climate of the British Isles*. London: Macmillan & Co., Ltd., 1938.

Clapham, Sir John Harold. *A Concise Economic History of Britain from the Earliest Times to 1750*. London: Cambridge University Press, 1949.

Court, W. H. B. *A Concise Economic History of Britain from 1750 to Recent Times*. London: Cambridge University Press, 1955.

*Darby, H. Clifford (ed.). *Historical Geography of England Before 1800*. London: Cambridge University Press, 1936.

Demangeon, Albert. *The British Isles*. Translated by E. D. Laborde. London: William Heinemann, Ltd., 1939 (original French edition 1927).

Ekwall, Eilert. *The Concise Oxford Dictionary of English Place-Names* (3d ed.). New York: Oxford University Press, 1947.

Fox, C. *The Personality of Britain: Its Influence on Inhabitant and Invader in Prehistoric and Early Historic Times*. Cardiff: National Museum of Wales, 1933.

*Freeman, Thomas W. *Ireland*. London: Methuen & Co., Ltd., 1950.

*Great Britain. *Monthly Digest and Annual Abstracts of Statistics*. London: H. M. Stationery Office.

Great Britain, Chancellor of the Exchequer. *Economic Survey*. Published annually. London: H. M. Stationery Office.

Great Britain, Department of Scientific and Industrial Research, Geological Survey. *British Regional Geology* (2d ed.). Eighteen regional monographs on British rocks and structure. London: H. M. Stationery Office, 1948.

Great Britain, Ministry of Agriculture and Fisheries. *National Farm Survey of England and Wales*. London: H. M. Stationery Office, 1946.

*Hadfield, Charles. *British Canals: An Illustrated History*. London: Readers Union, 1952.

*Hoskins, W. G. *The Making of the English Landscape*. London: Hodder & Stoughton, Ltd., 1957.

JONES, LL. RODWELL. *The Geography of London River.* London: Methuen & Co., Ltd., 1931.

*MACKINDER, HALFORD J. *Britain and the British Seas.* New York: Appleton-Century-Crofts, Inc., 1902.

OGILVIE, ALAN G. (ed.). *Great Britain: Essays in Regional Geography.* London: Cambridge University Press, 1930.

SMITH, WILFRED. *An Economic Geography of Great Britain.* London: Methuen & Co., Ltd., 1949.

*STAMP, L. DUDLEY. *British Structure and Scenery.* London: William Collins Sons & Co., Ltd., 1946.

————. *The Land of Britain: Its Use and Misuse.* London: Longmans, Green & Co., Ltd., 1948.

*————. *Man and the Land.* London: William Collins Sons & Co., Ltd., 1955.

————. (ed.). *The Land of Britain.* Report of the Land Utilisation Survey of Britain. London: Geographical Publications, Ltd., 1943–46.

*STAMP, L. DUDLEY, and BEAVER, S. H. *The British Isles* (4th ed.). London: Longmans, Green & Co., Ltd., 1954.

TANSLEY, ARTHUR G. *The British Islands and Their Vegetation.* London: Cambridge University Press, 1939.

WOOLDRIDGE, SIDNEY W., and LINTON, DAVID L. *Structure, Surface, and Drainage in South East England.* London: George Philip & Son, Ltd., The London Geographical Institute, 1939.

Articles

DARBY, H. CLIFFORD. "The Changing English Landscape," *Geographical Journal* 117 (1951): 377–98.

————. "Some Early Ideas on the Agricultural Regions of England," *Agricultural History Review* 2 (1954): 30–47.

EMBLETON, C. "Some Stages in the Drainage Evolution of Part of North-East Wales," *Transactions and Papers: Institute of British Geographers* 23 (1957): 19–35.

MAXWELL, I. S. "The Geographical Identification of Domesday Vills," *Transactions and Papers: Institute of British Geographers* 16 (1950): 97–121.

SIMPSON, E. S. "Milk Production in England and Wales," *Geographical Review* 49 (1959): 95–111.

SMITH, WILFRED. "The Location of Industry," *Transactions and Papers: Institute of British Geographers* 21 (1955): 1–18.

4

Northern Europe

If asked to define "Northern Europe" as a region, many persons would have only the haziest notion as to which countries should be included. Most of them would certainly begin by naming the Scandinavian countries, that is, Norway, Sweden, and Denmark, but which other nations to include (if any) would be a point of serious debate. In the following chapter, therefore, the author has chosen to define Northern Europe in terms of an areal concept which long has been an integral part of Scandinavian geographical thought: the so-called *Norden* concept.

The term itself means simply "the North," but in this connection is specifically intended to designate five nations in Northern Europe which are more closely related to one another than they are to any of the countries surrounding them. They are the three Scandinavian countries, together with Iceland and Finland. A sixth area, the Faeroes, while constituting an administrative part of Denmark, is usually regarded as a distinct geographic unit within the region.

The *Norden* concept derives its validity not so much from the facts of physical geography as it does from those of cultural and historical geography. To demonstrate this point one need only cite a few of the characteristics which distinguish the countries of Northern Europe as a regional group. They are, for example, all nations of relatively small populations, the ethnic and linguistic compositions of which are both simple and uniform. In fact, the same ethnic and linguistic stock finds representation in all five countries, though in one of them it exists only as a minority. Moreover, the overwhelming majority of the peoples profess the same religious faith.

In each of these nations illiteracy has long since been abolished and the regional standards of education, health, and sanitation can scarcely be equaled elsewhere on the continent. Though their resources are neither varied nor abundant, the nations of Northern Europe have achieved a level of economic well-being which is among the highest in the world. Because there are no great discrepancies in the distribution of their national wealth, these countries are often regarded as working models of economic democracy. In the field of social legislation the nations of Northern Europe are outstanding pioneers, having long set the pace for the rest of the world. Though three of them retain a monarchial form of government, they all have well-established traditions of political freedom and democracy. Also, despite an earlier history marked by bloodshed and violence, the nations of Northern Europe have demonstrated such exemplary harmony and cooperation in the conduct of international affairs for the last century, that the region as a whole has come to be called "Europe's quiet corner." When seen in the light of such considerations, Northern Europe will be appreciated as a distinct geographic region with a character and qualities of its own.

THE PHYSICAL LANDSCAPE

Location, Size, and Configuration

The region of Northern Europe occupies a position in the Old World which is almost directly comparable to that of Alaska in the New World. Its southern border, the Danish-West German boundary, is situated in the same latitude as the southern tip of the Alaskan Panhandle (55° N.), while the North Cape of Norway, the northernmost point of continental Europe, is located on the same parallel as Point Barrow (71° N.). Longitudinally these two regions show a similar correspondence, for the distance is just as great from the eastern boundary of Finland to the western extremity of Iceland as it is from the Alaskan Panhandle to the outermost islands of the Aleutian chain. When the Norwegian islands of Spitsbergen (Svalbard) are included, however, the plane of reference must be altered, for the only regions in the New World which are located at a corresponding latitude (namely 74°–81° N.) are the northernmost islands of the Canadian archipelago and the northern quarter of Greenland.

In point of size, Northern Europe is about seven-eighths as large as Alaska. With an area of nearly 500,000 square miles, it constitutes just over one-eighth of the European land mass and has close to 19 million people. Unlike Alaska, however, Northern Europe is not a single, relatively unbroken expanse of land (Fig. 4–1). Instead, it is a region of peninsulas and islands, each separated from the other by

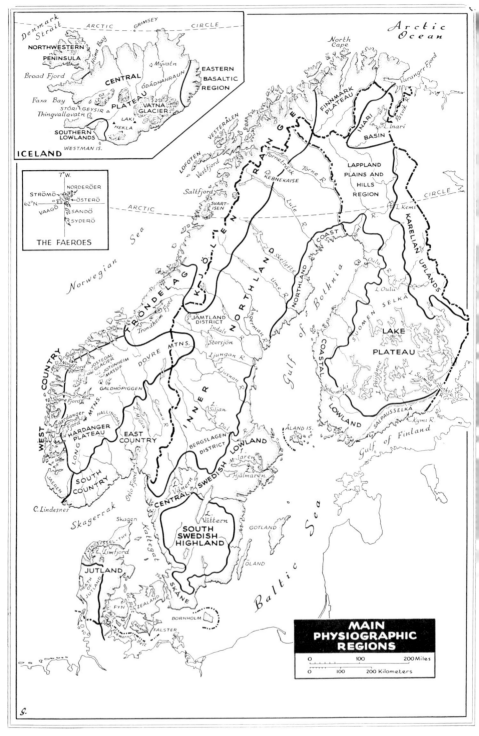

Fig. 4–1. Main physiographic regions.

varying widths of open sea. By far the largest continuous land mass in Northern Europe is what we may call the Fenno-Scandinavian peninsula. Joined to the subcontinent along a front extending from the Gulf of Finland to the White Sea, this compound neck of land stretches northward between the Gulf of Bothnia and the White Sea and then mushrooms out into the Scandinavian peninsula (which extends 1,200 miles to the southwest) and the Kola Peninsula (which extends some 300 miles to the east). The fact that this appendage is divided politically among Finland, the Soviet Union, Norway, and Sweden in no way detracts from either the physical continuity or the essentially peninsular character of the area as a whole. Northern Europe's only other land contact with the subcontinent is the peninsula of Jutland in Denmark. Owing to its location, this peninsula has been infinitely more important as a link between the northern countries and the remainder of Europe than the broader but less accessible Fenno-Scandinavian peninsula.

Apart from these two peninsulas, however, Northern Europe has no physical continuity, for its remaining areas are composed of islands. Among these are Iceland and the Faeroes in the Atlantic, Spitsbergen and Jan Mayen in the Arctic, the Danish archipelago and the Swedish islands of Gotland and Öland in the Baltic, and the Åland Archipelago at the entrance to the Gulf of Bothnia. As a consequence of this peninsular and insular configuration, Northern Europe stands somewhat apart from the rest of the subcontinent. This relative isolation has in turn played an important role in the historical and cultural development of the region and in large part explains the sense of community which exists between these nations today. A brief introductory description of the individual countries follows.

Norway. The Kingdom of Norway occupies the western and northern sides of the Scandinavian peninsula, extending through 13° of latitude and 26° of longitude. Lindesnes, its most southerly point, is located in the same latitude as Juneau, Alaska, while its northernmost extremity, North Cape, is situated on the same parallel as Point Barrow. The country has an extremely attenuated shape, stretching some 1,100 miles from north to south. From a maximum width of 280 miles near 61° latitude, it constricts to less than 4 miles near 68° (measured from the Swedish border to the head of Tys Fjord) and then broadens out again to 160 miles in the Finnmark Plateau in the far north. If embayments are not included, its coast line measures about 2,100 miles, but if they are reckoned in, this figure rises to 12,500 miles, or roughly half the circumference of the earth. On its landward sides Norway is bounded by Sweden in the east (1,025 miles) and by Finland and the Soviet Union in the northeast (452

and 125 miles, respectively). Its total area is 124,556 square miles
(slightly larger than the state of New Mexico), of which almost
10,000 square miles are made up by the 150,000 islands and skerries
which line its coasts. In addition to its continental area, Norway has
sovereignty over Spitsbergen and Jan Mayen in Arctic waters and
Peter I and Bouvet islands in the South Atlantic. Norway also claims
a portion of the Antarctic continent under the name of Queen Maud
Land.

Sweden. The Kingdom of Sweden is situated on the eastern side
of the Scandinavian peninsula. Its shores face the Gulf of Bothnia
in the north, the Baltic Sea in the southeast, the Skagerrak and
Kattegat in the southwest, and the Sound (Öresund) separates it from
Denmark. Like Norway, it has an elongated shape, extending 975
miles from north to south and 310 miles from west to east at its widest
point. Its coast line measures about 1,600 miles in length, embayments excluded. On its landward sides it is bordered by Norway in
the west (1,025 miles) and Finland in the northeast (332 miles).
With a total area of 173,035 square miles, of which 158,450 are land,
Sweden is the fourth largest country in Europe and is slightly larger
than the state of California.

Finland. The Republic of Finland is situated east of the Gulf of
Bothnia and north of the Gulf of Finland. The total length of its
coast line along these bodies of water is about 680 miles, embayments
not included. On its landward sides Finland is bounded by Sweden in
the northwest (332 miles), Norway in the north (452 miles), and the
Soviet Union in the east (787 miles).

Like both Norway and Sweden, Finland has an elongated shape,
measuring over 700 miles between its northern and southern extremities. Except for the northernmost tip of Lappland and the Hangö
(Hanko) Peninsula in the southwest, the entire country lies between
60° and 70° north latitude. With a total area of 130,125 square miles,
of which 117,935 are land (somewhat larger than the combined areas
of Michigan and Wisconsin), Finland is the sixth largest country in
Europe (Fig. 4–1).

Denmark. The Kingdom of Denmark is located between the
North and Baltic seas and is composed of the peninsula of Jutland
(Jylland) and the islands lying to the east of it. At the same time it
commands the sea approaches to the Baltic and the southern land
approaches to the Scandinavian peninsula. In such a key position,
Denmark can truly be called the "Crossroads of Northern Europe."

The largest continuous land area in the country is the peninsula
of Jutland, which totals 9,186 square miles. Lying just north of it

across the Lim Fjord is the island of Vendsyssel-Thy, which for all intents and purposes can be considered a part of the peninsula itself. Together, their combined areas total 11,410 square miles, or roughly two-thirds that of the entire country. On the west they face the North Sea, on the north the Skagerrak, and on the east the Kattegat. Near the base of the peninsula, Denmark shares a 42-mile land boundary with West Germany.

The Danish archipelago consists of some 480 islands, of which about 100 are inhabited. Most of them are very small, but together their areas come to 5,166 square miles. For the sake of convenience, we can consider them under three principal headings: (1) the Fyn group, (2) the Zealand group, and (3) Bornholm. The group centered on the island of Fyn is separated from the peninsula of Jutland by the Little Belt, a strait which is about a half mile wide at its narrowest point. On the east it is separated from the Zealand group by the Great Belt which averages 10 miles in width. This group in turn is separated from Sweden by the Sound, which constricts to a width of less than 4 miles near Helsingör. On the south both groups are separated from the German coast by the Fehmarn Belt. The most distant of the Danish home islands is Bornholm, about 90 miles east of Zealand and 25 miles off the coast of Sweden. Together the archipelago and the peninsula have an area of 16,576 square miles, or slightly less than the combined areas of Massachusetts and New Hampshire. The country's over-all coast line is 4,612 miles in length. Denmark also has sovereignty over the Faeroes and Greenland, in the North Atlantic.

Iceland. The most remote member of the European family of nations is the Republic of Iceland, lying just south of the Arctic Circle between 13° and 25° west longitude. Its nearest neighbor is Greenland, 200 miles to the west across the Denmark Strait, but it lies some 500 miles from the coast of Scotland and over 600 miles from the mainland of Norway. Despite this offside position with respect to the main currents of European life, Iceland served as a steppingstone to the West in the days of the Vikings and occupies a similar strategic position in the Air Age of today.

Roughly rectangular in shape, the island has a total area of 39,709 square miles (slightly less than the state of Virginia). Its coast line, about 3,600 miles long, is broken in the west by three large peninsulas and in the north and east by numerous fjords. Only the south coast is relatively unindented.

The Faeroes. Situated some 400 miles west of Norway and 250 miles southeast of Iceland are the Faeroes (Föroyar), located at 62°

north latitude and 7° west longitude. Composed of 18 larger islands and numerous skerries, the archipelago has a total area of 540 square miles, or roughly half that of Rhode Island.

Geologic Structure

Within the limits of Northern Europe, rocks of both the most ancient and most recent geologic ages are found. Over most of Finland and Sweden, the eastern portions of Norway, and the northern coast of the Danish island of Bornholm one finds resistant granites, gneisses, and schists which date from the Pre-Cambrian period.[1] These outcrops are remnants of the so-called Fenno-Scandian Shield (Baltic Shield). Though the surface of this region was originally warped into several extensive mountain systems, by the beginning of the Cambrian period these had been all but eroded away and reduced to a peneplain. From Cambrian to Silurian times large sections of this plain were invaded by epeiric seas (shallow seas of temporary duration) and vast areas were covered with fossil-bearing sediments. By far the greatest accumulation of sediments took place in the west, where a geosyncline, or trough, had developed. About the end of the Silurian period, the sediments in this trough were compressed, folded, and faulted into a vast mountain range which extended from Scotland northward through Norway and Spitsbergen to the northeastern coast of Greenland. After this mountain-building process (the so-called Caledonian orogeny) had subsided, the entire shield area was once more subjected to a prolonged period of erosion. Only in Spitsbergen and the region of southernmost Sweden and Denmark did any noteworthy deposition take place. In Spitsbergen all geologic ages from the Cambrian to the Tertiary are represented, but of greatest importance are the coal-bearing deposits of the Carboniferous period. In southern Sweden and in Denmark, beginning in the Mesozoic Age and continuing into the Cenozoic, thick layers of limestone and chalk were laid down.

During the Tertiary period, the North Atlantic area was convulsed by a great diastrophic upheaval in which the relative land and sea levels were considerably altered. In the west, great outpourings of lava built up an island which embraced large parts of present-day Iceland and central Greenland and may have extended from Jan Mayen in the north to the Faeroes in the south. Concurrent with the appearance of "Greater Iceland," as this island is known, was the faulting and sinking of the western and northern portions of the

---

[1] For geological terms, see Appendix I.

Fenno-Scandian Shield. As the land west of the present Norwegian coast sank into the sea, the land to the east was elevated once more, with the greatest rise taking place along the newly formed coast. This caused a rejuvenation of all the watercourses in the vicinity and particularly intensified the erosion on the western slope, which then fell abruptly into the sea. Here the steep gradient and copious moisture allowed the streams to cut into the peneplained plateau with such vigor as to capture several drainage basins from the less active southeastward-flowing rivers.

Scarcely had Greater Iceland appeared and the Scandinavian peninsula been re-elevated when vast snow fields began to accumulate in the higher districts of both regions, eventually consolidating into great ice sheets. In Iceland the advancing ice met strong opposition in the flame and fury of the continuing vulcanism. Further tectonic disturbances had already reduced the island to more nearly its present proportions, however, for there is evidence that the ice sheet which covered the Faeroes was purely local in nature. Here, what was originally a single basaltic block that was slightly tilted to the south and east was progressively cut along old fault lines, by the combined forces of ice and sea, into a number of smaller islands.

Over the remainder of Northern Europe the ice sheets alternately expanded and contracted several times, rounding off the resistant uplands and broadening the existing valleys and depressions. In Finland, Sweden, and Norway most of the surface mantle was carried away, while Denmark became the resting place for much of this glacial material. During the final glaciation, the edge of the ice remained stationary over central and southern Jutland for some time, building up an extensive terminal moraine. In Finland too, one finds evidence of a stationary ice lobe in the two great recessional moraines which parallel the south coast—the so-called *Salpausselkä* (ridge). As the glaciers finally melted back for the last time, the lower-lying areas were inundated by postglacial seas (forerunners of the modern Baltic and its appendages), while numerous lakes formed in the ice-scoured fissures of the interior. At the same time the areas which had been depressed so long by the great weight of the ice began rising back into isostatic balance. This process is still in operation over much of Scandinavia and can be noted most effectively on the Bothnian coasts of Finland and Sweden. Here, near the cities of Vaasa and Umeå, respectively, the rise amounts to about one foot in thirty years. Though the Pleistocene ice sheets have long since disappeared from northern Europe, several plateau and valley glaciers of more recent origin are to be found in the highlands of Scandinavia and Iceland.

The Regions of the North

Using its geologic structure as a basis, we can distinguish five major subdivisions within Northern Europe, each of which embraces one or more physiographic regions. They are (1) the Scandinavian mountains, (2) the Fenno-Scandian Shield, (3) Sweden's Baltic islands, (4) Denmark and Skåne, and (5) the Faeroes and Iceland.

The Scandinavian Mountains. Norway has fallen heir to most of Scandinavia's mountain backbone. Fully 72 per cent of its land area is composed of unproductive highland wastes of rock and swamp. In its various portions the mountain ridge is known by several local names. The southern part of the ridge is called the Long Mountains (Langfjellene) and separates the country into the East Country (Östlandet) on the east-facing slopes and the West Country (Vestlandet) on the western side. In the Jotunheim Massif, where the highest peaks are located (Galdhöpiggen—8,097 feet), the ridge turns in a more east-west direction and bears the name of Dovre Mountains (Dovrefjell), separating the East Country in the south from Tröndelag in the north. Here the main ridge is broken by the Tröndelag-Jämtland gap, but is resumed once again to the north as the Kjölen Range. Associated with this range is the mountain bulwark which makes up the Lofoten Islands and the coast of Finnmark. In its northern reaches, the main ridge of the Kjölen runs through Swedish territory, reaching its highest point in Kebnekaise, 6,965 feet. Finland's highest mountain, Haltiotunturi—4,344 feet, is likewise found in this section.

The Scandinavian mountains have a marked weather-divide effect, for they separate the distinctly maritime west coast from the more continental eastern interior. Thanks to the moderating influences of the North Atlantic Drift and the prevailing westerlies, winter temperatures average above freezing along the coast as far north as the Lofotens. Although the maximum precipitation in these coastal districts comes in winter, most of it falls as rain. Over the mountains and to the east, winter temperatures are considerably colder, so the moisture which falls at that season contributes to a deep and stable snow cover. Indeed, virtually all transmontane roads linking eastern and western Norway are blocked by snow from 6 to 7 months of the year. Everywhere on the western slopes the average annual precipitation exceeds 40 inches, and in the higher parts of the West Country it totals between two and three times that amount. In the area between Sognefjord and Nordfjord as much as 230 inches of moisture fall each year, helping to nourish the Jostedal Glacier, one of the largest ice sheets in continental Europe. East of the mountains the average annual precipitation everywhere drops to under 40 inches and, in some sheltered valleys and in the far north, to less than 20 inches. Summers are warmer and sunnier than they are to the west, though this is also the season of maximum precipitation.

In the southern portions of the Scandinavian mountains, the coniferous tree line is reached at an elevation of less than 3,000 feet. In Tröndelag the limit falls to 2,000 feet and in the far north to 1,200 feet. Though scrub birches struggle upward an average of 800 feet higher, the greater part of the mountains lie well within the zone of alpine meadows. It is these open highland wastes that best typify the *fjell* of Scandinavia.

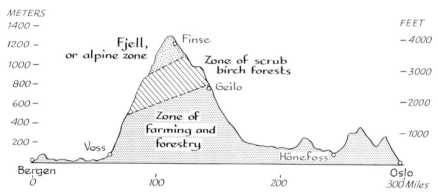

Fig. 4–2. Profile across the Scandinavian mountains, along the Oslo-Bergen railway. More than 30 miles of this railway, which links Norway's two largest cities, are above the timber line and another 30 miles are above the limit of permanent agricultural settlement. Due primarily to a difference in climate, the limits of the respective zones are lower on the west than they are on the east. (Source: Rutebok for Norge.)

Although their height is not impressive when compared to such ranges as the Alps, the Scandinavian mountains have always constituted a distinct barrier to movement. Except near their northern and southern extremities, they are crossed by only one pass at less than 2,000 feet elevation. This is the strategically located Tröndelag-Jämtland gap which breaks across the range near the middle of the Scandinavian peninsula. With two exceptions (at either end of the Dovre Mountains), all of the passes within Norway itself are higher than 3,300 feet, and hence above the tree line. The Bergen Railway, which is the only all-land, year-round connection between Norway's two largest cities, makes its crossing at 4,271 feet, but only by burying 15 per cent of its total mileage in tunnels and snowsheds (Fig. 4–2).

Three similar but nevertheless distinct subdivisions make up the western slope of the mountains. They are, from south to north, the Norwegian West Country, Tröndelag, and the Kjölen Range province. The most distinctive feature of the Norwegian West Country is its narrow steep-sided valleys which in many instances have been scoured by the ice far below the level of the sea, producing deep fjords. The greatest of these is Sogne Fjord which measures some 125 miles in length and is over 4,000 feet deep near its outer end. Hardanger Fjord to the south is 105 miles long and over 2,900 feet in depth at its deepest point. Tributary streams have been left far up the fjord sides in hanging valleys; as a consequence, waterfalls are numerous. Places of habitation are limited to the more sheltered of the islands which line the coast, to the low strandflat which rims much of the shore, or to small patches of lowland at the heads of the fjords. The Jaeren district south of Stavanger affords a noteworthy exception, for here the coastal lowland is covered with rolling moraine deposits. Jaeren's early spring and long growing season help to make it one of Norway's best agricultural areas. Although the more sheltered parts of the West Country were once covered by a mixed forest, this region today possesses only a small fraction of Norway's productive woodland.

North of the Dovre Mountains, centered on the Trondheim Fjord, is the region of Tröndelag. Thanks to its easily eroded Cambro-Silurian deposits, this region is Norway's second most extensive lowland area and agricultural district. Though its clayey soils have been cultivated for centuries, the region is still largely clothed in a forest of spruce and pine.

Northward from Tröndelag, Norway is squeezed into the lower western slopes of the Kjölen Range. The varying geologic character of the range gives it a very broken relief, ranging from the sharp alpine peaks of the Lofotens to the relatively broad interior valleys which extend from Trondheim Fjord to Salt Fjord. In the more sheltered valleys good stands of conifers are found, while along the coasts a cover of scrub birch is characteristic.

The Arctic Circle, which bisects the Kjölen Range province, is scarcely evidenced by the relative mildness of the climate, though its presence is keenly felt in the marked seasonal variations in insolation which are experienced. In common with Lappland (the region where Norway, Sweden, and Finland meet in the north), this region at midsummer knows no darkness at all. In the latitude of the North Cape the sun remains constantly above the horizon from the middle of May until the end of July, and in Spitsbergen this period of continuous sunlight extends from mid-April until the end of August. In contrast, at the winter solstice (December 22), the regions north of the Arctic

Circle receive no sunlight whatsoever, with the North Cape in continuous darkness from mid-November to the end of January. In Spitsbergen the sun does not rise from the end of October until the middle of February. Though the southern portions of Northern Europe likewise experience days and nights of very unequal duration, it is in these northerly areas that the most pronounced effects upon the activities of man are observed.

The Fenno-Scandian Shield. East of the Scandinavian mountains lies the vast Fenno-Scandian Shield. It may be likened somewhat to a broad, shallow saucer, for it is upturned not only on its western edge but also on the east where it culminates in the Karelian Uplands of eastern Finland. Its southernmost outliers, found in the South Swedish Highland, northeastern Skåne, and the northern part of Danish Bornholm, do not show this same east-west warping, but they do show evidence of the extensive faulting which has left its imprint on much of the rest of the region.

The eastern slope of the Scandinavian mountains (the highest and westernmost part of the Shield) is shared by both Norway and Sweden, though by far the larger part lies in the latter country. The long, gradual southeasterly slope is drained by Northern Europe's largest rivers, among them the Glomma (365 miles) in Norway and the Dal (323 miles) in Sweden. Many of the valleys are occupied by deep, finger-like lakes, the east slope's counterpart of the western fjords. Typical examples are Mjösa, Norway's largest lake (140 square miles), and Siljan, Storsjön, and Torneträsk in Sweden.

The valleys of the Norwegian East Country and the Inner Northland of Sweden are relatively broad and open. Those of the East Country converge in the region of the Oslo Fjord, though in the southern portion of the area (the South Country) the valleys are narrower and their axes are more nearly north-south. There is also a tendency toward the convergence of several large valleys near the center of the Swedish Northland; there the mouths of the Ångerman, Indals, and Ljungan are located within a few miles of one another. In both of these areas the hilly terrain of the interior comes down to the edge of the sea without a bordering coastal plain.

Most of the Norwegian East Country and Sweden's Inner Northland lie well above the highest postglacial marine limit; hence their soils are almost entirely derived from coarse morainic materials. In the lower valleys of the East Country, however, easily eroded Cambro-Silurian deposits have contributed not only to the essentially lowland character of the region but also to its distinction as the most productive farming area of Norway. Apart from those in the Jämtland district, no similar deposits are found in Inner Northland. This fact, coupled with higher latitude and a more severe climate, make this vast region the least productive agricultural area of Sweden.

The irregular terrain of Sweden's Inner Northland merges imperceptibly into that of the Finnmark Plateau of northern Norway and the Lappland Plains and Hills region of northern Finland. Moraine deposits interspersed with resistant monadnocks and swampy plains characterize both regions. A major difference is in the orientation of their drainage. In Finnmark, which slopes toward the Arctic, the edge of the plateau meets the ocean in a series of bold and barren headlands, that of the North Cape rising nearly 1,000 feet out of the water. Most of Finnish Lappland, on the other hand, drains by way of the Kemi River system into the Gulf of Bothnia. Finland's only area of Arctic drainage, the Inari Basin, centers on the lake of that name, which is also the country's largest body of water. Its most important outlet is the Pasvik (Paats) River, which serves as the Norway-U.S.S.R. frontier through most of its length.

South of the Oulu River, the character of the Finnish countryside changes as the interdigitation of land and water becomes increasingly complex. This part of the Shield constitutes the Lake Plateau, Finland's most distinctive landscape. Delimited on the south by the Salpausselkä (two great moraines which run roughly parallel to the Gulf of Finland) and on the north by the Suomen Selkä (a secondary watershed), the Lake Plateau rises into the Karelian Uplands in the east and is even less well defined in the west. Its distinctive character, however, is its great profusion of lakes, interspersed with eskers, drumlins, and low crystalline hills. Its elevation averages between 300 and 500 feet, and its drainage is effected chiefly through the Vuoksi River in the east, the Kymi River in the south, and the Kokemäki River in the west.

The Karelian Uplands form the watershed between the Gulf of Bothnia and the White Sea. Compared to the Scandinavian mountains, they are merely a low ground swell, averaging between 500 and 700 feet in elevation. In the southern half of the region individual points top 1,000 to 1,200 feet, while in the north a number of summits range from 1,400 to 2,100 feet. The Soviet-Finnish boundary is drawn through this region but does not coincide with the watershed in all areas.

Those portions of the Shield which were downwarped sufficiently to be inundated by the postglacial antecedents of the Baltic Sea differ in several important respects from the remainder of the Shield. They became, first of all, areas of deposition for marine clays, a fact which distinguishes their soils very markedly from those above the highest marine limit. They are inherently more productive and hence have long been preferred in terms of agricultural settlement. Besides contributing to a difference in soil, however, the marine deposits have largely tended to obliterate local variations in relief, producing in the process the most extensive and unbroken plains areas within the Shield region. For example, the plains which form the Coastal Lowland of western and southern Finland average from 20 to 80 miles in width, and their continuation, the Northland Coast of Sweden, is from 20 to 30 miles wide. Although the Northland Coast is pinched out by the hills of Inner Northland south of Umeå, it is resumed near Sundsvall and broadens out into the Central Swedish Lowland. Though not a coastal plain in the strict sense of the term, the Central Swedish Lowland served as a strait between the Baltic and the ocean for the postglacial seas. It is characterized by relatively extensive flat plains, broken at intervals by low crystalline fault-block hills and large lakes. In the eastern half of the Lowland the fault blocks are aligned principally east-west, and off the coast they continue as a chain of steppingstone rocks and islets through the Stockholm skerry guard and the Åland Archipelago into southern Finland. In the western half of the Central Swedish Lowland, the fault lines trend more north-south. Vänern, the largest of Sweden's lakes, has an area of 2,140 square miles and owes its existence partly to faulting and partly to inundation of the low plain. Vättern to the east occupies an ancient fault valley and, with an area of 735 square miles, is Sweden's second-largest lake.

South of the Central Swedish Lowland is an upland region which, like most of the higher portions of the Shield, was not covered by the postglacial lakes. This is the South Swedish Highland, whose moraine-strewn crystalline hills culminate at an elevation of 1,237 feet about 20 miles south of Lake Vättern. Traversed by numerous fault lines running in a roughly north-south direction, the region's uneven surface is accounted for by an alternation of horsts and grabens. Small lakes and swamps are especially common in the southern half of the area. On either coast the region slopes down to a narrow coastal lowland. The southernmost outcrops of the Shield are to be found in the horsts which trend northwest-southeast through the northeastern parts of the province of Skåne, and in the granite cliffs that line the northern coast of the Danish island of Bornholm.

With the exception of the South Swedish Highland, most of the Shield region lies in the lee of the Scandinavian mountains. As a consequence, the greater part of eastern Norway, Sweden, and Finland receives between 20 and 30 inches of precipitation a year, with the maximum concentration coming in the summer. Along the more exposed western edge of the South Swedish Highland, the annual average is nearly twice as great. Cloudiness is less pronounced than west of the mountains, and summers are warmer. Winters are correspondingly more severe than along the Norwegian coast, with temperatures falling off progressively toward the northeast. The snow cover over most of the Shield region is deep and stable, ranging from 2 to 3 months duration in the south to more than 7 months in parts of Lappland. Ice normally interrupts navigation in the Baltic for about 2 months each year, in the southern reaches of the Gulf of Bothnia for 3, at the inner end of the Gulf of Finland for 5, and in northern Bothnian waters for as many as 7 months.

Apart from those areas of good soils where extensive clearings have been made, the Shield region is primarily a land of forest. In southern Sweden and along the south coasts of Norway and Finland one finds a mixed-forest type where both deciduous and coniferous species occur, but by far the greater part of these countries falls into the zone of northern coniferous forests where spruce and pine are dominant. In Norway the proportion of land in forest to total land area is almost a quarter, while in Sweden it is more than half and in Finland it is nearly two-thirds. In no other region of Europe are the per-capita ratios of productive woodland as high as they are in these countries of the north.

Sweden's Baltic Islands. Sweden's two Baltic islands, Gotland (1,160 square miles) and Öland (519 square miles), afford a unique variety of landscape within the Northern European area. Both of them are composed of tabular limestones of Cambro-Silurian age which dip slightly to the south-southeast. On southern Gotland sandstones from the same period are found. Owing to their generally level surface, low rainfall, and porous bedrock, there are no true valleys anywhere on the islands. On the southern half of Öland—an area known as the Alvaret—the limestone is clothed by a short-grass vegetation reminiscent of the steppe. Elsewhere on the islands patches of mixed forest are found in which both the drought-tolerant pine and the lime-loving ivy are common.

Denmark and Skåne. Thanks to their common geological background, the landscapes of Sweden's southernmost province, Skåne, and most of Denmark are very similar. Structurally the lowland of southwestern Skåne, the Danish islands, and eastern Jutland comprise a gently to moderately rolling plain separated only by shallow arms of the sea. This till plain, composed as it is of lime-rich moraine deposits and clays resting on a bedrock of limestone and chalk, is among the most productive farm land in all of Northern Europe. Only in a few scattered localities is the bedrock exposed at the surface, as for example on the eastern end of the island of Mön, where the chalk cliffs rise more than 400 feet out of the Baltic. Running through central and southern Jutland is a chain of hills which marks the terminal moraine of the last glaciation. It is in these hills that Denmark's highest point —Yding Skovhöj, 567 feet—is located. To the west of the moraine, glacial streams built up extensive outwash plains of sand and gravel, an area which today constitutes Denmark's least-productive region— the so-called Heath of Jutland. Sweeping sand beaches and shifting dunes characterize Jutland's low western coast.

Owing to their location on the extreme southern margin of Northern Europe, Denmark and Skåne enjoy the mildest climate of any part of the region. Temperatures average near or above freezing during most winters and in the mid-60's during the summer. Precipitation, the bulk of which falls as rain, totals between 20 and 30 inches a year. The native vegetation supported by this mild, moist climate was a dense deciduous forest in which the beech tree was particularly common. However, as the land was taken under cultivation the forests gradually disappeared until today less than ten per cent of Denmark and Skåne remain in woods. Owing to man's long exploitation even these remaining groves have a parklike character, and they can in no way be compared with the forests found over most of the rest of Northern Europe. But if man has left his mark on the forests of the region, so has he also altered the originally barren Heath of Jutland, for there numerous plantations of spruce and pine have been made and considerable cultivation taken place.

The Faeroes and Iceland. Having once comprised parts of the same tabular island (Greater Iceland), the Faeroes and large sections of Iceland demonstrate a striking similarity of landscape. Gently dipping layers of basalt form bold headlands over 2,000 feet in height along the northwestern edges of the Faeroes and in eastern and northwestern Iceland. In the Faeroes the inclination is toward the southeast, so nearly all of the habitations are located on this lower and more accessible side of the islands. In Iceland the layers dip chiefly toward the interior of the island, reflecting the presence there of a zone of subsidence. In all of the basalt areas, mountain glaciation has produced numerous U-shaped valleys, many of which are partially submerged as fjords, and other boldly etched features such as cirques, arêtes, and horn peaks.

In the subsidence zone which runs diagonally across Iceland from southwest to northeast, volcanism and diastrophism (movements of the earth's crust) continue as active agents of landscape formation. As a result, the features are jumbled and chaotic. Most of interior

Iceland is a plateau which averages about 2,000 feet in elevation, though numerous isolated mountains rise above the general level to heights of 5,000 feet and more. Some of these are horsts, others are volcanic cones, and still others are old volcanic necks which remained after the volcano itself had been eroded away. Great fault scarps like that at Thingvellir and extensive lava flows (of which the largest is the Ódádhahraun in the northeast) add to the broken nature of the terrain. In the higher parts of the island, particularly athwart the height of land that crosses the country from east to west, lie several plateau glaciers, of which Vatna Glacier (2,200 square miles) is the largest. Extensive lowlands are found only in the south and southwest, though even there large areas are uninhabitable due to lava flows and the continuing deposition of outwash from the great glaciers.

Iceland is one of the most intensively volcanic regions in the world. Best known of its volcanoes perhaps is Hekla which has had more than a dozen eruptions within historic times, the most recent occurring in 1947–48. Occasionally, volcanic activity takes place beneath one of the glaciers, resulting in a spectacular and destructive phenomenon known as a "glacier-burst." Hot springs are found in virtually every part of the island and total several thousand in all. Many of them boil over periodically, sending great columns of superheated water and steam into the air. The most famous of these springs is the Stóri Geysir in Haukadalur, from which our word "geyser" was derived.

Due to their insularity, both the Faeroes and Iceland have climates which are decidedly maritime in character. In the Faeroes winter temperatures rarely dip to the freezing point and summer temperatures seldom get much above 50° F. About 60 inches of precipitation are received each year, with the maximum coming in the winter season and almost all of it falling in the form of rain. There are long periods of overcast, and winds of gale force are not infrequent. As might be expected, such a climate has not been conducive to tree growth; hence, most of the Faeroes are covered with grass.

In Iceland, the very size of the island contributes several aspects of "continentality" to the climate. The south and west coasts, bathed by the Irminger Current, a branch of the North Atlantic Drift, have a milder and wetter climate than the north and east coasts, which come under the influence of the cold East Greenland Current. Winter temperatures in the southwest seldom average below freezing, but in the north and east they normally drop into the low 20's; snow is thus more common and longer lasting in the latter region. In summer, temperatures in the low 50's are common to the coastal districts in all parts of the island. Precipitation, which in the south and west averages between 30 and 60 inches a year, usually amounts to less than 20 inches a year over most of the northern half of the island.

The dominant vegetation in Iceland today is grass, though at the coming of the first settlers there were rather extensive wooded areas (composed chiefly of scrub birch) in the lowlands. Small birch groves are now found only in isolated or sheltered valleys where they are protected by law. The greater part of the island is covered by a sparse mountain vegetation consisting of mosses and lichens, together with grasses, heather, and dwarf birches. In recent years conifers have been successfully introduced from other subarctic regions, demonstrating that the climate is not hostile to their growth. The country's largest experimental forest is located at Hallormstadhur in the northeast.

THE CULTURAL AND HISTORICAL BACKGROUND

Prehistoric Settlement

Although Northern Europe was the last major region of the subcontinent to be inhabited by man, owing to its long immersion in ice, Germanic tribes established themselves on the peninsula and islands of Denmark at an early date and later spread northward into Sweden and Norway. The earliest settlements in Finland appear to have been made on the southwest coast, and these too may have been Germanic in origin. About the beginning of the Christian era, however, the second and last major ethnic group to settle in Northern Europe began moving into southern and central Finland—these were Finno-Ugrian tribes. Apart from these two peoples, however (i.e., the Germanics and the Finno-Ugrians), no other ethnic group of importance is today represented in Northern Europe.

For some time, the chief forms of economic activity in Northern Europe continued to be hunting and fishing, though in those areas where easily cleared deciduous forests coincided with patches of good, easily worked soil, hunting and fishing were gradually replaced by agriculture. The greater part of Denmark early became the home of a relatively dense agricultural settlement, though this was much less true in Sweden, Norway, and Finland. In these countries, deciduous forests were formerly much more widespread than they are today, and while this served as an inducement to the primitive farmer, the paucity of good soils served as a strong deterrent. Early cultivation in these countries was largely restricted to easily tilled soils derived from Cambro-Silurian and/or marine deposits, as it is even to this day. When iron came into more general use, it not only allowed agriculture to spread into the coniferous-forest areas but also made possible the construction of better boats, a factor which greatly improved the communications of the time, particularly in Norway. A simultaneous deterioration of the climate soon nullified the gains made in farming, however, and in some areas, notably Norwegian Tröndelag, it is probable that all previous cultivation had to be abandoned. In the regions remaining, animal husbandry became the dominant form of agriculture and shelters had to be provided for the animals, which up until then had been pastured out-of-doors the year around.

The major lineaments of the present-day settlement pattern of Northern Europe appear to have already been well established in prehistoric times. Both agglomerated villages and dispersed farmsteads, found in Denmark today, were common at an early date. The oldest of the villages tended to be located in plains regions, the rolling hill regions being still largely in forest. In the wooded areas a more dispersed settlement was the rule. Main roads ran along water divides, and villages were located on watercourses only where fords had to be made. A much more important determinant of village locations was access to ground water in the form of ponds where animals could be watered. The Danish villages tended to take two general forms—a round village comprised of farms situated roughly in a ring around some central nucleus such as a pond or common pasture, and a linear village, usually comprised of two rows of farms strung out along a roadway. Round-village types were common on Zealand and on Jutland south of Limfjord and east of the Heath; the linear type was more prevalent on Fyn and in southern Jutland. Danish farm buildings were commonly made of bricks which were plastered over and whitewashed, and the roofs were often of thatch.

Although much of Sweden was early characterized by a settlement pattern of dispersed farms, villages have also been common since prehistoric times. The farms themselves fall into a half-dozen separate types, each distinguished from the other by the varying location of the animal shelters with respect to the dwelling house. The villages fall into three main groups—the linear village, the round village, and the family village, the latter being created through the subdivision of the original farms into smaller units. The linear-village type is most prevalent in east-central and southeastern Sweden and on the island of Öland. The round-village type is limited to those regions of the country where the Danish influence was the strongest, namely, Skåne and the adjacent west and south coasts. The family village was most common in the South Swedish Highland, west-central Sweden, and the southern parts of Swedish Northland. Though most construction was of wood, the form in which it was used varied from planks in Skåne to notched logs in Swedish Northland.

In Norway the settlement pattern was conditioned by the country's physical relief almost as strongly as it was by access to good soil. Apart from the lowland regions near the coast, early agricultural settlements were made on the sides of the more open valleys in the southeast. Such locations combined the advantages of soil (in this case, lateral moraines) and exposure to the sun, advantages which locations either higher up or lower down the valley sides did not possess. From these *midtligårder* (literally, "farms on the middle of the slope"), settlement spread up into the high mountain pastures where the women would usually spend the summer in small huts (*seter*) tending the animals. The farms themselves were widely scattered and true agricultural villages did not exist. Unlike Danish farms, which might be centralized in one or two large buildings, those in Norway were composed of often as many as 20 to 30 smaller buildings, each with its specific use. Along the coasts the location of fishing settlements was determined not only by proximity to good fishing banks but also by suitable harbors and access to small patches of land where subsidiary agriculture might be carried on. As early as the ninth century Norwegian fishermen from the western and northern coastal districts made annual expeditions to the Lofoten fisheries. Thus, with transhumance being practiced in the farming regions and seasonal migrations taking place along the coast to fish or into the mountains to hunt, the population of prehistoric Norway can hardly be thought of as permanently situated.

The rural settlement pattern of Finland was likewise characterized by small, dispersed farms, and agricultural villages in the Central European sense are quite unknown even today. In so far as possible, the farms were located on river terraces or on small knolls or eskers, so that they would not only have better exposure to the sun but also some degree of protection from the frost. Finnish farm buildings were then and are today customarily built of wood, and besides the dwelling house there may be from a dozen to 30 separate outbuildings, each with its own specific purposes. Almost invariably one of these will be a *sauna* (steam bathhouse), usually located somewhat apart from the rest of the buildings and in close proximity to a lake or stream. In the Åland Islands, small, protected harbors early gave rise to little fishing villages.

Of the five Northern European countries, only Denmark and Sweden can be said to have towns which date back to prehistoric times. These originally grew up around heathen centers of worship or at tribal meeting places, but somewhat later advantageous trading sites were also selected. Among the earliest Danish towns were Aarhus, Viborg, and Ribe on Jutland, Odense on Fyn, Ringsted and Roskilde on Zealand, and Lund in present-day Swedish Skåne. The earliest Swedish towns grew up in the vicinity of the Mälaren, among them Uppsala and Birka, though the latter has since become extinct.

Originally, all the Germanic tribes spoke the same language, though by the beginning of historic times this had already evolved into three principal dialectal variants. Two of these were spoken in Northern Europe, namely, Gothic (now extinct) in the Baltic area and Old Norse (or North German) in Denmark, Sweden, and Norway. Both dialects used the runic characters of the Gothic alphabet in their written language. Among the Finno-Ugrian tribes there also were several spoken dialects but no written language at this time.

The Viking Period (800–1100 A.D.)

About the close of the eighth century the story of the Scandinavian peoples suddenly emerges from the realms of legend into the pages of written history. For the next three hundred years these northern peoples demonstrated such a tremendous surge of activity that scarcely any part of Europe escaped their impact. Norwegians ranged from Spitsbergen and the White Sea in the north to the Mediterranean in the south, and likewise pushed westward to Iceland, Greenland, and the coasts of North America. In the east the Swedes coursed up and down the river systems of European Russia and ultimately reached Byzantium and the lands of the Caspian. The Danes were no less active, for they turned their attention to the lands bordering the North Sea and most particularly concentrated on the British Isles. Begun as voyages of exploration and trade, in many areas these expeditions took on the character of sporadic pirate raids and later developed into organized campaigns of conquest and settlement. Named for the audacious seamen who led these expeditions, this dynamic chapter of Scandinavian history has come to be called the "Viking period" (Fig. 4–3).

What the causes for this outburst of peoples may have been is not known with certainty, though they have variously been attributed to overpopulation with respect to the level of technology, to large-scale political dissatisfaction (particularly in Norway), to the attractive realization that the countries of Western Europe were too weak to defend the wealth they were accumulating, and to a sheer love of adventure. Indeed, all of these factors may have played a part, but far better known are the effects of this dispersal. In Northern Europe

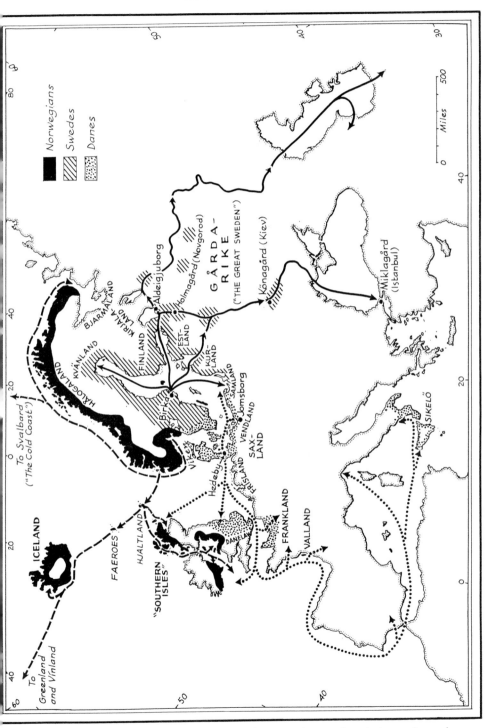

Fig. 4–3. Viking expeditions and settlements during the ninth, tenth, and eleventh centuries.

there was not only a northward movement of peoples in the Scandinavian peninsula itself but also the beginning of a large-scale Swedish movement into Finland. It was during this same period that the Faeroes and Iceland were permanently settled, though both of these areas had probably been visited somewhat earlier by the Irish. Norwegians landed in the Faeroes sometime during the eighth century, and the first permanent settlement was made in Iceland in 874, near present-day Reykjavík. Once begun, the tide of emigrants from Scandinavia (particularly Norway) and from the Viking possessions in the British Isles swelled rapidly, and by 930 there were some 60,000 to 70,000 people on the island. This original period of settlement in Iceland, the so-called *Landnám*, saw all of the coastal areas populated while the interior remained virtually uninhabited, a pattern of distribution which has continued unchanged to this day. The story of this settlement has been preserved in one of the most complete works of historical geography in existence, the so-called *Landnáma-bók*.[2]

It did not take long for the settlers in Iceland to realize that their new environment offered them fewer opportunities (and greater obstacles) for making a living than had the lands they had left. As a consequence, various aspects of their culture had to be modified to conform to this more exacting milieu. The construction of wooden buildings, for example, was a virtual impossibility, for there was little suitable timber on the island. Instead the settlers were forced to build their homes of stone, earth, or peat. As the birch forests disappeared, the problem of fuel became more pressing and the people had to resort to burning driftwood and sheep dung. Furthermore, only the hardiest of the grains they had brought with them would ripen in the short, cool summers of Iceland, and during the fifteenth century, possibly because of the deterioration of the climate, even this cultivation had largely to be abandoned. With local exceptions, agriculture in Iceland came to mean harvesting hay during the summer to carry the livestock through the winter.

The Viking period saw the introduction of Christianity into Northern Europe and the respective unification of the three Scandinavian countries. In Sweden, both the Swedes and the Goths had been brought under one king and the country's borders had been pushed westward against the Norwegians and southward against the Danes. During this same period, the island of Gotland rose to prom-

---

[2] Written during the twelfth and thirteenth centuries, the *Landnámabók* contains the names of 417 of the earliest colonists and describes in detail how the land was apportioned. About a third of the persons so mentioned appear to have come from the British Isles.

inence as a trading center, its chief town being Visby on the west coast. Though Christianity was introduced into the country early in the ninth century, its triumph was not complete until the middle of the thirteenth century, making Sweden the last great nation in Europe to bow to the authority of Rome.

In Norway the settlement pattern became more fixed as trade increased and as Christianity gained a foothold. The country's first trading center was founded near Larvik in the ninth century and shortly afterward Tönsberg became Norway's first town. In the next two centuries a number of other towns came into being—Bergen, Nidaros (present-day Trondheim), Oslo, Stavanger, Borg (now Sarpsborg), and Hamar. When Christianity came in about the year 1000, these embryonic trading towns were selected as sites for its churches, and from then on the growth of both church and town was reciprocal. In 1153 Norway became a separate ecclesiastical province, with an archbishopric established at Nidaros.

It was likewise during the Viking period that the Danish trading town of Hedeby (now the West German city of Schleswig) grew to importance. Also dating from this period are the *Dannevirke*, an extensive earthenwork defense line built across the narrows of Jutland just south of Hedeby, and several large, circular Viking encampments on Jutland and Zealand. As Christianity gained ground in Denmark during the tenth century, churches were established in the more important administrative and trading towns, and in 1104 a Danish archbishopric was created at Lund. First mention was made of Copenhagen (Köbenhavn) in about 1043 when it was referred to as a fishing and trading village, but after 1167, when a castle was established there, the town grew in importance. In Iceland the first *Althing*, or legislative assembly, convened at Thingvellir in 930, and it is from this date that the republic reckons its birth.

During the Viking period, a further step in the evolution of the language pattern of Northern Europe took place. Old Norse, which up until then had been the language common to all three Scandinavian countries, split into two parts—an East Norse spoken in Denmark and Sweden and a West Norse spoken in Norway, the Faeroes, and Iceland.

The Middle Ages

Soon after the close of the Viking period, the countries of Northern Europe began turning their energies to a more intensive development of their own resources and trade began to develop with Western and Central Europe. From Tönsberg in Norway timber was early exported to the Low Countries, and Bergen likewise became an early center for the marketing of fish. In fact, by the thirteenth century Bergen had managed to gain control of all Norwegian fish exports from the mouth of Hardanger Fjord to Finnmark, and in order to maintain this dominant position foreign merchants were forbidden to sail north of that city. In Sweden the mining of iron had probably begun during Viking times, and the production of so-called "osmund iron" in central Sweden (particularly the Bergslagen district at the southern edge of Swedish Northland) soon led to an appreciable export due to its relatively high quality for the period. Stockholm grew up as an important iron-shipping port, as did Göteborg some-time later, when iron exports from the Vänern district began. In the thirteenth century copper was also being mined in the Bergslagen, and together these two metals dominated Swedish exports for several centuries. Whereas Birka had been superseded by Stockholm, the ancient town of Visby was continuing to grow and prosper. In the south of Sweden the salting and marketing of Baltic herring was already a thriving business.

It was not long before the commercial league of the north-German cities (the so-called "Hansa") began casting covetous eyes on this grow-ing trade of Northern Europe. Through a combination of shrewd business tactics, economic sanctions, and the threats or actual use of force, the Hanseatic merchants soon managed to gain control of the greater part of the region's commerce. When the Hansa established its factory in Bergen in 1343, it secured control of virtually the entire Norwegian coast, thanks to the dependence of this vast region upon imported bread grains which the Hanseatic League was in a position to monopolize. Though the exchange of dried fish and butter for grain, meal, and salt soon made Bergen the leading trading center of all Northern Europe, the general effect on the Norwegian economy was detrimental. When the Hansa's privileges were finally revoked in the sixteenth century, Bergen nevertheless continued its domination of northern Norway, and it was not until the middle of the nineteenth century that this region began to enjoy a measure of economic inde-pendence, thanks largely to improved communications.

In Sweden, the Hansa early monopolized the salting and marketing of fish in the south, and its influence was likewise strongly felt in mining and in the local government of the many new towns which came into existence at this time in the central portion of the country. Though a German settlement had been made in Visby as early as the twelfth century, that city gained its greatest prominence about the end of the thirteenth century, when it became the chief trading center of the Hanseatic League in the Baltic. Near the height of its power, however, it was sacked by the Danes (1361), and it never regained its former importance. In 1370, after long opposition, Denmark was likewise obliged to grant trade privileges to the Hansa.

During the Middle Ages several political changes took place in Northern Europe which have had a considerable influence on the subsequent development of the region. About the middle of the thirteenth century Norway reached the height of its power when all of its far-flung colonies recognized the Norwegian king as their sovereign. Within a century, however, the country's fortunes had been seriously reversed, for, with the extinction of her royal line in 1380, Norway and its possessions were joined to Denmark, first as an equal kingdom but then as a dependent area in 1536.

Throughout the medieval period Sweden continued to focus her attention on the east, turning her energies first to the Christianization and conquest of Finland, a task which she largely completed by the defeat of the Russians in 1323. This conquest was followed by such an influx of Swedes to East Bothnia that, from 1362 on, that region was recognized as an integral part of the Swedish realm. Though this political status was later altered by the course of events, the Swedish conquest of Finland had other consequences which were more enduring. In addition to bringing the country under the jurisdiction of the Western church, the Swedes considerably altered the Finnish settlement pattern. Not only were many Finns pushed north and eastward into the interior of the country, in turn dislodging the seminomadic Lapps, but the urban development of Finland was also initiated. The oldest Finnish town is Turku (in Swedish, Åbo), which was founded in 1229 and became the country's first capital. Rauma and Pori were founded in 1365, and Viipuri (in Swedish Viborg, in Russian Vyborg) was established in 1403. While the locations of these towns were largely determined by reason of their harbors and their opportunities for trade, the towns of the interior tended to grow up around fortresses. Savonlinna, Hämeenlinna, and Kajaani are examples of such towns. Helsinki was not founded until 1550. Furthermore, by introducing their own language, the Swedes had a profound influence on the linguistic character of the country. Not only is there a considerable Swedish-speaking minority in Finland today, but the Finnish language itself has incorporated many words of Swedish origin. It was during this period too, that the dialect of Turku became the national standard for the written language, having been used in the Finnish translation of the Bible.

After Norway was joined to Denmark in 1380, the Danes attempted to complete the union of the Scandinavian countries by attacking and conquering Sweden. In 1389 the Swedes were forced to join the Danish-sponsored Kalmar Union but, after a long series of bloody wars, broke out of this alliance in 1523. From then until the middle of the eighteenth century Denmark and Sweden were almost constantly at war with one another as they both struggled for mastery of the Baltic. By the middle of the seventeenth century it appeared that Sweden would ultimately be triumphant, for she had not only driven the Danes off the Swedish mainland in the south and annexed the Norwegian territories of Bohuslän (on the west coast of Sweden north of Göteborg) and Jämtland but she had also turned the Baltic into virtually a Swedish lake by consolidating her hold on Finland and annexing Estonia, Latvia, the region around present-day Leningrad, and portions of the north-German coast at the mouths of the Oder and Weser rivers. Her dominance in the Baltic was short lived, however, for, with the rise of Russia under Peter the Great, Sweden was forced to yield or cede all of her overseas possessions except Finland. Thus, by 1750 the countries of Northern Europe had already passed the peak of their political greatness and were in a state of decline.

During the Middle Ages there was a further development of the urban settlement pattern of the Scandinavian countries as well as a further evolution of the language pattern. In Denmark there were 50 towns by the year 1300, most of which were situated on the coast at the shortest crossings between the islands, on fjords, or at river crossings. Several towns grew up at road junctions, near castles, and at the sites of monasteries. In 1416, when the Danish king chose Copenhagen as his capital, he further spurred the town's growth, and it became the country's leading center of learning when a university was established there in 1479. In Sweden, where there had been some 30 towns previous to 1600, a like number arose during its period of greatness. Among them was Eskilstuna, which has ever since been renowned for its fine-quality steel products. In Norway the seventeenth century saw the rise of several mining settlements, among them Kongsberg, Röros, and Lökken. The influence of King Christian IV of Denmark is witnessed in such place names as Kristiania (since renamed Oslo) and Kristiansand on the south coast. The Norwegian language also bears the imprint of the country's long association with Denmark, for throughout this period Danish was the official literary and commercial language of Norway and as such made its strongest inroads in the towns of the southeast. In the less accessible rural and mountain districts, however, old West Norse dialects continued to be spoken throughout the Danish period. In Sweden the strong influence of the Hansa is evidenced by the many German words which entered the Swedish language at that time.

No discussion of the Middle Ages in Northern Europe would be complete without some mention of the untold hardships which the people of Iceland were forced to bear during this period. In the centuries following the Landnám, it is reasonable to assume, the population grew gradually to something over 80,000 persons, but about the beginning of the fifteenth century a series of natural calamities struck the island, carrying away a great number of inhabitants. The Black Death is said to have wiped out nearly two-thirds of the population, while several volcanic eruptions and the deterioration of the climate, with its attendant starvation, also took a heavy toll. In 1602 the Danes imposed a trade monopoly on the island which only further aggravated the people's suffering. When the first census was taken in 1703, there were only about 50,000 inhabitants remaining. This number was further reduced by nearly one-fifth as a consequence of the catastrophic eruption of Laki Volcano in 1783. In the Faeroes, the Black Death is believed to have killed virtually everyone, with a resettlement of the islands taking place from western Norway somewhat later. This is believed to account for the fact that the present Faeroese population speaks a medieval Norwegian dialect rather than Old Norse as in Iceland.

The Modern Period

Since 1750, the countries of Northern Europe have abandoned all dreams of political expansion and greatness and instead have devoted their energies to the improvement of their economic and social conditions at home. Beginning about the end of the eighteenth century, land reforms were initiated in both Denmark and Sweden to correct the continually worsening situation which was created by repeatedly subdividing farm properties into ever-smaller units. In both countries a more scattered settlement pattern has resulted and new areas have been taken under cultivation. In Finland, land reforms were also begun after the country gained its independence and since that time an area as large as Swedish Skåne has been opened to new agricultural settlement. During the modern period, the strongest influence on the urban settlement pattern of Northern Europe has been the Industrial Revolution. Because it came rather late, in most instances after the middle of the nineteenth century, it was not attended by the overcrowding and congestion which have plagued much of industrialized Western and Central Europe. Instead, owing to the nature of its raw materials and sources of energy, industry in Northern Europe has tended to be rather evenly divided between rural and urban locations. Where towns already existed, it has spurred their growth, but where they did not exist, industry has given birth to them. Because many of its raw materials and most of its fuel must be imported, industry has found it of particular advantage to locate in port cities.

The past two centuries have seen a steady rise in the standard of living in Northern Europe and with it the transition from aristocratic monarchy to social democracy. During this same period, great numbers of Northern Europeans emigrated to North America, and the release of this population pressure on the land undoubtedly did much to promote the rapid economic advances which have since taken place. Throughout the modern period, the political destinies of the Northern European countries have rested largely in the hands of the Great Powers which surround them. In 1808–9, Sweden was expelled from Finland by Russia, and Finland became a grand duchy of the Russian Empire. During the Napoleonic Wars Denmark reacted against British pressure by joining the French. As a result of this mistake, Norway was taken from her and joined to Sweden, though she still maintained sovereignty over Iceland, Greenland, and the Faeroes. The duchies of Schleswig and Holstein (on the southern frontier of Jutland) had always been a bone of contention between the Germans and Danes, and, when Denmark attempted to extend her constitution of 1849 to cover the Duchy of Schleswig, Prussia used this as an excuse to attack her in 1864 and take both territories from her. In 1905, Norway chose to end its union with Sweden and the two countries parted in peace. Throughout World War I the Scandinavian countries successfully maintained a policy of neutrality, though the war nevertheless had several important repercussions within the region. In 1917 Finland declared its independence from Russia, in 1919 she drew up a democratic constitution, and in 1920 she was recognized as an independent republic. In 1918 Iceland became a sovereign state in personal union with the king of Denmark, and in 1920, on the basis of a plebiscite, north Schleswig was returned to Denmark. In 1925, pursuant to a treaty signed in 1920, the Spitsbergen islands became a constitutional part of the Kingdom of Norway, followed by the annexation of Jan Mayen and the Antarctic islands of Bouvet, in 1930, and Peter I, in 1931. In 1939 Norway laid claim to a portion of the Antarctic Continent under the name of Queen Maud Land.

When World War II broke out, the countries of Northern Europe announced their intention to remain neutral, but this hope was shattered in November, 1939, when the Soviet Union launched the so-called "Winter War" against Finland. In the peace of March, 1940, Finland was forced to cede the city of Viipuri and the Karelian Isthmus, as well as a border region in the central Karelian Uplands.

In addition, the Hangö Peninsula was to be leased to the Soviet Union for a thirty-year period. Then in April, 1940, Nazi Germany invaded and occupied both Denmark and Norway, and in order to forestall a similar move in the Faeroes and Iceland, these latter areas were occupied by the British. In 1941 the Americans took over the defense of Iceland. In June of the same year, three days after the Nazis attacked the Soviet Union, the Finns entered the war on their side but were forced to sign a separate peace in September, 1944. Likewise in 1944, the people of Iceland voted to sever their ties with Denmark and become an independent republic. In May, 1945, with the end of the war in Europe, Denmark and Norway were liberated. In the peace treaty signed in September, 1947, Finland lost Viipuri and the Karelian Isthmus in the south once more, and the region in the central Karelian Uplands. In addition, the Petsamo (now Pechenga) region was taken from her, the Porkkala Peninsula was leased to the Soviet Union for 50 years, and $300 million in reparations were levied against her, payable over an eight-year period ending in 1952.[3] Of the Northern European countries, therefore, only Sweden escaped the direct effects of the war, though her neutrality was strained and precarious throughout. In the postwar period, Denmark, Norway, and Iceland joined the North Atlantic Treaty Organization, while Sweden elected to refrain from joining any alliance outside of the Scandinavian area which might precipitate an invasion of Finland.

Each of the Northern European countries is divided into several administrative subdivisions, and, though they have a different name in each country, they correspond most closely to the American county. In Norway, the unit is called a *fylke* and they number 20 in all, including one each for the cities of Oslo and Bergen. In Sweden the unit is a *län*, of which there are a total of 25 including one for the city of Stockholm. The Finnish unit is a *lääni*, of which there are 12, including the Åland Islands which enjoy a large measure of self-government. In Denmark the administrative subdivision is called an *amt*, and the country has 24 in all, including one for the Faeroes, which has the right to use its own language and flag and is to a large extent self-governing, and one for Greenland. The Faeroes and Greenland each elect two members to the Danish Parliament. The Icelandic unit of local administration is the *sýsla*, of which there are a total of 22.

The modern language pattern of Northern Europe is a direct product of the region's historical development. In Iceland, the language is the direct descendant of the Old Norse which was introduced during the Viking period. Owing to Iceland's isolation, Ice-

---

[3] As evidence of Soviet "good will," the reparations were scaled down to $227.5 million in 1948 and the Porkkala Peninsula was returned to Finland in 1955.

landic has preserved its old grammatical system virtually unchanged
since the days of the Sagas, in contrast to the more simplified Scandinavian languages. In a further effort to preserve this purity, original
Icelandic terms have been coined to take the place of foreign words.
This attempt to correlate a medieval language with modern technology and items of culture which are not native to Iceland has produced
some rather imaginative compounds. Electricity, for example, is
literally translated as "amber power," while a telephone is called a
"talking wire." Many of the younger people speak English, and many
of the older generation know Danish. The Faeroese language has
likewise retained its medieval grammar and is accordingly very difficult
for most Scandinavians to understand. Both Danish and Faeroese are
recognized as official languages in the archipelago, however. In Denmark itself, Danish is the only official language, though there is a
small German-speaking minority in Schleswig. Norway has two official languages, both of which are Norwegian but which differ in their
historical development. They are *bokmål* (literally, "book language")
and *nynorsk* ("new Norwegian"). *Bokmål* is a derivation of Dano-
Norwegian, the official language of Norway during its long association
with Denmark. *Nynorsk* is a composite of the rural dialects which
continued to be spoken throughout the Danish period in the more
isolated regions of the country, and was first given written expression
about the middle of the nineteenth century. In Sweden there is only
one official language, namely, Swedish, though there are small Lapp
and Finnish minorities in the northern part of the country. In north
Norway the Lapps number about 20,000 and in north Finland about
3,000. In the latter country both Finnish and Swedish are recognized
as official languages. In their written forms, the three Scandinavian
languages are mutually intelligible in all three countries, although
this is considerably less true of certain of the spoken languages, particularly Danish and Norwegian *nynorsk*.

In addition to their language ties, the countries of Northern
Europe have several other cultural bonds of an enduring nature. In
all of these countries the Evangelical Lutheran church has been the
state church ever since the Reformation, though there is almost complete freedom of worship in the region today. In the fields of education, labor relations, customs, travel, and humanitarianism the nations
of Northern Europe have demonstrated a strong sense of regional
unity. Each year an inter-Nordic parliament with advisory powers is
held in an attempt to correlate the economic and social policies of
the region. Many of these advances in regional cooperation have
come about as the result of efforts of an organization known as the
"Nordic Union" which was founded in 1919. Of a less official nature,

but no less important in strengthening the bonds of friendship between these northern countries, is the vast tide of tourists which flows between these nations every summer. With a uniformly high standard of living, a great variety of scenic and cultural attractions to visit, and travel restrictions reduced to a minimum, the peoples of Northern Europe are perhaps the most tourist-minded of any region on the continent. In all but a political sense, *Norden* is a symbol of the unity of Northern Europe.

NORWAY

Population

In 1957 Norway had a population of 3½ million, of whom about half lived in cities, suburbs, or rural agglomerations. The largest city is Oslo, the capital, with about 455,000 inhabitants (with suburbs, 525,000). In second place is the west-coast port of Bergen with 115,000, followed by Trondheim with 59,000, Stavanger with 53,000, Drammen with 30,000, and Kristiansand with 27,000. Sixteen other towns number over 10,000 inhabitants each. About four-fifths of the total Norwegian population lives along the coasts and on some 2,000 adjacent offshore islands; a like proportion make their homes south of the Tröndelag region, with over half in the East Country alone. In the period from 1820 to 1940 about 800,000 Norwegians emigrated to the United States, the bulk of them coming from the South and West countries.

Present Economic Life of Norway

Agriculture and Fishing. For reasons of topography and climate, less than three per cent of Norway's land area has been brought under cultivation (Fig. 4–5). The country's most fertile agricultural regions are those lowland areas which are underlain by Cambro-Silurian deposits and/or covered with postglacial marine sediments. Such regions are found in three sections of the country, namely in the lower valleys of the East Country, the district of Jaeren in the West Country, and central Tröndelag. Together these three districts comprise only eight per cent of Norway's total area, yet they contain almost one-half of her total land under cultivation. In the lower valleys of the East Country both animal husbandry and an intense cultivation of field crops are carried on, with grain being grown on the better soils and potatoes in the sandier tracts. About three-fourths of Norway's total area in wheat is to be found in this region. In Jaeren, main attention

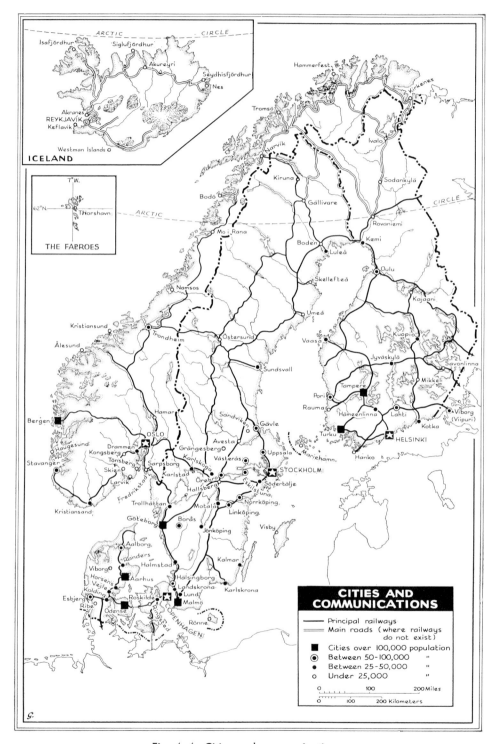

Fig. 4–4. Cities and communications.

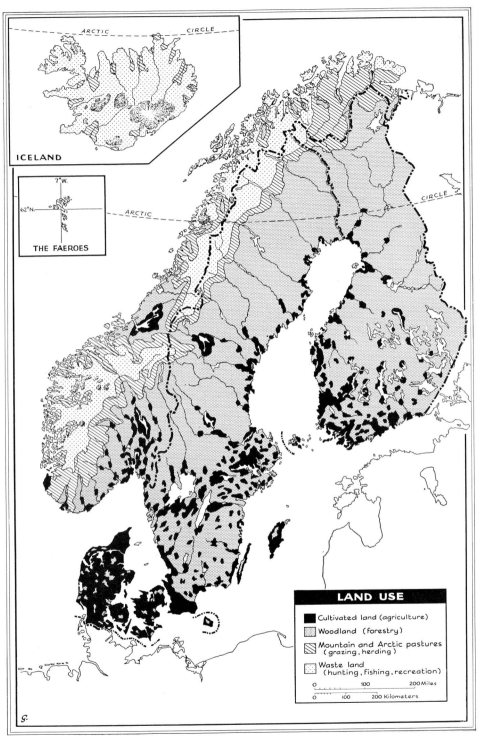

ARCTIC CIRCLE

ICELAND

7° W.

62° N.

ARCTIC

THE FAEROES

CIRCLE

LAND USE

- ■ Cultivated land (agriculture)
- ▨ Woodland (forestry)
- ▨ Mountain and Arctic pastures (grazing, herding)
- ▨ Waste land (hunting, fishing, recreation)

0   100   200 Miles

0   100   200 Kilometers

G.

Fig. 4–5. Land use.

223

is given to the production of animal products, based both on locally grown fodder crops and imported fodder concentrates. The district is a leading producer of butter, cheese, poultry, eggs, and early vegetables. In the central Tröndelag district, due to its shorter growing season and lower summer temperatures, hay and fodder crops are dominant, with barley occupying over four-fifths of the acreage devoted to grains. Elsewhere Norwegian agriculture is limited to small plots on the valley sides of the East Country, in the valley bottoms or on the strandflat of the West Country, and to the high pastures in the mountain districts. The inner parts of Hardanger and Sogne Fjord are noteworthy for their production of fruit, including apples, pears, plums, and cherries.

With the exception of a few large farms in the lower valleys of the East Country, Norway is essentially a country of small family farms. More than half of all Norwegian farms are smaller than 5 acres in size, and 98 per cent of them have less than 50 acres.[4] Over nine-tenths of all farm properties are owned by their operators, and more than 90 per cent of all farm labor is supplied by the individual farmer's family, with women comprising over half of the total labor force. Due to the small size of the farms, their often prohibitively steep slopes, and scattered distribution, the use of machinery is limited and, even when operated on a cooperative basis, rather inefficient (Fig. 4–6).

Hay is by far the most important crop, normally constituting from two-thirds to three-fourths of the total acreage under cultivation. Next in order come barley, oats, potatoes, and wheat. With four-fifths of its cultivated area in fodder crops, Norway must import the greater part of her bread grains, but by concentrating on the production of animal products she can generally cover her domestic needs of dairy products, meat, and eggs. In order to do even this, however, a considerable quantity of fodder concentrates must be imported each year and margarine must be made to meet the nation's fat requirements. Sheep and goats make up a sizable part of the country's livestock herds, and in recent years fur farming has become an important adjunct to agriculture. In the coastal districts farming is often found in combination with fishing, and in the wooded regions a joint farm-forest economy is common. In all, about one-fifth of the Norwegian population earns its living from agriculture.

Though Norwegian fishermen normally catch a larger volume of fish each year than do the fishermen of any other European nation, the average value per ton of the catch is lower than that of any country in Europe save Iceland. This is explained in part by the varieties

[4] See the statistical summation, Appendix III.

of fish caught, in part by the seasonal nature of the occupation making preservation of the catch a serious problem, and in part by the form in which the catch is sold. Herring makes up about two-thirds of the volume of the catch each year but only about 40 per cent of its total value. This species is taken off the west coast from Lindesnes to Trondheim Fjord from December to March, and, whether it is marketed fresh or salted, it does not command a very high price. The problem of processing such huge quantities of fish in a short time is

Fig. 4–6. Farms in the upper part of Hallingdal, in the Norwegian East Country. Typical *midtligårder*, they are located on the middle of the slope, where the soils and exposure are best. Note the striking contrast in land use between the cultivated south-facing slope and the forested north-facing slope. (Photo: Normanns Kunstforlag.)

so acute that much of the herring has to be reduced to fish meal for fertilizer or to oil for margarine if it is to have any value at all. Cod, on the other hand, accounts for about one-fourth of the volume and one-third of the value. This species spawns along the north coast from January to April, with the largest concentration being found in the Lofoten Islands. Because of the long distance even to Norwegian markets, the bulk of the cod catch must either be dried or salted to prevent spoilage in transit; as a consequence, it commands a much lower price when it does reach the market. Brisling, a small variety of herring, is taken off the coast of the West Country from July to September and forms the basis of the Norwegian sardine industry.

Nearly half of Norway's 87,000 fishermen live in the counties north of Tröndelag—forceful testimony to the importance of the sea in the economic life of that remote region. That Norway's fishing industry is still primarily a small-scale, individualistic type of operation is demonstrated by the fact that over half of the more than 80,000 craft in use are open boats without motors.

Fig. 4–7. The settlement of Lofthus, on the southern arm of Hardanger Fjord, in the Norwegian West Country. This district is a foremost producer of fruit, including apples, cherries, and pears. The edge of Folgefonni, an extensive plateau glacier, may be seen on the mountains in the background. (Norwegian National Travel Office.)

Whaling has been an important Norwegian livelihood for several centuries, but the modern period began in the 1860's with the invention of the explosive harpoon. From then until 1904 Norwegian whaling was carried on in the Arctic Ocean from a series of coastal stations in Finnmark, Iceland, and Spitsbergen. The number of whales was so reduced, however, that the center of operations shifted to the Antarctic, with land stations being established in the South Shetland and South Georgia islands. In 1905, the first floating factory ship began operations in the Antarctic, anchoring in sheltered harbors to carry on its work. Since 1925 such factory ships have been able to operate completely on their own, without recourse to protected anchorages. Whales are towed by small catching ships to the floating factory, where they are hauled on board through a slipway in the stern. Norwegian whalers normally account for about one-third of the world's annual production of whale oil, the bulk of which is used for the production of margarine. The principal ports of the Norwegian whaling fleet are Sandefjord, Larvik, and Tönsberg, all near the mouth of the Oslo Fjord.

Industry and Raw Materials. The industrialization of Norway began about the middle of the last century, when steam power was introduced into sawmilling and a number of small industries were begun using imported coal as fuel. The greatest industrial expansion has taken place since the turn of the century, however, thanks to the development of part of the country's vast hydroelectric resources. Now, over one-third of the Norwegian population earn their living in industry and almost three-fourths of the country's exports are derived from it.

With the greatest waterpower reserves of any country in Europe, Norway has been generously compensated for its otherwise serious lack of energy sources. Estimated at 9,200,000 kilowatts when operated at 75 per cent efficiency, these reserves have as yet been only 30 per cent developed, yet Norway is already producing over 25 billion kilowatt-hours annually. About 80 per cent of the reserves are advantageously located in the more densely populated southern half of the country (i.e., in the East and West countries). Of the total production of electric energy about five-eighths is used in industry, with the largest single consumer being the chemical and electrochemical industry.

The raw materials for Norway's industries come principally from her forests, mines, and fisheries. After an early start in the timber trade, Norway has given her main attention to the production of pulp and paper ever since Sweden, Finland, and Russia, with their vaster stands of saw timber, came into competition with her. In contrast to both Sweden and Finland, which export much greater quantities of better-grade chemical pulp than they do of the lower-grade mechanical pulp, Norway normally exports roughly equal quantities of each type. On the other hand, Norway exports finished paper to a greater degree than does either Sweden or Finland. The country's largest pulp and paper mills are located near the mouths of the larger rivers, for convenience of floating and shipping. The chief centers of the industry are Sarpsborg, Drammen, and Skien—all in the East Country, but there is also some pulp production in Tröndelag. Norway's export of pulp and paper generally makes up about one-quarter of her total export trade.

Norway has a variety of mineral deposits, but, like those of Finland, they are for the most part of low metallic content (Fig. 4–8). The largest mining operation in the country is open-pit iron mining in the Syd-Varanger district near Kirkenes. The ore here contains about 33 per cent iron in a natural state, but it is beneficiated and shipped in briquettes of 65 per cent purity. Norway's next most important mineral resource is copper pyrite, with more important centers of operation being Sulitjelma in the Kjölen Range and Lökken, southwest of Trondheim. Apart from the production of metallic copper, sulphur is extracted for use in the cellulose and chemical industries. Limestone is quarried in the southern portions of the East Country and plays an important role in the production of artificial fertilizers as well as being used in the making of cement.

Norway's vast resources of hydroelectric energy have enabled her to build up a considerable electrometallurgical industry based on imported raw materials which often come from great distances. This industry is largely localized in the West Country, for there nature has concentrated bountiful supplies of electric energy in close proximity to sheltered, deep-water harbors. Ocean-going freighters unload their raw ore directly at the factory where it is processed with cheap power and then exported as finished metal. A typical example is the large aluminum factory at Höyanger in Sognefjord, which uses bauxite from France, Italy, and Yugoslavia. A large refinery at Kristiansand on the south coast processes semifinished nickel shipped in from Canada. Other plants along the coast process manganese, zinc, and chromium ores. Pig iron is produced in electric smelters at Stavanger and Bremanger at the entrance to Nordfjord. The country's largest electric steel mill began production at Mo i Rana, just south of the Arctic Circle, in the spring of 1955.

Another Norwegian industry which is based on hydroelectric power is the electrochemical industry, and foremost among such enterprises is the famous Norsk Hydro Corporation which produces saltpeter from air, water, and limestone. Its method based on a Norwegian process requiring tremendous amounts of electric energy, the corporation built three large power stations near Rjukan and began production there. Switching later to an improved German process, the company transferred about half of its operations to a plant located on the coast, near Skien, although the Rjukan power stations still supply the energy for both installations. Another branch of the electrochemical industry is the production of carbide and cyanamide, the largest of such plants being located at Odda on Hardanger Fjord.

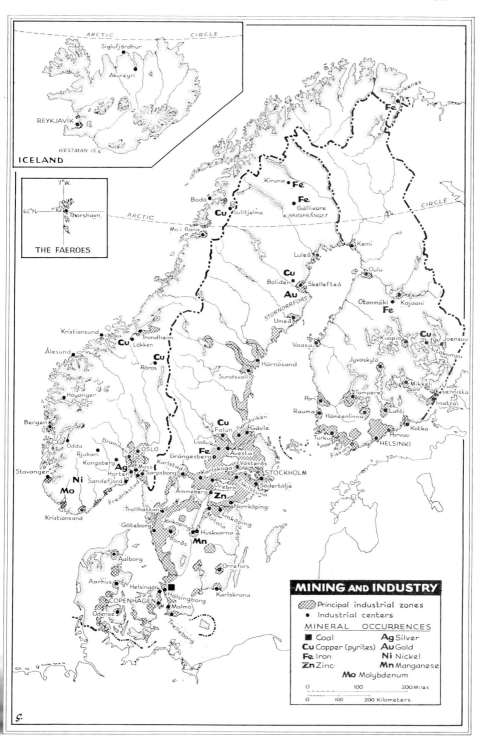

Fig. 4–8. Mining and industry.

Measured in terms of the value added by manufacture, Norway's leading industries are: the manufacture of transport equipment (especially ships), chemicals, paper, basic metals, and food processing. Of these, the chemical and paper industries are strongly oriented toward export, while the others produce chiefly for the home market. The largest single industrial center is the city of Oslo, with one-fifth of the country's factory workers and one-fourth of the total value added by manufacture.

Fig. 4–9. The industrial town of Höyanger, on an arm of Sogne Fjord. This view testifies to the dispersed nature of Norway's settlement pattern. In the foreground is the factory of the Norwegian Aluminum Corporation, which gave rise to the town in 1916.

Transportation and Foreign Trade. Transport in Norway has always been confronted with tremendous topographic and climatic obstacles, as well as by great distances between widely scattered settlements. It is not surprising, therefore, that the sea has been the dominant theme in Norwegian transportation all through the country's history; even today, it continues to play a decisive role in Norway's communications. In 1893 the so-called *hurtigruten* (express route) was begun between Bergen and Finnmark and this still remains the only dependable year-round connection between northern and southern Norway. Daily sailings are maintained between Bergen and Kirkenes, and the entire distance can be covered in 5½ days.

Begun in 1854, Norway's rail net now totals about 2,790 miles in length, of which all but 40 miles belong to the state. By 1957 about one-third of the mileage had been electrified, accounting for nearly two-thirds of the total traffic. All major trains on non-electrified lines are now diesel powered. Although a rail link to Bodö in north Norway is presently under construction, no further additions to the system are contemplated. Since the war, the railways' operational deficit has grown from year to year, in part because of the increasing competition from motor traffic.

Norway's road system totals about 30,300 miles in length, of which 10,000 miles are maintained by the national government and just over 2,000 miles are hard surfaced. Nearly all inhabited districts are reached by regular bus services, which, since 1951, have consistently carried a larger volume of passenger traffic than the railways. Though most transmontane routes are closed by snow in winter, about 91 per cent of the mileage of Norway's main roads is held open by plowing. Ferry routes, which comprise integral links in the road net of the fjord and island districts, total 1,350 miles in length.

Domestic air services in Norway are carried on by three companies, two of which are state subsidized and one of which is distinctly regional in character. Regular flights by land planes are made on routes linking Oslo-Kristiansand-Stavanger, Oslo-Bergen, Oslo-Ålesund, and Oslo-Trondheim-Bodö-Bardufoss (near Tromsö). Smaller seaplanes are used on routes between Bodö, Narvik, and the towns of the Lofoten islands, as well as on flights from Tromsö along the coast to Kirkenes. Winter flying schedules, particularly in north Norway, are sharply reduced due to darkness, poor weather conditions, and the absence of tourist traffic at that season.

Norway's merchant marine has often been called her "floating empire," for without it the country could not maintain its high standard of living. Profits accruing from her overseas shipping make up the discrepancy in her foreign trade, allowing Norway consistently to import a greater value of goods than that which she herself is able to export. Before the war her merchant navy was the fourth largest in the world, totaling 4.8 million gross tons, two-thirds of which were motor ships and 40 per cent oil tankers. By 1950 Norway had replaced all the tonnage lost during the war, and by 1959 the fleet had more than doubled its prewar size, totaling at the beginning of that year not less than 10 million gross tons. Motor ships comprised nearly seven-eighths of this tonnage, over half of which were tankers, and three-fourths were less than 9 years old. The gross earnings of this great fleet have in recent years totaled the equivalent of some $750 million, more than four-fifths of which has been earned in trade which never touched the home country.

Norway is dependent on many imported goods for maintaining her standard of living, and most of these must be in finished or semi-finished form, for with her small population and lack of capital Norway is unable to support a diversified industry of her own. Among her chief imports are transportation equipment (including ships and automobiles), base metals for processing, mineral fuels, machinery, textiles, grain, and coffee. In return for such goods Norway exports refined base metals, pulp and paper, fish products, whale oil, and artificial fertilizer. In the prewar period her best customers, both for imports and exports, were Great Britain, Germany, Sweden, and the United States, and since the war this pattern has again re-established itself.

Norway's Arctic Possessions. In the European Arctic Norway has two territorial possessions—Jan Mayen and Spitsbergen. The former is a single volcanic island located at 71° N. latitude and 8° W. longitude. Earlier used as a base for whaling and sealing operations, its principal importance today is as a weather station. The territory of Spitsbergen is composed of the island of West Spitsbergen and the archipelago lying to the east of it, as well as Bear Island situated halfway between Spitsbergen and the north coast of Norway. With the exception of Bear Island, the archipelago is largely covered by inland ice sheets. Formerly important as whaling and sealing bases, Spitsbergen has more recently served as a "jumping-off place" for Arctic expeditions and as the site of three Norwegian weather stations. Since 1900, coal mining has been carried on in West Spitsbergen, first by a United States firm but now by the Norwegians and Russians. The Norwegian population numbers about 1,200 persons, most of whom reside in the mining camps at Longyear City and New Ålesund. The Soviets number about 2,700 and are concentrated in the settlements of Barentsburg and Grumant City. The annual production of the Norwegian mines averages nearly 400,000 tons, of which the greater part is used in north Norway or by the state railways. The Soviet-mined coal, about 300,000 tons per year, is shipped to Murmansk. All export must take place during the short summer season when the coasts are not blocked by ice.

SWEDEN

Population

In 1958 the population of Sweden totaled 7.4 million persons, of whom half lived in cities and towns. From 2 million in 1767, the Swedish population had doubled by 1864 and tripled by 1924, passing the 7-million mark in 1950. In the period from 1820 to 1940 about 1.2 million Swedes emigrated to the United States. Since the end of World War II Sweden has opened its doors to numerous Baltic and Central European refugees. In recent decades the over-all population growth has been slow, because Sweden has the lowest birth rate of any country in the world.

Sweden's population is very unevenly distributed, with nearly four-fifths living in the southern two-fifths of the country. The greatest densities are found in the Central Swedish Lowland and in Skåne. The country's largest cities lie at opposite ends of the Central Lowland. In the east is Stockholm, the capital, with some 800,000 inhabitants (with suburbs, over one million). Göteborg, the major port on the west, has over 440,000 inhabitants. Malmö, the regional center of the rich Skåne Lowland, ranks third with some 245,000 inhabitants. In addition Sweden has nine other cities with over 50,000 population each, nineteen more which range in size between 25,000 and 50,000, and forty-six with populations between 10,000 and 25,000.

Present Economic Life of Sweden

Agriculture and Forestry. About 9 per cent of Sweden's land area is under cultivation, though the percentage varies widely from one region to the next (Fig. 4–5). In the Skåne Lowland, for example, over 70 per cent of the land has been brought under the plow, in the Central Swedish Lowland from 40 to 50 per cent, and in the South Swedish Highland about 10 to 20 per cent. Inner Northland, on the other hand, has less than 0.5 per cent of its land under cultivation, while the Northland coast averages from 3 to 8 per cent and the Jämtland district, 3 per cent. Nearly three-fourths of all Swedish farms have less than 25 acres of tilled land each, though two-thirds of the country's total land under cultivation is in farms with larger averages. As might be expected, the larger farms are located in the lowland regions of Skåne, central Sweden, and insular Sweden, while small farm units are the rule in the South Swedish Highland and in Northland (Fig. 4–11). About one out of every five Swedish farms is tenant operated, and over one-fourth of all cultivated land in Sweden belongs to such farms. In 1950 less than one-fourth of the Swedish population was employed in agriculture.

In terms of the total acreage devoted to its cultivation, hay leads all other Swedish field crops, for almost 45 per cent of the nation's cultivated land is dedicated to this commodity. Oats are second in importance, followed by wheat, mixed seed, rye, and potatoes. When grain prices fell in the 1880's, Sweden, like Denmark, turned its attention more strongly toward animal husbandry but, unlike Denmark, also maintained its production of bread grains for domestic consumption. Before the outbreak of World War II, Sweden was nearly 99 per cent self-sufficient in wheat, despite the fact that the domestic level of consumption had sextupled since 1870. Moreover she was almost 96 per cent self-sufficient in rye, the consumption of this grain having fallen as the standard of living rose. Barley and oats, which

Fig. 4–10. The *Gamla Staden* or medieval center of Stockholm. Founded on the islands in the foreground, the Swedish capital city has gradually embraced a number of neighboring islands and spilled over onto the mainland on both sides of the Mälaren. Because of Stockholm's many waterways, it is often called "the Venice of the North."

were formerly exported to some degree, are now all used domestically, and small additional amounts are imported. The export surplus of butter has risen greatly even though the Swedes continue to consume more butter than they do margarine. The export surplus of eggs has also increased, and though the country maintains a small import of meat, this need could also conceivably be filled by curtailing the small export of livestock which now takes place. In all, the country's production of vegetable products rose by 77 per cent from 1870 to 1940, while the volume of animal products increased by no less than 218 per cent in the same period. Bad weather and a shortage of fertilizer occasioned a slight drop in production during World War II, but by

1958 Swedish farms were producing about 10 per cent more than their prewar levels. Output per man-hour rose about 60 per cent during the same period.

Wheat finds its greatest acreage in the Skåne Lowland, the Central Swedish Lowland (particularly the Plain of Östergötland east of Lake Vättern), and insular Sweden. The cultivation of rye is rather evenly distributed over the country south of the Dal River, though in the

Fig. 4–11. View of the Central Swedish Lowland near the inner end of the Mälaren. Once covered by postglacial seas, this region is now one of Sweden's most fertile agricultural areas. At the right is a wheat field. Forests are found on the crystalline outcrops, one of which shows in the foreground. At the left is a *linbana*, or cableway, which transports limestone from a quarry to a large cement factory in Köping.

better agricultural regions it has lost considerable ground to wheat. Oats take up a large part of the cultivated land in the western Central Swedish Lowland (especially around Lake Vänern) and in the South Swedish Highland. Barley is grown over most of the country, though in Skåne and insular Sweden it is the finer two-row variety used for malt and in Inner Northland it is the more tolerant six-row variety used for bread grain. The cultivation of potatoes is uniformly distributed over all of Sweden with the exception of the mountain districts, but sugar beets are limited to the Skåne Lowland and insular

Sweden. Cattle are rather evenly distributed over the country, while swine are almost entirely confined to Skåne.

In addition to her soils, Sweden has an extremely valuable resource in her forests. It was not fully appreciated, however, until the middle of the nineteenth century, when the industrial nations of northwestern Europe demanded more timber. From that time on, the forest regions of Sweden (especially Northland) took on the character of a new Swedish frontier and sawmills sprang up rapidly. During the next half century there was a tremendous expansion in the production of sawn timber, culminating about 1900. In the last decades of the nineteenth century the pulp industry also started production, and, thanks to the continually growing demand for newsprint and wrapping paper, the pulp industry now ranks as Sweden's most important forest industry in terms of the value of its production. Of lesser importance are a number of other forest industries engaged in making paper, mill goods such as finished window frames and doors, furniture, plywood, wallboard, and prefabricated houses.

Though the forest regions of southern Sweden have likewise benefited by this expansion of the wood-using industries, it has been of especial importance to Northland, where other means of economic livelihood are considerably more limited. Regrowth is slower there, but the quality of the wood is better. Moreover, the region is admirably suited for the transport of timber, for the heavy winter snow cover facilitates the movement of logs by sled during this season. In the spring the logs are floated down the larger rivers (among them the Ångerman, Indals, Ljungan, Ljusnan, and Dal) to the sawmills and pulp factories situated at their mouths. One disadvantage, however, is the long period during the winter when the ports are blocked by ice, making necessary the concentration of exports during the summer season.

The country's largest sawmills are found along the Northland coast, with particular concentrations near the mouths of the Indals, Ångerman, and Ume rivers. There are numerous smaller mills in the southern portion of Inner Northland and in the eastern half of the South Swedish Highland. It is in this latter area that the greatest concentrations of woodworking shops and furniture factories are also found. The distribution of pulp mills largely parallels that of the sawmills, though the two greatest concentrations are along the Northland coast (particularly between the mouths of the Dal and Ume rivers) and in the Lake Vänern area. Those along the Northland coast account for over half of the country's chemical pulp production as well as nearly all of Sweden's pulp exports. The production of the southern pulp mills goes largely into domestic paper making, hence most of the country's paper factories are located in central and southern Sweden, especially around Lake Vänern and in the South Swedish Highland.

A century ago, wood products made up about 10 per cent of Sweden's exports by value, though this percentage rose rapidly as an increasing demand spurred production. In 1897 an export peak of 1.2 million standards of timber was reached, and not until 1929 was this figure surpassed. During the '30s a considerable diversification of the sawmill industry took place and the production of plywood, wall-board, and prefabricated houses began to assume a more important position. Just before World War I the pulp and paper industry had supplied 20 per cent of Sweden's total exports by value, but by 1937 this percentage had risen to 30 per cent, and in some recent years it has approximated 40 per cent. Although Sweden's own paper require-ments are fulfilled by domestic production and small quantities are exported, about 90 per cent of the pulp produced is exported to be made into paper elsewhere. The same thing is true with artificial fibers, the bulk of which is processed in other countries.

The wood industries of Sweden have now reached a transitional period, for the age of virgin forests is past and exploitation of second-growth forests has become the order of the day. Even before the last war, the shortage of raw materials was so acute that the forest-products industries were operating at only 85 per cent of capacity. During the war the forest reserves were further reduced when it became neces-sary to use a considerable amount of wood for fuel. The labor supply in the Swedish forests is largely derived from farmers who work in the woods during the winter and tend their farms during the summer. Even so there are about 150,000 full-time employees in the Swedish forest industries. About one-fourth of Sweden's forests are owned by the state, another one-fourth by corporations, and one-half by private individuals.

Mining and Manufacturing. The subsoil of Sweden is the most richly endowed of any nation in Northern Europe. Metal-bearing ores are found in three principal districts of the country, namely the Bergslagen district near the southern edge of Inner Northland, the Skellefte district centered on the river system of that name in northern Sweden, and the Lappland district in the far north of Northland.

In the early Middle Ages the mining of iron and copper was already important in the Bergslagen district, and by the middle of the four-teenth century these two metals made up almost 40 per cent of all Swedish exports by value. Two centuries later these metals consti-tuted over three-quarters of the country's total exports. However, as Sweden's copper reserves gradually became exhausted, as the foreign competition of coke-smelted ores began to be felt, and as new domestic industries came into being, the relative importance of iron and copper in the country's economy declined. Without good coal reserves of her own, Sweden has met the challenge of foreign competition by continuing the production of high-quality charcoal-smelted pig iron, a commodity for which she has had a leading reputation ever since the production of "osmund iron" began about the close of Viking times. About 40 per cent of the total Swedish pig-iron production is made up of such high-quality pig iron, its principal raw material being the relatively phosphorus-free iron ores of the Bergslagen. This production not only forms the basis of the Swedish domestic steel industry (discussed below) but also provides an important export of quality steels. Though methods for smelting ores which have a high phosphorus content were developed in the late 1800's, the bulk of these ores goes into export (chief mining center: Grängesberg). Copper production at Falun has now all but ceased, though the mining of a number of other metals has become increasingly important in recent years. Among them are pyrites, lead, zinc, manganese, tungsten, and molybdenum.

The mineral resources of the Skellefte district are for the most part covered by a heavy overburden, and their discovery and exploration have depended largely on geophysical prospecting with special electric equipment. Composed chiefly of pyrites, the metal-bearing ores contain a great variety of minerals, among them gold, silver, copper, lead, zinc, and nickel. The chief center of operations in the Skellefte district is Boliden.

Sweden's greatest mineral deposits by far are the vast iron reserves in the Lappland district in the far north. Averaging between 60 and 70 per cent pure iron, these ores have a relatively high phosphorus content, and the greatest part of their production is exported. During the summer season, shipments go by electric railway to the port of Luleå at the head of the Gulf of Bothnia and to the Norwegian port of Narvik, but during the winter, when the Gulf is blocked by ice, all ore is shipped via ice-free Narvik (Fig. 4–12). The two principal centers of production are Kiruna and Gällivare, with most of the mining now taking place below the surface rather than in open pits as was formerly true.

Among the non-metallic resources of Sweden mention should be made of coal, peat, building stone, lime, and quartz. Coal of rather low quality is found in northwestern Skåne near Hälsingborg, and though production was increased to 600,000 tons a year during the last war, it normally averages about 300,000 tons annually. Most of the production is used by local industries and railways. Peat is found in virtually all parts of Sweden, and it is estimated that the country has in this resource the fuel equivalent of nearly 4 billion tons of coal. Before the outbreak of World War II the average production for fuel was 25,000 tons a year, but, with the serious shortage of imported fuel during the war, production rose to a maximum of 1.25 million tons in 1945. In the west-coast province of Bohuslän, the quarrying of granite building stone is an important industry and most of its production is exported. Lime and limestone are found in Skåne, insular Sweden,

Fig. 4–12. Part of the mechanized iron-ore-loading facilities at Narvik. Giant cranes feed the ore onto conveyor belts, which deliver it into ships' holds at rates up to 4,000 tons per hour. Now north Norway's largest city, Narvik owes its existence to its facilities for shipping the rich iron ores brought overland from Swedish Lappland. (SJ Press.)

and the Central Swedish Lowland, and it is in these regions that the country's cement industry is localized. The production of tiles is concentrated in Skåne and in the Mälar Valley of the Central Swedish Lowland. The Swedish glass industry is centered in the southeastern part of the South Swedish Highland, around Orrefors, and has long enjoyed a reputation for fine quality.

In the middle of the seventeenth century Sweden was the world's leading producer of iron, annually turning out an amount equal to one-third of the world's total consumption. She owed her foremost position not only to her rich iron-ore deposits but also to her extensive forests which supplied charcoal for fuel. As iron smelted with coke became increasingly important, however, she gradually lost ground to the coal-rich nations of the earth, and today Sweden accounts for only about one per cent of the world's total production of iron and steel. Though she is now far down the list in terms of quantity production, Sweden still remains one of the world's foremost producers of quality iron and steel. In the years preceding the outbreak of World War II, about 37 per cent of her total production was exported, though on the other hand an appreciable amount of lower-grade iron and steel was imported each year. Since the war, exports of Swedish steel have fallen to less than 20 per cent of production, while imports have continued to increase. The main concentration of iron and steel mills is found in and near the Bergslagen district, one of the largest mills being located at Sandviken. Gold, silver, and copper are smelted at a plant near the mouth of the Skellefte River. Aluminum is produced near Avesta in the Bergslagen from imported Norwegian aluminum oxide, though a large part of Sweden's aluminum requirements are filled by imports, especially from Canada. Of the nearly 35,000 persons engaged in metal production in Sweden, about 30,000 are employed in iron and steel mills.

The manufacture of iron and metal products is spread over a number of localities in the central and southern parts of the country, though the two largest concentrations of such industry are located in Eskilstuna and Stockholm. In the seventeenth century the groundwork for Eskilstuna's diversified production of high-quality goods had already been laid, and since then this Swedish city has become world famous for the matchless quality of its knives, scissors, carpenter tools, surgical instruments, locks, keys, machine tools, hardware, precision instruments, and silverware.

The Swedish manufacturing industries are the most diversified of any nation in Northern Europe, and many other products besides steel and glass have attracted world attention. Swedish trade-names in cream separators, refrigerators, vacuum cleaners, calculating machines, and various types of precision and electrical equipment are known the world over. The Swedish Ball-Bearing Company (SKF), with headquarters in Göteborg, is the world's largest exporter of ball bearings. The L. M. Ericsson Company, centered in Stockholm, supplies a large part of the world with its telephone equipment, and the name of Bofors is recognized as a world leader in armaments production, particularly of antiaircraft artillery. In addition, Sweden has a number of other mechanical industries, whose markets are less embracing. Motor vehicles, for example, are produced in Göteborg, Södertälje, and Stockholm. The country's largest shipyards are located at Göteborg, Malmö, Karlskrona, and Stockholm, and much of their work is done under foreign contract. Among the other centers of the mechanical industry are Linköping (aircraft and steam locomotives), Malmö (milling equipment), Trollhättan (aircraft engines, diesel motors, and turbines), Huskvarna (bicycles, sewing machines, and firearms), and Västerås (high-tension electrical equipment including electric locomotives). Two out of every five Swedish industrial workers earn their living in the metal and engineering industries.

Though most of its raw materials must be imported, the Swedish textile and clothing industry normally supplies 90 per cent of the country's needs for cloth and wearing apparel. Norrköping is Sweden's largest center for the production of woolen goods and also has an important production of cotton products. The Borås-Göteborg district is the country's chief cotton-spinning center, however, with a center of secondary importance in Malmö. The linen and jute industries are also concentrated near Sweden's west coast. Rayon and artificial wool are made in Borås and Norrköping. The chief clothing centers are Stockholm, Borås, Göteborg, and Malmö, and the production of shoes is concentrated in and near Örebro. The country's largest rubber factories are located in Skåne at Hälsingborg and Trälleborg.

The Swedish chemical industry engages in the production of a number of items, among them being superphosphate fertilizers, explosives, matches, wood distillates, plastics, and pharmaceuticals. Bofors holds the lead in explosives production, while Jönköping remains the center of a match industry which is a mere shadow of the monopolistic enterprise it constituted before 1932. Though today about one Swede in ten is employed in an industrial plant of some kind, more than 90 per cent of the country's factory workers are employed in enterprises with 100 or fewer workers.

Though she has no petroleum and only small, poor-quality coal reserves, Sweden is bountifully supplied with hydroelectric energy. Of her total waterpower resources, about 80 per cent are situated in Inner Northland, north of the Dal River. The remaining one-fifth south of the Dal has already largely been utilized, so Sweden's future needs must be fulfilled from Northland. In fact, about half of her total hydroelectric energy now comes from this region, the power being made available to the more densely settled and industrialized regions of central and southern Sweden through five great high-tension systems, each carrying 200,000 volts. A sixth transmission line carries 380,000 volts from the Harsprånget power station on the Lule

River over 590 miles to Hallsberg in the Central Swedish Lowland and is one of the world's longest and most heavily charged high-tension systems. Likewise linked to this system is the Stornorrfors station completed in the autumn of 1959. Located on the Ume River near the city of Umeå, Stornorrfors is not only the largest waterpower station in Sweden, but also in all Europe west of the Soviet Union. The total hydroelectric potential which Sweden might feasibly develop is estimated at between 40 and 45 billion kwh annually. In 1957 the country's production of electric energy topped 28 billion kwh, the bulk of which was produced by waterpower. To cover her fuel requirements, Sweden is normally dependent on coal and coke imported from Poland, Germany, and Great Britain, though in periods of emergency she is afforded some measure of substitution from her forests and from her peat and oil-shale deposits.

Fishing. Fishing plays a relatively minor role in the Swedish national economy, yet the largest part of the domestic demand for fish products is satisfied by Swedish fishermen. Centered chiefly in the west-coast province of Bohuslän, most Swedish fishing takes place in the Kattegat and Skagerrak, with herring, cod, and mackerel representing the most important varieties caught.

Transportation and Foreign Trade. Until the early nineteenth century, most transport in Sweden was by lakes and streams during the summer and by "winter roads" during the winter. In the first half of the last century, however, Sweden, like most of the other nations in Europe, was seized with a canal-building fever, and the most important project of this period was the so-called Göta Canal joining Göteborg with the east coast of Sweden through lakes Vänern and Vättern. In the 1860's railway construction began in earnest in Sweden, and today the country has over 10,000 miles of railroad, of which over 90 per cent are state owned and some 45 per cent are electrified. Of the country's total rail traffic, however, about seven-eighths is carried on the electrified lines.

In 1957 Sweden had 57,000 miles of roads, of which some 2,700 miles were maintained by the national government and 6,000 miles were hard surfaced. In the same year Sweden had one automobile for every 10 inhabitants.

Domestic air transport is carried on in Sweden by two companies, one operating on the longer-distance trunk routes (Stockholm-Göteborg, Stockholm-Malmö, and Stockholm-Luleå-Kiruna) and the other providing local feeder service to the smaller provincial cities. To conduct international flying, Sweden has joined with Denmark and Norway to form a corporation in which Sweden holds three-sevenths of the stock.

In 1957 Sweden's merchant marine totaled some 3 million gross tons, having grown by nearly one-third since 1950. Four-fifths of the tonnage consisted of motor ships, and one-half was less than 9 years old. In recent years the gross earnings of the Swedish merchant fleet have amounted to the equivalent of more than $250 million annually. The ports of Göteborg and Stockholm handle about an equal volume of traffic and together account for 30 per cent of Sweden's total foreign trade. Before the war (1938) Sweden's chief sources of imports were Germany, Great Britain, and the United States. In the same year her greatest exports went to Great Britain, Germany, and the United States. In 1955 West Germany, Great Britain, and the United States led the list of import sources, while Great Britain, West Germany, and Norway were the most important recipients of Swedish exports. Paper pulp, wood products, machinery (including ships), metals, and paper were her most important exports in 1955, while fuel, base metals, transport equipment, machinery, and foodstuffs constituted her chief imports.

FINLAND

Population

Finland had just over 4.25 million inhabitants in 1957, or more than ten times as many as in 1750. Some Finnish migration to the neighboring countries of Northern Europe took place before 1890, and in the ensuing half century almost 350,000 persons emigrated to the United States and Canada. Following the territorial cessions at the end of World War II, the country was obliged to absorb 480,000 Karelian refugees who chose to move rather than become Soviet citizens. Of the present population, slightly more than a third live in urban areas. Helsinki, the capital, is the country's largest city and has about 437,000 inhabitants (with suburbs, 511,000). The industrial city of Tampere has edged into second place with 119,000, surpassing the historic cultural and political center of Turku which has 115,000 inhabitants. Three other Finnish cities have more than 50,000 inhabitants each, seven have between 25,000 and 50,000, and twenty number more than 10,000 each.

Though the tide of Finnish settlement has been advancing inexorably toward the northeast during the centuries, about half of the total population still resides in the coastal districts of the south and west. It is in these areas that the country's Swedish-speaking minority, amounting to just under 9 per cent of the total population, is concentrated. In the Åland Islands Swedish is the language of 96 per cent of the populace, though in no mainland province does the proportion exceed 30 per cent.

Present Economic Life

Agriculture and Fishing. About 7 per cent of Finland's land area is under cultivation, the percentage varying from more than 30 per cent in sections of the coastal plain to less than 1 per cent in Lappland. Before the war, the average Finnish farm consisted of 20 acres of tilled land, but, as a result of the emergency resettlement of nearly 40,000 Karelian farm families, agricultural holdings were further splintered until today the average Finnish farm has less than 17 acres of tilled land. Fully 90 per cent of the country's farms have less than 40 acres of cultivable land each, though the farms larger than 40 acres comprise about two-fifths of the total land under the plow. These larger farms are concentrated in the southern and western portions of the country, especially on the Coastal Lowland, while small farm units are the rule in the interior, to the north and east. In the latter areas particularly, farming is combined with hunting, fishing, and forestry and is at best a part-time occupation. Formerly a very large proportion of Finnish farms were tenant operated, but a series of land reforms begun about 1920 has reduced this proportion to less than 5 per cent. At the present time about one-third of the Finnish population gains its livelihood from agriculture.

Like Norway and Swedish Northland, Finland has a climate which is best suited to the growing of fodder crops, and hence animal husbandry has become the dominant theme in Finnish farming. Over three-fourths of the country's cultivated land is in fodder crops, and, of the total, over half is in hay alone. In terms of acreage under cultivation, oats are second in importance, followed by barley, wheat, and rye. Hay is the principal crop in all regions of the country, but oats as a second crop give way to wheat in the more fertile soils of the Åland Islands and to barley in the far north. Though the Finnish yields per acre were the lowest of any country in Northern Europe before the war, they nevertheless were better on the average than those of countries, like France, whose climates are considerably more favorable for agriculture.

The aim of Finnish agriculture has been to make the country as self-sufficient as possible with respect to its food supply. Before World War II this goal had largely been achieved in such commodities as milk, butter, meat, eggs, and potatoes but had not yet been reached in bread grains. Even in bread grains, however, a tremendous advance in this direction had been made, for whereas Finland produced only 40 per cent of its requirements of bread grains before World War I, it was almost 90 per cent self-sufficient in this commodity by 1938, thanks both to increased acreages under cultivation and higher yields per acre. Unfortunately, World War II and its subsequent cessions of territory largely nullified these remarkable gains and today Finland must import nearly five times as much wheat and rye to feed her people as she did in 1938. Moreover, to maintain what self-sufficiency she does have, Finland must continue to import considerable quantities of fodder concentrates and artificial fertilizers.

Fishing plays a smaller part in the economy of Finland than in that of any of the other countries of Northern Europe. This is due, of course, to the fact that Finland lacks access to the open sea, which the other nations possess. Of the annual catch, about three-fourths is Baltic herring and over half of these are taken in the skerries off the southwest coast. Sealing has also been carried on since ancient times off the west coast, and seals are likewise found in Lake Saimaa in eastern Finland. Only about 10,000 persons live by hunting and fishing in Finland, including the Lapps who tend their reindeer herds in the far north.

Forest Industries. Though less than one-fourth of Finland's population derives its living from industry, this branch of the country's economy is steadily growing in importance. Aside from her agricultural land, Finland's greatest single resource is her forests (Fig. 4–13) and in normal times over 70 per cent of her exports are wood products of one sort or another. Of the country's total number of industrial employees, nearly one-third work in forestry and in the elaboration of forest products.

Sawmilling in Finland began in the sixteenth century, with the eastern districts of the country around Viipuri taking an initial lead. The greatest impetus to growth, however, came about the middle of the nineteenth century, when Great Britain adopted a free-trade policy and steam power was introduced. Though the earliest mills were located at waterpower sites, since the advent of steam the newer mills have grown up at the mouths of the larger rivers. Using their own waste for fuel, these plants are ideally located with respect both to floating and shipping possibilities. Since the loss of Viipuri, Kotka has become the country's largest timber port, handling over onefourth of the export trade. Among the other large timber ports are Pori, Oulu, Kemi, and Rauma. Though Finland had nearly 30,000 miles of floatable waterways before the war, the loss of Viipuri and the outlet of the Saimaa Canal has seriously complicated the movement of timber from eastern Finland. The postwar cessions likewise cost Finland about 12 per cent of her sawmill capacity.

In addition to sawn timber, box wood, and planed timber, the Finnish wood industry also produces spools, plywood veneer, and prefabricated houses for export. Once the world's leading producer of spools, Finland has steadily lost ground since World War I, because of both the loss of the Russian market and competition elsewhere. Also, using birch as a raw material, the Finnish plywood industry has grown rapidly since its founding in 1912, and before the outbreak of the Second World War Finland had risen to first place

Fig. 4–13. Part of Lake Saimaa in eastern Finland. This landscape is characteristic of the Lake Plateau—Finland's most distinctive natural region. Settled within relatively recent historical time, the region is still sparsely populated and shows few evidences of human occupancy. (Finnish Tourist Association.)

in the world's export of plywood, supplying nearly one-third of the total entering foreign trade. A more recent development in the wood-products industry is the production of prefabricated houses, most of which have been exported to the Soviet Union.

Side by side with her sawmills there have grown up pulp and paper mills, using the sawmill waste both for fuel and raw materials. In addition to the production of cellulose (both mechanical and chemical), the Finnish pulp and paper industry has a number of by-products which have given rise to further branches of industrial activity. Among them are rayon, fodder cellulose, turpentine, pine oil for soap and varnish, distilled spirits, and, during the war at least, motor fuel and lubricants. While the by-products go chiefly to the home market, pulp and paper are among Finland's foremost exports, with Great Britain as the country's best customer. In the postwar cessions to the Soviet Union, Finland lost about one-fifth of the productive capacity of her cellulose industry and one-tenth that of her paper industry.

More than half of Finland's forests are owned by private individuals, while another one-third belong to the state. The state exercises a strong influence in the Finnish forest industry and engages in considerable production itself. The motives for its entry into such production have been varied, ranging from acquiring fuel for the state railways to opening up less-accessible forests in the north and preventing foreign capital from getting control of the forests. Corporations own only 8 per cent of the total forest area.

Manufacturing. Producing principally for the home market are a number of other industries. The largest of these is metalworking, which since the war has become the country's largest single industry in terms of the number of persons employed. This is primarily the result of Soviet reparation demands which forced the industry to expand in order to meet delivery deadlines. Pig iron is produced by a coke oven in Turku and by an electric furnace near Imatra (Vuoksenniska), using scrap and some ore. Malleable-iron production is carried on in Martin ovens and electric furnaces on the southwest coast (Dalsbruk and Fiskars) and also at Vuoksenniska, where steel rails are rolled. Locomotives are built in Tampere, and the country's largest shipyards are located at Turku and Helsinki. The Finnish metal industry also produces farm implements, machinery, structural steel, boilers, and turbines. Important as this industry is to her domestic economy, however, Finland must continue to import most of the metal she uses in semifinished form.

Though most of its raw materials are likewise imported, the Finnish textile industry is centered about 90 miles inland, in the city of Tampere. This choice of location was originally due to Tampere's abundant waterpower, though the later construction of the railway network has also tended to give Tampere an added distributional advantage. Secondary centers of production are located in Helsinki and Turku. Because the production of the Finnish textile industry is neither adequate nor sufficiently diversified to meet domestic requirements, textile goods still constitute a considerable item of import.

Like Sweden's industry, that of Finland is rather evenly divided between rural and urban locations. Though its principal concentration is in the more densely settled Coastal Lowland of the south, access to forest resources and relatively good water and rail transport have encouraged an increasing industrialization of the Lake Plateau and the northern Coastal Lowland. The Åland Islands, owing to their "offside" position, are the least industrialized province of the entire country. A particular feature of Finnish industry as a whole is its large proportion of women employees, amounting to almost 40 per cent of the total. Indeed, an important factor in the growth of Finland's home-market industries has been her supply of cheap labor.

Minerals and Power. Finland's bedrock contains a great variety of minerals, but for the most part their metal contents are so low that mining is not profitable. At the present time Finland's most important mining operation is the copper mine at Outokumpu in Karelia. Discovered in 1910, this deposit of copper pyrite annually yields nearly 20,000 tons of metallic copper from some 600,000 tons of raw ore, as well as sulphur concentrates which are used in the cellulose industry and iron residues which go into the making of steel. At Otanmäki, in the north-central part of the country, the exploitation of a large titanium-iron deposit was started in 1953. With an iron content of about 37 per cent, the ore is scheduled for mining at the rate of 500,000 tons annually. The Petsamo nickel mines, which were just coming into production before World War II, were lost to the Soviet Union in 1947.

Without coal, Finland's industry was originally very closely tied to her waterpower sources. The introduction of steam changed this situation somewhat, but the advent of hydroelectric power once more shifted the centers of concentration back to waterfalls. Because of the nature of her topography, Finland's waterfalls generally have low heads of water, averaging 20 to 30 feet. Of advantage, however, is the fact that almost half of her waterpower reserves are located in the southern part of the country, where the large lakes also serve as natural regulators of the water level. With reserves estimated at 10 billion kwh, Finland was producing more than 7.7 billion kwh in 1957, of which about one-fifth was thermally generated. The recent completion of large generating stations on the Oulu and Kemi rivers (as well as elsewhere) and their interconnection with the existing power grid has helped to offset the loss occasioned by the cessions of 1947, when one-third of Finland's developed waterpower was turned over to the Soviet Union. The country's largest hydroelectric plant is located at Imatra on the Vuoksi River and has a capacity of 150,000 kw. Its power is distributed by high-tension lines as far west as Helsinki and Turku. About 80 per cent of all Finnish hydroelectric power is used by industry.

Transportation and Foreign Trade. Finland's earliest communications were by her lakes and rivers during the summer and by winter roads over the snow and ice through the rest of the year. The country now has about 21,900 miles of main roads, most of which have been built since the coming of the automobile. Only those in the vicinity of the larger cities are hard surfaced. In 1957 there was one automobile for every 35 persons in Finland.

As early as 1500, discussions began about the feasibility of joining Lake Saimaa and the eastern lake district with the Gulf of Finland by a canal, but nothing was done until the first half of the nineteenth century. Once completed, the Saimaa Canal became Finland's busiest inland waterway. In the 1930's, the tonnage passing through the canal averaged 3.5 million a year, though much of the north-bound traffic was empty bottoms. During the war the canal was within the fighting zone and accordingly unusable, and after the war it was lost to the Soviet Union by the territorial concessions. Whether Finland will find it practical to link the Saimaa district with the Kymi River by a new canal is still being debated.

Begun in 1862, when a line connecting Helsinki and Hämeenlinna (Tavastehus) was completed, the Finnish railway system now has about 3,170 miles in operation, of which all but 100 miles belong to the state (Fig. 4–4). Finland's railways have played an important role in the economic development of the country by opening up new forest and farm lands, expanding the hinterlands of several timber ports, and by providing a trade link with the Soviet Union. Inasmuch as most of the lines were built during the Russian period, the tracks are of broad gauge, and, despite the railway bridge across the Tornio River to Sweden, Finland has direct rail traffic with the Soviet Union only. The Finnish rail net has not yet been completed, however, and several additional lines are under construction or being planned.

Domestic air transport is carried on by a state-operated corporation, regular service being maintained between Helsinki and the other main towns of the country. The Finnish capital is also linked by air with the Scandinavian capitals and Moscow.

Sea transport is the decisive factor in Finland's foreign trade, for only her rail connections with the Soviet Union permit through shipments by land. Because of the nature of her exports, Finland's foreign trade experiences wide seasonal fluctuations compared to that of Denmark, for instance. The export of wood products, which comprise some 70 per cent of the total, is concentrated in the summer and early autumn, with the result that efficient year-around use of domestic shipping in home waters is impossible. Moreover, because her exports are more bulky on the whole than her imports, almost half of the freighters arriving in Finnish ports are in ballast, while only 10 per cent of the ships depart in ballast. Winter ice conditions likewise mean a decrease in traffic, since only specially constructed ships or limited ports (Hanko and Turku) can be used. Helsinki is the country's largest import port, followed by Turku, Hanko, and Kotka. Kotka leads in export, with Helsinki second and Turku third. The war caused a catastrophic drop in the Finnish merchant marine, the total gross tonnage falling from 649,000 tons in 1939 to 269,000 tons in 1945. By 1957 it had grown to 777,000 tons, of which, however, about half consisted of steamships more than 25 years of age.

Until she won her independence in 1917, about 40 per cent of Finland's trade was with Russia. Germany was her second-best customer and Great Britain took third place. After Finland's independence, however, Great Britain climbed into first place, where, with the exception of a few years, she has remained ever since. Germany held second place until the close of World War II, when trade with the Soviet Union became important once more. Today, with nearly one-fifth of her total trade being conducted with her eastern neighbor, Finland is especially sensitive to whatever politico-economic pressures Moscow chooses to apply. Finland's principal exports are paper pulp, newsprint, and timber products, while chief among her imports are fuels, iron and steel, bread grains, and textiles.

DENMARK

Population

In 1958 the population of Denmark totaled 4.5 million, having more than quadrupled since 1800. From 1820 to 1940 about 300,000 Danes emigrated to the United States, though this is considerably less in proportion to the emigration from the other Scandinavian countries during the same period. Of the present population, 44 per cent reside in Jutland and 56 per cent live on the islands to the east. In terms of its rural-urban distribution, the Danish population may be divided roughly into quarters, with Copenhagen and its environs, the outlying provincial towns, suburbs and rural agglomerations of over 500 persons, and scattered rural habitations each giving residence to about a fourth of the total. Copenhagen reached the peak of its growth in 1950, though its subsequent decline has been offset by continued growth in the suburbs. Today the metropolitan area of the Danish capital has 1.25 million inhabitants. Copenhagen so dominates the country as a whole that no other city even remotely approaches it in size. Aarhus, the regional capital of Jutland, ranks second with about 160,000, suburbs included, and is followed by Odense on Fyn with 115,000 and the North Sea port of Esbjerg with

53,000. Seven other Danish towns have more than 25,000 inhabitants each and twenty-three more have between 10,000 and 25,000 persons.

Present Economic Life of Denmark

Agriculture and Fishing. Although agriculture has always played an important role in the economic life of Denmark, the specialized export nature which characterizes this occupation today dates back only to the latter part of the nineteenth century. When it became clear to Denmark that she could no longer compete with America and Russia in growing cheap bread grains for the industrial nations of Western Europe, the little nation turned to a concentrated production of livestock products, placing chief emphasis on the growing of fodder crops. Thanks largely to the high level of scientific instruction given to the farmers, to the adoption of the cooperative principle of organization, to a self-imposed regulation of quality, and more recently to the widespread mechanization which has taken place, Danish agriculture has become a model of rational management, whose products can command the highest prices in the world markets.

In proportion to its area Denmark has more land under cultivation than any other country in Europe—64 per cent. Even on the relatively infertile western plains of Jutland over half of the land is under cultivation. In general, the percentage of land devoted to the various crops is relatively uniform from one section of the country to the next, though this is least true in the Heath of Jutland. The greatest proportions of land in wheat are found on Bornholm, Zealand, and Fyn, where about 10 per cent of the cultivated area is devoted to this crop. Malt barley likewise finds its greatest concentrations east of the terminal moraine, and on the islands of Laaland and Falster it constitutes over one-third of the acreage. Sugar beets are also confined to the better soils and particularly to Laaland and Falster, where they make up another 20 per cent of the cultivated area. Oats, hay, green fodder, and root crops are quite uniformly distributed over the entire country, and in the sandy districts of western and northern Jutland crops of rye, potatoes, and mixed seed (barley and rye) reach their greatest extent.

About 64 per cent of the Danish farms are under 40 acres in size, and an additional 34 per cent have areas of between 40 and 150 acres. When the total acreage of cultivated land is broken down into the same categories, we find that only 29 per cent belongs to the farms with less than 40 acres but that 56 per cent belongs to the farms in the 40- to 150-acre group. Accordingly, against the background of Europe as a whole, it would not be erroneous to think of Denmark as a nation of middle-size farms (Fig. 4–14). Hired labor is much more common on Danish farms than it is elsewhere in Northern Europe, and annually constitutes about 35 per cent of the work done. Nearly three-fourths of all Danish farms either own or have access to tractors, and more than two-thirds are equipped with milking machines. Evidence of the intensive and careful use the Danish farmer makes of his soil is seen in the fact that an average of 430 pounds of artificial fertilizer are applied annually to each acre under cultivation.

Fig. 4–14. View looking eastward from the lighthouse near the southeastern tip of Bornholm. In the foreground is a typical Danish farmstead. Built around three sides of a central courtyard are whitewashed, half-timbered barns and implement sheds, with a brick dwelling house occupying the fourth side.

In sheer volume, the Danish production of livestock products dwarfs that of the rest of Northern Europe. Each year the farms of Denmark produce more milk than Norway and Finland put together, more cheese than Norway and Sweden combined, and more meat and butter than is produced in all three of her neighboring northern countries.

Denmark's specialized production of livestock products has had a number of interesting, and occasionally serious, consequences. Before the last war she was the world's foremost exporter of butter, bacon, and eggs, but, because she cannot produce all of her own fodder requirements, Denmark has also become one of the world's leading importers of fodder concentrates. To fatten her swine she has had to maintain a considerable import of corn, and to maintain the fertility of her soils she has become a leading importer of artificial fertilizers. Despite her foremost position as an agricultural nation, Denmark has to import almost one-third of the bread grains used for domestic consumption, and, in order to release as much butter for export as possible, vegetable oils are imported in large quantities to make margarine. Hence we have the apparent inconsistency that, in a nation which is one of the world's largest producers of dairy products, the domestic consumption of margarine per capita is two to three times that of butter. With her economy so utterly dependent on such exports and imports it is easily understood why Denmark's per-capita foreign trade is among the highest in Europe.

Though Denmark's revolution in agriculture has been largely responsible for the high standard of living which the Danes now enjoy, it has also made the country's economy extremely vulnerable to international economic crises, such as that of the 1930's. The fact that only about one-fourth of the Danish population is today employed in agriculture belies its tremendous importance to the life of the nation.

The Danish fishing industry likewise has an importance out of proportion to the numbers it employs. In 1957, for example, Denmark's 17,000 fishermen landed more than half a million tons of fish. In volume, this represented less than one-third of the Norwegian catch in the same year, yet its total value was more than two-fifths that of its northern neighbor. In some years the Danes may catch only 15 per cent as much as the Norwegians and still earn nearly 60 per cent as much when it is marketed. This is due, first of all, to a greater abundance of more-valuable species in Danish waters, particularly the plaice and the eel. Secondly, Denmark's proximity to the consuming markets allows a greater proportion of the fish to be sold fresh rather than dried or salted. The chief ports of the fishing fleet are Esbjerg on the west coast of Jutland and Skagen on its northern tip.

Industry. The industrialization of Denmark has paralleled the shift of Danish agriculture to specialized production for export, and food processing has quite naturally become one of the most important branches of industry. Its gross value of production is greater than that of any other industry, though in value added by manufacture it ranks second and in number of workers employed it ranks fourth. With the exception of the more than 1,400 dairies scattered over the country which handle fluid milk, the food-processing industry has tended to locate in advantageous shipping ports rather than in rural districts near the source of supply. Despite the fact that Denmark has no resources of coal, iron, wood, petroleum, or waterpower, a number of other industries have grown up within the country, most of them designed to produce for the home market but some of them also producing for export. Among the latter are the engineering and shipbuilding industries. In 1898 a Danish firm acquired the patent of the diesel engine from its inventor, and in 1912 the first diesel-powered ocean-going ship sailed from Denmark. Since that time, the country has been a foremost builder of motor ships and marine engines. Today Danish engine works and foundries employ more workers than any other branch of industry and contribute the largest share to the value added by manufacture. Branches of industry which are based at least in part on Danish raw materials include the making of porcelain and cement. Others, like the textile and apparel industries, depend almost exclusively on imported raw materials. The fact that all Danish industries are dependent on imported fuel for power further heightens the desirability of port cities as industrial sites. Nearly one-third of the Danish population makes its living in industry today and about two-fifths of all industrial workers are concentrated in the Copenhagen area.

Transportation and Foreign Trade. Transport in Denmark is encumbered by the country's lack of physical continuity. In 1957 Denmark had 2,710 miles of railway, of which nearly half were privately owned. However, the disproportionately small role that the private railways play in the country's transportation scheme is seen in the fact that the state railways annually carry fifteen times as much passenger traffic and forty times as much freight traffic as the private lines. Joining the various islands and linking Denmark's rail net to those of Sweden and West Germany are 153 miles of ferry routes.

Denmark's highway net in 1957 consisted of 5,200 miles of roadway, of which the greater part was hard surfaced and nearly 1,400 miles were classed as main roads. In addition to a rapidly swelling volume of domestic road traffic—with one passenger car for every 17 Danes in 1957—a sizable transit traffic between the Scandinavian peninsula and the continent has developed, in recent years involving as many as 1.5 million entries and exits into and out of Danish territory.

With 28 of its 35 cities over 10,000 in population located on navigable water bodies, it is not surprising that a considerable part of the domestic traffic of Denmark goes by sea. The greater part of such movement is made up of bulky goods such as coal, petroleum, stone, and cement. In terms of volume of traffic handled, Denmark's busiest ports are Copenhagen, Aarhus, Aalborg, and Esbjerg.

At the end of 1957 Denmark had a merchant marine which totaled just over two million gross tons. Of this tonnage, seven-eighths consisted of motor ships, two-thirds were less than 9 years old, and nearly one-third was made up of tankers. The gross freight earnings of Danish ships in foreign trade annually contribute the equivalent of about $225 million to the Danish national economy.

Lacking great internal distances and possessing well-developed forms of surface transport, Denmark has experienced a rather modest growth in its domestic air services. However, regular flights are maintained between Copenhagen-Aarhus, Copenhagen-Aalborg, and Copenhagen-Rönne (on Bornholm). Denmark has joined with Norway and Sweden to form a cooperative international airline in which Denmark holds two-sevenths of the stock. Kastrup Airport at Copenhagen is its main traffic center, and from it emanate many intercontinental flights including transpolar services to both Los Angeles and Tokyo.

Owing to the specialized nature of its economy, Denmark's foreign trade is not only large but also relatively unbalanced. In normal years, about four times as many tons of goods are discharged at Danish ports as are loaded for shipment. This is because her imports, of which fuels, base metals, transport equipment, textiles, and machinery lead the list, are much bulkier than her exports, among which meat, dairy products, and machinery rank highest. Denmark's chief sources of imports are the United Kingdom, West Germany, the United States, and Sweden. These same countries provide the best markets for her exports, though Sweden normally buys more from Denmark than does the United States.

THE FAEROES

The present population of the Faeroes numbers about 35,000, of whom some 6,000 live in the capital, Thorshavn. Fishing and whaling support about three-eighths of the islands' inhabitants and account for more than seven-eighths of their exports. The annual catch runs to more than 100,000 tons, with cod constituting about three-fourths of the total and herring about one-fifth. Fully nine-tenths of the catch is marketed after being salted, smoked, or marinated. The Faeroes' best customers are the countries of Mediterranean Europe and South America. Though Faeroese fishermen range as far afield as Iceland, Greenland, and Spitsbergen, all whaling activities take place in the vicinity of the islands themselves, particularly during the summer, when the small *ca'ing*, or grind, whales swarm along the coast. As recently as 1890 about half of the Faeroese population lived by agriculture, but today this proportion has fallen to five per cent. Sheep raising is the chief form of agricultural activity, and the islands' flocks total upward of 70,000 animals. Less than four per cent of the islands' area is under cultivation, and there is a small annual harvest of hay, potatoes, and root crops. Most foodstuffs and other commodities must be imported, with Denmark normally supplying about two-thirds of the total. In some localities, fowling along the cliffs and on the skerries provides an important adjunct to the food supply,

Fig. 4–15. View overlooking the town of Vaag on Syderö, most southerly island of the Faeroes. Note the broad U-shape of the valley and how the fjord has almost cut through to the ocean, seen in the background. Also, note the complete absence of trees.

though on the whole this activity is declining owing to the attraction of other less dangerous and more remunerative occupations. Coal of fair quality is mined on Syderö, though peat remains the islanders' chief source of fuel. The larger settlements have communal generating plants for electricity, but most outlying districts continue to depend on wind-operated generators for their power. Industry, including such marine-oriented activities as ship repair and fish processing, together with handicrafts, especially home knitting, gives support to about one-sixth of the islands' inhabitants. In recent years as many as 1,400 Faeroese have been enticed by high wages into service in the Icelandic fishing fleet.

Interisland communications are maintained by ships operating between Thorshavn and the other main towns, though at a considerable deficit. There are about 120 miles of motorable roads and several hundred motor vehicles on the islands, but a large part of the goods which are moved overland still goes by horseback or on the backs of men. During the summer, steamship connections between the Faeroes and Copenhagen are maintained on a schedule of once each week and during the winter, once every three weeks.

ICELAND

In 1957 the population of Iceland totaled 167,000 persons, of whom about three-quarters lived in towns and villages of 300 or more inhabitants. Reykjavík, the capital and largest city, had 67,000 (with suburbs, 73,000), while Akureyri, the regional center of the north, was second in size with a population of 8,300. Because it has the highest birth rate of any country in Western Europe and the lowest death rate in the world, Iceland is presently undergoing something of a "population explosion." Concurrently, the migration from the rural districts into Reykjavík has swelled to such proportions that today 44 per cent of all Icelanders live in the one city and its suburbs.

As recently as 1880 almost three-quarters of the people of Iceland gained their living through agriculture, but since that time a great expansion has taken place in both fishing and industry. Today only about 20 per cent of the population is engaged in agriculture, with animal husbandry still constituting its central theme. Less than one per cent of the island's area is under cultivation and the chief crops are hay, potatoes, and turnips. Marked fluctuations in yield from year to year testify to Iceland's location near a climatic frontier. Another ten per cent of the island is covered with grass which affords pasturage for numerous sheep, cattle, and horses (Fig. 4–16). In the Southern Lowlands and the western half of the north coast, where local transport is best developed, fluid milk forms the chief source of agricultural income; elsewhere, mutton constitutes the principal farm commodity entering commerce. In recent years water from hot springs has been used to heat greenhouses and forcing-gardens, and Reykjavík now derives much of its fruit, vegetables, and cut flowers from such sources.

The backbone of Iceland's modern economic life is fishing, for although only 11 per cent of her population is engaged in this occupation, some 97 per cent of her exports are derived from it. Cod and herring constitute the principal species caught, cod being taken off all coasts and herring more especially along the north coast. Because about half of the country's trawlers are based in Reykjavík, the Icelandic capital has the distinction of being the largest fishing port. During and since World War II the movements of herring off the north coast have been extremely erratic, and in recent years most fishing activity has shifted toward the east. Landings at Siglufjördhur, the "herring capital of Iceland," have fallen off sharply, and many processing plants located farther west have lain idle for several seasons.

Fig. 4–16. Icelandic ponies grazing near Lake Myvatn, in the northeastern interior. Until rather recently the sturdy Icelandic pony served both as the primary means of overland transport and as a valuable adjunct to the food supply. Part of a lava flow and a table mountain (horst) may be seen in the background.

In order to protect the spawning grounds of the fish on which the country's livelihood is so overwhelmingly dependent, Iceland extended its fisheries limit to 4 nautical miles in 1952 and then to 12 in 1958. The refusals of some other countries, notably the United Kingdom, to recognize these claims have engendered considerable friction and ill will.

Industry now supports over 20 per cent of the population, and, because most of its raw materials come from fishing and agriculture, its most important branch is food processing. Formerly the bulk of the fish catch was marketed after being dried and salted, but now a large part of the catch is sold iced or frozen. A considerably smaller proportion of fish is canned for export, as well as some mutton, shrimp, and lobster. In the last decade a number of subsidiary industries have grown up, among them the preparation of fish meal for fertilizer, herring oil for margarine, and cod-liver oil for medicinal purposes. A large electrochemical plant which began operations on the outskirts of Reykjavík in 1954 fills the country's needs for nitrate fertilizer and provides an additional item for export. A state-owned cement plant at Akranes commenced production in 1958 and promises to substantially reduce the country's dependence on imported building materials.

Save for a poor-quality peat, Iceland largely lacks fossil fuel resources. It is, however, bountifully supplied with hydroelectric power, the reserves being estimated at between three and four million kilowatts, of which half might feasibly be utilized. To date only about 80,000 kilowatts have been developed, but even this rather limited development has largely been responsible for the country's recent strides in industrialization. During World War II another economic advance of great importance was made when an installation was completed for heating most of the city of Reykjavík by water piped from hot springs 11 miles to the northeast. Investigations into the possible utilization of earth heat as a source of power are currently under way.

Until relatively recent times, all transport in Iceland was either by ship along the coasts or by overland horse caravan. While shipping still is of great significance, the automobile has completely revolutionized the country's land transport. Today Iceland has about 5,600 miles of motorable roads and one motor vehicle for every nine persons —the highest ratio of any country in Europe. Air transport is also of great importance, as evidenced by the fact that one Icelander in every four travels by plane each year. One company maintains frequent services between Reykjavík and the other main towns of the island, and this and another Icelandic airline engage in international traffic, the latter flying between New York and the major cities of northwestern Europe. Keflavík Airport, about 30 miles west of the capital, was reactivated as an American military base during the Korean War but also serves as a regular stop for several foreign airlines operating between Europe and North America.

With its small population dependent on imports for most of the essentials of life, Iceland has the highest per-capita trade of any nation in the world. To pay for its required imports, Iceland exports fish and fish products (including oil and meal) and some mutton, wool, hides, and skins. Before World War II, the United Kingdom was Iceland's best customer, normally taking one-fifth of her total exports and supplying one-fourth of her total imports. During the war the bulk of

Iceland's trade shifted to the United States, which remained her most important trading partner until the mid-1950's when she in turn was displaced by the Soviet Union. By 1958 one-third of Iceland's total trade was being carried on with countries behind the Iron Curtain. In most prewar years Iceland had a favorable trade balance, but during and since the war imports have consistently exceeded exports. In order of their value, the chief imports are mineral fuels and lubricants, textiles, transport equipment, and machinery. The port of Reykjavík normally handles seven-eighths of the country's imports and two-thirds of its exports.

*   *   *

To each of the countries of Northern Europe, diverse as they are, the challenge remains the same: how to make a living in an environment which offers many obstacles and provides few resources. That these countries have largely succeeded in meeting this challenge in the past is witnessed by their high standard of living today. How well they will succeed in meeting this challenge in the future will in large part depend on their ability to work together in ever closer and more harmonious cooperation and on their ability to avoid involvement in the intrigues of the Great Powers which surround them. Northern Europe, like all other regions of the world, can prosper only in an atmosphere of peace.

BIBLIOGRAPHY

(Major references are asterisked.)

Books in English

ADAMSON, OLGE J. (ed.). Industries of Norway. Oslo: Dreyers Forlag, 1952.

Danish Agriculture. The Danish Agricultural Organizations. Copenhagen: J. B. Qvist & Komp., 1954.

*MALMSTRÖM, VINCENT H. A Regional Geography of Iceland. Washington: National Academy of Sciences–National Research Council, 1958. Publication 584.

*MEAD, WILLIAM R. An Economic Geography of the Scandinavian States and Finland. London: University of London Press, Ltd., 1958.

*O'DELL, ANDREW C. The Scandinavian World. London: Longmans, Green & Co., Ltd., 1957.

OSVALD, HUGO. Swedish Agriculture. Swedish Institute, Stockholm. Uppsala: Almqvist & Wiksell, 1952.

*PLATT, RAYE R. (ed.). Finland and Its Geography. American Geographical Society Handbook. New York: Duell Sloan & Pearce, Inc., 1955.

*SÖMME, AXEL (ed.). The Geography of Norden. Oslo: J. W. Cappelens Forlag, 1960.

*Suomi: A General Handbook on the Geography of Finland. Geographical Society of Finland. Helsinki: Valtioneuvoston kirjapaino, 1952.
THORARINSSON, SIGURDUR. The Thousand Years Struggle Against Ice and Fire. Reykjavík: Bókaútgafa Menningarsjódhs, 1956.
WESTERMARCK, NILS. Finnish Agriculture. Pellervo Society. Helsinki: Yhteiskirjapaino Osakeyhtiö, 1954.

Books in Foreign Languages

*AHLMANN, HANS W:SON. Norge: Natur og Naeringsliv (Norway: Nature and Economic Life). Norwegian edition by Fridtjov Isachsen and Hallstein Myklebost. Oslo: Universitetsforlaget, 1957.
CHABOT, GEORGES. L'Europe du Nord et du Nord-Ouest: Tome II—Finlande et Pays Scandinaves (Northern and Northwestern Europe: Volume II—Finland and the Scandinavian Countries). Paris: Presses Universitaires de la France, 1958.
KAMPP, AAGE H. Faeröerne: Folk og Erhverv (The Faeroes: People and Economy). Copenhagen: Det Danske Forlag, 1950.
PIPPING, HUGO E. Finlands Näringsliv efter andra Världskriget (The Economic Life of Finland After the Second World War). Helsinki: Söderstrom & Co., 1954.
SÖMME, AXEL. Jordbrukets geografi i Norge (The Geography of Norwegian Agriculture). Bergen: Grieg, 1949.
Sveriges Industri (Sweden's Industry). Översikt utgiven år 1948 av Sveriges Industriförbund. Stockholm: Esselte AB, 1948.
Vår Industris Geografiske Fordeling (The Geographical Distribution of Norwegian Industry). Oslo: Grieg, 1952.

Articles

ALEXANDER, LEWIS M. "Iceland," Focus 10 (October, 1959).
GOODWIN, WILLIAM F. "Scandinavia," Focus 5 (January, 1955).
HAUPERT, J. S. "The Impact of Geographic Location upon Sweden as a Baltic Power," Journal of Geography 58 (January, 1959): 5–14.
MALMSTRÖM, VINCENT H. "The Norwegian State Railways: 1854–1954," American Scandinavian Review 42 (September, 1954): 360–71.
———. "The Rise of Reykjavík: A Study in Historico-Economic Geography," Proceedings of the Minnesota Academy of Sciences (1957–58).
MEAD, WILLIAM R. "Finnish Karelia: An International Borderland," Geographical Journal 118 (1952): 40–57.
———. "The Cold Farm in Finland," Geographical Review 41 (October, 1951): 529–43.
SOMMERS, LAWRENCE M. "Svalbard: Norway's Arctic Frontier," Scientific Monthly (June, 1952): 338–45.

5

Western Europe

France, Belgium, the Netherlands, and Luxembourg together constitute the western gateway to the Eurasian continent. A maritime outlook has come readily to these countries which have an extensive coast line stretching from the Ems River mouth to the western reaches of the Pyrenees. Their eastern borders join Central Europe without serious land barriers. The Iberian Peninsula to the south is accessible at either end of the Pyrenees, and Italy along the Riviera coast. The British Isles lie only 21 miles across the English Channel at the narrowest part of the Strait of Dover.

The Western European countries can be regarded as both maritime and continental in character. France, for example, has a coast line 1,925 miles long, and no part of the country is more than 300 miles from the sea. At the same time, Strasbourg is located only 400 miles from Vienna and 360 miles from Berlin. At their nearest points, the French and Dutch borders are only some 140 miles from Communist East Germany. Belgium and the Netherlands share only a short coast line, but they occupy the delta area of three of Europe's most important rivers for trade and transport. Thus, while France borders on four seas and extends from southern to northern Europe, the Low Countries have a bridge location providing direct connections between the heart of Central Europe and the sea.

Western Europe includes the largest state in Europe outside the Soviet Union, as well as one of the smallest. France has more than twice the area of the German Federal Republic (West Germany) or the United Kingdom, but it has a smaller total population than either of them. Luxembourg, on the other hand, is one of the smallest states of Europe, having an area of only 998 square miles. Western Europe, also, can take pride in the successful formation of the first economic union of several states—the Benelux union—and in active participation of all four states in other regional organizations of the mid-twentieth century, such as the European Coal and Steel Community, the European Economic Community, and others.

The surface configuration of Western Europe is extremely diversified, ranging in elevation from the highest peaks in Europe, in the Alps, to below sea level, in the polders of the Netherlands. Yet, the alignment of the terrain is such that maritime air masses penetrate easily, providing much of Western Europe with a temperate marine climate.

THE PHYSICAL LANDSCAPE

Upon general observation the physical landscape of Western Europe appears to be simple (Fig. 5–1). The grain of the terrain is arcuate, with the convex side toward the Atlantic Ocean, English Channel, and North Sea. There are three principal concentric bands of landforms: (1) Bordering the coast is the European Lowland which extends from the western Pyrenees into northern Germany and eastern Europe; (2) adjoining the lowland arc in the interior is an irregular area of hills and plateaus, stretching from the Carcassonne gateway to the Vosges and Ardennes; (3) framing Western Europe on the south and southeast are the high and rugged mountains of the Alps and Pyrenees.

A closer examination of the physical landscape reveals, however, that uniformity is only superficial and that there is great diversity within each of these belts. Hills appear in the lowland, and river valleys and wide corridors break up the continuity of hills, plateaus, and mountains.

The European Lowland

The southwestern section of the European Lowland is the Aquitaine Basin covering about 15 per cent of the area of France. It is a basin in which sediments have accumulated from the adjacent higher lands since late Tertiary times. The sedimentary layers are horizontal, so that the countryside is level or gently rolling and without scarplands.

The southern and southeastern part of the basin is a large piedmont alluvial fan deposited by the ancestral streams issuing forth from the last Pleistocene glaciers of the Pyrenees. The present Garonne River, its southern tributaries, and the streams of the Adour watershed have carved the fan in recent times into an undulating to rolling foothill area.

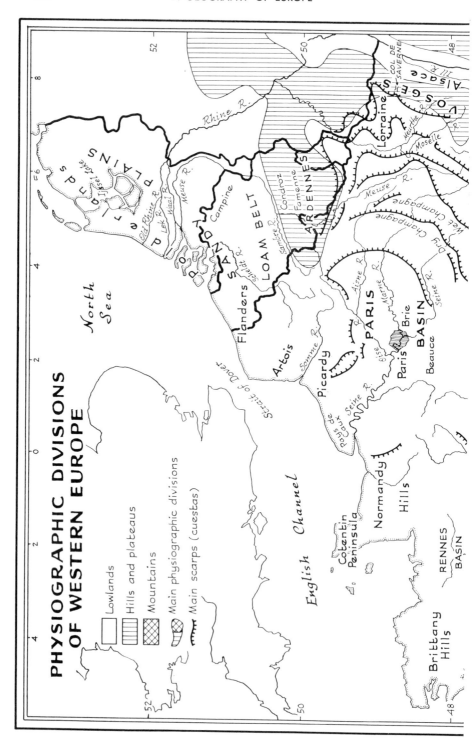

PHYSIOGRAPHIC DIVISIONS
OF WESTERN EUROPE

Lowlands

Hills and plateaus

Mountains

Main physiographic divisions

Main scarps (cuestas)

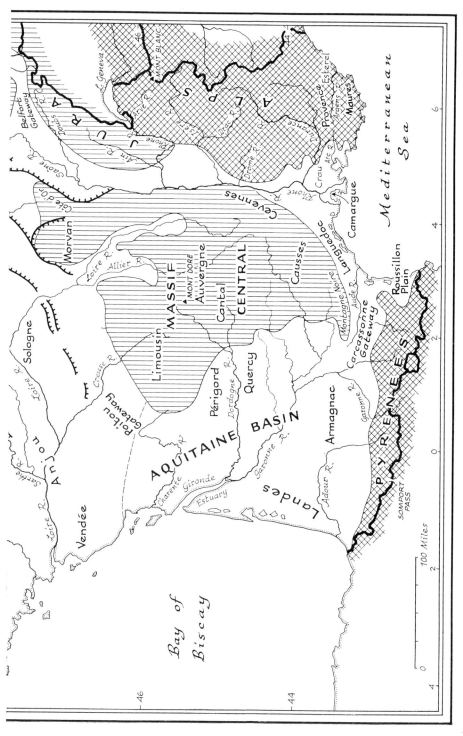

Fig. 5–1. Main physiographic divisions.

Between this fan and the Gironde estuary lies the Landes region—a low, flat, sandy plain behind the coastal dunes. These sands are of recent marine origin. Until only a century ago, the landscape presented a picture of desolation—shifting sand dunes and intervening marshlands and swamps—for a subsurface hardpan formation interfered with normal drainage processes. In the latter half of the nine-

Fig. 5–2. The Landes forest between Bordeaux and Bayonne. The sandy plain has been drained and planted with maritime pine. Note the movable sawmill on the edge of the forest. Pines are valuable as a source both of naval stores and timber.

teenth century, land was reclaimed, dunes stabilized, and extensive forests of maritime pine planted. Thus, the Landes became and remains a principal producer of lumber and naval stores (Fig. 5–2).

North of the Garonne-Gironde estuary, limestone bedrock is at or near the surface. Near the coast it is covered with unconsolidated sediments. However, eastward toward the Massif Central the surface rises gradually and culminates in the Périgord and Quercy limestone plateaus, which have karstic features at higher elevations but contain wide, fertile valleys.

There are three gateways leading out of the Aquitaine Basin into other physiographic provinces. The gateway of Carcassonne, a wide, sweeping corridor between the Pyrenees and the Massif Central, connects the Basin with the Mediterranean coastal plain. In the north, the low, featureless coast continues to the Loire estuary. Inland, the gateway of Poitou between low Hercynian massifs provides a connection between the Aquitaine and Paris basins.

The Paris Basin, occupying roughly one-fifth of the area of France, is a structural basin composed of a series of alternating strata of Jurassic and Tertiary limestones, sandstones, and clays of marine origin. During the Alpine mountain-building period, a gentle uplift and downward arching of the rock strata set the stage for subsequent erosion and the present landscape. Toward the east, these layers outcrop as far as Lorraine, southern Luxembourg, and southernmost Belgium. Differential erosion has produced the scarplands, with more resistant steep forested limestone scarps facing eastward toward Central Europe. Famous examples are the Île de France escarpment east of Reims and Épernay which bears the vineyards of the Champagne, the Côtes de Meuse of the western Meuse Valley, and the Côte de Moselle—the western slopes of the Moselle Valley where the iron-ore-bearing strata are exposed. The prevailing bedrock in the Paris Basin is limestone, but over wide areas in the north and west it is covered with deep, fertile loam called *limon* [1] (Fig. 5–3). Variations in slope, the irregular distribution of loam, and the deeply incised rivers, often with wide floodplains and terraces, give considerable regional diversity to the landscape. The flat, featureless Beauce, south and southwest of Paris, contrasts with the undulating to hilly Artois between Picardy and Flanders.

Within the Paris Basin the portions not covered by loam either have a dry, almost karstic landscape in spite of an abundance of precipitation or they are poorly drained where residual clays are at the surface or where clay beds emerge. Conspicuous examples are the Dry Champagne and Wet Champagne. The former is dry chalk country, partly forested, partly used for grazing and some crop cultivation; the latter, adjoining the Dry Champagne on the east, was originally wooded, waterlogged clay country but is now in the main a drained and reclaimed prosperous agricultural area.

Two large river systems drain the Paris Basin. In the south, the Loire and its tributaries have a general east-to-west orientation and empty into the Bay of Biscay; the greater part of the Basin is drained by the Seine River system which extends from interior highlands northeastward through the center of the Basin to the Seine estuary on the English Channel. A few other streams outside these two systems are important, notably the Meuse and Moselle rivers in the east and the Somme River in the north. Generally, streams meander and are deeply incised. Where erosion has reached softer layers of sand and clay beneath the limestones, the floodplains are wide and soils

[1] *Limon* is loess that has been redeposited by running water.

on the lower slopes vary in composition and fertility, depending on the nature of the parent material.

West and southwest of the Paris Basin are the old worn-down Hercynian massifs of Normandy and Brittany, also known as the Armorican Massif. Although a few rounded hilltops reach elevations of over 1,000 feet, local relief is not pronounced.

Fig. 5–3. Undulating landscape in the Picardy near Amiens. Fertile loam soils give rise to a prosperous agriculture. (Standard Oil Company of New Jersey.)

In the Brittany peninsula there are two parallel east-west rows of granitic hills, of which the northern one has the greater height and continuity. The general elevation gradually increases from east to west until the highest peak is reached not far from the drowned valleys of the western end of the peninsula. For the most part, the landscape is not forbidding but a well-dissected, continuously rolling hedgerow country, known as *bocage* (Fig. 5–4), with deeply weathered granite yielding residual soils of low fertility. The coastal plain to the north and south slopes gently from the interior upland to the cliffy irregular and indented coast.

Between the Brittany peninsula and the Normandy hills is the Rennes Basin, a former lake bottom and now an extensive undulating lowland. Loose sediments largely have been eroded away and old Hercynian rocks are exposed at the surface.

Granitic rocks again come to the surface to form hills in Normandy east and northeast of the Rennes Basin and near the northern end of the Cotentin Peninsula. The slopes rise fairly rapidly from surrounding lowlands. At close range, however, these hills, as those in Brittany, present a rounded, well-dissected *bocage* landscape. The low sections of the Cotentin Peninsula as well as the coastal plains are marshy,

Fig. 5–4. The *bocage* landscape of Brittany. Undulating to rolling country-side, with fields and pastures enclosed by hedgerows. Some of the farmsteads are isolated, others are clustered in hamlets and villages. (French Embassy Press and Information Division, New York.)

and in part reclaimed like the polders of Belgium and the Netherlands.

Northeast of the Paris Basin is the Belgian Gate, a narrow section of the European Lowland, between the English Channel and the Ardennes. Here and in the adjoining Netherlands the bedrock is composed of Cretaceous and Tertiary sedimentary rocks dipping gently toward the northwest. However, it is covered with masses of unconsolidated sediments of fluvial, marine, and glacial origin. This part of the lowland has distinctive belts, each paralleling the coast.

A strip of sand dunes, sometimes 2 miles wide and 30 to 60 feet high or higher, borders the coast itself. In Belgium the northeastern section of the shore line near the Dutch border has recently been attacked by the sea and has retreated, resulting in destruction of even some older dune formations, whereas in the Netherlands sediments have been deposited by currents. Such deposition, combined with works of man, has resulted in a seaward shift of the Dutch shore line, creating several parallel dune belts.

Immediately behind the dunes, stretching from western Flanders to northern Groningen, are the "polder lands." These are generally below sea level in the Netherlands—amounting to between one-fourth and one-third of the Dutch land area—and just barely above sea level in Belgium. Formerly these lands were peat bogs, wet clay areas, and lakes, but now they have largely been drained and reclaimed for agricultural use. In Belgium, the polder region attains a maximum width of some 12 miles inside the dunes, but in the Netherlands the belt is much wider, with a maximum of some 30 miles south of the Ijssel Lake (Ijsselmeer) and in the low delta lands. Man's creation of the polder landscape has been a continuing process since the tenth century A.D.

Adjoining the polders are the sandy plains stretching from eastern Flanders and the Campine northeastward to southern Groningen. These range in elevation from at or near sea level on the polder side to 150 to 300 feet in the interior. They are interrupted by extensive river clay deposits in the delta lands of the Rhine and Meuse, and, further north, glaciation has altered the landscape considerably. In Belgium, the sandy plains are of recent fluvial origin and the sandy soils have been used for agriculture in Flanders ever since the Middle Ages. In the Campine, on the other hand, an impermeable subsoil delayed effective exploitation by man; some sections have remained heath land, others have been afforested with coniferous vegetation. With increased demand for food, large tracts have been improved and, together with stream valleys, are being utilized for pasture and crops. The discovery of coal there in the present century has created mining and manufacturing communities and transformed the original physical landscape even more.

In the delta lands, river beds can be recognized which at one time held glacial streams but which are now abandoned. Valleys, now occupied by the arms of the Rhine and Meuse rivers, are separated from one another by wide strips of low, flat clay land, protected from floods by dikes.

North of a line connecting Nijmegen, Wageningen, and Utrecht, or roughly north of the Meuse River, continental glaciation has been the agent chiefly responsible for shaping the landscape. The outwash sands were covered by ground moraines which subsequently were eroded away again in many places. Where they have remained, the ground moraines have a depth ranging from 3 to 15 feet and, in some localities, as much as 50 feet. The glaciers, moreover, have left a series of north-south ridges of morainic hills, most of them east and southeast of the Ijssel Lake. The higher, sandy morainic and, in part, poorly drained areas of the eastern and northeastern Netherlands have provided a meager habitat for man, and, understandably, these were the last sections of the country to be settled. Some high moors still exist in the far northeast, but most of the area has been put to agricultural use, and recent planning calls for a vitalization through introduction of industries there.

The fourth belt of the European Lowland in Belgium and the Netherlands is a band of low plateaus between the sandy plains and the Ardennes. This region includes what has been called the heart of Belgium, as well as a small section in southern Limburg in the Netherlands. The undulating surface rises gradually in elevation to about 600 to 650 feet in the interior. Like parts of the Paris Basin, this section is covered with thick loam (*limon*) which has yielded rich soils and, therefore, is agriculturally one of the most productive areas of the Low Countries. The southern limit is the Sambre-Meuse corridor which marks the beginning of the Ardennes. Only southern Limburg is northeast of the corridor and adjoins the Ardennes directly.

The drainage in the lowlands of Belgium and the Netherlands is dominated by the three great rivers which have contributed so much to the formation of this particular landscape—the Rhine, Meuse, and Scheldt. The Rhine at present has three distributaries which are, from north to south: (1) the Old Rhine, flowing through Utrecht and Leyden; (2) the Lek, on which Rotterdam is located; and (3) the Waal, which is interlaced with the Meuse just above Dordrecht (Fig. 5–5). The Scheldt, with its main course in Belgium and its mouth in the Netherlands, is the principal gateway of Belgium for maritime traffic. The three rivers have formed a series of long estuaries along the coast. The western Scheldt estuary must remain open for free access to Antwerp, but the Dutch are planning to close off the eastern Scheldt estuary and those of the Meuse and Waal in order to shorten the coast line, reduce dangerous salt infiltration from the sea, and create fresh-water lakes for irrigation.

Hills and Plateaus

The hill and plateau areas of Western Europe, such as the hills of Normandy and Brittany within the lowland, are of Hercynian origin. Only the Jura is an exception, because it was formed during the Alpine orogeny. Four principal massifs can be distinguished.

In the northeast, extending into southeastern Belgium, northeastern France, and northern Luxembourg, are the Ardennes, which have three distinct subdivisions. The Condroz adjoins the Sambre-Meuse corridor on the south. Formerly a plateau, it is now a dissected ridge-and-valley region also referred to as the Lower Ardennes. The wooded northeast-southwest trending ridges are of resistant sandstones, while the intervening valleys developed in softer, more easily eroded limestones and shales. General elevation increases from 650 feet near the corridor to about 1,150 feet in the south. On the south, and separating the Condroz from the Higher Ardennes, is the Famenne depres-

Fig. 5–5. The Rhine-Meuse estuary. The Hollandsch Diep (foreground) is the principal outlet of the Rhine-Meuse system. (KLM Aerocarto n.v.)

sion, a poorly drained clay lowland lying at approximately the same elevation as the Sambre-Meuse corridor. The main massif is the Higher Ardennes south of the Famenne—a deeply dissected, largely wooded plateau surface noted for being flat and poorly drained and having both the highest annual precipitation in Benelux and the lowest density of population. The rocks are old and metamorphosed and yield a thin, infertile soil cover. The elevation of the plateau in Belgium and Luxembourg averages between 1,200 and 1,500 feet. It is highest in the east near the German border, where it rises to more than 2,200 feet, and lowest (about 900 feet) in the west in France. In Luxembourg the Ardennes cover roughly the northern third of the country, a region known as Oesling, as opposed to the Gutland further south, which is structurally a part of the Paris Basin.

The second principal Hercynian massif is represented by the Vosges Mountains between Lorraine and Alsace. This massif is divided into two sections by the low Col de Saverne, located northwest of Strasbourg at an elevation of 1,086 feet. Through it pass the major transport routes connecting the Paris Basin with the southern Rhine graben. To the north of the Col de Saverne are the densely forested Lower Vosges which adjoin the Hardt Mountains in Germany. Hercynian rocks are covered by younger sandstones, the terrain is strongly dissected, and the general elevation of hilltops is between 1,200 and 1,500 feet. Elevation increases south of the Col de Saverne, and old metamorphosed rocks are exposed at the surface. Slopes are smooth and hilltops rounded even where the highest elevations are reached, close to 5,000 feet. The western slopes toward Lorraine are gentler than those in the east, where strong faulting delimits them against the Rhine graben. As in the Lower Vosges, this section has dense coniferous forests, but here the timber line is reached at about 3,500 feet. Above that level are grasslands utilized for summer grazing. On the rainier slopes originate some of the most important streams of eastern France, such as the Moselle and Meurthe. In the east, however, streams are shorter and have steep gradients down into the Rhine Plain.

The Rhine graben is a rift valley filled in with hundreds of feet of alluvial sediments and loess deposits. Parts of the plain are poorly drained, especially the southern floodplain between the Rhine and Ill rivers; in general, however, the graben is one of France's most fertile and prosperous areas. Farther south, between the Vosges and the Jura Mountains, lies the Belfort Gateway, also called the Burgundy Gate. This low rolling corridor, about 15 miles wide, makes a major break in the landscape of hills and plateaus, and has been of great economic and strategic importance. The significance of the gateway for transport and communication has not diminished, but strategically it is no longer of consequence.

The Jura Mountains, beyond the Belfort Gateway to the south, form a 180-mile arc around the Swiss lake country, attaining their greatest width in France—approximately 45 miles—south of Besançon. The massif is composed largely of folded and horizontal limestone which does not give the appearance of mountainous country even though the highest elevation is more than 5,000 feet. The higher parts of the Jura rise along the Franco-Swiss border on the inside arc, where the strata have been folded into many anticlines and synclines. This section often has been compared with the Ridge and Valley Province of the Appalachian Mountains, and indeed it has many similar characteristics, except that anticlinal valleys are rare. The trellis drainage pattern prevails, and stream capture has reduced the number of main streams to two—the Doubs and Ain rivers. The slopes are steep and carry a dense coniferous vegetation; settlements are located chiefly on lower slopes, in valleys, or at water gaps. Adjoining the folds on the west is the much wider plateau section of the Jura. Here the limestone strata are horizontal and underground drainage prevails. Three plateau levels can be distinguished, descending in a steplike manner westward toward the Saône Valley.

The fourth major section of hills and plateaus is the Massif Central, by far the largest of the four and the most diversified. This is one of the Hercynian massifs uplifted last during the Alpine orogeny and, in part, subsequently modified through extensive lava flows. Moreover, a tilting of the Massif Central in Tertiary times resulted in higher elevations along the southern margin and a general downward slope toward north and west.

The heart of the Massif Central is the Auvergne, a region where past volcanic activity is very much in evidence. Old volcanic cones in the western Auvergne provide the highest elevations in the Massif Central—Mont Dore and Plomb du Cantal, 6,186 feet and 6,094 feet, respectively. Their slopes have been dissected by running water and by Pleistocene ice. To the southeast of these domes are extensive basaltic lava flows, while to the north more recent volcanic activity has created a rugged, little-eroded landscape dotted with many volcanic cones (*puys*). The older basalts to the south are well weathered and have yielded fertile soils, but the choice of crops is limited by climatic conditions. In the eastern Auvergne, lava flows have been largely eroded away and have left rolling granitic surfaces and occasional volcanic plugs standing in the landscape like monuments (Fig. 5–6).

Elsewhere, the old crystalline rocks are exposed at the surface in the Limousin Plateau northwest of the Auvergne and in the highlands of the eastern rim, from the Morvan in the north to the Cevennes and Montagne Noire in the south. The Limousin Plateau is a flat to undulating old erosion surface at an elevation of close to 3,000 feet in the east with a gentle downward slope toward the west. The entire eastern rim, on the other hand, has been affected by faulting along the Rhone-Saône corridor and the Languedoc. Slopes rise steeply from adjacent lowlands to form a crest line which is high, forbidding, and continuous in the south but becomes lower, more dissected, and less of a barrier in the north. Northwest of Nîmes the continuity of the Hercynian rocks is broken by the Causses, a rugged karstic area of limestone having an average elevation of 2,500 to 3,000 feet. Here underground drainage is pronounced, leaving the surface dry and with little soil cover except for residual clay pockets.

Fig. 5–6. Volcanic plugs in the Le Puy Basin. The Rocher de l'Aigville domi-nates the town of Le Puy in the foreground, and the town of Polignac lies at the foot of the basalt plug in the background. (French Government Tourist Office, New York.)

The Massif Central, particularly the higher ranges, has heavy precipitation, and all of France's major river systems receive contributions of its surface runoff. The continental divide is located near the eastern and southeastern rim of the Massif, so that streams flowing toward the Rhone and Saône rivers and the Mediterranean Sea are short and swift and have steep gradients. In other directions, however, rivers descend gradually, cutting narrow gorges into the hard basement rocks and widening occasionally in sedimentary or structural basins.

Corsica can perhaps be considered transitional between hill lands and mountains. A longitudinal depression separates the young folded mountains, occupying the eastern third of the island, from the granitic Hercynian block to the west. Mountains and hills are well dissected and almost everywhere they reach to or near the coast where they descend precipitously (see Fig. 1–18). While the east coast is straight and runs approximately north-south, the west coast bulges westward and displays a ria shore line.

Mountains

The Pyrenees. France and Spain partake of the Pyrenees, the mountain ranges extending some 260 miles from the Mediterranean to the Bay of Biscay. Although the Pyrenees represent an almost continuous barrier for man as well as for climate, their structure and appearance differ greatly from one part to another.

In the west, from the ocean to the Somport Pass, the mountains are composed mostly of limestone and their average elevation is below 6,000 feet. Precipitation is heavy, and stream erosion has dissected and lowered the terrain sufficiently to create several fairly easy passes between France and Spain. From Somport eastward to the headwaters of the Garonne River are the Central Pyrenees—the most rugged and highest section of the mountain system. Hard crystalline rocks produce peaks of more than 9,000 feet, and the landscape has been much modified by glaciation. The mountain façade, however, is broken up by a series of transverse valleys, whose streams flow from glacial cirques northward across the ranges through a succession of gorges and basins filled with glacial debris.

The Pyrenees of the Ariège, between the headwaters of the Garonne and Aude rivers, east of the Central Pyrenees, present a strong contrast by their longitudinal rather than transverse orientation of landforms and drainage. The innermost section is the axial zone where, as in the Central Pyrenees, large areas are above the timber line and where meadows are used for summer pasture. In fact, here as elsewhere in the Pyrenees, as also in the Alps, forests have suffered and the timber line has been lowered because of the destructive custom of burning woodlands to gain additional pastures. The axial zone is flanked on the north by the "North Pyrenean Massif" or the "Middle Mountain," as it has been called, lying almost entirely below the timber line. This is a land of forests where relief has been produced in large measure by running water on resistant granites and schists and strips of infolded younger sedimentary rocks. The Pre-Pyrenees, or "Little Pyrenees," still farther north, are situated in juxtaposition to the Aquitaine Basin. The gently folded sedimentary rocks are for the most part densely forested and assume the character of a foothill country. Longitudinal drainage is typical of the Pyrenees of the Ariège, with streams flowing between ranges and cutting through them in steep, narrow, short defiles.

Finally, east of the Aude River are the Mediterranean Pyrenees—massive crystalline forms with high, isolated intermontane basins. Slopes descend steeply into the Roussillon Plain and to the Mediterranean, but only some 30 miles from the coast a pass of less than 1,000-foot elevation provides an easy route between France and Spain. The Mediterranean climate and vegetation extend from the coast to the lower slopes; at higher elevations, however, above 2,000 feet, rainfall becomes more abundant and the slopes are forested to the timber line, with alpine meadows at still higher elevations. Thus, the combined influence of altitude and distance from the sea has produced several zones of vegetation.

The Alps. The French Alps occupy the southeastern corner of the country. Bordered by the Mediterranean coast and Lake Geneva in the south and north, respectively, they extend toward the Rhone corridor in the west, and in the east and northeast they continue into Italy and Switzerland. In the northern French Alps four longitudinal divisions manifest themselves. The central core is composed of high crystalline massifs whose granites and schists are of Hercynian origin. The northernmost of these and also the most notable is Mont Blanc, which, at 15,781 feet, is the highest peak in Europe. Mont Blanc, like some peaks in the other massifs, is still extensively glaciated, the snow line reaching down to about 9,000 feet. Pleistocene glaciers have left a majestic and beautiful landscape of cirques, U-shaped valleys, hanging valleys, and other erosive features. Moraines are visible as far away as the Rhone corridor. Outliers of the Hercynian massifs further south can be found along the border of France and Italy, not far north of the Riviera, in the form of the Maures-Estérel Massif, which parallels the coast between Cannes and Toulon, and in the high, rugged mountains of Corsica.

To the east of these massifs rise the folded internal Alps, composed of massive sandstones and limestones, much distorted by big overthrusts. Bordering the central core on the west and separating it from the Pre-Alps is the Alpine furrow (*Sillon Alpine*), a structural depression extending from Chamonix to south of Grenoble. It is followed by some important Alpine streams such as the Drac, middle Isère, and upper Arve rivers, which have deepened it through erosion. The Pre-Alps, west and south of this depression, are composed chiefly of Mesozoic limestones and form a wide arc from Lake Geneva to the Riviera coast. The Drôme River Valley, however, marks a notable change in orientation and dissection of the ranges. North of that valley the Pre-Alpine zone is quite narrow, and its continuity is broken up by transverse valleys eroded by streams descending from the internal ranges and forming gaps (*cluses*) as they pass through north-south ridges.

South of the Drôme Valley, the Pre-Alps widen to some 60 miles or more and the alignment veers to east-west, very much like that of the Pyrenees. This southern region, the Provence, has the semblance of a jumble of broken blocks 1,500 to 2,500 feet in elevation, with occasional higher peaks, and there is only one major valley—that of the Durance River. Moreover, a depression lies along the zone of contact between the Maures-Estérel Massif and the limestone ranges, providing an important routeway between Toulon and Fréjus; and the valleys of the Arc and Argens rivers form a corridor between the Rhone Delta region and the Riviera coast. The Mediterranean climate becomes increasingly pronounced southward, the periods of summer droughts lengthen, and forests give way to slopes that are either barren or covered with drought-resistant shrubs. All major streams draining the French Alps find their way into the Rhone River which, together with the Saône, follows a structural trench. This is the Rhone-Saône corridor, the southern gateway which has been of great significance in the historical development of Western Europe.

THE CULTURAL AND HISTORICAL BACKGROUND

The significance of location of the Western European states for human occupancy has been borne out by their function as gateways for movement of goods, people, and ideas to, from, and within the continent of Europe. Nevertheless, at some periods in history they have been on the periphery of activity and movement and have experienced slowdown or stagnation. By virtue of their maritime and land position, however, these states have contributed greatly to the political, economic, and social development of Europe as a whole and of many land areas across the seas, where they gained temporary colonial control or settled permanently.

The Maritime Position

Of the countries in Western Europe, all but Luxembourg border on the sea. It should not be assumed, however, that France, by virtue of the longest coast line, necessarily occupies the most important maritime position now. In the past, France was actively participating in overseas colonization, in direct competition with Belgium and the Netherlands, as well as with Britain and Germany. Thus, the sea position of France between the British and Germanic areas has encouraged rivalry with these other European maritime states both in medieval and modern times.

Mediterranean traders provided the early cultural contacts from across the seas, in the south and southwest of France. In the sixth and seventh centuries A.D., some Celts, fleeing from the Angles and Saxons, crossed the English Channel to France, invaded the old Armorica, and created a new Brittany there which has persisted to this day. The Celtic imprint was a lasting one, as people in western Brittany still speak a variety of Celtic. In the ninth century the Vikings, or Norsemen (later called Normans), after moving in and plundering the French shores, settled in the Bay of Normandy, between the Cotentin Peninsula and the Pays de Caux. The Normans, in turn, invaded England in the eleventh century and enriched English culture and, eventually, American culture with their Romance heritage.

In the Middle Ages the rudiments of a manufacturing complex developed in the North Sea area, through the zeal of the Hanseatic merchants and shippers. Wool weaving was the most strongly established industry. It was centered in Flanders and thrived there for many centuries. With mercantile and industrial growth tied closely to the area's seaward relations, a greater agricultural production was needed to sustain the increasing urban population. New lands were put into crops and agricultural methods improved. Gradually, land reclamation and crop rotation became widely accepted.

England moved across the English Channel into Western Europe as a continental power in the middle of the twelfth century when Eleanor, Duchess of Aquitaine, married Henry Plantagenet, who shortly afterward became Henry II of England. Three hundred years later British power on the continent declined. In the middle of the fifteenth century France's sea boundary on the English Channel as well as on the Atlantic Ocean became secure, and it has been accepted without question ever since. The only remnants from this period are the Channel Islands, a cluster of small islands off the coasts of Brittany and Normandy, which Britain has owned since 1259.

In the age of discovery and colonization, global aspects of maritime relations began to develop—first of France, then of the Netherlands, and lastly of Belgium. Antwerp had been one of Europe's most important ports since 1315 when the city joined the Hanseatic League. Traffic stagnated, however, beginning with the pillaging of the city by Spaniards in 1567 and with the closing of the Scheldt estuary by the Dutch until Napoleonic times. On the other hand, French and Dutch ports, particularly Bordeaux and Amsterdam, became gateways to the continent, especially during the eighteenth century. Since the emergence of Germany as a modern political and industrial power on the European continent the center of gravity in the ocean transport pattern has shifted from France to the Low Countries and the German North Sea coast, so that the maritime position of France has been weakened accordingly and has become peripheral in relation to the rest of Europe.

On the Mediterranean Sea also, maritime relations began in ancient times, with Marseille becoming France's gateway there. The port's role was vastly strengthened in the nineteenth century, when France began to colonize North Africa and when, after the opening of the Suez Canal in 1869, Marseille assumed the main function of colonial port, not only for North Africa but also for French possessions and commercial interests in Asia beyond Suez.

The Land Position

Traveling overland from where they had settled earlier in the south of Germany, the Gallic Celts arrived in Western Europe about 500 B.C. The incumbent population, an already rather numerous Neolithic people largely devoted to farming, amalgamated with them. The Roman conquest brought the influence of Mediterranean culture, especially the Latin language, over the greater part of the conquered territory, as far as the *limes* along the river Rhine, where the threatening Germans were held back. The Vandals, Alamanns, Burgundians, and Visigoths from northeastern and central Europe eventually moved sporadically into the West in varying numbers. They were followed by another Germanic people, the Franks, who created a number of kingdoms in Western Europe. Thus the Franks were imposing their rule over much of Gaul contemporaneously with the Celtic invasion of Brittany. The prevailing language remained Low Latin except in Brittany and in the peripheral Low Countries, Alsace, and eastern Lorraine, where a Germanic tongue evolved. The enduring power of the Franks in the old Gaul finally provided France with her name.

The division of Charlemagne's large empire into three north-south parts under the Verdun Treaty of 843 set up a long border zone, Lotharingia, later perverted to Lorraine, between the western and eastern Frankish kingdoms. It is especially noteworthy that the western kingdom returned to its Celto-Latin tradition and eventually became France, while the eastern kingdom, where both land and people were German, later developed into Germany. The intermediate zone, extending from the marshes of Friesland to the olive groves of Italy, was fought over and shifted one way and another up to the present century. Boundaries, whether linguistic, political, or religious, developed slowly and spasmodically.

France has enjoyed a longer continuous period as an independent state than her three neighbors to the north. Most of the present area of France has been effectively integrated since the fifteenth century. Some later expansion did take place toward the east into central Europe, as well as in the Mediterranean realm.

Alsace and Lorraine had been associated with tribal kingdoms and other medieval-type units until they were incorporated into France in the seventeenth century. On two occasions since then, Alsace and parts of Lorraine have been taken over by the Germans, but there is no longer any doubt that these areas are now integral parts of France. In the southeast, the Alpine zone of Savoy-Nice was a wide area of sparse population and an effective barrier to communication and transportation. It was joined to France permanently in 1860. Following World War II, a few changes on the Franco-Italian border extended French control still further eastward. In the south, land boundaries with Spain were stabilized in the Treaty of the Pyrenees of 1659.

The formation of France as a modern state took place by early unification in the Paris Basin, the core area, by expansion to include the greater part of France by the end of the fifteenth century, and by final border adjustments on the east and south in later centuries. The significance of the land position of France in relation to German, English, Spanish, and Italian areas has shifted in the past according to the political and economic developments which have taken place in these neighboring states.

In the Middle Ages, France and Flanders were bound closely to the Apennine peninsula. Trade routes led from Italy by way of the Rhone Valley to the fairs of Champagne and thence to the free cities of Flanders. During the Renaissance, Italy held supreme mastery in all arts and crafts, and new ideas and techniques were brought home by French soldiers during the fifteenth and sixteenth centuries. The luxury silk industry of Lyon is, in fact, of Italian origin.

In the sixteenth century Spain had driven out the Moors and was looked upon as a strong colonial power. Spain, France, and England were all integrated states, functioning effectively, while Italy, although culturally pre-eminent, remained disorganized politically. France occupied a central land position between England and Spain. With the subsequent decline of Spain as a continental power, France emerged as the strongest state on the continent in the seventeenth and eighteenth centuries. This strength was accompanied by a shifting of mercantile interests away from the Mediterranean states to Western Europe. With industrialization in northwestern Europe and with the unification of Germany in 1871, Europe's balance of power shifted again and France's land position between Britain and the unified Germany assumed an importance which has persisted to this day.

Since World War II, the combined land and maritime position of France has taken on new significance with respect to strategy in the East-West power struggle. France has become an essential unit in the NATO alliance, because of her location between the United States and the Soviet Union.

For the Benelux countries the land position has been, and is, of paramount significance. The emergence of these three states can, at least in part, be ascribed to the ineffectiveness and eventual failure and breakup of the Holy Roman Empire. The Netherlands fought for and gained its freedom at the time of the Reformation; in 1648 it was recognized as an independent state. Already exploitation of its land and sea position had made the Netherlands a major power in European trade and overseas colonization. The right to control the Scheldt estuary, obtained in the Peace of Westphalia, eliminated competition from Antwerp in the Spanish Netherlands by closing that port off from the sea. Moreover, the immigration of Portuguese and Spanish Jews and French Huguenots brought new talent and resources to the recently founded country. Although the Scheldt estuary was reopened by Napoleon in 1803, the supremacy of the Dutch, astride the Rhine estuary, has not been challenged successfully in continental European trade and transport.

Belgium represents that portion of the former Spanish Netherlands which was unable to throw off the foreign yoke in the wars of independence. After a futile attempt to reunite Belgium and the Netherlands in 1815, Belgium finally was created in 1830–31 as an independent kingdom. Too many differences and animosities had evolved between the two countries in the two centuries of separation.

Having only land frontiers, Luxembourg has been by far the most land-oriented of the states of Western Europe. A remnant of larger feudal units, it gained political independence in 1839 and was declared neutral territory in 1867. Since joining a customs union with Belgium in 1922, an orientation toward the sea has become increasingly pronounced. With the creation of Benelux, the European Coal and Steel Community, and the European Economic Community, the land and sea positions have both assumed great significance in the economic life of the country.

It is of particular interest to note that none of the three Benelux countries first emerged as a buffer state, but that in the power struggles of the nineteenth century they all assumed that role.

Evolution of the Human Landscapes

Man has had a hand in shaping most landscapes in Western Europe. It may be difficult or impossible to determine the beginnings of some cultural landscapes, for their origins lie in prehistoric time and have never been recorded. During the Middle Ages the landscape was changed by the barbarian invaders or colonists, as the case may have been. The agricultural plots which had been cultivated in prehistoric times could be found here and there, but generally forests, marshes, and heath prevailed. Feudal rulers or missionaries of the Church led the drive to clear the forests in unsettled areas. It was in this period that the organization of the agricultural systems began and the settlement patterns were finally crystallized. However, neither physical factors nor human circumstances in themselves are sufficient for a penetrating analysis of these patterns. Wherever possible, an explanation of the many forms of rural and urban landscapes must be found in terms of total relationships among which one factor, physical or human, may or may not have predominated.

The Rural Landscapes. A glimpse of an aerial photograph of almost any part of Western Europe will reveal a maximal utilization of land and its division into many small fields and meadows. The plots appear to be extremely intricate, by virtue of both field pattern and colors of crops. They are larger than rice paddies in the Far East but far smaller than farm plots in the United States.

Four main rural landscapes stand out:

1. Open-field country is found in nearly all of France north of a line drawn from Geneva to Besançon, Dijon, Orléans, Blois, Chartres, and Rouen, and in Belgium south of a line leading from Tournai, Ath, Nivelles, Brussels, Vilvoorde, Louvain, Tongeren, and Maaseik, and in all of Luxembourg (Fig. 5–7). The landscape stretches without interruption, open and unadorned, without trees except in forests, without hedges, earth banks, isolated or scattered farm houses. The farmers live clustered in villages with a church at the center and surrounded by their fields.

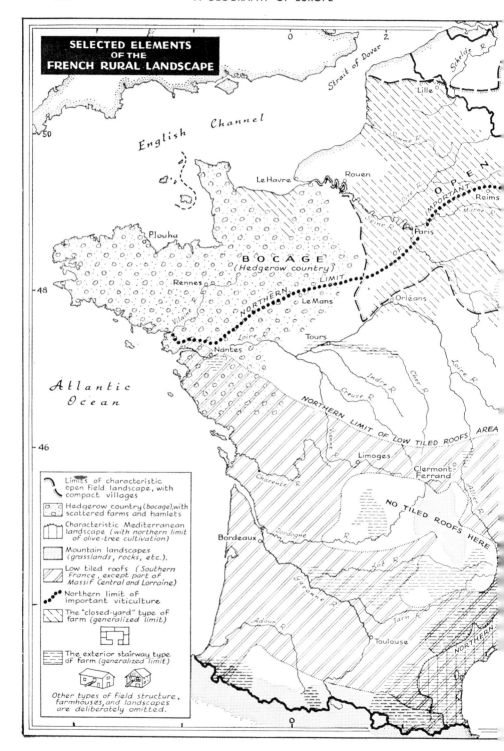

SELECTED ELEMENTS OF THE FRENCH RURAL LANDSCAPE

English Channel

Strait of Dover

Le Havre

Rouen

Lille

Schelde R.

Somme R.

Reims

Marne R.

Paris

Oise R.

Seine R.

Plouha

B O C A G E
(Hedgerow country)

Rennes

NORTHERN   LIMIT

Le Mans

Orléans

Vilaine

Loire R.

Nantes

Tours

Indre R.

Creuse R.

Cher R.

Loire R.

Atlantic
Ocean

NORTHERN LIMIT OF LOW TILED ROOFS   AREA

Vienne R.

Limoges

Clermont-
Ferrand

Charente R.

NO TILED ROOFS HERE

Bordeaux

Dordogne R.

Lot R.

Garonne R.

Adour R.

Tarn R.

Toulouse

NORTHERN

Legend:

- Limits of characteristic open field landscape, with compact villages
- Hedgerow country (bocage), with scattered farms and hamlets
- Characteristic Mediterranean landscape (with northern limit of olive-tree cultivation)
- Mountain landscapes (grasslands, rocks, etc.).
- Low tiled roofs (Southern France, except part of Massif Central and Lorraine)
- Northern limit of important viticulture
- The "closed-yard" type of farm (generalized limit)
- The exterior stairway type of farm (generalized limit)

Other types of field structure, farmhouses, and landscapes are deliberately omitted.

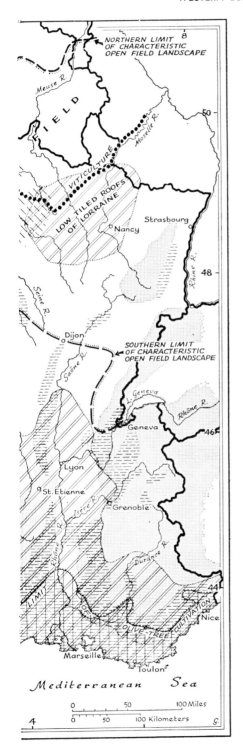

Fig. 5–7. Selected elements of the French rural landscape.

Until the end of the eighteenth century, open-field cultivation was a community enterprise. A three-way division was made of the cultivated parish land, known as the three-field system: one for winter cereals (wheat, rye), one for spring cereals (barley, oats), and the third was left fallow. This sequence was first made compulsory by Charlemagne probably in the latter part of the eighth century. Rotation took place every year, and every year, in the absence of chemical fertilizers, one-third of the land was left fallow in order to reduce the ill effects from overworking the soil and to permit collective grazing of livestock. Following the harvest, animals could graze in the fields of stubble as well. While the individual farmers owned their tiny plots, the land had to be worked at the same time and under identical conditions as that of their neighbors. Announcements of prescribed times for plowing, sowing, and harvesting were made in church on certain Sundays. In deference to the rotation system and to allow livestock free movement on the common pastures, all plots of land were required to remain unenclosed. By the same token, each family head had to hold land in each of the three parts to secure for himself and his family a supply of all crops grown in the community.

The community system was closely tied in with the evolution of communal tenure practices during feudal times. Under this system, citizens of the community had certain property rights in communal lands, among which were rights in arable land, in forests, and in alpine pastures. In fact, one of the compelling reasons for the long endurance of the community system was the right to graze on fallow and harvested land. Farmers needed a large area for pasturing their herds, so open fields were essential. The number of animals that each family head could graze was determined by the extent of his holding, but a minimum of one cow and six sheep could be pastured even if no land was owned.

During the nineteenth century the practice of compulsory crop rotation gradually became outmoded. A decree early in the French Revolution had established freedom of cultivation and exploitation, which made possible individual improvement in rotation without community action. Nevertheless, the peasants resisted stiffly any changes in the time-honored practices. The introduction of previously unknown or little-known plants, especially clover, fodder turnips, Indian corn, potatoes, and sugar beets brought about the development of different crop successions. Besides, the widespread raising of fodder and the use of fertilizers and modern farm machinery all combined to bring about the abandonment of the traditional system.

2. The second chief type of rural landscape is the *bocage* of western France (Fig. 5–4). It is an enclosed, confining landscape, characterized by small, elongated fields and meadows encircled by high

hedgerows or trees growing from ground level or from earthen dikes, deep-rutted twisting wagon lanes, scattered isolated farms, or occasional hamlets or villages. From aloft, the countryside appears like an immense compartmented forest riddled by thousands of clearings, yet actual forests and woods are rare. The Armorican Massif and the southwestern part of the Paris Basin are landscapes of this sort, as are many parts of the Massif Central.

The massive uniformity of the *bocage*, in part, might be related to the extremely individualistic character of the people and their desire to maintain overt evidence of ownership of their land. But what was the origin of the *bocage?* Several hundred years ago the landscape was more open heath than today. In the eighteenth century the semiwooded heath or the *lande*, as it is called, covered between half and one-third of Brittany. Today it still persists on as much as 14 to 18 per cent of all land on the peninsula. Over the years, many open *landes* have become cultivated fields, enclosed by hedges in order to protect the cropland against livestock grazing in open areas beyond. In that way, the *bocage* landscape was created in an area where agricultural practices go back to Neolithic times.

One wonders whether the hedgerows and farm plots were laid out haphazardly or with some intent. Some 20 years ago a study of aerial photographs revealed that Neolithic farmers had small enclosed fields similar to the *bocage* country of western France today. Furthermore, it was shown that most of the fields, still rectangular rather than square, point in certain directions and that these directions appear to be the same as those of the main alignments of the Megalithic monuments along the southern coast of Brittany at Carnac. In this area the directions correspond to the position of the sun at sunrise and sunset on certain days of the year, such as the solstices. This startling disclosure gives strong support to the supposition that the field patterns were laid out in Neolithic times by a sun-worshipping people. The tradition, once established, has been followed to our day when woods and heaths were cleared and returned to cultivation.

3. One might call the remaining portion of France, loosely speaking, the southern landscape, while pointing out the regional variations among southwestern, central, and Mediterranean sectors. Historically, the southern landscape developed an agriculture characterized by the relatively less productive two-field system, in which half the cultivable land was left fallow for one or more years, depending on local conditions of soil and slope. Enclosure was more common in the south, though no definite system prevailed, with individual buildings in hedged fields and compact hilltop villages built during the Middle Ages for defense. A predominantly hilly terrain doubtless contributed to the variety of field patterns. Often, size and dimensions of the

plots were extremely irregular as a result of the necessity of finding the best location and soil for each crop. Except for the Mediterranean area, long specialized in horticulture, the farming was mainly unspecialized, and a great diversity of crops could be found throughout the countryside.

The land use of today reflects to a large extent these historical patterns. In the Mediterranean area the meadow is noticeably absent and wheat, olives, and vineyards fill the landscape, together with certain intensive truck-farming regions. Grazing lands are almost ubiquitous in the Massif Central and the other highlands, while a mixed livestock-and-crop economy has evolved in the Aquitaine and the Saône Valley. Nearly everywhere are vines used for the production of quality or ordinary wines in large amounts or only for the domestic needs of the farmer.

4. The rural landscape of Flanders and the western Netherlands represents a fourth main type. Reclaimed farmlands wrested from the sea or from lakes and poorly drained valley floors are known as polders —landscapes made up of canals, rows of poplars, green wet meadows, rectangular plots, and large, isolated or loosely grouped farmhouses. The appearance of the land changes toward the east. It becomes higher, plots are more irregular, and small woods are interspersed with fields and pasture land. The polder landscape is spectacular and its origin is well understood. Its evolution can be traced through the centuries and consists of four principal stages.

The sea polders were the earliest to be developed, beginning in the tenth and eleventh centuries.[2] Sea walls were built out from shore on sections of the coast where dunes were absent. The resulting slowdown in the ocean currents would create an area of sand and silt accretions which then could be diked off from the sea. In such a way, a complex of adjoining sea polders came into existence and to the present day some 940,000 acres of land have been reclaimed from the sea.

The second stage—the creation of inland polders—began in the fourteenth century in Holland, earlier in Flanders. Much of maritime Flanders was drained by the thirteenth century, because of the great demand for food in the flourishing Flemish textile towns. The windmill, which was first used for pumping water out of bogs early in the fifteenth century, accelerated land-reclamation processes so that, by the end of the sixteenth century, most of the mainland of Holland behind the dunes was settled. Moreover, it had become clear that joint efforts were necessary to coordinate drainage work and dike maintenance. For this purpose, the Dutch *waterschappen* and the

[2] W. W. Reys, "The Dutch Polder Country," *Geografisch tijdschrift* 7 (August, 1954): 146–58.

Flemish *wateringues* were formed—autonomous syndicates which became drainage authorities.

Although reclamation and drainage were well organized, the settlement of the land was not. A peasant would obtain the right to a parcel of land extending from the dike into the polder; the strip of land could be extended on both sides of the dike to the boundaries of the village, so that a narrow elongated field pattern, possibly several miles long, came into existence. This type of land use was as uneconomical to operate as the fragmented properties in other parts of Western Europe.

In the third stage of land reclamation, beginning in the seventeenth century, land division was based on more rational considerations of land use and hydraulic conditions. This stage consisted of the drainage of inland lakes which, in turn, created the lowest polders in the Netherlands, reaching depths of nearly 22 feet below mean sea level. The largest of these, Haarlem Lake, could not be drained until the middle of the nineteenth century, when steam power was available for pumping. Even as late as this, water control was defective and general land-use planning was inadequate. The growth of rural settlement was spontaneous and unplanned, and transportation facilities were poor, making public services and administration extremely difficult.

In the twentieth century attention returned to the sea. With modern technology it was possible to isolate the Zuider Zee from the North Sea by means of a dike 19 miles long (Fig. 5–15) and to carve out five large polders with a total area of some 885 square miles (when completed). Even here, the distribution of centers of population was not adequately planned in the Wieringermeer polder, the first to be settled, and administrative problems were encountered in connection with the Northeast Polder because of its large area.[3] For the remaining polders, economic and social planning is proceeding in the greatest detail in the hope that all major problems can be anticipated. Moreover, the even more ambitious Delta Plan for the diking of all but two Scheldt-Meuse-Rhine distributaries has been begun.

The open-field country, the *bocage*, the landscapes of southern France, and the polder landscape of the Low Countries are the four main types of rural landscapes. Transitional forms are numerous, and occasionally islands of *bocage* are found in the open-field area, and open fields in the hedgerow country.

The appearance and arrangement of the farmhouse complex varies greatly from one region to another. Many regional types have evolved according to local resources, traditions, and economies.

[3] C. A. P. Takes, *Physical Planning in Connection with Land Reclamation and Improvement*, Wageningen, Netherlands: H. Veenman & Zonen, 1958.

The high mountains of the Alps are practically the only area of Western Europe where there are frame houses or where houses have been built entirely of wood, often on a stone foundation. The use of wooden beams, moreover, on the walls and ceilings is not uncommon, and numerous picturesque half-timbered farmhouses can be seen in Normandy, the Basque country, and Alsace. Brick farmhouses are the custom in northern France and in the plains of Belgium and the Netherlands (Fig. 5–8). The use of brick has been increasing, grad-

Fig. 5–8. Typical Saxon farm building in the eastern Netherlands, near the Schoonebeek oil field. The thatched roof covers both the living quarters and the barn. (Standard Oil Company of New Jersey.)

ually replacing stone, the traditional building material since Roman days. Brick is now used widely in new construction, particularly in the Benelux countries. The great diversity of local stones, so often of warm colors, contribute to the artistic aspect of many farms. The farm buildings of Brittany and Limousin have granite walls; those of the Loire country are of white, soft, and easily carved chalk; in the Auvergne the black volcanic blocks blend with the landscape. Some places have little stone available and houses are built with walls of pressed dried mud often strengthened with straw.

Roofing materials and roof styles are also a matter of utility and local tradition. The Roman half-cylindrical tiles can be seen throughout most of southern France, as in neighboring Italy and Spain; they require little slant of the roof. There are islands of such tile in Lorraine, and of small flat tiles arranged in a scalelike fashion in some rural areas of the Paris Basin. In southern France, on the other hand, there are islands of slate roofs in some Pyrenean valleys, such as the upper watershed of the Gave de Mauléon (the *Pays de Soule* in the Basque country) and adjacent valleys farther east in the Béarn, where slate is readily available locally. In Alsace and some other regions shingles are used. Steep roofs thatched with straw or reed are still seen in Normandy, Brittany, the Beauce, and the Low Countries, but, because they represent safety and sanitation hazards, they are gradually disappearing. Stone roofs occur in the Auvergne and in sections of the Jura and the Alps. In general, however, local color and artistry are slowly giving way to more utilitarian tiles.

Three traditional layouts of rural farmsteads can be recognized in the Western European countries, and all three reflect directly the economic requirements of rural life.[4] First, the *maison-bloc* plan, as it is called by French geographers, combines several farming functions under one and the same roof. There are two subtypes of this layout. In one, all parts of the building are on the ground floor, with the actual layout of functional space varying from one region to another (*maison-bloc en terre*). This type is widespread. It occurs everywhere in France—except in the Mediterranean region and in the Paris Basin —as well as in the Belgian Campine and Ardennes, the Luxembourg Oesling, and the Dutch Brabant. Occasionally, in the Basque country, the roof over this assembly is centered on the living quarters, so that it appears asymmetrical, with the longer side of the roof extending over part of the building housing the livestock, fodder, equipment, etc. However, this asymmetrical feature does not occur as frequently as one is led to believe from the literature. The other subtype is a two-story house (*maison-bloc en hauteur*) where living quarters are on one floor above or below stable and barn. In vine-growing areas, the latter are generally on the ground floor, together with the wine cellar.

The second layout is the farmstead with an enclosed yard. Farmhouse, stable, barn, carriage house, and outbuildings are laid out in a quadrangle within which the well or possibly a pond may be found, as well as the manure pile. The buildings are contiguous, or nearly so. This type of farmstead predominates in areas of intensive grain cultivation in northern France, central Belgium, and Dutch Limburg.

The third plan is the open-yard farmstead which is favored in the cattle-raising areas of western and central France—Normandy, Brittany, and parts of the Massif Central—of the Flanders Plain in northernmost France and western Belgium, and of the western Netherlands. The open-yard farm has gained popularity, since expansion of farm facilities is made easier with more space.

[4] Albert Demangeon, *La France*, Vol. 6 of Vidal de la Blache, ed., *Géographie Universelle*, Paris: Librairie Armand Colin, 1946.

Everywhere in Western Europe farmsteads can be observed which do not adhere strictly to any one of these major types of layout. There are many transitions, none of which, however, appears to be localized in any one area.

The Urban Landscapes. France was the first of the Western European countries to evolve an urban landscape. Many French cities and towns can look back to the pre-Roman era. Analysis of place names of innumerable French towns points to the enduring influence of the Gallic tribes in whose domain the chief present-day French cities were already capitals. Cities like Le Havre, built on the commission of King Francis I, or Lorient, which was the port of the French East India Company, are some of the few towns that were established within the last few centuries.

Of the ancient towns no visible traces remain. In the south of France many of the old sites as well as newly selected ones became foci of Roman settlements. The core of the colony was called the "castrum" (*cité*), which was a stronghold surrounded by walls.[5] The cathedral, generally built within the castrum in late Roman or early medieval times, became the principal landmark. Later, in the Middle Ages, when crafts and trade developed, these cores of urban growth expanded and the market place, the *ville*, with its surrounding residences and shops, emerged contiguous with the *cité* and replaced it as the real focus of medieval urban life. In northern France and Flanders during the early Middle Ages, merchants developed small market colonies along main transport routes, frequently next to strongholds called *bourgs* or *burgs*, but often independently without walled protection. The original functions of these towns were manufacturing by artisans and trade and transport, linked with marketing the goods. By 1000 A.D., copper and iron work became the specialty of the Meuse Valley, while Brugge, Ghent, Ieper (Ypres), and others flowered into prosperous commercial and industrial towns famed for textile manufacture.

From the outset the market place was the pivot of regional economic activity and the core of future urban growth. The cathedral, the high ornate guildhall, the town hall, and the belfry usually flanked this central square, and the houses extended along roads leading out from it in various directions. Most of these towns enjoyed virtual independence from the ruling lords, and were granted self-government sooner or later.

In certain parts of France and Belgium during the Middle Ages the cores for future town life appeared in such forms as the medieval

---

[5] Robert E. Dickinson, *The West European City*, London: Routledge & Kegan Paul, Ltd., 1951.

castles and manor houses, which had in their immediate vicinity the settlement of vassals (as Chateauroux and Niort), and monasteries and ecclesiastical seats around which urban settlements clustered (Chartres and Limoges, for example). Occasionally the town core might merge with another core already existent nearby, to add to its size, but more often the core remained separate, evolving into a town on its own. Today the central core of an old city is easily identified by the narrow twisting streets, the presence of a cathedral, some medieval houses, possibly a castle, and remnants of old ramparts. In France an outer core has a good number of seventeenth and eighteenth century houses, as in Bordeaux and Nantes, whose ports brought them prosperity at a time when new ideas on city planning were afoot from both the aesthetic and the functional standpoints. Recent industrial developments generally have grown up on the urban fringes. Belgium, however, experienced stagnation of urban activities from the end of the Middle Ages until the nineteenth century, because of foreign domination and the closing of the Scheldt estuary by the Dutch. In the nineteenth century, first industrialization and then the emergence of Belgium as an independent kingdom brought a long-delayed but very vigorous growth of urban areas and activities, with principal concentrations in the Sambre-Meuse corridor, at Antwerp and Brussels.

In Holland, the founding of towns and general urban development took place at a later time. The low, marshy terrain of what is now the most densely settled part of the Netherlands was uninviting to colonists and, in fact, hazardous. The Romans penetrated only to the old Rhine River and founded such towns or garrisons as Utrecht and Nijmegen. The barbarians who migrated into Gaul bypassed the area or moved through it, destroying existing settlements. Higher ground to the east had soils of low fertility, and sparse population. It was not until Carolingian times that urban settlements were founded again. However, the majority of towns did not appear on the map until the twelfth and thirteenth centuries, which have been called the golden age of medieval new-town planning in the Netherlands.[6]

Once the Dutch realized their advantageous position with respect to currents of European trade, new centers grew rapidly and became prosperous. These centers were established primarily for the crafts, trade, transport, and local administration, as had been the Flemish towns two or three centuries earlier. Sites were selected in accordance with requirements of trade and transport—at road junctions (Groningen), ferry or fording points (Utrecht, Zwolle), or transshipment points (Arnhem, Rotterdam, Amsterdam). Little or no regard was

[6] Gerald L. Burke, *The Making of Dutch Towns*, London: Cleaver-Hume Press Ltd., 1956.

given to site conditions. The central feature of many of these towns was a bridge across a river or canal in the case of dike towns, or a dam in the case of so-called dike-dam towns. In either case the bridge or dam assumed the function of market place. Around this center were grouped the other buildings and facilities necessary for the town's function. Some towns, such as Delft, were founded in the middle of a polder reclamation project to serve at first as a rural market. Later, however, the town was replanned in order to take on various urban functions. In fact, most Dutch towns have grown by continuous replanning and by effective integration of new surrounding areas into the urban patterns. Thus, urban growth, which has been continuous to the present day, has occurred chiefly by extension of existing towns rather than by establishment of new ones.

Regionalism. There appears to be a marked correlation between the long and relatively stable history of settlement in Western Europe and the development of regionalism. Long before the surrender of Vercingetorix to Julius Caesar in 52 B.C., settlement had taken place in much of France and the Low Countries outside the poorly drained lowlands. In contrast, Germany and other parts of Central Europe were inhabited by tribes that were more transient. With time, distinct characteristics became indelibly imprinted on the landscape as well as on the people living in it, resulting in pronounced regional differentiations of speech, customs, land use, and other visible features. The operative factors involved in this regionalism were many and varied. In some cases, natural barriers or physical uniformity contributed to a certain amount of homogeneity and kinship within a region. Or it may have been land use, form of settlement, or a combination of human and physical factors which formed the traditional *pays* in France and Belgium. A number of regions are known to have grown out of *pagi*, which had been small Gallo-Roman territorial divisions.

In France the old provinces were political units until they were abolished during the Revolution and replaced by the smaller *départements*. The area of each of these *départements*, of which there are now 90, was sufficiently small for citizens to reach the administrative center from any point in less than a day's ride on a horse. The ancient provinces, however, have retained their identity, and people are more prone to think and talk of "Brittany" or "Normandy" than of "Finistère" or "Manche." Generally, ancient provinces have no clear-cut delineation, and marginal or adjacent areas may be identified with the provinces but may not be true bearers of the old traditions. For example, only about the western two-thirds of the Brittany peninsula is culturally Breton, but Brittany as an ancient province includes the

Rennes Basin and parts of the lower Loire region. The ancient provinces in the Netherlands and Belgium still represent the official administrative divisions of these countries.

In addition to the traditional regional concept, larger economic regions have been evolving since the end of World War II. For purposes of economic planning and statistical compilation, several *départements* of France were grouped together in 1946 to form 18 economic regions. At an international level, the European Coal and Steel Community, the European Economic Community, and others, are all indications of the increasingly great role of economic relationships in the regionalism of Western Europe.

FRANCE

The People

Although France is by area the largest state of Western Europe, it is today among the less densely populated. France ranks fifteenth in Europe with 209 inhabitants per square mile in 1958, lower than any of her neighbors except Spain.

At the last census, in 1954, the population numbered close to 43 million, and at the beginning of 1960 the population was estimated at 44,754,400. For Western Europe as a whole, the rural density of France is low (Fig. 5–9). Although the rural population is fairly evenly distributed throughout much of the country, some differentiation can be indicated. There are areas of very sparse population in the Causses—the dry limestone plateaus in the southwestern Massif Central—and the high sections of the southern Alps. An almost continuous belt having a population density ranging from 50 to 124 per square mile extends from the chalk plateaus of the eastern Paris Basin, through parts of the limestone plateaus in the southern Paris Basin not covered by loess deposits, to the Massif Central, the Pyrenees, the sandy Landes in the southwest, and Corsica in the Mediterranean. On the other hand, areas of relatively dense rural population include the coasts of Brittany, the rich loess-covered plateaus of Picardy, the fertile alluvial Rhine Valley of Alsace between Strasbourg and Mulhouse, and the valleys of the Loire and Garonne rivers.

With agriculture still the backbone of the French economy, only a few large, densely populated industrial or urban areas can be delineated. In fact, urbanization in France has been very slow, and in 1954 there were but 28 cities, including Paris, with more than 100,000 inhabitants. The population gap between Paris and other urban agglomerations is astonishingly large. Greater Paris in 1954 contained

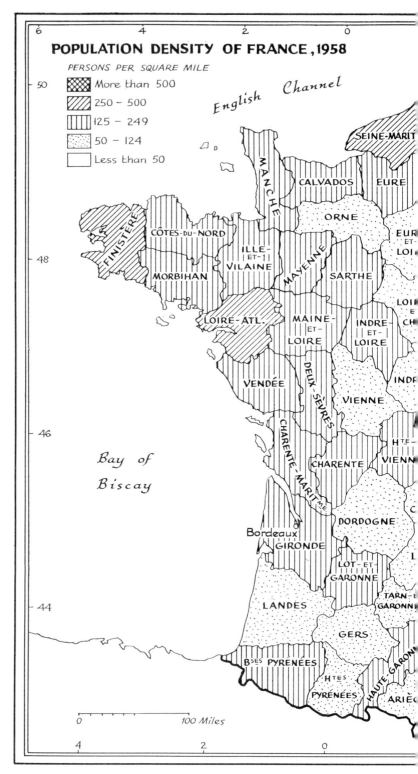

Fig. 5–9. Popula

ity of France.

close to 6.5 million inhabitants, about 15 per cent of the total population, or as many people as in the next 34 urban areas combined.[7] This has been of great concern to the French government, which is attempting to develop plans for decentralization of population and industry. Other regions of high urban concentration are the northern industrial region—a cluster of cities on and near the principal coal fields of France—and the metropolitan areas of Marseille and Lyon.

Demographically, France has attained a unique position in relatively recent times. Until the middle of the nineteenth century, France had the largest population in Western and Central Europe, having reached 20 million by the end of the sixteenth century and 26 million by the time of the French Revolution. In 1801, with more than 27 million, she surpassed Great Britain with only 11 million, Germany with 22 million, and Italy with 17 million. France's population continued to increase until the middle of the nineteenth century, when it numbered nearly 36 million inhabitants. In the second half of the nineteenth century, however, population increase as a whole fell off with continued industrialization and urbanization, and with the agricultural depression which began in the 1880's. Germany exceeded France in total population in the 1850's, Great Britain toward the end of the nineteenth century, and Italy in the 1930's. Between 1851 and 1938 France's population increased by only a little over 6 million, while in the same period the population of the United Kingdom increased by some 25 million, and even that of the Netherlands by some 5.5 million. Germany, between 1870 and 1938, gained about 28 million people. At the same time, urban areas, especially Paris and the north, increased their population at the expense of rural areas—a gradual population shift which is still continuing.

While the low birth rate created a population problem in the century before World War II, the situation has been reversed since that war. In the last 15 years, the birth rate has increased to its highest level in the present century, so that France now leads most European countries in the rate of population growth. Simultaneously, life expectancy has increased because of a declining death rate. By 1951, France had regained the 1938 population level.

On the other hand, the French population-density pattern in the last 25 years has changed very little. Areas, in both the north and south of France, which had a high density of population in the 1930's increased their density in the 1950's. They include Greater Paris, the Industrial North, Lorraine, the Rhone Basin, and the Riviera coast, as well as some cities such as Lyon, Toulouse, Nantes, and Bordeaux. Sections which had manifested a decreasing popula-

[7] République Française, Institut National de la Statistique et des Études Économiques, *Annuaire Statistique de la France*, 1958.

tion in the 1930's for the most part continued to decline in the late 1950's, at the same time facing a more impoverished local economy. Such areas include Brittany, the Massif Central, and Corsica. The major exception is the Haute-Savoie, where population has increased in the wake of hydroelectric power and manufacturing developments.

The Nation

Language, one of the vital forces of French national consciousness, has been instrumental in unifying the somewhat diverse parts of France into a cohesive whole. The fact that the language of Île de France, a Romance dialect, has been accepted as the official language throughout France is an indication of the early political control and cultural dominance of the Paris Basin—the core area of the French state. Provincial dialects still remain, and other languages are spoken in some areas, but these areas are nonetheless integral parts of the French nation.

The Breton language, a tongue derived from Celtic, is spoken in the Brittany peninsula west of a line extending from Plouha in the north to the mouth of the Vilaine River in the south. At the Atlantic end of the Pyrenees some 100,000 people speak Basque, a language the origin of which has never been determined; and at the eastern end of the Pyrenees live 185,000 people who speak Catalan, a Romance language. In Corsica an Italian dialect known as Corsican has its roots in the Pisan period (1077–1312) and probably earlier. Flemish is spoken in the area around Dunkerque, and German dialects are used throughout Alsace and parts of Lorraine. Practically all these people, however, are bilingual.

Minority problems are virtually non-existent in France. Despite an autonomist Breton movement and a separatist Alsatian party, in the past little actual support has been rallied around these causes. There are regional movements whose aims do not conflict with French unity itself. They exert pressures on the central government for protection and preservation of regional languages, dialects, customs, and traditions. The cohesion of the French nation was amply demonstrated during World War II when the Germans were unable to split France effectively. The Bretons as a whole remained loyal to the Free French; in fact, the population of Brittany was a large contributor to the French underground movement.

What factors, other than language, contributed to this common bond? Certainly not race. There is no such thing as a French race, for the French have absorbed many races and peoples who have invaded the country throughout history from all directions. Religion is another factor which has not been involved, at least not in recent times. The struggle between the Catholic Church and the state had been a divisive factor, but one which could not be traced to any regional distribution. During the French Revolution, however, religious equality was initiated, and since then the Church has not been officially recognized by the state. Although most French people are Roman Catholic, religious tolerance is extended to all sects.

It was the French Revolution that provided new national consciousness and strengthened regional homogeneity throughout the land. The Revolution spread common ideas of "liberty, equality, and fraternity" over the entire country and, indeed, over many parts of the modern world. General adherence to these ideas, as well as the long historical association of the various parts of France through wars, the Reformation, revolutions, overseas colonization, etc., all strengthened the common bond.

Finally, there has been the close tie of all parts of the country in its social and economic life. The social structure has evolved since the days of the Revolution. The most significant aspect is that there is no regional concentration of any one class or group. The only distinction that can and should be made is that between Paris and the rest of France. The Parisian considers people from outside Paris provincial, and, at the same time, all of France looks to Paris for political, economic, social, and intellectual leadership. Moreover, outlanders from the provinces have always been lured to the capital, seeking its cultural and economic advantages and, in the process, contributing to the total character of the city themselves. Indeed, the leadership of Paris is undisputed.

From the economic standpoint, a considerable integration of the various parts of France has been favored by the fact that a great variety of natural resources has promoted internal trade. A heretofore adequate and efficient network of highways and railroads has facilitated this trade and has tied the regions closely together.

Present Economic Life

France is a rich country from the standpoint of basic resources, yet the average income of the French people is relatively low. The reasons are manifold. As was pointed out earlier, the population of France had been stagnant until recent years. Moreover, a considerable immobility has existed between various occupations. Industrialization was very slow in the first half of the present century and has been concentrated in very few nuclei, especially around Paris. This heavy concentration of industrial growth has left most of the country in an underdeveloped state which has created patterns of social life inimical to economic progress. In 1959, however, President de Gaulle stabilized France politically and financially, and the nation appears to be on the threshold of rapid economic progress.

Agriculture in France has also been backward, a condition which can be attributed partly to the fact that industry has not given agriculture tools or machinery at prices which the farmers will or can pay. There are too many persons on the farms who produce, at high cost, too little. Such circumstances have created a deterioration of the farmers' economic position in relation to the rest of the working population. Moreover, farmers have had a deep-seated reluctance to leave their land, and a scarcity of housing has impeded movement from rural to urban and industrial areas.

In general, France still remains a land of shopkeepers, small proprietors, and craftsmen, dedicated to the rights of the individual over those of the group. This structure has forestalled full conversion to mechanized industry, with the result that France has lagged behind other, more progressive states.

In 1958, France had a total labor force of about 19.7 million people, or 44 per cent of the total population, including some 7 million women. Nearly one-third of the women worked on farms, and about one-fourth were engaged in industry. About 29 per cent of the total labor force was engaged in agriculture, forestry, and fishing, and close to 35 per cent in industry. These percentages represent a relative decline in the labor force engaged in primary activities since World War II, and a relative increase in the labor force engaged in manufacturing. This would indicate that industry is slowly gaining ground, while the relative economic importance of agriculture has declined.

In spite of the decline of the agricultural labor force, the number of French workers engaged in purely agricultural work is very high, compared with the Benelux countries. There is strong popular opinion, perhaps based more on tradition than realism, that agriculture should be kept on a par with industry in national importance. The fact remains that the agricultural labor force is at a low level of productivity and represents a drain on the French economy, although the average French farmer is well known as being thrifty and industrious.

Agriculture. Some 62 per cent of the total area of France is utilized for various agricultural pursuits. More than one-third of this is cultivated land, while another one-quarter is permanent grassland. France is normally self-sufficient in food except, of course, for tropical products, and even has some exportable surplus.

In general, France is a country of small farms. According to the latest agricultural census, in 1956–57, some 35 per cent of all farms were smaller than 12 acres and another 45 per cent were between

12 and 50 acres. There are, of course, regional variations. Smaller farms are more numerous along the Mediterranean coast, where there is also a scarcity of cattle, and in Alsace-Lorraine. Larger farms, on the other hand, are concentrated in the eastern half of the Paris Basin. About two-thirds of the farms were owned and operated by the farmers themselves; in fact, there was no hired help on 82 per cent of the farms. Some 27 per cent of the French farms were operated by tenants, and about 5 per cent by sharecroppers. Although tenant farmers are scattered throughout the country, there are notable concentrations in the Breton peninsula and in the northern regions, especially the *départements* Seine-Maritime, Nord, Côtes-du-Nord, Pas-de-Calais, and Oise. The sharecropping system is practiced chiefly in the Aquitaine Basin, where the Landes *Département* alone had some 40 per cent of all sharecroppers in France.

Various factors hinder an increase in French agricultural production, aside from those already discussed. High production costs make it impossible for agricultural products to compete on the international market, and mechanization has proceeded very slowly. In 1956–57, 72 per cent of the French farms owned no tractor, nor did they make use of any.

Perhaps the greatest single factor underlying most of the difficulties is land fragmentation, which has been proceeding throughout the centuries. Most plots are too irregular in shape and too small to be worked efficiently. A farmer may own many small plots located in different directions from the village, sometimes long distances away. The waste of time is enormous in terms of travel; crop rotation, irrigation, soil-erosion control, and other general aspects of farm operation are made difficult.

There are four principal reasons for this excess of fragmentation. Firstly, compulsory crop rotation, which began in medieval times and which no longer exists, has nevertheless left its imprint upon the French agricultural landscape. As was already pointed out, this system resulted in every peasant family obtaining holdings in each of the three basic sections of arable land belonging to the village. Subsequently, rights to individual pieces of land were divided again and again, resulting in the splintering of the arable land. Secondly, the basic law of France, the *Code Civil*, since its adoption in 1803 has required that land be divided up evenly among heirs upon the death of the head of household. The law was aimed at breaking up large feudal estates and at asserting and strengthening property rights of individual peasants. A third important reason for land fragmentation is what has been called "the narrowness of the land market." [8] The

[8] Frederic O. Sargent, "Fragmentation of French Land: Its Nature, Extent and Causes," *Land Economics* 28 (1952): 218–29.

eagerness of peasants to buy more land but their inability to pay for large pieces, the piecemeal sale of domains when cash was needed, plus land speculation, all contributed to fragmentation. Finally, the village type of rural settlement in many parts of France facilitated, indeed perpetuated, the holding of many individual lots.

The seriousness of this situation was recognized as early as the seventeenth century, but all attempts to consolidate property holdings had been in vain until a sensible and flexible law was passed in 1941. This law represents a combined effort of the national and local governments and groups of resident farmers of each area where a consolidation project has been decided upon. The law became operative in 1943, and by October, 1956, close to 3,000 projects in sixty-four *départements*, involving some 5 million acres, had been completed; more than 1,000 projects affecting 2 million acres of farm land were in process; and approval for another 1,700 projects had been requested.[9]

A recurrence of fragmentation will be avoided because, once a project has been completed, subdivision will no longer be permitted. Although in the majority of these projects complete consolidation cannot be effected at once, the reduction in the number of parcels of individual properties, and, thereby, the increase in the size of lots, makes possible the more rational planning and utilization of farms. This, in turn, will release several million people now on the land, for employment in manufacturing, professions, and services—all activities which advance the standard of living. Furthermore, the speed of penetration of modern ideas, machines, and methods will be increased, ingrained routine will gradually change, productivity per agricultural worker will rise, and there will be an accumulation of capital so urgently needed for progress.

Agricultural Regions. In general, eight types of agricultural landscapes can be distinguished in France (Fig. 5–10).

1. THE LOAM-COVERED PARIS BASIN. A thick layer of loam (*limon*) covers most of this area which stretches from Belgium to the Loire River and from the Seine estuary to the Champagne. Open, undulating to rolling plains and plateaus such as interior Flanders, Picardy, Brie, Beauce, and the Paris area fall within this section. It contains some of the most fertile soils and is among the technically most advanced agricultural areas of France, characterized by high yields and large farms with good equipment and permanent or temporary hired workers. This area covers about 15 per cent of the surface of France but grows more than 92 per cent of the sugar beets and more than 40 per

[9] République Française, Institut National de la Statistique et des Études Économiques, *Annuaire Statistique de la France, 1958*.

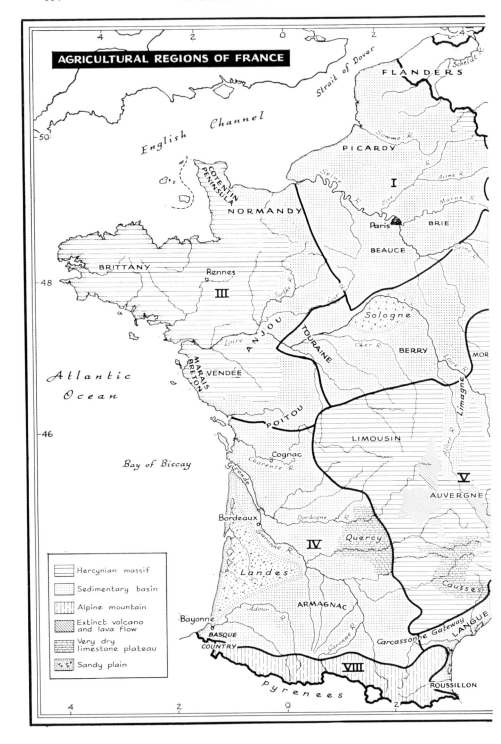

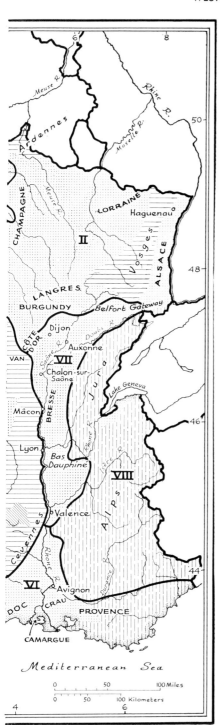

Fig. 5–10. Agricultural regions of France.
(After Sourdillat, J. M. *Géographie Agricole
de la France.* Paris: Presses Universitaires,
1950.)

  I. Loam-covered Paris Basin
 II. Forest Belt
III. *Bocage* Areas of Western France
 IV. Basin of Aquitaine
  V. Massif Central
 VI. Mediterranean Area
VII. Rhone-Saône Corridor
VIII. The High Mountains

cent of France's wheat and oats. The beets are harvested every year with the help of numerous migrant workers from Belgium. Beet pulp and molasses are used as cattle feed, and leaves are fed to the sheep or are plowed under. Associated with primary crops are many secondary crops included in complex rotations, and the raising of cattle and sheep.

The wide valley bottoms are used for truck and dairy farming, particularly the production of cheese. Dairying and poultry farming are also widespread on the Brie Plateau. The slopes of the Île de France escarpment, which delimit the Brie against the Dry Champagne to the east, carry the carefully tended vineyards of Champagne. The Paris region itself is an area of intensive horticulture. In the sandy and alluvial plains of maritime Flanders in the far north, extensive pasturing prevails.

This agricultural region is located in proximity to the industrial north. It has easy access to urban and industrial areas where employment is available and where the rural surplus population can be absorbed. Thus, favorable human and physical factors have combined to produce the most prosperous rural area in France.

2. THE FOREST BELT. This area includes the southern and eastern Paris Basin, as well as the Vosges, the Ardennes, and, for the sake of convenience, also the Rhine Valley. This section of the Paris Basin is composed of calcareous plateaus and plains which are not covered with loam. Precipitation, therefore, sinks readily into the ground, leaving the surface dry. Over wide areas the soils are thin residual clays, and much fertilizer is required for the growing of crops. Large sections of the plateaus are forested or fallow and open pasture. For example, in Berry, the southern Dry Champagne, and the plateau of Langres, sheep raising assumes considerable importance. Where crops are grown, cereals predominate. Crop yields are low, as are income and living standards of the farmers. Therefore, rural depopulation has been striking in this region, especially in the plateau of Langres (Burgundy), which has the lowest population density.

Where the clays are thick, such as in the Wet Champagne and in parts of the Sologne, soils have been drained and used to advantage for crops. The most intensive rural land use and relatively high population densities can be found in the river valleys, such as those of the Loire, Meuse, and Moselle. There, a great variety of crops are grown in rotation and vines and deciduous fruit abound. Cattle are associated with agriculture everywhere.

The Hercynian massifs of the Ardennes and the Vosges Mountains also have extensive forests, with livestock and crop farming on the lower slopes and the valley floors. The eastern slopes of the Vosges descend steeply to the broad valley of the Rhine River in Alsace. On the lower hillsides are terraced vineyards growing grapes for quality wines. Between the Rhine and the Ill rivers lies a marshy floodplain. However, between this floodplain and the Vosges foothills is a terrace with rich loam soils, where both livestock and crop densities are high and where the major settlements are located. The soils are deeper and more fertile in northern Alsace. Tobacco, asparagus, and other vegetables are grown; the Haguenau region is one of France's outstanding hops-producing areas.

3. THE BOCAGE AREAS OF WESTERN FRANCE. This part of France has been called "the green lands," because, throughout most of it, fields are surrounded by hedges or trees on the same level as the fields or on earth mounds. Only in the *Marais Breton* along the Atlantic coast of the Vendée are there wide expanses of open, low-lying, poorly drained land given over either to pasture or to the production of salt from sea water (Fig. 5–11).

In general, farms of the *bocage* areas are scattered, small, and have an oversupply of labor. Wheat, dairy products, meat, apples, and vegetables are the leading agricultural products, but there is considerable regional variation. Cider competes with wine as the favorite beverage.

In Normandy, meadowland is three or four times more extensive than cropland. In the western part of the Cotentin Peninsula, up to 95 per cent of the land may be pasture and meadow. Crops are grown primarily for the feeding of livestock, and the entire economy is dominated by dairy farming—the production of butter, cheese, and milk for the Paris metropolitan area. Apple orchards dot the landscape, and one of the provinces, Calvados, has given its name to brandy distilled from apples.

Toward the west, Brittany presents very interesting contrasts. On the coast there is truck farming in several small areas,[10] but, on the whole, Brittany is primarily a producer of cereals, potatoes, and animal products. Since World War II, meadows and pastures have been gaining at the expense of cultivated land. On the other hand, the French government has encouraged the removal of apple trees, for the dual purpose of reducing the production of alcohol and increasing that of cereals. Since 1953, some wheat has been exported to the Netherlands and Germany directly from small Breton ports by means of Dutch and German vessels.

[10] There are six principal areas: on the north coast in the vicinity of St.-Malo, St.-Brieuc, and north of Morlaix; on the west coast on the Plougastel peninsula opposite Brest; and on the southwest coast in the Concarneau area and southwest of Quimper.

In the rolling Rennes Basin the landscape is somewhat more open, the fields are larger, and the production of cereals, particularly wheat, is emphasized more than in other parts of Brittany. On the wide, gentle banks of the Loire Valley are the famous vineyards of Anjou, while in the floodplain the thick alluvial soils are used for truck farming and the growing of flowers. South of the Loire, livestock becomes more important again, particularly the fattening of beef, but a gen-

Fig. 5–11. Salt-evaporation ponds in the *Marais Breton,* a section of the coastal plain, south of the Loire estuary, which is barely above sea level. (French Embassy Press and Information Service, New York.)

erally successful balance is maintained between livestock and crop farming.

4. THE BASIN OF AQUITAINE. Southwestern France also presents a great many contrasts in land use. Its intensity ranges from that of the very sparsely populated areas of the Landes between Bordeaux and Bayonne to that of the densely populated Bordeaux vineyard and truck-farming areas.

To the south of the Vendée and Poitou a landscape begins which is composed largely of open fields, nucleated settlements, and some scattered vineyard areas. This is the northern Charente which was one of the earliest viticultural areas of France, but where few vineyards have remained since the destruction of the European vines by the phylloxera in the late nineteenth century. Instead, the area has specialized in dairy farming. Milk and butter cooperatives have been formed throughout to improve purchasing and marketing procedures.

Farther south in the Charente, the percentage of land in vineyards increases, although even in the Cognac region vineyards take up less than 20 per cent of the land. The highest vine-growing densities there are south and southeast of Cognac, where up to 30 per cent of the land has been planted into vineyards. The entire region is known as the Cognac appellation area, where white grapes are grown for distillation and the manufacture of wine brandy named after the town of Cognac.

Southeast of Bordeaux, largely in the *département* of Gers, is the Armagnac area where the growing of white grapes for distillation into wine brandy is also significant. Here, also, vineyards do not cover more than 30 per cent of any one commune.

The highest vineyard densities are in the valleys of the lower Garonne and Dordogne and their tributaries, together with the slopes along the Gironde estuary. Grapes are grown here for the production of quality wines (Bordeaux wines) rather than brandies. The region includes many appellation areas, such as the famous *Sauternes*, *Médoc*, and *Graves*.

In the Basque areas south of the Landes forest (Fig. 5–12) as well as in the eastern part of the Aquitaine Basin, drained by the middle Garonne and Dordogne and their tributaries, corn has taken an important place, together with wheat, in crop rotation. In general, this is a prosperous agricultural region and, in some sections, farmers have formed efficiently run cooperative organizations. Thus, mechanization is more apparent there than in any other part of western and southern France. Cattle are part of the economy everywhere, and sheep are numerous in the foothills of the Pyrenees.

5. The Massif Central. In the Limousin and other crystalline massifs further east, such as part of the Auvergne and Morvan, the soils developed from the old hard Hercynian rocks. They are thin, of low fertility, and often poorly drained. Climatic conditions at higher elevations are severe and limit the choice of crops somewhat. On the high plateau surfaces, pasture land predominates and cattle are raised for beef and veal. At lower elevations and in a number of fertile alluvial basins, rye, oats, potatoes, forage crops, vegetables, and fruit are of considerable importance. Although rye is the basic cereal, wheat has been gaining ground where soil and climatic conditions are favorable.

In the volcanic portion of the Auvergne, agriculture consists of a livestock and crop combination. Soils are fertile and permeable, the cattle density is high, and farms are relatively large. Dairying is a specialty of this area, particularly the production of milk and cheese.

Sheep are raised throughout the southern portion of the Massif Central, especially in the dry limestone plateaus of the Causses. This is the home of the world-renowned Roquefort cheese for which ewe milk and partially processed cheese are collected, not only locally but from an area extending from Corsica to the Basque country.

6. The Mediterranean area (Midi). The Mediterranean slopes represent a blend of traditional Mediterranean agriculture and mod-

Fig. 5–12. Basque village in the foothills of the Pyrenees. Corn, wheat, forage crops, and pasture are the principal uses of the land. Farmers live in such hamlets and villages, or on isolated farmsteads.

ern commercialized farming under irrigation. The traditional combination of wheat on the narrow plains, vineyards and olive trees on the hillsides, and sheep on the denuded mountains can be found in much of the Provence and in Corsica. Transhumance is the custom, and each summer the sheep and goats are driven to high alpine pastures. Actually, pasture land is scarce and the practice of transhumance has declined with an increase of fodder grown under irrigation. In the Languedoc, commercial viticulture has become the principal activity. In the *département* Hérault, close to 70 per cent of the cultivated land is in vineyards, and more wine is produced there than in any other *département* of France. This specialization has been of great concern to the French government. A plan calls for extensive irrigation to diversify agriculture by enlarging the fruit and vegetable acreages.

Vineyards can be seen as far as the small fertile Roussillon Plain and the lower slopes of the Pyrenees. The former, however, also produces a great variety of vegetables, with the aid of irrigation, as well as peaches and apricots.

Perhaps the greatest specialization can be found along the lower Rhone River. In the vicinity of Avignon year-round agriculture is practiced; vegetables and grapes are grown in small fields, surrounded by high cypress hedges which serve as a protection against the mistral winds. All fields are irrigated in the dry summer half year, with water from the Durance River. Farther southeast, the Crau—a large, deltaic rocky plain—serves as winter pasture for sheep, and in the poorly drained delta area proper, the Camargue, a large reclamation project has been under way since 1947, for the production of sufficient rice for the home market (Fig. 5–13). In this area there are also some large land holdings on which fighting bulls are raised.

7. THE RHONE-SAÔNE CORRIDOR. Diversity is the key word for the Rhone-Saône Corridor. The Mediterranean crop combination extends up the Rhone Valley from the coastal plain into the interior. Slopes are covered with vineyards, and in the alluvial basins and on river terraces is an intensive cultivation of wheat, sugar beets, forage crops, some tobacco, and a great variety of fruit. The mulberry tree, which used to be significant for sericulture, has been on the decline.

Between Valence and Lyon the Rhone River clings to the slopes of the Massif Central, while from the left bank a hill land, the Bas Dauphiné, extends eastward. There, coarse gravels are covered with fertile, more recent alluvial and morainic deposits. In the wide valley floors one finds the wheat and sugar beet combination and planted, irrigated meadows interspersed with pastures for dairy cattle. On the lower slopes deciduous fruit abound. In fact, the hill area, together with this section of the Rhone Valley, is the heart of the fruit belt where apples, apricots, peaches, and cherries are grown, mostly for table use. In the Lyon Basin is a high density of dairy cows, providing milk and other dairy products for the large urban area.

North of Lyon, where the recent alluvium of the Saône Valley is very fertile but in places poorly drained, meadows are used as common pasture after the grass has been cut; on the better-drained soils, wheat, sugar beets, and legumes are grown. Of great fame are some localized agricultural pursuits such as the Burgundy vineyards on the slopes of the Côte d'Or between Dijon and Chalon-sur-Saône as well as those farther south around Mâcon, the raising of poultry on the plain of Bresse, and truck farming in the Auxonne region.

8. THE HIGH MOUNTAINS. In the high mountains the agricultural economy is primarily pastoral. Nearly everywhere, depopulation of

the higher areas has been accompanied by an extension and intensification of agriculture on lower slopes and valleys as well as in the forelands. Where the growing of rye, oats, and potatoes has been continued at high elevations, the yields are meager and not sufficient for subsistence. Thus, cropland gradually is giving way to meadow and pasture land where grass is cut for hay, and sheep and cattle graze in summer.

Fig. 5–13. Experimental rice fields in the Rhone River Delta. This is a state farm, employing Spanish migrant labor.

In the northern Alps and in the Jura, cow's milk is used for the production of many kinds of cheese, particularly the well-known Gruyère, or Swiss cheese, which is marketed everywhere in France. Throughout the Pyrenees, except in the westernmost section, sheep milk goes through the first stage in the cheese-production process, to be collected periodically for further processing in the Causses into Roquefort cheese. Adjacent to the Bay of Biscay, in the Basque areas, cattle, for milk and meat, and fruit and vegetable growing are emphasized to satisfy the demand for these products in summer when tourist trade is most active. On the Pyrenean slopes in the east, olives, vineyards, and chestnuts become important. Chestnut trees, however, have been on the decline everywhere because of a blight for which no control has yet been found. Experimentation with some foreign species not subject to the disease is in progress.

In both the Pyrenees and the Alps, valley floors and basins contain thick alluvial and glacial deposits whose fertile soils support a profitable livestock-and-crop-combination type of agriculture. Forests have maintained their traditional importance on the slopes all through the mountains except in the southern Alps where deforestation and depopulation have been particularly severe.

Agricultural Production. Wheat remains the leading single crop of France in terms of number of acres dedicated to it, in spite of the fact that the total wheat acreage has declined in the last few decades, especially since World War II. Gradually here, as in other parts of Western Europe, marginal lands have been converted to grassland or abandoned. This decline in acreage, however, was more than compensated for by an increased yield, so that the total production of wheat and other cereals rose significantly. The yield of wheat, for example, has risen from 23 bushels per acre in the years before World War II to 34 bushels in 1957, that of barley from 26½ bushels to nearly 41, and that of corn from 20½ bushels per acre to almost 40 bushels in 1957. These increases reflect the general improvement in French agricultural techniques, such as better seed selection and a considerable increase in the use of commercial fertilizers and lime. Total production of wheat and other cereals varies from year to year with climatic conditions. In 1957 wheat production reached an all-time high of over 11 million metric tons, which was surpassed only by the United States, China, and the Soviet Union.[11]

Another characteristic of French agriculture has been the increasing importance of fodder crops which in their totality cover an area exceeding that devoted to wheat. Moreover, of all the cereals grown about one-half represents cattle feed. It has been estimated, in fact, that the total area used for the production of feed for animals is double the area used to grow products for human consumption, so animal husbandry has become the main focus of attention. In 1958, France tied for fourth place with the United Kingdom in world production of meat, after the United States, the U.S.S.R., and West Germany.

In 1956, the lead of France in the world production of wine was taken over by Italy, whose production has increased steadily.[12] France's wine production, on the other hand, has declined in recent years in the wake of a government-sponsored program to convert some of the vineyard areas to other crops. By January, 1957, some 81,500 farmers had applied to the government for the conversion of about 260,000 acres from vineyards to other crops.

A line can be drawn roughly from the Loire estuary through Paris, the Reims area, and toward southern Luxembourg, to demarcate the northern limit of viticulture. The distinguished quality-wine produc-

[11] For statistical data, see Appendix III.

[12] In 1956 France and Italy combined produced more than one-half of the world's wine.

tion areas are those of the Garonne-Dordogne valleys in southwestern France, the Loire Valley in the west, the Champagne and Alsace regions in the north and northeast, and the Rhone-Saône corridor from Dijon to Avignon. The abundant vineyards of the Languedoc produce the largest quantities of ordinary table wine.

A startling development has been the production of rice on the reclaimed lands of the Rhone River Delta and in the Languedoc. This crop has been so successful that, by 1957, France produced some 114,000 tons, which was sufficient for domestic use and even permitted some export.

Specialized horticulture has been on the increase in the Mediterranean region, the Rhone Valley, the valleys of the Garonne and the Loire rivers, the coast of the Breton peninsula, and the Paris area. However, in addition, large quantities of fresh vegetables and fruit are imported from North Africa, especially in winter and early spring. Efficient distribution systems radiating from the major ports have been developed so as to enable rapid delivery of the perishable products to all parts of France, mainly by truck.

Fisheries. In summer, the number of fishermen reaches 66,000. This figure is notably lower in the off season, during the winter, when many fishermen seek employment in other occupations. In addition, some 20,000 to 25,000 people are employed in industries associated with fishing, such as canning, shipbuilding and ship repairing, refrigeration, and transport.

French fisheries are characterized by family-type ownership. About half the number of fishermen and vessels have home ports on the Atlantic coast between the western tip of Brittany and the Spanish border. The largest catch, however, is brought into ports on the Channel and North Sea. Boulogne, alone, by far the most important fishing port in France, accounts for about one-third of the fresh fish catch. Of least importance in terms of number of fishermen and boats, as well as catch, is the Mediterranean coast. Most of the fishing vessels are small. With the number of sailing ships diminishing rapidly, the fishing fleet is becoming more and more motorized.

Fishing activities fall into three categories: The first, deep-sea fishing, involves a small number of trawlers—about thirty in all of France—covering long distances to fish for cod in North Atlantic fishing grounds, especially the Grand Banks of Newfoundland, including waters around the French islands of St. Pierre and Miquelon and around Greenland and Spitsbergen. Two ports, Bordeaux and Fécamp, account for about 80 per cent of the cod catch unloaded in France, and St.-Malo for another 10–12 per cent. Much of the catch is marketed dried or salted, but consumption of fresh cod has been increasing. Because the total catch exceeds home consumption, export of cod has been significant, the major markets being in Mediterranean Europe, Brazil, and the Caribbean. The second type, classified as "sea fishing," occurs in the open ocean and the Mediterranean, mostly beyond 50 miles from shore. Three-fourths of the fresh fish marketed in France are caught by vessels belonging to this category. The third type is called in France *pêche artisanale*, which includes fishing in coastal waters as well as from the shore line without fishing boats. Of the total yield of about 536,000 metric tons of fish (and seaweed) in 1957, 63 per cent was marketed as fresh fish.

During World War II, the fishing fleet suffered very heavily. Some 60 per cent of the deep-sea fleet and 70 per cent of the sea-fishing fleet tonnage was destroyed. Postwar recovery was very slow, but the fleet is younger and much better equipped than it was before the war. Fish consumption per person in France is considerably below that of other maritime countries in northwestern Europe, such as Great Britain, Norway, and Sweden. This has been interpreted to mean that the national market is far from being saturated and that an expansion of fisheries can take place.

Industrial Raw Materials.

ENERGY RESOURCES. Consumption of energy in France did not change appreciably in the twenty-year period between 1929 and 1949; since then, however, total energy requirements have risen rapidly as a result of the modernization and equipment plans, the second of which was completed in 1957. It has been estimated that by 1965 consumption of energy will have increased by some 35 per cent over 1955 and that by 1975 it will have nearly doubled.[13] Consumption has exceeded energy production by far, and, therefore, France has been the biggest net importer of energy in Western Europe. In 1955 approximately one-third of the energy consumed had to be imported, and in 1956 about 41 per cent. For this reason, assurance of an adequate power supply has become a major problem in France's economic development.

In order to increase home production of various forms of energy, elaborate plans have been made and are being executed for more effective exploitation of domestic coal, gas, and waterpower, for discovery of more crude oil and gas, and for development of nuclear energy. A main handicap has been the peripheral location of the fuel reserves—coal in the north and northeast, crude oil and gas in the

[13] A. Gamblin, "La Situation Énergétique de la France," *L'Information Géographique* 22 (January–February, 1958): 15–25.

south and southwest, and waterpower in the south and southeast of France (Fig. 5–14).

COAL. About 65 per cent of all energy consumed in France is derived from coal. In 1957 this amounted to 73 million metric tons, while French collieries produced only 57 million metric tons. The deficit was made up by imports which have been costly in terms of foreign exchange. While coal production has been rising, its consumption has been increasing at a greater rate, widening the gap to be covered by imports. Furthermore, foreign sources have changed, for before World War II the principal foreign suppliers of coal were Great Britain and Germany with smaller quantities coming from Belgium, the Netherlands, and Poland; in 1957 the principal suppliers were the United States and Germany.

In spite of the need for more fuel, the French coal industry has not displayed much vitality. Thousands of miners have left the pits in the last decade, to seek jobs with better salaries under better working conditions; hence, a serious labor shortage exists. New miners are difficult to recruit, even through immigration, and it takes time to develop the necessary skills. On the other hand, many technical improvements have been made in existing mines, and in spite of the fact that coal is difficult to mine, except in Lorraine, output per man-shift underground in 1956 was second highest in Europe, after West Germany. With 3,619 pounds, France had increased its 1938 output per man-shift underground by one-third and was surpassed only by the Saar coal field the high output of which gave Germany first place. If productivity is calculated by individual fields, the Lorraine coal field has reached an all-time high in Europe with 5,082 pounds per man-shift underground. New coal seams have been discovered, but the development of new pits is costly and time-consuming. It takes nearly ten years before maximum production can be reached. All in all, the coal industry has little flexibility, and increases in demand have been met, in the main, by increased use of petroleum products and hydroelectric power.

Unfortunately, much of the French coal is not good coking coal, making it necessary to import considerable amounts of coking coal and coke. France has tried to evolve new coking processes through which coke can be produced with types of coal available locally. For example, a new method of blending and coking Lorraine and Saar coal yields a soft, friable metallurgical coke, so Lorraine coal is increasing considerably its relative importance in the French economy. In 1952, about one-fourth of the metallurgical-coke supplies for the Lorraine iron and steel works originated in Lorraine, and 41 per cent in the Ruhr. By 1957, Lorraine coke represented nearly 39 per cent of the total while that coming from the Ruhr had declined to 34 per cent.

The two principal coal fields are located in northern and northeastern France. One-half of French coal production in 1958—close to 29 million metric tons—came from the *Bassin du Nord et du Pas-de-Calais*, located in a deep syncline along the northern slope of the Artois Ridge. The coal seams, an extension of the southern-Belgium field, are thin, displaced, and broken up by faulting into several basins. Thus, mining is difficult, especially by mechanical processes. The other field, contributing 26 per cent of total French coal production—15 million metric tons in 1958—is a continuation of the Saar coal field and is located in Lorraine east of Metz, only 40 miles from the iron-ore fields. It is much easier to work than other French coal fields because the thickness of the coal seams facilitates the use of modern equipment. Although production from this field is smaller than from that of the north, the Lorraine contains more than half of the known coal reserves of France. Over the next 20 years, the exploitation planned in this field will increase its relative importance, so that by 1975 it should contribute 30 per cent of coal production as against 47 per cent for the northern coal field.

All other coal fields are secondary by comparison. Coal in the Massif Central was the earliest to be developed and to attract industries in the first half of the nineteenth century. For example, the St. Étienne field, at one time thought to be the best in France, attracted various metallurgical and mechanical industries, while the Blanzy-Le Creusot coal field was and still is utilized for high-quality-steel production by the great Schneider armament works. Only three of these fields are significant today, all situated along the eastern edge of the Massif near Blanzy-Le Creusot, St. Étienne, and Alès. The other smaller fields lie along a north-south line farther west in the Massif, a fault line extending from Décize and Commentry in the north to Décazeville and Carmaux in the south.

In recent years, new discoveries have been made. Of these, the most noteworthy is a small deep field at Lons-le-Saunier at the foot of the Jura Mountains. There may be several seams, and the probable reserves have been estimated at 260 million metric tons. Although it is anticipated that some coal will be sent to Lorraine, much of it, as that of other small fields, will be used locally for the generation of thermal electricity, the production of gas, etc.

Lignite has been only little used. Several deposits occur in the Provence, in southeastern France, and in the Landes south of Bordeaux. In 1958, total lignite production in these areas amounted to 2.3 million metric tons.

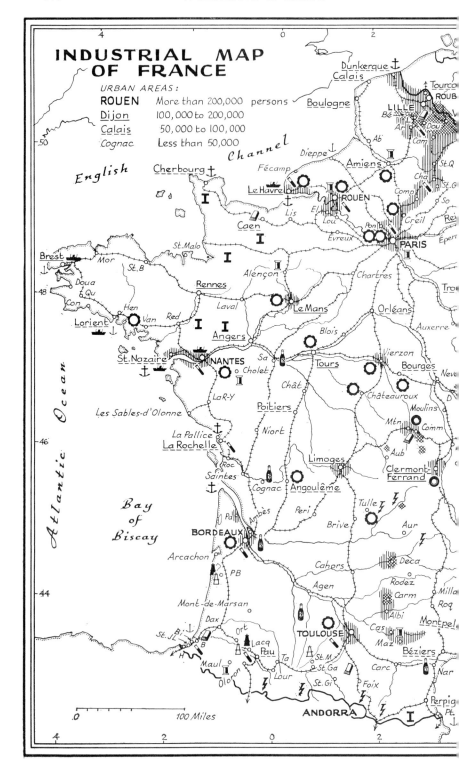

INDUSTRIAL MAP
OF FRANCE

URBAN AREAS:

ROUEN   More than 200,000 persons
Dijon   100,000 to 200,000
Calais   50,000 to 100,000
Cognac   Less than 50,000

Main industrial area
Main railroad line
P Potash   B Bauxite
Coal   Gas   Oil   Iron
Primary metallurgy
Shipbuilding
Mechanical industries, engineering
Textiles   Rubber
Chemicals   Wine or brandy
Port   Very important port
Hydroelectric power

Fig. 5–14. Industrial map of France.

France's coal reserves are not very great. The total proved and probable reserves in 1957 amounted to about 5.7 billion metric tons, which will be exhausted in 100 years at the 1955 rate of production. Even if possible reserves are included, this resource will be depleted in 150 years at most. Thus, development of alternative energy sources has been uppermost in the minds of French planners.

PETROLEUM AND NATURAL GAS. In 1957, some 23 per cent of the energy consumed in France was produced from petroleum and natural gas. More than 90 per cent of the required crude-oil tonnage had to be imported, chiefly from the Middle East.

Prior to 1937, France made no concerted efforts to explore the home territory for petroleum and natural-gas resources. All crude oil and oil products were imported, except for about 60,000 metric tons produced at a small oil field at Péchelbronn in northern Alsace. Since 1937, however, organized exploration for oil and gas has been proceeding. In 1938, the Saint-Marcet gas field was discovered near St. Gaudens some 45 miles southwest of Toulouse, and in 1949 oil was struck at Lacq near Pau at the southern margin of the Aquitaine Basin. More recently, oil and gas have been discovered in the Parentis-Lugos region of the Landes, southwest of Bordeaux, and small fields were found in southern Alsace and near Lons-le-Saunier in the Jura. Moreover, a large field of sulphurous gas was found at Lacq, below the oil-bearing strata. These and the significant finds in Algeria have raised the hopes of France that natural gas and petroleum products refined from domestic crude oils may assume a more important role in the future energy balance of the country.

The Péchelbronn and Lacq oil fields are not significant in terms of quantity or quality. Annual production from these two fields has been roughly 300,000 metric tons, and reserves are small. The first oil strike in the Landes was made in 1954. Estimates of total reserves are so encouraging that the Esso Standard Oil Company is laying a pipeline from Parentis to Bec d'Ambès at the confluence of the Garonne and Dordogne rivers, where a refinery is being built in addition to one already there. As a result of these developments, crude-oil production in France rose to about 1.5 million metric tons in 1958. It is hoped that domestic French crude-oil production will be increased to some 3.5 million metric tons in 1961.

The oil fields in Algeria, first discovered in 1956, are the most promising.[14] Their full extent is not yet known. In spite of transport difficulties, production plans call for 9 million metric tons of crude oil by 1961, about one-third of France's estimated need in that year.

[14] Maurice Kamen-Kaye, "Petroleum Development in Algeria," *The Geographical Review* 48 (October, 1958): 463–73.

The possible gas reserves in the fields of southern France have been estimated to be as high as 800 billion cubic meters. A pipeline distribution network has been constructed, connecting the principal consumption centers of the southwest, the city of Nantes, and the St. Étienne-Lyon-Chalon-sur-Saône region. Another line to Paris is planned. The output of natural gas has risen from less than 100 million cubic meters in 1945 to 1.054 billion cubic meters in 1958. The chief disadvantage of these fields has been their great distance from centers of population and industry. The southwest, however, hopes that its oil and gas resources will attract industry and revitalize its regional economy.

Another problem directly connected with future production of crude oil and petroleum products is the development of a large national refining capacity. Before 1930, there was no modern petroleum refinery in France. Since then, refineries have been put into operation in or near the major seaports, the largest ones in the environs of Le Havre and Marseille. In 1956, the total refining capacity was 31 million metric tons of crude oil per year, with an expansion planned for 44 million metric tons by 1961.

HYDROELECTRIC POWER. Of the total electric power produced in France in 1958 (58.6 billion kwh) 54 per cent was generated by hydroelectric stations, representing some 12 per cent of all energy consumed. In all, France has harnessed more than 40 per cent of its estimated waterpower potential.

The great hydroelectric power potential is in the hilly and mountainous regions of the Alps, the Pyrenees, and the Massif Central, and in the valleys of the Rhone and Rhine rivers. By far the largest and most spectacular power plants are located in the Alps and in the Rhone Valley. The construction of the Génissiat Dam across the Rhone River, 30 miles from Lake Geneva, began in 1937 and was carried on even during World War II. In 1948 work was completed on the dam and power plant with a total installed capacity of 325,000 KW, and generation of power began in that year. Provisions were made for a bypass for inland shipping, which can be built should a Rhone-Rhine waterway connection through Switzerland materialize.

Along the middle Rhone, the Donzère-Mondragon project north of Avignon was begun after World War II, and power production was initiated in 1952. With a capacity calculated at 300,000 KW, this plant and the Génissiat installation are designed to generate about two-thirds of the Rhone River potential. If all plans materialize, there will be a total of 21 power sites on the river in France and several bypass canals in addition to the one already in operation between Donzère and Mondragon.

In the French Alps proper, streams have been utilized for power for electrochemical and electrometallurgical industries since the early part of this century. Planning for large-scale developments in this region has been proceeding since World War II and has revolved chiefly around the Isère and Durance watersheds. Thus far, only a fraction of the potential has been tapped.

Elsewhere, the most notable recent undertakings have been in the valleys of the Dordogne and Rhine rivers. In the upper course of the Dordogne, seven dams are in operation or under construction, having a total annual output of 2.2 billion kwh. In the Rhine Valley the Grand Canal d'Alsace is under construction, paralleling the Rhine River from Basel to Strasbourg. Two power plants are already in operation, one at Kembs, the other at Ottmarsheim, and five more are planned. Upon completion of this project an annual power production of some 6.5 billion kwh will have been reached, which is the recognized potential of this section of the Rhine River.

France has been developing the best sites first. By 1965 it is expected that dam and power-plant construction at less suitable sites will begin, and, by 1975, 96 per cent of the waterpower resources will have been exploited.

ENERGY FROM NUCLEUS, TIDES, AND SUN. These sources of energy are for the future. The first nuclear-power plant is being built near Chinon at the confluence of the Loire and Vienne rivers, designed for a capacity of 60,000 KW with operation expected to begin in the early 1960's. Other plants are under construction. By 1965 nuclear-power plants are expected to supply 5 billion kwh, and by 1975 some 50 billion kwh, or about one-fourth of the total assumed energy requirement for that year.

In an attempt to utilize the tides, a power plant is being erected in the estuary of the Rance River, on the coast of northern Brittany near St.-Malo. It is an experimental plant which when completed, presumably in 1965, is expected to yield 800 million kwh annually. If this one is successful, much larger projects are being contemplated to utilize the strong tidal flows, particularly those of the Bay of Mont St. Michel.

Another experimental undertaking in progress involves several solar furnaces which have been constructed in the Pyrenees to determine whether direct energy from the sun can be harnessed successfully.

FERROUS AND NON-FERROUS MINERALS. France is fortunate in having been endowed with an abundance of iron ore, bauxite, and potash. She is less fortunate with other minerals, and much must be imported.

Exclusive of the Soviet Union, France has the largest iron-ore reserves of Europe, some 35 per cent of the total. This means some 6.56 billion metric tons of measured, indicated, and inferred ore, containing approximately 2.309 billion metric tons of iron. The bulk of it is minette ore, located in the Lorraine region roughly between Nancy in the south and Longwy in the north. Iron-bearing seams outcrop all along the west slopes of the Moselle Valley, where they have been exposed to fluvial erosion. The seams dip gently toward the west and south beneath the Brie Plateau. They are relatively undisturbed over large areas, in spite of faulting which has taken place in the geologic past. Thus, modern mechanized methods can be employed with ease at the surface as well as underground. The ore varies in iron content between 32 and 40 per cent, and may be either predominantly calcareous or silicious. Until the latter part of the nineteenth century, the high phosphorus content had precluded its exploitation in the modern iron and steel industry. In 1878, however, the Thomas-Gilchrist process was introduced for the removal of phosphorus from the metal. Mills in Lorraine began to employ the process only one year later, and early in the twentieth century the minette region had become one of the principal suppliers of pig iron and steel in Western Europe. More than 90 per cent of the total French iron-ore output of 59.5 million metric tons in 1958 was Lorraine ore. Mining methods are so efficient that in spite of the leanness of the ore it can be delivered at competitive prices in the industrial regions of northern France and western Belgium.

Other iron-ore deposits occur in Normandy south of Caen, in Anjou and southeastern Brittany, and in small scattered areas in the Massif Central and the Pyrenees. The Normandy ores are richer than those of Lorraine, having an iron content of 45–46 per cent. Reserves are considerable, nearly 1.4 billion metric tons, but only one bed is exploitable under present conditions. In 1957, production from this field amounted to 2.7 million metric tons. The Anjou-Brittany ores, contributing 950,000 tons in 1957, contain 48–52 per cent iron; they are chiefly magnetites, difficult to reduce.

There are ample bauxite reserves in southern and southeastern France, the extent of which has been estimated variously from 200 million metric tons in the mid-1940's to 68 million tons in recent years. Eighty per cent of the deposits are found in two *départements* —Var, in the Provence, and Hérault, in the Languedoc. The mines are located in western Var (northeast of Marseille) and west of the Rhone Delta. The remaining deposits are in Bouches-du-Rhône where bauxite was first discovered; in the vicinity of the medieval, now nearly depopulated town of Les Baux, six miles northeast of Arles;

and in the *département* Ariège in the Pyrenees southeast of Toulouse. Before World War II, France had been the leading world producer of bauxite, but in 1958 she occupied fourth place, with the lead taken over by Caribbean producers. Moreover, while world production during that period increased nearly fivefold, France lagged behind with a 2½-fold increase.

France possesses the fourth-largest potash deposits in Europe, after the Soviet Union, Germany, and Spain—some 400 million metric tons. The mines are located in southern Alsace near Mulhouse. France ranks fourth in the world production of potash, following the United States and the two Germanys, with a total of 1.6 million metric tons of potash content in 1957. In view of the vital importance of potash in the manufacture of fertilizers for agriculture, special efforts have been made since World War II to modernize the mines and increase their production.

A few other mineral resources have some importance as, for example, the rock-salt deposits in the Luneville area in Lorraine, which form the basis for a local salt-refining and chemical industry. Also, there are widely scattered lead and zinc deposits in the Pyrenees, the Massif Central, Brittany, the Alps, and Corsica. The deposits are small, yielding only a fraction of the domestic requirements, but they are significant in times of crisis.

Manufacturing. About 35 per cent of France's active population in 1957 was engaged in mining and manufacturing. Close to one-third of these were employed in the iron, steel, and metal-working industries. The Lorraine since before World War I has contributed to the French economy some two-thirds of total steel and more than three-fourths of total pig-iron production. This region is, therefore, recognized as the single most important center for such manufacturing.

The Lorraine has not always held this dominant position. When charcoal was used as fuel, iron works were scattered widely on the basis of availability of ore and charcoal and of proximity to markets. After the introduction of coke as a fuel in about 1820, there occurred a gradual concentration of iron and steel manufacturing on coal fields, first in the Massif Central and then in the Nord-Pas-de-Calais region. When the Thomas-Gilchrist process made possible the use of minette iron ore in the Lorraine, that region gained momentum in spite of such drawbacks as its peripheral location in relation to its major markets, the absence of suitable low-cost water transport, and the lack of good coking coal.

The Lorraine iron and steel plants are grouped in three areas. Outstanding among these is the Metz-Thionville complex in the Moselle Valley. The mills there contribute about three-fifths of the Lorraine iron and steel output, and, in view of recent developments, chances for greater industrial expansion within this area have been enhanced considerably. It has already been pointed out that technological advances have made it possible to produce coke from Lorraine coal, only a short distance away. Moreover, an agreement with Germany has assured canalization of the Moselle River, from Thionville to Koblenz where it flows into the Rhine River. Completion of this project will lower transport costs for coking coal moving in, as well as for iron, steel, and metal products being marketed abroad.

The second area is the Longwy-Villerupt area near the Belgium-Luxembourg border, often referred to as the Northern District. This area produces a scant one-third of Lorraine's iron and steel. It is closest in land distance to the northern coal fields of west and central Europe, but there is no waterway system, a situation which may become crucial from the competitive standpoint when the Moselle canalization from Thionville to Koblenz is completed.

The remainder of the iron and steel output in Lorraine comes from the Nancy region, which finds itself at a disadvantage relative to the other two and is not likely to expand its basic industries. The region is farther from coking coal and good iron-ore deposits. The iron ore is not self-fluxing like that of the other areas, so limestone or calcareous ore has to be shipped in. Although the city of Nancy is a focal point for inland waterways, they are insufficient for present-day traffic.

The interdependence of Lorraine iron ore and Ruhr coal has been much overemphasized in past literature. Pounds pointed out [15] that in the past the Lorraine industrial region has obtained up to two-thirds of its fuel supply from the Ruhr, and that it could have absorbed even more. On the other hand, the Ruhr industrial region has been geared to higher-grade foreign ores, so that imports of minette ore have never exceeded 20 per cent of the total needed—and, in fact, imports from Lorraine have been much less than that for over a half century.

It is further significant that the French Industrial North and the Paris region are the best markets for Lorraine steel products. The Lorraine itself, and industries between the Lorraine and the North, also consume a considerable share. This again emphasizes the imbalance which exists in France between the high concentration of manufacturing in a few areas and the relative underdevelopment of the rest.

As production centers of iron and steel, the Industrial North and the Massif Central are relegated to second and third place, although

[15] Norman J. G. Pounds, "Lorraine and the Ruhr," *Economic Geography* 33 (April, 1957): 149–62.

industries there were founded earlier than in Lorraine. The North contributes less than one-sixth of France's pig iron and 20–22 per cent of her steel. However, it benefits from a good supply of scrap from the numerous local engineering industries, so the steel produced here is of higher quality than Lorraine steel. Iron, steel, and engineering industries are centered in the Valenciennes and Douai regions, and the Sambre Valley southeast of Valenciennes. Production in the Massif Central, on the other hand, is quite specialized. High-grade alloy steels are produced primarily for the manufacture of armaments. Industries cluster around coal fields, notably at St. Étienne and Le Creusot.

In 1958, France ranked fifth as a world steel producer, with 14.6 million metric tons, and plans were under way for further expansion. For example, Dunkerque is to be added to other French ports having heavy port industries. A new iron and steel plant is under construction which, by 1965, will contribute 3 million metric tons of steel annually.

In the category of light engineering industries, the manufacture of automobiles has been one of the most active and rapidly growing enterprises. France's production lines turned out 1,128,000 units in 1958 82 per cent of them passenger cars. Export of cars has now become a vital factor in the French economy. Production is centered largely in the Paris region, where labor is abundant, cars are most easily marketed, and excellent land and inland-waterway transport is at hand.

Among other metallurgical industries the production of alumina and aluminum stands out significantly. The original process for the manufacture of aluminum was developed in France in the middle of the nineteenth century. Production first began in northern centers, including Paris, and later moved to Salindres near Alès in the Languedoc. The introduction of the electrolytic process in 1889 relocated the primary industry toward hydroelectric-power sites in the Alps and the central Pyrenees. There are now two companies which obtain bauxite from their own mines, produce alumina and aluminum, and have their own marketing outlets. In 1958, France produced 209,580 metric tons of aluminum, the highest output in Europe and the third largest in the world. Roughly 15,000 tons were exported to Belgium. An even greater tonnage of bauxite and alumina was shipped out of the country. Refineries for other metals, such as lead and zinc, are located either in the major ports, because nearly all the ores are imported, or in the vicinity of coal fields, chiefly in the Industrial North.

The chemical industry in France is relatively young but has made great strides, especially since World War II. Between the two world wars, chemical production was associated almost exclusively with coal, hydroelectric power, and imported phosphates and pyrites. Plants had grown up chiefly around coal fields, for the manufacture of coal distillates, or in ports, for the production of chemical fertilizers from imported raw materials. Electrochemical works were located in the Alps and Pyrenees where hydroelectric power is available.

Although the same basic distribution exists today, new types of chemical industries have been added. Sulphur is being produced from natural gas at Lacq; by 1960, the expected output will be 550,000 metric tons, which may cover the home demand and permit export of the mineral. Other chemical plants, primarily for plastics, have been added to the array of chemical industries at coal fields, and have also been located near petroleum refineries to utilize their by-products.

The textile industry has a long tradition in France and, at one time, was widely scattered in many small regional centers of production. Since the conversion to modern factory-type manufacturing, however, the textile industry has concentrated more and more in four principal regions. The industry, which employs some 600,000 workers, produced about 650,000 tons of textiles of all kinds in 1957.

The largest concentration of textile manufacturing is in the Industrial North, which has the heritage of Flanders. The character of the textiles made in this area is diverse—wool, linen, cotton, jute, and synthetic fibers—although a certain amount of specialization exists within the area. Lille, for example, has the bulk of French linen manufacturing, while cotton and wool processing focus on Roubaix and Tourcoing. Family ownership prevails. This means that the majority of enterprises are small in size, specializing in one type of operation and, since World War II, unable to withstand national and international competition without far-reaching governmental protective measures. Textile raw materials are imported from all parts of the world through Antwerp, Dunkerque, and Le Havre. Although the proximity of coal facilitated the factory-type development, it was not a major factor, inasmuch as the regional concentration had already taken place before coal was used. More significant were the presence of initiative, skilled labor, and well-established merchant houses which had commercial connections throughout the world.

In Normandy, the textile industry centers around Rouen, and consists primarily of cotton spinning and weaving. Practically all cotton used in France is imported through Le Havre, which operates a cotton exchange. Another cotton-processing area is in eastern France, particularly in the valleys of the Vosges Mountains and in the Alsatian Plain. Availability of soft water and rural labor were prime factors in establishing the industry there, as were proximity of Swiss capital and technical knowledge. Moreover, southern Alsace is well located with respect to transport and communication through the Belfort gateway,

into Switzerland and Germany. The earliest industry was fabric printing, a specialization which is still prominent. Cotton processing developed in the nineteenth century, and between 1871 and World War
I, while Alsace was part of Germany, it spread to the eastern and
southern slopes of the Vosges, the Épinal and Belfort regions, respectively.

The fourth major region is the Lyon area where most of the manufacturing of silk, artificial, and synthetic fibers is pursued. The rearing
of silkworms, which had been introduced into Mediterranean France
in the fifteenth century and spread north into the Rhone Valley, has
all but disappeared; most of the silk is imported from China and
Japan. Capital and initiative of Lyon merchants, available rural labor,
nearby water and waterpower, were factors in the concentration of
the industry in this particular area. The cycles of fashion have meant
long periods of alternating depression and prosperity in the silk industry, and the invention of artificial and synthetic fibers has presented a serious challenge. Some existing textile mills have been
converted and new plants built, designed especially for the manufacture of the new fibers and their fabrication.

Closely linked with the textile industry is the production of many
specialized items which have brought renown to certain cities and
towns, such as the manufacture of lace in Le Puy, Alençon, and
Valenciennes, of velvet in Amiens, and of ribbons in St. Étienne.
Of far-reaching effect, however, has been the garment industry in
general, which provides employment for some 600,000 to 700,000
persons, many more women than men. This industry is scattered
widely throughout France, but the focus, of course, is on Paris, which
provides world leadership in fashion design.

A myriad of other manufacturing industries could be named, too
numerous for analysis here, ranging from shipbuilding in the chief
ports to the manufacture of china in Limoges and watches in the
Jura Mountains.

To recapitulate, it might be helpful to outline briefly the main
industrial regions.

1. THE INDUSTRIAL NORTH encompasses a great variety of manufacturing, including iron and steel, chemicals, textiles, glass, and products
of the engineering and food industries. This area is contiguous to
Belgium and is part of the European industrial belt which extends
discontinuously from the British Isles to the Soviet Union. There
are local coal supplies and good communications with the sea and
with the rest of France and Western Europe, as well as with Central
Europe. Accompanying these advantages are a large skilled-labor pool,
the old Flemish tradition, and a vigorous group of industrialists and
merchants.

2. ALSACE-LORRAINE's industrial structure is less balanced than that of the Industrial North. The iron and steel industry of Lorraine, the textile industry, particularly cotton processing, of the Vosges and Alsace, dominate the industrial scene. Local resources which aided industrial development have been Lorraine iron ore and coal, plentiful water and waterpower, good transport connections within France as well as with neighbors to the south and east, and an available supply of rural labor. In progress are improvements of inland waterways, more intensive development of hydroelectric power, and a greater diversification of industry than now exists, which, if they materialize, will provide a great degree of economic stability.

3. THE CENTRAL INDUSTRIAL REGION has Lyon as its principal focus. From there, industries extend in all directions—along the Rhone-Saône corridor into valleys of the Alps, to St. Étienne and valleys of the northern Massif Central. Here metallurgical, chemical, and textile industries are the prominent ones, utilizing local coal supplies, water, and waterpower, and drawing labor from rural areas.

4. THE PARIS AREA has no raw materials and no local power resources, yet it has become France's paramount manufacturing region. Paris—the hub of transport; the seat of government and administration; the center of commerce, finance, and culture; and the site of a large number of small handicraft factories—has become a large labor pool and market area as well. The *département* of Seine alone contains more than one-fourth of France's working population. Nearly all types of manufacturing are represented here in numerous workshops and small factories, as well as in some large plants. Outstanding are the engineering industries, including the manufacture of automobiles. Of greatest renown, however, is the function of the city as a fashion center, with all its associated luxury industries.

All raw materials must be imported from within or outside of France. This is facilitated by easy land and water transport routes which converge upon the city from all directions. Moreover, in addition to thermoelectric power produced locally, Paris obtains hydroelectric power from generating stations in the Massif Central.

5. There are many secondary industrial centers in and near ocean ports, in other major cities, and near sources of energy not included in the industrial areas above.

Communication and Trade. France has developed a dense network of railroads and highways. Paris is the principal focus of both networks to such an extent that it may be difficult to travel from one peripheral area to another without passing through the capital.

The railroads are nationalized and carry about 70 per cent of all freight hauled in France. The major project, after repairing the damage sustained in World War II, has been electrification. Some lines had been electrified between the two world wars, as, for example, the lines Toulouse-Dax-Bayonne and Bordeaux-Hendaye on the Spanish border, completed in the late 1920's. Power was available from nearby generating stations, and passage through the Landes forest of coal-burning engines, which were fire hazards, could be eliminated. With renewed efforts in the 1950's, the lines carrying the heaviest traffic have had priority and, by 1958, nearly 15 per cent of the track mileage had been electrified.

Although the French highway network is the densest in the world, it is outdated and not suited to the rapidly growing vehicular traffic. A program to widen existing highways and to construct new express highways has been begun. One of the most notable projects is the construction of a tunnel through Mont Blanc which will be 7½ miles long and will provide an all-weather route through the Alps between Italy and France. The entrance in France will be at an elevation of 3,947 feet and that in Italy at 4,528 feet, both sufficiently low for keeping roads passable at all times.

France has some 9,300 miles of navigable inland waterways and canals, but only about half of them are actually used commercially. The network is densest in the northeastern part of the country. Nearly all inland navigation takes place within an area delineated by a line from Le Havre to Dunkerque, Strasbourg, Lyon, and back to Le Havre. About 50 million metric tons of cargo are carried annually, which is one-third of the tonnage carried by railroads. Nearly all cargo is bulk, such as coal, petroleum products, and construction materials. The Seine River is the most used waterway, but Strasbourg is the largest inland shipping port, handling more than 8 million metric tons in 1956. Strasbourg's position was achieved by virtue of its location on the Rhine River and not because of inland-waterway connections with the rest of France. Such products as potash from southern Alsace and manufactured goods from Lorraine arrive by railroad which gives the port the best service with its hinterland.

The main drawback of the inland-waterway system has been that most of it was constructed in the nineteenth century, which means that for modern barge traffic the canals are too narrow and have too many locks. Moreover, the canals are operated on an inadequate budget and are poorly maintained. An important agreement made between France and Germany in 1956 in conjunction with the Saar treaty provided for canalization of the Moselle River between Thionville and Koblenz. In a separate treaty with Luxembourg, France agreed to aid that country in the building of certain port installations on the new canal and in electrification of the Luxembourg railroad system. The canal, when completed, will be 169 miles long and will accommodate 1,500-ton barges. Canalization is being achieved by construction of 14 dams, including one at Koblenz built by Germany during World War II. For France, and specifically for the Lorraine manufacturing area, realization of the canal will mean greatly reduced transport charges to and from Germany and ocean ports. Germany, on the other hand, will gain hydroelectric power because nine of the ten powerhouses to be built will be located in Germany between Trier and Koblenz, and the tenth one on the border of Germany and Luxembourg.

The development of the Rhone River has so far been mainly for generation of hydroelectric power and for irrigation. A scheme has been proposed for improvement of existing inland navigation and for an extension of the waterway to Geneva, from whence a connection with the Rhine River could be made. This would put Marseille in direct competition with Dutch and German seaports. As yet, this project is visionary.

French airlines service nearly all parts of the world. Air France is the largest airline in Europe. Again, Paris is the undisputed leader, handling some 57 per cent of all air traffic in French airports in 1956.

The French merchant marine in 1957 ranked ninth in the world; 33 per cent of its ships were tankers. War destruction had been heavy, so France's fleet is one of the most modern in the world. French ships carried about one-half of France's total overseas exports and imports. Marseille and its associated ports handled by far the largest tonnage, 22.5 million metric tons in 1958. Le Havre was second, with 14 million tons, but, in combination with Rouen, a total of more than 24 million tons of sea cargo were handled on the lower Seine River. Other important seaports are, in order: Dunkerque, Nantes, St. Nazaire, Bordeaux, and Sète.

France's foreign trade has been imbalanced for decades. Imports have exceeded exports by an average of 20 per cent since 1878. The deficit has been covered by invisible imports of foreign exchange through tourist trade, offshore purchases, transport services, insurance, etc., as well as by direct financial aid. France must import industrial raw materials, including ores, metals, and textile fibers, as well as crude oil, coal, and tropical and subtropical foods. The upswing in French manufacturing has resulted in a precipitous increase of these imports without a compensating increase of exports.

In recent years, nearly half of France's exports by value have been bulk goods and semimanufactured products, chiefly of the iron and steel industry. For example, Lorraine iron ores have been shipped to Belgium and semifinished materials to Germany, Benelux, and the United Kingdom. Only some 43 per cent of the exports have been finished products which, from the standpoint of economic well-being, should be at the top of the list. Included are machines and machine parts, textiles and clothing, chemical products, and automobiles. The marketing of automobiles (especially Renaults) in the United States and other countries has been of particular importance. However, because French prices of finished products in general have been higher than competitors', a considerable proportion of these products has been marketed in "France overseas," especially Algeria. This, again, is unfavorable to the foreign trade balance, inasmuch as finished goods should find markets in the dollar and sterling areas, where the great foreign exchange gaps exist. The remainder of the exports have been food products, chiefly wheat and wheat products, wine, and beet sugar. The biggest sales of wheat and wine have been to the United Kingdom and Germany, those of sugar to Algeria. France's function as food exporter has been declining ever since before World War I, but in the late 1950's there was hope that agricultural production could be revitalized and that France would increase food exports to become a granary of Europe.

In the over-all trade picture, imports have been heaviest from countries having dollar and sterling currencies, while exports have been chiefly to the French Community. This has created serious financial problems, particularly because an expansion of French trade into non-franc areas has been very difficult, because of empire preference, United States protectionism, and the poor competitive price position of French manufactured goods. However, 1958–59 showed a significant increase of exports to the United States, and prospects for increased trade within the European Economic Community seem brighter.

The French Community

In order to grasp the full significance of France as a world power, brief mention must be made of her areas of influence outside Europe. Many changes have taken place since World War II in parts of the world where France at one time was the colonial ruler. Nations in southeast Asia, formerly under French political control, have gained complete independence and statehood and, in 1958, an entirely new system was evolved regarding the relationship to France of all remaining overseas territories. Under the new constitution confirmed by all territories except Guinea, a French Community was created—a federal system of autonomous states, nearly all of them in Africa. At that time, the cumulative area of the Community, except for France proper, was about 3.8 million square miles, nearly 18 times the area of France and about the same total area as the 50 states of the United

States. The total population occupying this area was about 41 million, nearly as high as the population of France.

Since then, some members of the Community have formed economic unions and others have become independent states. In contrast to the British Commonwealth, many parts of which were settled by English-speaking people, the population in the French Community is composed almost entirely of natives. Only Algeria has a sizable European element, about 1.2 million people, or some 14 per cent of its total population.

THE BENELUX COUNTRIES

Belgium, the Netherlands, and Luxembourg—the Benelux countries—occupy an area of about 25,300 square miles, equivalent to 12 per cent of the area of France or half the area of North Carolina. The Netherlands accounts for about 50 per cent of the total area, and Belgium 45 per cent. Commerce, the *raison d'être* since the time of the Middle Ages in the Low Countries, has provided a mutual if competitive interest over the centuries. Thriving trade relations have grown from the unique location of Belgium and the Netherlands astride the deltas of the Rhine, Meuse, and Scheldt rivers. The Rhine River provides easy access to Central Europe, and the North European Lowland makes these two countries corridor lands between Central Europe and France, and thence to Mediterranean lands. The United Kingdom lies only 21 miles away at the narrowest part of the English Channel. Altogether, site and situation of the Low Countries is such that circulation of goods and people developed freely and effectively, making trade the basis of all economic activity. Only in periods when man interfered with this process did temporary economic stagnation result. Even Luxembourg has had the same *raison d'être* since the end of the nineteenth century, when, through utilization of its iron-ore reserves, it became a manufacturing state dependent on foreign trade for a higher standard of living.

The People

In 1958, the Benelux countries had reached a total population figure of about 20.5 million, of whom a little more than half were Dutch and some 9 million were Belgians. Thus there is a fairly close correlation between percentage of area and population among these three countries. Beyond that, however, an examination of population structure and growth since World War I brings to light very important differences.

In the eighteenth century and before World War I, population growth in the Netherlands and Belgium proceeded at approximately the same rate, so the population of the Netherlands, on the average, was consistently about 1.5 million below that of Belgium.[16] Luxembourg's population, in contrast, grew more slowly than that of the other two countries. By World War I it had increased by only 50 per cent since 1840, while that of the Netherlands and Belgium had doubled.

Population Growth of Benelux Countries *
(thousand)

Country	1840	Pre-World War I	1958
Belgium	4,300	7,450	9,053
Netherlands	2,900	6,000	11,173
Luxembourg	172	261	322

* Estimates from statistical yearbooks.

World War I marks an important turning point. Population growth in the Netherlands accelerated, while that in Belgium began to slow down to such a degree that by 1933 the total population in each of the two countries was the same—about 8,200,000. Since then, the Netherlands has continued to outdistance Belgium, despite the facts that emigration from the Netherlands has exceeded immigration (except in 1958 when 23,000 persons emigrated but 35,000 were repatriated from Indonesia) and that to Belgium in the first half of this century some 300,000 people were added as a result of an excess of immigration over emigration.

The principal reason behind the shift in population growth has been the differing birth rate – death rate balance in the two countries. While between 1900 and 1956 the Netherlands had a surplus of 6 million births over deaths, Belgium's surplus was only 2 million. In the 1950's, the Netherlands has had the highest birth rate in northwestern Europe and the lowest death rate in the world. In Luxembourg, both birth rate and death rate were somewhat below that of Belgium, so the net increase in population there was the slowest among the three Benelux countries. Moreover, the Netherlands has a greater percentage of young people than either Belgium or Luxembourg. Thus, the Netherlands during the next 10 years will have a larger increase of productive population than Belgium, whereas in Luxembourg a decline is anticipated.

[16] T. Van den Brink, "Structure et Évolution Démographique dans les Pays de Benelux," *Benelux Kwartaalbericht*, Bull. Trimestriel 2 (1958): 1–11.

A rapid population growth has given the Netherlands some of the highest population densities in Europe and in the world. In South Holland, which includes The Hague and Rotterdam, the density is 2,400 per square mile, and in North Holland, where Amsterdam and Haarlem are located, it is nearly 2,000. In Belgium, only three provinces reach densities of more than 1,000 per square mile—Brabant (including Brussels), Antwerp, and East Flanders (including Ghent) —but none approaches the high Dutch densities. Combining the density pattern in both countries, one nearly continuous belt of dense population emerges. It extends from North Holland between the North Sea and the Ijssel Lake, southward, skirting the delta area toward Brussels, and thence northwestward into East Flanders. The only gap appears in the Campine in Antwerp province. A second belt of dense population extends from the southern section of Dutch Limburg southwestward along the Sambre-Meuse-Vesdre corridor to the French border.

The transition from high to low population densities is sharp in some areas, such as south of the Sambre-Meuse corridor. The sparsest-populated sections of Benelux are in the Ardennes of Belgium and Luxembourg and in the Northeast Polder of the Netherlands, which is in the process of being settled. Other areas of relatively low population density are Zeeland—the province occupying the Rhine-Meuse-Scheldt delta region—and the poorly drained sections of the northeastern Netherlands.

The Netherlands and Belgium are highly urbanized. While Belgium has the most populous city—Brussels and suburbs, with 1 million people—the Netherlands has many more large urban agglomerations. There are nine cities in Belgium with a total population of more than 50,000 each, while in the Netherlands there are 31. In Luxembourg the capital city, with a population of 70,000, is the only one falling into that category. It is difficult, in fact, to differentiate between urban and rural population in Belgium. The two are interwoven to a considerable degree, and commuting between places of residence and work is very common. Many workers, especially among the Flemish, are also part-time farmers who have been reluctant to leave their inherited property, for reasons of security as well as family tradition. The combination of housing shortages near the places of work and excellent transportation facilities has encouraged commuting to such a degree that, according to estimates, as much as 40 per cent of Belgium's active population may work outside their places of residence.

The Benelux Nations. In Benelux, sharp cultural divides can be found. The most significant is the Walloon-Flemish language divide in Belgium which follows an approximate east-west line through a point just south of Brussels. The capital itself, and the province of Brabant in which it is located, are considered bilingual. To the north and east of the divide the languages are Germanic—Flemish and German in Belgium; Dutch, Frisian, and German in the Netherlands. To the south, Walloon is spoken—a French dialect which has never become a literary language.

The Walloons, occupying interior southern Belgium, did not share in the maritime activity of the Flemish and Dutch. They were not so much affected by the Reformation and Counter Reformation, and came under closer cultural influence from adjacent French-speaking areas. Historically, the Walloons have been the controlling ethnic group in Belgium, through their economic and political predominance, particularly in the early development of modern industry. Although French or Flemish was spoken locally, French had become the official language under Spanish rule, and its continued use as such produced a profound cleavage between those people speaking one or the other language. Only after long and often bitter struggles were both French and Flemish recognized as the official languages of Belgium.

Uneasiness persists and the cleavage is as yet unresolved. The maintenance of an equilibrium between the Flemish and Walloon populations has been one of the motivations in Belgian economic and political thinking. Of concern to the Walloons has been the rapid growth of Flemish population and a corresponding decline in Walloon areas. While in 1896 only some 26½ per cent of Belgium's working population was Flemish, 57 per cent Walloon, and 16½ per cent bilingual, by the middle of the twentieth century 43 per cent of the working population (46 per cent of the total population) was Flemish and only 37 per cent of the working population (32 per cent of the total population) was Walloon. The number of people speaking both languages increased to 20 per cent of the population, most residing in Brabant province. Thus, by the middle of the twentieth century the Flemish-speaking population had gained numerical superiority.

A further difficulty has been the gradual loss of economic superiority of the Walloon sector. While Belgian industry at first was located in the southern coal fields, the newer industrial and mining developments have been in the Flemish sections—in the Campine and in Antwerp—as well as in bilingual Brussels. In general, however, the world wars have done much to reconcile the two factions and to promote a Belgian national feeling and a spirit of partnership.

The religious wars of the Reformation forced the separation of the Netherlands from the territory which was to become Belgium much later. The Calvinist section known as the Netherlands was able to throw off the foreign yoke and to establish an independent state, while the south remained Roman Catholic and under the rule of the Hapsburgs. As a result of this separation, a sharp divide soon manifested itself, which deepened and became formidable when the Dutch throttled Antwerp by closing the Scheldt estuary from 1648 until 1795. The political separation, therefore, originally resulting from religious differences, was an important factor in the creation of two different nations. The boundary between the two states no longer represents a religious one. While Belgium remains almost solidly Catholic, less than half of the Dutch are Protestant and close to 40 per cent are Roman Catholic. Thus, religion as a factor of national consciousness has waned.

With respect to the degree of integration of the various factors contributing to a feeling of "nationality," Belgium faces problems, chiefly of ethnic origin, with which neither of the other two Benelux countries has had to contend. In the Netherlands, such ties as the traditional importance of religion and the religious wars, one principal language, the long common memories of struggles against the sea, centuries of commercial wealth, and a political association of 300 years have all welded a nation corresponding closely with the territorial area of the state. Luxembourg, a remnant of a larger duchy, has never been united politically with any other state. It is a solidly Catholic country. The language spoken has been chiefly Luxembourgeois—a Germanic dialect which has been evolving into a literary language—since the French-speaking sections were incorporated into Belgium in 1839. However, many people are bilingual, and both Luxembourgeois and French are official languages. Culturally, the people of Luxembourg have been oriented toward France, despite the country's long economic association with Germany as a member of the Zollverein. Thus, in the middle of the twentieth century the Luxembourgers are a nation speaking a Germanic language and having strong cultural ties with France, while at the same time linked to a customs union with Belgium and the Netherlands.

The Present Economic Life of Benelux

The idea of an economic union among the three Benelux countries was conceived in London during World War II by the three governments-in-exile. Steps toward effective union were begun on January 1, 1948, with the adoption of a common tariff. A series of further steps culminated in a treaty which was signed by the three countries in 1958, by which a full economic union was established for a period of 50 years.

This union was achieved in spite of economic competition and in
the face of grave initial differences between the Netherlands and the
other two states over money, wages, trade balance, etc. The great
desire for an increasing economic security outweighed all other considerations, and seemingly insurmountable difficulties were being overcome by the end of the 1950's.

Economic pursuits in all three countries are parallel and, to some
extent, competitive. Although recent statistical information about
occupational structure is complete only for Belgium and Luxembourg,
it is evident that Belgium has the lowest percentage of its active population engaged in agriculture, forestry, and fishing, and it probably
has the highest percentage in manufacturing. In fact, it appears to
be Belgium which, in the last forty years, has undergone the most
pronounced change in occupational structure. In 1920, nearly one-
third of the working population was engaged in agriculture, while
by 1958 it was only 10 per cent. The principal reason for this decline
has been an exodus from rural areas in the Ardennes into the Walloon
industrial region, which has created a labor shortage in the Ardennes.

Agriculture. Agriculture is still of great significance in all three
Benelux countries. For home consumption, they all produce sufficient
amounts of meat, dairy products, and vegetables. In addition, the
Netherlands is geared to export agricultural goods, especially vegetables and dairy and horticultural products.

The size of farms differs considerably. They are smallest in Belgium, where there are one million holdings, of which nearly three-
fourths are smaller than 2½ acres. Furthermore, of the remainder—
256,000 farms—some 40 per cent are between 2½ and 7½ acres.
Thus, while Belgium has about 20 per cent less farm land than the
Netherlands it has twice the total number of farm enterprises. If all
farms are included in the calculation, the average-size farm in Belgium
is only 5 acres as against 17 acres in the Netherlands. Even if only
farms of more than 2½ acres are considered, the average for Belgium
is 16 and for the Netherlands 20 acres.

Luxembourg has the largest farms. Only 18 per cent of the total
number have an area of less than 5 acres; among the other 82 per
cent, the average-size farm is 36 acres, with at least half of them having an area between 12½ and 50 acres.

Of the three Benelux countries, the Netherlands uses more of its
total area as farm land than Belgium or Luxembourg—some 72 per
cent. However, only 44 per cent of the Dutch farm land is actually
used for crops, with the remainder utilized chiefly as permanent
meadow and pasture. Belgium and Luxembourg both have considerable areas in the forested Ardennes, so only 57 per cent of the total

area is farm land in Belgium and 55 per cent in Luxembourg. Half of the farm land in Luxembourg and more than half in Belgium is given over to crops. However, in all three Benelux countries a considerable proportion of the crops harvested is consumed by livestock, so that, as in France, animal husbandry emerges as the mainstay of the agricultural economy. Cattle are raised for the production of both dairy products and meat, except in the Netherlands, where meat production definitely assumes a secondary role.

In terms of area devoted to individual crops and of total production of each, oats and wheat vie for first place in Belgium and Luxembourg, and oats and rye in the Netherlands. This indicates a heavier emphasis on crops for livestock in the Netherlands than in the other two countries, mainly because of the importance of export of dairy products in the Dutch economy. The acreage in sugar beets has been increasing since World War II, so as to meet the home demand for sugar. Yields in the Low Countries are the highest in the world for the principal grains, yet needs are so great that large quantities must be imported to complement domestic production. Wheat yields are between 55 and 58 bushels per acre in the Netherlands and Belgium, as against 15 to 20 bushels in the United States. Oats yields are more than 90 bushels and rye close to 50 bushels per acre, compared with 40 and 14 bushels, respectively, in the United States.

The cooperative movement has been developed most strongly in the Netherlands. It began in the latter part of the nineteenth century, when grain imports from the New World impoverished farmers and forced them to reorient their agricultural economy as well as their social attitudes. Dairy farming gradually supplanted the growing of grain, and cooperatives replaced the strong individualism which had formerly prevailed.

The movement toward cooperatives began in 1877 when a group of farmers in Zeeland made a joint purchase of fertilizers. The first cooperative dairy plant was founded in 1886 at Warga in Friesland. Now there are some 4,000 cooperatives, specialized in practically every field of agricultural pursuit. More than 75 per cent of all milk, more than 80 per cent of the butter production, and approximately 80 per cent of the total cheese production are now processed in cooperatives. Many buying cooperatives have been formed, also, for the purchase of fertilizer, fodder, seeds, etc., as well as sales cooperatives for the sale of agricultural products.

Especially noteworthy are the cooperative auctions for the sale of vegetables, fruits, and flowers. Farmers who belong to cooperatives of this type are obliged to sell through these auctions; nearly all marketed vegetables are sold in this way. In recent decades the cooperative movement has expanded into sales and slaughtering of cattle, and has strengthened successfully the social and economic position of those farmers who have specialized in that branch of activity.

Agricultural Regions. In Benelux seven agricultural landscapes can be distinguished:

1. THE POLDER LANDS. Along the inner fringe of the sand dunes are the polder lands, the development of which has been noted. The surface is flat, and the soils are heavy marine or river clays of widely ranging fertility. Meadows and pasture land predominate, although grains, sugar beets, and potatoes are important as well, especially in Zeeland, the new Ijssel Lake polders, the northern margin of Groningen and Friesland, and parts of maritime Flanders. Some areas have become quite specialized and are of world renown. For example, along the western margins of the Holland polders dune sand has mixed with heavier polder clay, resulting in a soil particularly favorable for intensive horticulture, including fruits, vegetables, tulips, hyacinths, and other flowers. The bulb area—some 16,000 acres—lies between Leyden and Haarlem. Between The Hague and the Hoek van Holland is the Westland, where 49,000 acres of land are used for the growing of fruits and vegetables, mostly under glass.

Drainage canals and ditches perform the function of fences, and gates are visible only at bridges across the waters. Farmsteads in the older polder lands of the Netherlands and Belgium form widely scattered clusters on dikes and along roads, while in recently developed Dutch polders modern regional planning has grouped them into villages and towns, spaced at regular intervals from one another in a calculated hierarchy.

In Belgium, West Flanders has only a small percentage of its area in polder lands, and those were reclaimed in the Middle Ages. In the Netherlands, land reclamation is a continuing process. The big project of this century thus far has been the draining of the Zuider Zee. This body of water became an inlet of the North Sea in the thirteenth century and had been a flood menace ever since. During World War I there were disastrous inundations and, simultaneously, wartime conditions created food shortages. The conviction grew that both problems could be solved by isolating the Zuider Zee from the North Sea and by draining sections of it so as to increase the agricultural acreage of the Netherlands and simultaneously to produce a fresh-water lake.

The project was begun in 1918, and the first polder—the Wieringermeerpolder, with an area of some 49,000 acres—was completed in 1930, two years before the main dike was closed (Fig. 5–15; for the locations of projects discussed here and in the following pages see Fig. 5–19). With the completion of the 19-mile-long dike in 1932, the

Fig. 5–15. The main dike separating the Ijssel Lake (right) from the Wadden Zee (left), an arm of the North Sea. The tall building is the monument commemorating the closing of the dike in 1932. (KLM Aerocarto n.v.)

Zuider Zee became the Ijssel Lake, named after the Ijssel River, one of the distributaries of the Rhine. The dike's crown is 20 to 22 feet above sea level, and the width of the base is some 600 feet. It was constructed of material available locally, chiefly sand, and on the seaward flanks a thick layer of resistant, impregnable boulder clay taken from the floor of the Zuider Zee. In order to prevent scouring of the flanks of the new dike by wave action, they were covered with large willow and brushwood mattresses weighted down with boulders.

The completion of the dike had two immediate benefits. It shortened the coast line of the Netherlands from 1,150 miles to 840 miles, thereby reducing the area in danger of attack by the sea; the shores of the Ijssel Lake were no longer exposed to the open ocean. Secondly, the dike provided direct communication with the northern provinces of the Netherlands.

The new lake has become a fresh-water reservoir which, at the completion of the entire project later this century, will have an area of about 300,000 acres. It is a reservoir for inland drainage as well as a source of fresh water for agriculture and industry.

Since the construction of the dike in 1932, the Northeast Polder, with an area of about 118,000 acres, was completed and is being settled (Fig. 5–16) and the East Flevoland polder has been pumped dry and is being readied for settlement. There are two more polders to be drained, South Flevoland and Markerwaard, which will form a single large homogeneous area enclosed on three sides by existing lands. After completion of the entire project, about 885 square miles will have been added to the surface area of the Netherlands—approximately 7 per cent of the total present area, or 10 per cent of the total farm land—and roughly 300,000 people will have been settled on these new lands.

The second major project of the twentieth century is the Delta Plan through which three principal distributary arms of the Scheldt-Meuse-Rhine delta will be closed by means of four main dams. The western Scheldt estuary and the New Waterway will be left open, however, so as not to impede maritime traffic to Antwerp and Rotterdam, respectively. This project received its immediate impetus in 1953 when high tides and strong onshore winds combined to produce higher flood waters than ever known before. Many dikes broke, and more than 350,000 acres of land were flooded in the delta area, resulting in a great loss of life and property.

The Delta Plan was designed and initiated as a multiple-purpose project. Its aims are to protect the polder lands in Zeeland in the future, shorten the coast line still further, stop infiltration of sea water, and make available bodies of fresh water for irrigation. Moreover, a tideless inland water body will improve transport and communication, thereby contributing to the economic and social development of Zeeland and South Holland. Work began in 1958; when it is completed, two arms of the sea will have been sealed off against the North Sea while the northernmost arm, the Haringvliet, will have sluice gates for the escape of surplus waters of the Rhine and Meuse rivers. The technical difficulties encountered here will eclipse those the Dutch have had to solve in the Zuider Zee project. The tidal range in the estuaries is 13 feet against 3 feet at the former Zuider

Fig. 5–16. Farmsteads in the newly settled Northeast Polder reclaimed from the former Zuider Zee. (KLM Aerocarto n.v.)

Zee entrance, dams will have to be built on shifting sands instead of boulder clay, and depths are much greater. However, new techniques and materials, combined with traditional Dutch determination and skill, will bring this project also to a successful conclusion.

It has been predicted that its completion later in the century will alter the landscape and its economy profoundly. With good transport links, the delta region is expected to become suburban to the large cities of South Holland. Agriculture will change from the growing of grains and dairying to truck farming, and lakes and beaches will become a tourist and vacation paradise.

Whatever the future may bring, one industry is certain to be eliminated. The eastern Scheldt has been the location of a highly successful and prosperous oyster and mussel industry, but, with the construction of the dam across the estuary, the water will become fresh and shellfish cultivation will cease. Unfortunately, no new suitable sites for this type of fishing have been found, so this industry will die out.

The third major project involves the separation of the Wadden Zee from the North Sea by linking the Frisian Islands with dams and by anchoring the two ends to the mainland. This will again shorten the coast line and add more land to the Dutch area. Still in the planning stage, this project is only a dream and hope, but some day it will become a reality.

2. THE EASTERN NETHERLANDS. East of the Ijssel Lake the expanses of peat bogs, high moors, and unconsolidated sands remained essentially sparsely settled until the seventeenth century. Then, drainage was begun by means of ditches and canals, and peat and other organic material were mixed with sand and fertilizer, thereby producing fertile soils for the growing of various small grains for livestock and man, and potatoes suitable for the production of starch. Dairy farming is important here, also, and pigs are being raised on by-products of dairies as well as on imported feed. Oat and rye straw are used for the manufacture of mats and cardboard.

Since the time when agricultural expansion began in this area, population has increased rapidly, mostly nucleated in rural hamlets and villages. This, plus mechanization of agriculture, gradual exhaustion of peat reserves, and poor land and water transport, has created problem areas the economy of which the Dutch government is attempting to improve through a program of industrialization.

3. THE CAMPINE. In northern Belgium and the southern Netherlands lies an undulating to rolling sandy landscape where an impermeable subsoil created poor drainage conditions and delayed human occupancy. The Campine has been typified as a "forest-animal region." [17] Certainly this is true in the Dutch and Belgian border zones, the heart of this area. In either direction, however, toward

[17] Fritz Quicke, *Les Régions Agro-économiques de la Belgique*, Liége: Sciences et Lettres, S. A., 1950.

large population centers more land has been reclaimed for the growing of crops, the percentage of land in forest declines, and that under grass cover increases. For the Campine as a whole, one can generalize that cropland, chiefly rye, oats, and potatoes, is widely scattered on better-drained soils, while along stream courses and canals are permanent pastures and irrigated meadows. Settlement is primarily in clusters of farmhouses interspersed with individual farmsteads situated along roads. Younger rural settlements and coal-mining towns appear among older established villages.

4. INNER FLANDERS. This is yet another section of the sandy belt which extends through Belgium and the Netherlands. Inner Flanders adjoins the polder land of maritime Flanders and Zeeland on the south, and stretches from the Campine westward into France. Like the Campine, this area is undulating, and rye and other crops, chiefly for livestock, are abundant. This belt, however, has been developed agriculturally since the Middle Ages, when the growth of Flemish towns necessitated an increase in local food production. Rural population density is very high and farms are small. Farmhouses are strung out loosely along roads, giving the impression of considerable scattering of rural settlement. Dairy farms and market gardening prevail near Antwerp and Ghent. Toward France in the west and in areas adjoining the fertile loam region in the south, there is a specialized production of industrial crops, notably sugar beets, flax (Fig. 5–17), chicory, and tobacco.

5. THE LOAM BELT. South of the sands of East Flanders and the Campine, elevation increases and fine, permeable fertile loam gives rise to the most prosperous agricultural region of Benelux. The belt extends roughly between the Meuse and the upper Scheldt rivers from France across central Belgium into Dutch southern Limburg and Germany. It is a mixed zone of livestock and crop farming, where wheat and sugar beets are principal crops for man, and rye and oats for animals. An infinite variety of secondary crops has produced a variegated rural landscape. On the other hand, some localities are highly specialized in the growing of industrial crops, fruits, and vegetables (Fig. 5–18).

In the west, in areas adjacent to France, flax, chicory, tobacco, and hops are grown, especially in the valleys of the Lys and Scheldt rivers. Truck farming predominates near urban concentrations, as in the Brussels, Liége, and Malines regions. In the latter, vegetables cover as much as 40 per cent of the cropland and, near Brussels, a considerable amount of vegetable growing is done under glass. In the truck-farming region, farms are among the smallest in Benelux, land division is extreme, and exploitation is as intensive as in the vegetable- and bulb-growing areas of the polders.

Fig. 5–17. Flax fields in Inner Flanders. Processing plants are scattered throughout the area. (Belgian Government Information Center, New York.)

Fig. 5–18. Hothouses at Hoeilaart, 8 miles south of Brussels. (Belgian Government Information Center, New York.)

In the northern section of this region the landscape is open, except for frequently fenced-in meadows, and settlement is loose, consisting of clusters of four-sided farmsteads or open villages at road junctions. In the south the loam belt, like the Ardennes and Lorraine, was under the three-field system until the end of the eighteenth century, so that fences become rare and hedges have been planted around orchards which, in turn, surround compact farm villages.

6. THE ARDENNES. South of the Sambre-Meuse line is another region where livestock and forests predominate. In the Ardennes proper in Belgium and Luxembourg, closed agricultural villages, meadows, and fields appear as islands of various sizes in the forest. The soils are thin and of low fertility, and much more of the cleared land is in meadow than is in crops. Cattle raising predominates over all other agricultural pursuits. Wet, narrow, deeply incised valleys as well as higher elevations have been avoided for settlement.

Toward the north and south from the main plateau, the percentage of land in forest decreases and population density and cropland for human consumption increase, although livestock remains the mainstay of the economy. In the Herve, the northeasternmost section, forests almost disappear and meadows and orchards dominate the landscape.

7. LORRAINE. In southernmost Belgium and southern Luxembourg extends a rolling landscape of scattered small rural settlements, but there are also many individual farms on fertile soils cleared in medieval times. A mixed type of livestock and crop farming prevails; oats occupy the greatest area, but potatoes and winter wheat are also important. Here as elsewhere in Western Europe, the trend in the last 50 years has been toward a livestock economy and the percentage of meadow and pasture land has been increasing. On the slopes of the Moselle Valley, vineyards provide Luxembourg with domestic wines, including the sparkling variety.

Industrial Raw Materials.

ENERGY RESOURCES. Of the three Benelux countries, Luxembourg alone has practically no energy resources, with the exception of a small waterpower potential and her forests in the Oesling—the Ardennes plateau section. In conjunction with the Moselle canalization, a hydroelectric-power plant is being built where the river forms the Luxembourg-Germany boundary. Coke and coal are imported from Belgium, the Netherlands, and Germany, and petroleum products from Belgian and Dutch refineries.

Belgium and the Netherlands both have their own fuel—the former, coal, and the latter, a combination of coal, petroleum, and natural gas (Fig. 5–19). However, production is far short of domestic needs. The Netherlands must import nearly one-half of its energy requirements, but Belgium only about 14 per cent, much of it in the form of petroleum and petroleum products.

COAL. Both the Netherlands and Belgium have coal deposits at their disposal, which have been and will continue to be vital in the economy of the two countries. In Belgium some 90 per cent of all energy consumed is derived from coal mined there. Belgium ranks as the fourth-highest producer in Europe west of the Iron Curtain. Additional amounts of coking coal and coke have had to be imported, chiefly from Germany. Although labor productivity has been slowly increasing ever since World War II, the output per man-shift underground, at 2,550 pounds, has been consistently the lowest among the coal-producing countries of free Europe.

The coal mines in Belgium are located in two general areas. The southern or Walloon fields have the oldest coal mines in Europe. Lying in the Sambre-Meuse corridor, they can be divided into four mining regions. The Borinage, centered on Mons, and the Tournai region, northwest of it, are economically depressed areas where mines are small, numerous, and poorly equipped, and where the better seams have been exhausted. The closing of the pits and various industrial enterprises has brought about a great deal of unemployment and unrest. Many Belgians from this area have sought better and more attractive employment in adjacent mining and manufacturing areas of France, to which they commute, while Italians have immigrated to go into the pits at low wages. A third mining region is that between Mons and Namur, centered on Charleroi. Here are employed more than 40 per cent of all Belgian coal miners, and the heavy concentration of many industries provides a better regional balance and a prosperous economy, in spite of the difficult mining conditions. Finally, coal is being mined in the Liége area where it also forms the basis of a great variety of industries.

The number of pits in these four mining regions declined from 265 in 1900 to 113 in 1957, the latter operated by 48 companies and producing less than two-thirds of Belgium's coal.

The remainder of coal in Belgium comes from the Campine region, where large-scale mining did not begin until 1917. There seven large companies each operate one mine, producing more than one million tons of coal annually apiece. The Carboniferous coal seams lie in an area extending some 50 miles east-west from Dutch Limburg toward Antwerp. Their depth at the Dutch border is about 1,400 feet and they dip westward, so that about one-half of the estimated reserves are below a depth of 3,000 feet. In spite of the great depth, however, mining operations are easier and output per man-shift underground

Fig. 5–19. Industrial map of Benelux.

larger than in the southern coal fields, because the seams are thick and regular. The mines are widely scattered in open heath land, and, as yet, no industrial concentrations have been formed; rather, the coal is shipped out mostly by inland waterway to the leading industrial concentrations in the Sambre-Meuse corridor, Brussels, Antwerp, and Ghent.

The Belgian coal reserves workable under present conditions have been estimated as being about 2.8 billion metric tons, which means that at the current production rate they will be exhausted in less than 100 years, unless technology is improved or new seams are discovered.

In the Netherlands the situation is more favorable. The coal seams in southern Limburg are a section of the measures extending from Aachen in Germany into the Belgian Campine. Because of the westward dip already mentioned, the seams are at a depth of only 300 feet at the German border and 1,400 feet near the Belgian border.[18] However, the seams vary in thickness from 2 to 8 feet and have been disturbed by folding and faulting. Output per man-shift underground is 3,300 pounds, which is somewhat higher than the output in the adjacent Belgian Campine and considerably more than that of the German Aachen mines. The principal mining areas are at Heerlen and Kerkrade.

In 1958, the Netherlands produced from this field 11.9 million metric tons of coal, of which about half was high-grade coking coal, sufficient for home demand of coke as well as for some export of high-grade metallurgical coke. The over-all coal production could not meet Dutch demand and an additional 7.3 million tons had to be imported in 1958.

In northern Limburg there is a second coal field, which has not yet been exploited because of its great depth. It lies in the Peel district, extending in a southeast-northwesterly direction into North Brabant, and is located at depths ranging from 2,500 to 3,000 feet. The total estimated exploitable reserves of all Dutch coal fields are about 5 billion metric tons, which, at the current production rate, would be exhausted in 450 years.

PETROLEUM AND NATURAL GAS. Only the Netherlands is so fortunate as to have petroleum and natural-gas resources. The 1958 crude-oil production represented about one-fourth of all energy consumed and 10 per cent of crude oil refined in the Netherlands, the rest having been imported from the Middle East and the Western Hemisphere. About 60 per cent of the 1958 production total came from the oil fields at Schoonebeek, in eastern Drenthe near the German border.

---

[18] F. J. Monkhouse, "The South Limburg Coal Field," *Economic Geography* 31 (April, 1955): 126–37.

The remainder came from scattered small fields near The Hague, Delft, and Rotterdam, which have been producing since 1953. Proven reserves in 1955 were only about 13 million metric tons.

Domestic natural gas covers about 1 per cent of Dutch energy requirements and 10 per cent of total Dutch gas production. There are 15 natural-gas wells in the northeastern Netherlands near the Dutch-German border north of Enschede, and two wells in the vicinity of Delft in South Holland.

FERROUS AND NON-FERROUS METALS. The minette ores of the Lorraine Basin extend into southern Luxembourg as well as into the southern margin of the Belgian province Luxembourg. The ore layers are near the surface, but there is no uniformity in thickness or in areal extent. In Luxembourg they occur in at least five layers ranging in thickness from 3 to 12 feet and having an average iron content of a little over 30 per cent. In the Belgian section only one bed—4½ to 7½ feet thick—is workable. The Luxembourg fields have a proven reserve of 200 million tons of ore containing 56 million tons of metal. An additional 300 million tons of ore reserves, having an iron content of 78 million tons, are possible.

There are also hematite deposits in the Sambre-Meuse corridor, which were worked until 1946 when further extraction became economically unfeasible. However, there still is a proven reserve of 30 million tons of ore containing 10 million tons of iron, with much greater possible reserves. The seams outcrop for some 40 miles and vary in iron content from 26 to 40 per cent, but locally it may be as high as 58 per cent. Finally, lenticular beds of ferruginous sands are found about 25 miles northeast of Brussels, containing limonite with varying iron content below 28 per cent. These beds, also not exploited currently, contain a proven reserve of 50 million tons and a possible reserve of 100 million tons, with 12 and 20 million tons of iron, respectively.

Iron-ore production in the latter 1950's approached 8 million metric tons annually in Luxembourg and was only about 140,000 metric tons in Belgium, both insufficient tonnages to cover the demand in either country. Luxembourg obtained additional supplies from the French Lorraine, and Belgium from France, Luxembourg, and Sweden.

Manufacturing. Our previous discussion has shown that the economy of all three Benelux countries is based almost entirely upon manufacturing and foreign trade.

LUXEMBOURG. Until late in the nineteenth century, Luxembourg was strictly an agricultural country with very little manufacturing. The standard of living was low, and its population was diminishing, in part because of heavy emigration. With the successful use of minette ores in the iron- and steel-making processes, beginning in 1878, the situation changed drastically. A series of industrial towns sprang up in southwestern Luxembourg along the French border, at the base of the ore-bearing cuesta; Esch-sur-Alzette became the most important town. Since World War II, iron and steel works have also been established in new suburbs north of Luxembourg City.

Before World War I, as a member of the *Zollverein* and then in customs union with Germany, Luxembourg's economy became closely integrated with that of Germany, including the Saar and Alsace-Lorraine. The customs union with Belgium in 1922, however, gave the country the added advantage of free access to the port of Antwerp. This, in turn, stimulated the further development of the iron and steel industry, the products of which now make up 80 per cent of Luxembourg's total exports. No coke is produced locally. All coke is imported from Germany and France, and, as already stated, additional ore is brought in from adjacent French mines. In 1958 only a fraction of the iron and steel products manufactured in the country were used locally, more than 95 per cent having been exported, chiefly to other European countries.

BELGIUM. In Belgium, the bulk of the iron and steel industry is located in the Walloon mining and industrial belt, with particular concentrations at Liége and Charleroi. Outside this area, iron and steel are produced in the Athus-Musson-Halanzy area in Belgian Luxembourg near the international border, based on minette iron ore, and at Clabecq on the Brussels-Charleroi canal. The industry is oriented predominantly toward the phosphoric minette ore of the Lorraine. All large plants have their own coke ovens, but coke production is not enough to cover home demand and some additional supplies must be obtained from Germany.

Steel production in Belgium has increased steadily from World War II until 1956 when its total figure was nearly three times as great as in 1938; it has been consistently the highest among the three Benelux countries.

In conjunction with these industrial and mining complexes, other important industries have grown up, such as chemical plants, gas works, thermoelectric-power plants, the textile, china, and glass industries, and refineries of various metals. As has already been pointed out, the industrial concentrations that have evolved in the Liége and Charleroi sections have given these areas considerable prosperity and economic security. The Namur area has no coal, but manufacturing began on the basis of local iron-ore deposits and waterpower. Excellent transport connections by water on the Meuse and Sambre rivers gave the city an advantage for further development, and today there are metallurgical and chemical industries, glass manufacture, zinc refining, and others.

The oldest industry in Belgium is the textile industry. It emerged in Flanders beginning in the eleventh century, with the processing of local and, later, English wool and the manufacturing of cloth, especially in Ghent, Brugge, and Ieper. Later, the linen industry developed, mainly localized in the valley of the Lys River whose lime-free waters proved particularly suitable for the retting of flax, and cotton spinning and weaving entered the textile complex in the seventeenth century. The most recent addition is the manufacture of artificial and synthetic fibers.

Today, the textile-manufacturing areas can be classified in two groups. There are the old specialized centers in Flanders where manufacturing of all types is widely scattered. Some Flemish cities are of world renown, such as Ghent, Kortrijk, and Roeselare in the linen industry, and Ghent in the manufacture of linen, cotton, and jute. Malines is known for the production of flannel, and Brussels for its shawls and tartans. Many other examples could be cited. Although wool gave the original impetus to the development of the Flanders textile centers, its manufacture is not concentrated there now to any degree.

Verviers in the Vesdre River Valley and its satellite towns represent the second group of textile mills, producing a great variety of wool and woolen goods. The woolens industry has been flourishing ever since the fifteenth century, when it moved there from Flanders to get away from local competition, guild restrictions, and high labor costs. The Vesdre River has pure, soft water suitable for washing and fulling, cheap rural labor was available, and Walloon industrial activity had extended into the valley from Liége. Later, coal from the Liége basin became an additional advantage. Since World War II there has been some shifting of large companies to towns in Flanders, such as Malines and Diest, where they have begun operation with new and modern plants.

Two manufacturing centers outside the Walloon industrial belt—Brussels and Antwerp—deserve special mention. Brussels is located at the head of inland navigation on the Senne River. Its industrial area extends southwestward along the Senne River and the canal to Charleroi. More than half the population of Belgium lives within a 30-mile radius of the capital city, pursuing a great variety of urban, industrial, and agricultural activities. Antwerp, at the head of ocean-going navigation on the Scheldt River, some 55 miles from the sea, also has a rich industrial hinterland, thanks to the city's function as a seaport. Among the more important industries are shipbuilding, petroleum refining, and the processing of colonial goods.

The port has been a prosperous center of trade and transport since the city received its rights in 1291 and since it joined the Hanseatic League in 1315, with the exception of a period extending from the Spanish Inquisition and the closing of the estuary by the Dutch until the reopening by Napoleon in 1795. The population of Antwerp increased from 74,000 in 1830 to 130,000 in 1845 and 295,000 in 1900. In 1955, the Antwerp urban agglomeration amounted to a population of nearly 606,000.

THE NETHERLANDS. Traditionally, Dutch industry like that of Flanders has produced luxury goods since the end of the Middle Ages, such as Utrecht velvet and Delft earthenware. To these were added, beginning in the seventeenth century, shipbuilding and the colonial industries, which evolved chiefly in the large port cities of Amsterdam and Rotterdam. The colonial industries consisted of preparation and conversion of raw materials from overseas, such as the manufacture of cocoa and chocolate, the production of vegetable oils, the distillation of gin, diamond cutting, and the re-export of the finished products. The Industrial Revolution virtually bypassed the Netherlands on account of the nature of her existing industries and particularly because no coal or other mineral resources were known, on which to base heavy industry.

Industrialization began in the latter half of the nineteenth century, first with the development of manufacturing of agricultural products. The economic plight of Dutch farmers, because of cheap foreign grain imports, and the resulting changes in the basic agricultural structure of the country, have already been discussed. The production of high-quality agricultural products and their export have been of great importance in the Dutch economy ever since. Moreover, the discovery of coal in Dutch Limburg in the twentieth century, the development of new scientific methods, and the ever-increasing population problem, particularly since World War II, have intensified the efforts of the Dutch to create a modern industrial nation.

Coal has given rise to a concentrated industrial complex in southern Limburg. The production of high-grade metallurgical coke is linked with a diversified chemical industry and the production of gas. A high-pressure pipeline system extends through Limburg and North Brabant. In addition, there are several thermoelectric-power plants which are essential links in the Dutch power grid. The Dutch iron- and steel-manufacturing center, however, is not located here but in Velsen on the North Sea Canal, two miles east of Ijmuiden. It uses imported iron ores in conjunction with coal and coke from the Limburg fields. Annual production of crude steel has been increasing steadily. In 1958 it amounted to 1.4 million metric tons, which covered nearly half the home demand for that year.

New scientific methods and modern technical developments have given rise to some very specialized varieties of manufacturing, some as port industries and others located inland. Rotterdam is one of Europe's chief oil-refining centers, and Rotterdam and Amsterdam have shipbuilding and its ancillary engineering industries. The production of chemicals and pharmaceuticals, flour milling, and the assembly of automobiles—all are based on imported raw materials and semimanufactured products, as are some of the older, traditional industries discussed above. Some large, outstanding plants are located in the interior, such as the tin smelters at Arnhem and the famous Philips factory at Eindhoven, producing radio sets, phonographs, and electrical equipment.

The Dutch textile industry is concerned chiefly with the processing of cotton. Spinning is concentrated largely in the Rotterdam area, while cotton weaving and further manufacturing is scattered in the eastern and southern Netherlands. Outstanding is the Twente, an area in southeastern Overijssel, where Enschede and Hengelo have become cotton-textile centers. Since 1936 the production of high-quality rayon has taken on importance in association with cotton-textile industries, particularly in the Twente.

To alleviate population pressure and to aid rural problem areas in the far northern and northeastern sections of the country and in parts of North Brabant (southwestern and northeastern) and northern Limburg, the Dutch government in 1952 initiated a policy of encouraging and giving state aid to industries which wished to establish themselves and expand in those areas. It is anticipated that such industrialization will absorb surplus rural population and improve road and water transport and the levels of regional economies, at the same time as it aids the over-all industrialization policy pursued by the Dutch government.

Communication and Trade. By virtue of their location on the Channel and North Sea, in the Belgian corridor of the North European Lowland, and astride the Rhine-Meuse-Scheldt deltas, both Belgium and the Netherlands are of paramount importance in terms of the European transportation pattern, and both have exploited their position to the fullest extent. But in the matter of highways modernization has, in general, been unable to keep up with the demands of present-day road traffic.

HIGHWAYS. Benelux, like France, is confronted with the problem of rapidly increasing traffic on the highways. In Belgium, for example, the number of private cars has increased by more than three times since 1939, and in Luxembourg it nearly doubled between 1953 and 1957. In general, the network of highways and secondary roads serves all sections of Benelux, but the ever-growing automobile and truck traffic cannot be handled adequately on these roads. A modernization program is under way to improve and widen the more important existing roads, and connect the principal ports, cities, and industrial centers with a network of superhighways which will also tie in with the international road network.

RAILROADS. Belgium has the densest railroad network in the world, a total of 3,100 miles of rail, the greatest track densities lying within the two Flanders provinces, in Hainaut and around Brussels. Belgium has been called the turntable of European railroad traffic because nine international lines traverse the country, among them those of the Orient Express, Nord Express, Tauern Express, and others.

Belgian railroads carry about 70 million tons of merchandise annually, 22 per cent of which represents transit and 46 per cent derived from the country's import and export trade. Thus, internal cargo transport by railroad accounts only for about one-third of the total traffic, a fact which emphasizes the international position of Belgium.

A government program to modernize the railroads and thereby reduce the costs and increase the speed of transport has high priority and is proceeding through electrification and the use of diesel engines. By 1957, 17½ per cent of the total rail net was electrified, including the main lines from Brussels to other major Belgian cities, and to Luxembourg.

In the Netherlands, railroads do not assume so vital a function as in Belgium. The railroad network was completed essentially by 1890, and by the turn of the century it was well integrated with the Belgian and German railroads. Only local additions made since then have increased the length of track which now amounts to 2,000 miles. Here, as in Belgium, modernization has been in progress; roadbeds have been improved, diesel engines put into service, and lines electrified. In 1958 one-half the Dutch network was operated with electricity. In that year, Dutch railroads carried only 23.6 million tons of merchandise as against 144 million tons carried on Dutch inland waterways.

INLAND WATERWAYS. The density of the inland-waterway network in the Netherlands (miles per inhabitant) is the highest in the world.

There are 4,200 miles of waterways, of which 84 per cent are canals. Small craft dominate the waterways, inasmuch as about three-fourths of all waterways can accommodate only barges having a carrying capacity of less than 1,000 tons. However, 790 miles can be used by craft carrying more than 1,500 tons.

The principal rivers used for navigation are the Rhine River, unequaled with its direct connection to Central Europe, particularly the Rhine-Westphalian industrial region, and the Meuse, which, together with the Juliana Canal, opens the South Limburg industrial and mining area to 2,000-ton barges. Rotterdam is located on the Nieuwe Maas, the estuary of the Lek River, which is a distributary of the Rhine River.

The most vital canals are those connecting the large ports with the North Sea—the 16-mile-long New Waterway for Rotterdam and the 18-mile North Sea Canal for Amsterdam. The latter is served also by the 40-mile-long Merwede Canal, which connects Amsterdam with the Waal River and thereby makes it a Rhine River port. The Juliana Canal was built to bypass an unnavigable section of the Meuse River. It parallels the Meuse along the right bank for some 21 miles from Maastricht to Maasbracht, where shipping returns to the river. Navigation is open for 2,000-ton barges which carry up to two-thirds of their total freight in coal and coke.

In Belgium the heavy emphasis on railroads noted above does not mean that inland waterways have been neglected or are not important. Belgium has 970 miles of navigable waterways, nearly half of them canals, as compared to the Netherlands' 4,200 miles, and yet the density of its network (miles per inhabitant) is second highest in the world after the Netherlands.

Canals originated in Flanders during the Middle Ages, but the great effort in canal building, as elsewhere, came in the nineteenth century, and by 1880 most of the present network was in existence. The chief objective was to connect the interior industrial areas with Belgium's ports, particularly with Antwerp. This meant the connection of the basins of the Meuse and Scheldt rivers, which, in some instances, was achieved only with great difficulties—the construction of many locks and the excavation of deep cuts.

The latest canal construction in Belgium was that of the Albert Canal, 81 miles long, connecting Liége and Antwerp by way of the Campine coal fields. Completed in 1940 but damaged during World War II, it was not until 1957 that its entire length could be used to capacity by barges having a 2,000-ton capacity or less. In the latter 1950's the Albert Canal alone carried one-third of the total cargo handled by inland shipping, as calculated in ton-miles. The canal has stimulated traffic and created industries along its course. It also serves as aqueduct and water-storage reservoir for the Antwerp metropolitan area.

The pattern of Belgium's inland waterways can be seen as three axial north-south lines connecting two east-west canal systems, one in the north and one in the south. The axial lines are the Albert Canal, the canal from Antwerp to Charleroi via Brussels, and the waterway connecting Antwerp with the Borinage (Mons) by way of Ghent. In the north the ports of Ostende and Zeebrugge are connected with Antwerp via Ghent, and in the south is the system of the Sambre and Meuse rivers. In 1947 a modernization program was undertaken which, when completed, will open all waterways to 1,350-ton barges.

Fifty-six million metric tons of merchandise were carried in 1957 on Belgian inland waterways, of which about one-half represented traffic generated by import and export, and 2 million tons were transit cargo.

MARITIME TRANSPORT. The Netherlands, with 4.6 million gross registered tons of merchant shipping (1959), has the fourth-largest fleet in Europe after the United Kingdom, Norway, and Italy, and stands seventh in the world. Belgium, on the other hand, is one of the smallest shipping nations, having only some 600,000 gross tons. The reasons for this contrast in orientation toward the sea were analyzed previously. In terms of port services, Antwerp, Amsterdam, and Rotterdam compete with one another and have overlapping hinterlands which in both countries are rich, heavily industrialized, and very densely populated. The Dutch ports handle the greatest tonnage of any one continental country—94 million tons of in-going and out-going cargo in 1958; this is 50 per cent more than the tonnage moving in and out of Belgian seaports. About 72 million tons of cargo were handled by Rotterdam alone (Fig. 5–20). Among world ports Rotterdam is second only to New York. Through expansion of facilities and industries the port is expected to handle 90 million metric tons by 1965 and 125 million metric tons by 1970.

All three ports—Rotterdam, Amsterdam, and Antwerp—are well equipped and take pride in having rapid and efficient service as well as excellent inland and seaward transport connections. Both Dutch and Belgian load indexes [19] are very unfavorable, because of the ever-increasing need for raw materials in Western and Central Europe.

---

[19] The load index, or load factor, is the percentage of space of a ship filled with cargo. It is to the advantage of a shipping line to have its ships sail with as high a load factor as possible.

AIR TRANSPORT. After France, the Netherlands and Belgium rank second and third, respectively, in terms of total mileage and passenger miles flown in 1957. Sabena, the Belgian airline, and KLM, the Dutch airline, have world-wide connections. Both countries have a number of commercial airdromes, but the airports of Brussels, Amsterdam, and Rotterdam handle most of the international traffic. Helicopters are used widely for local services and on some continental flights.

Fig. 5–20. Rotterdam, on the Nieuwe Maas River, looking upstream. The head of ocean navigation is at the bridges in the left background; the petroleum port is farther downstream. (KLM Aerocarto n.v.)

FOREIGN TRADE. As stated earlier, foreign trade is the most vital aspect of the economy of each of the three countries. Unhindered international trade and freedom of the seas are fundamental to the high standard of living enjoyed in the Benelux countries, and even to their survival under their present economic system. All three countries rely heavily on imports of food, raw materials, and fuels. They export manufactured and semimanufactured products. In the Netherlands the emphasis is on export of agricultural and horticultural goods, in Belgium on metallurgical products, and Luxembourg exports iron ore in addition to products of her iron and steel industry. A notable exception to this general statement is the Philips plant in

Eindhoven. Export of electric light bulbs from there to the United States represented 8 per cent of the dollars earned by the Netherlands in 1958.

The most active trading partners are the Benelux countries themselves. Outside the union, West Germany, the United States, and the United Kingdom are the most important in that order, and, for trade with Belgium and Luxembourg, also France.

The great dependence on foreign trade is indicated by the fact that about one-third of the gross national product of Belgium and Luxembourg is derived from foreign trade while in the Netherlands it averages about 40 per cent, as compared to a mere 10–11 per cent in the United States. In addition, Belgium and the Netherlands perform the important function of rendering services for the transit of goods to and from interior destinations, most importantly West Germany, as well as for transshipment of cargoes in their various ports.

*　　*　　*

Western Europe as defined in this book comprises four of the six members of the European Economic Community, or Common Market. Each state represents a great diversity of natural and human resources, and each is confronted with its own problems relating to the best use of these resources. However, collectively, as a community, they could develop the economic and political strength of a world power, if all plans for full economic union materialize.

BIBLIOGRAPHY

(Major references are asterisked.)

Books in English

EDELMAN, C. H. Soils of the Netherlands. Amsterdam: North-Holland Publishing Co., 1950.

GATES, P. LAMARTINE. Food, Land and Manpower in Western Europe. London: Macmillan & Co. Ltd., 1960.

MARTONNE, EMMANUEL DE. The Geographical Regions of France. Translated by H. C. BRENTNALL. London: William Heinemann, Ltd., 1933.

*MONKHOUSE, F. S. A Regional Geography of Western Europe. London and New York: Longmans, Green & Co., Inc., 1959.

*ORMSBY, HILDA. France: A Regional and Economic Geography. New York: E. P. Dutton & Co., Inc., 1950.

PANNEKOEK, A. J. (ed.). Geological History of the Netherlands. The Hague: Staatsdrukkerijen Uitgeverijbedrijf, 1956.

VEEN, JOHAN VAN. Dredge, Drain, Reclaim: The Art of a Nation. The Hague: M. Nijhoff, 1955.

Books in Foreign Languages

*FAUCHER, D. (ed.). *La France: Géographie Tourisme* (France: Geography and Tourism). 2 vols. Paris: Larousse, 1952.

Géographie Universelle
Vol. II: DEMANGEON, ALBERT. *Belgique, Pays-Bas, Luxembourg* (Belgium, the Netherlands, and Luxembourg). Paris: Librairie Armand Colin, 1927.
Vol. VI, Part 1: MARTONNE, EMMANUEL DE. *France Physique* (Physical Geography of France). Paris: Librairie Armand Colin, 1942. Part 2: DEMANGEON, ALBERT. *France Économique et Humaine* (Economic and Human Geography of France). 2 vols. Paris: Librairie Armand Colin, 1946, 1948.

*SCHMITHÜSEN, JOSEF. *Das Luxemburger Land* (Luxembourg). Leipzig: Hirzel, 1940.

Articles

AMERICAN GEOGRAPHICAL SOCIETY. *Readings in the Geography of France, Germany, and Netherlands.* Contributions by various authors. (Reprint Series No. 1.) New York: American Geographical Society, 1943.

BASTIÉ, JEAN. "La Population de l'Agglomération Parisienne" (The Population in the Parisian Agglomeration), *Annales de Géographie* 67 (January–February, 1958): 12–38.

DUSSART, FRANS. "Geographie der Ländlichen Siedlungsformen in Belgien und Luxemburg" (Geography of Rural Forms of Settlement in Belgium and Luxembourg), *Geographische Rundschau* 9 (January, 1957): 12-18.

DUSSART, FRANS. "Les Transports en Belgique" (The Transport Patterns of Belgium), *Zeitschrift für Verkehrssicherheit* 4 (1958): 1–16.

HOFFMAN, GEORGE W. "The Zuider Zee Reclamation Project," *Michigan Academy of Sciences, Arts and Letters* 35 (1949): 197–213.

MARTIN, J. E. "Location Factors in the Lorraine Iron and Steel Industry," *The Institute of British Geographers* 23 (1957): 191–212.

POUNDS, NORMAN J. G. "Historical Geography of the Iron and Steel Industry of France," *Annals: Association of American Geographers* 47 (1957): 3–14.

ROZENTAL, ALEK A. "The Enclosure Movement in France," *The American Journal of Economics and Sociology* 16 (October, 1956): 55–71.

SARGENT, FREDERIC O. "The Persistence of Communal Tenure in French Agriculture," *Agricultural History* 32 (April, 1958): 100–08.

STEIGENGA, WILLEM. "De Decentralisatie van de Nederlandse Industrie; . . . 1930–1950" (The Decentralization of Dutch Industry; . . . 1930–1950), *Tijdschrift voor economische en sociale geografie* 49 (June, 1958): 129–48. English summary: p. 148.

VINCE, STANLEY W. E. "The Agricultural Regions of Belgium," *London Essays in Geography* (ed. L. Dudley Stamp and S. W. Wooldridge). Cambridge, Mass.: Harvard University Press (1951), 255–88.

WEIGEND, GUIDO G. "The Basis and Significance of Viticulture in Southwest France," *Annals: Association of American Geographers* 44 (March, 1954): 75–101.

WEIGEND, GUIDO G. "Bordeaux: An Example of Changing Port Functions," *The Geographical Review* 45 (April, 1955): 217–43.

6

Central Europe

The term "Central Europe" (Mittel-europa, *Zwischeneuropa*), so frequently misused by the Germans as well as by others, can hardly be mentioned without introducing political overtones. At best, it can be considered a flexible political-geographical term describing an area whose borders shift in accordance with changes in national boundaries. In this chapter the term is used as a common denominator for the following countries: Germany within its post-World War II boundaries, Switzerland, Liechtenstein, and Austria.

It should be pointed out that, while concepts of Central Europe have differed, many writers and especially German geographers have stressed its geographical and cultural entity, and the fact that Germany constitutes its core. Furthermore, Central Europe has always been held to include that part of Europe in which at least a large portion of the population speaks a dialect of German. This region has at times included parts of France (Alsace and Lorraine) and the greater portions of Belgium and the Netherlands, in the west; the territory of the former Austria-Hungary, Rumania, Bulgaria, large sections of western Poland, the Baltic states, and some of the southern Alpine valleys extending into Italy, and Yugoslavia. Some geographers have tried to base their delineation of Central Europe on its physical geography and have seen a common denominator in the east-west alignment of the Alps, Central Uplands, and Lowlands. Others have considered Central Europe as a central transitional zone located between oceanic Europe in the west and essentially continental Europe in the east. All writers agree that Germany within its 1937 borders, Switzerland, Austria, Bohemia, and Moravia should be included in its area; Karl Sinnhuber and Henry Meyer, among others, have discussed the different interpretations attached to the elusive concept of Central Europe.[1]

The central position of the three countries—Germany, Switzerland, and Austria—in relation to other sections of peninsular Europe is of great significance. Central Europe is bordered by France, Belgium, Luxembourg, and the Netherlands—all in Western Europe; by Denmark, Norway, and Sweden—all in Northern Europe; by Italy, in Southern Europe; and by a great transitional region known by many names, but defined in this book as Eastern Europe. The borders of Germany have constantly shifted while those of the Alpine countries (Alpenländer) of Switzerland and Austria have remained relatively stable for many centuries. The North German Lowlands (plains), which form part of the great lowlands extending from western France deep into the Soviet Union (Fig. 1–3), have been used as a favorite invasion route from earliest historical times. The Vienna Basin has played an important role since the first century A.D., when the Romans used it as an outpost for offensive and as a base for defensive action. He who controls Vienna and its basin commands the narrows of the Danube, and gains access to the wide open spaces of the Carpathian (Pannonian) Basin. Vienna also lies astride the lowland route between the Adriatic Sea and the headwaters of the Oder (Odra) and Vistula rivers, and guards the southeastern entrance to Bohemia and Bavaria. Farther south, the several low passes across the Alps have facilitated the free interchange of peoples between Central and Southern Europe.

Most of the peoples of Central Europe, including those of the greater part of Switzerland, are German speaking. Their countries have a long and rich cultural tradition. Austria, with a glorious past and great power in the years of the Austro-Hungarian Monarchy, remained independent after 1919; Switzerland with its 25 cantons developed slowly from a nucleus (Urschweiz) formed in 1291 by a defensive alliance of the Forest Cantons (Waldstätten) Uri, Schwyz, and Unterwalden. Germany was politically unified in 1871. As a result of the outcome of World War II, it was divided into four occupational zones. While the western zones have united, the division between east and west has remained. In addition, the former capital, Berlin, also has been divided into four occupational zones. This division of Germany has left its impact, especially on the polit-

[1] Karl A. Sinnhuber, "Central Europe—Mitteleuropa—Europe Central: An Analysis of a Geographical Term," *Transactions and Papers: The Institute of British Geographers* 20 (1954): 15–39; and Henry Cord Meyer, "Mitteleuropa in German Political Geography," *Annals of the Association of American Geographers* 36 (September, 1946): 178–94.

ical and economic development of the two Germanys during the postwar years.[2]

However defined, Central Europe remains an area of transition. Structurally it ranges from sedimentary lowlands in north Germany, covered by thick continental glacial deposits, to crystalline highlands (Alps) with cirques and valleys carved out by Alpine glaciers; climatically, from the maritime climates of Western Europe to the transitional climates in the east, or from the subtropical type prevailing in some of the valleys along the southern flank of the Alps to the more variable climates of the Alpine region proper.

Central Europe has considerable mineral wealth: coal in the Ruhr, the Saar, Lower Saxony, and the southern part of the German Democratic Republic; petroleum in eastern Austria and Lower Saxony; iron ore in central Austria (Erzberg). Austria and Switzerland have ample hydroelectric power, and Austria and Germany have valuable deposits of various metallic minerals and rare salts. The industries of the whole region are highly developed.

THE PHYSICAL LANDSCAPE

Central Europe is characterized by a great diversity in its physical landscape. In addition, every part of the structural and tectonic elements is closely tied to surrounding regions (Fig. 1–3), e.g., the Alps in Western Europe, the North German Lowlands as part of the western and eastern European coastal lowlands, and the Alpine Foreland as a continuation of the Swiss Mittelland and the Austrian Alpine Foreland. To provide a clear picture of the physical landscape of Central Europe the discussions are presented under two regional headings, those of Germany and those of the Alps, including the Alpine countries of Switzerland, Liechtenstein, and Austria.

Germany

Location and Size. No matter how one defines Central Europe, Germany forms part of it. In 1871, it covered an area of 208,189 square miles. At that time it was third in size among European powers. Since then it has undergone four territorial changes. By the

[2] This chapter presents an over-all view of Germany with the Oder-Neisse rivers considered as its eastern boundary. Wherever a distinction between the two Germanys is needed, specific mention is made of West Germany (The German Federal Republic) and East Germany (The German Democratic Republic). When speaking of the territory east of the Oder-Neisse rivers, now part of Poland and/or the Soviet Union, Germans refer to these lands as "administered by Poland and/or the Soviet Union." This chapter refers to them as "lost territories."

Treaty of Versailles, Germany lost 27,200 square miles with a population of 6.5 million. It expanded again under Hitler, who incorporated the Sudetenland, Austria, and many other parts of Europe into the Third Reich between 1938 and 1944. But after the military defeat of 1945 it was reduced to 138,000 square miles (approximately the combined areas of Minnesota and Michigan). In the east, the former Prussian provinces of Pomerania, Brandenburg, and Upper and Lower Silesia have passed under Polish administration; East Prussia has been split up between the U.S.S.R. and Poland. Thus, present-day Germany is bounded by latitudes 47° and 55° N. and longitudes 6° and 15° E. Its greatest north-south extension is approximately 590 miles, and its maximum east-west extension 385 miles (Fig. 6–19).

Physiographic Divisions. Germany may be divided into five broad regions which resemble the main structural divisions (Fig. 6–1): (I) The North German Lowlands, a glaciated plain; (II) the Southern Transitional Borderlands, a belt of morainic material and highly fertile soil; (III) the worn-down fragments of the Hercynian system, collectively called the Central Uplands (*Mittelgebirge*); and (IV and V) the Alpine Foreland, once covered by the Alpine ice cap, together with the Alps, a young folded mountain system of which only a small fraction lies within Germany's boundaries. Each of these five main regions can be further subdivided according to structure, relief, climate, and soil characteristics.

Before discussing the regions and their subdivisions, it should be pointed out that in Germany the chief contrasts, both physiographic and cultural, appear between north and south. In the north, the glaciated lowlands include the transitional fertile borderlands. The south includes the diversified uplands of Central Germany, the Alpine Foreland, and the Alps. A dividing line, clearly marked on any physical map, may be drawn eastward from Aachen, along the southern margin of the Ruhr industrial area, along the edge of the Weser hills through Osnabrück and Hanover, along the northern edge of the Harz Mountains, and around the Leipzig Bay to Görlitz on the Neisse River (Fig. 6–1).

I. The North German Lowlands. The Lowlands escaped the uplift which has affected most of Southern and Western Europe since the Middle Tertiary. Unconsolidated deposits were laid down by the ice sheets which spread southward from Scandinavia in Quaternary times. Boulder clay, gravel, sand, and wind-blown loess deposits vary in thickness between 40 and 500 feet. In its successive advances the ice sheet encountered no obstacles short of the Central Uplands, where it was halted by the Ore Mountains (Erzgebirge), Harz Moun-

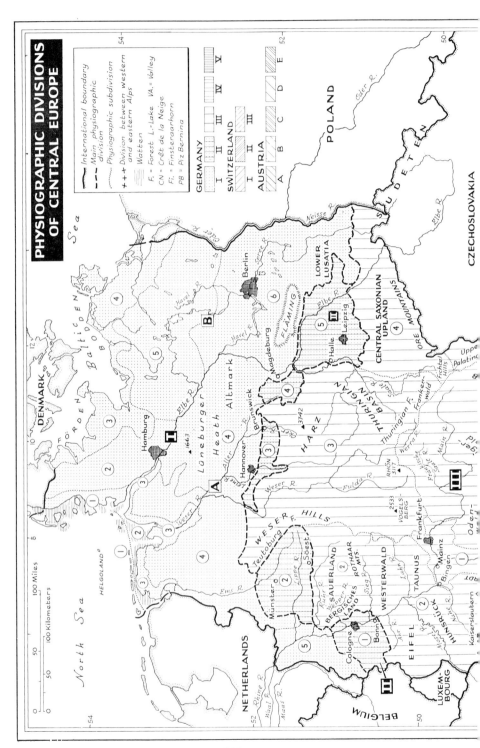

PHYSIOGRAPHIC DIVISIONS OF CENTRAL EUROPE

International boundary
Main physiographic division
Physiographic subdivision
+++ Division between western and eastern Alps
Watten

F. = Forest L.=Lake VA.= Valley
CN = Crêt de la Neige
Fl. = Finsteraarhorn
PB = Piz Bernina

GERMANY   I   II   III   IV   V
SWITZERLAND   I   II   III
AUSTRIA   A   B   C   D   E

North Sea

DENMARK

NETHERLANDS

BELGIUM

LUXEMBOURG

POLAND

CZECHOSLOVAKIA

Baltic Sea

HELGOLAND

Hamburg

Berlin

Hannover

Brunswick

Magdeburg

Halle

Leipzig

Frankfurt

Mainz

Bingen

Bonn

Cologne

Münster

Lüneburger Heath

Altmark

Alte R.

WESER HILLS

Teutoburg

MÜNSTER

BERGISCHES LAND

SAUERLAND

ROTHAAR MTS.

WESTERWALD

TAUNUS

EIFEL

HUNSRÜCK

HARZ

THURINGIAN BASIN

FLÄMING

LOWER LUSATIA

CENTRAL SAXONIAN UPLAND

ORE MOUNTAINS

SUDETEN

RHÖN

VOGELSBERG

Oder R.

Elbe R.

Weser R.

Havel R.

Neisse R.

Ems R.

Rhine R.

Waal R.

Maas R.

Main R.

Fulda R.

Werra R.

Spree R.

Leine R.

Aller R.

Moselle R.

Lahn R.

Ruhr R.

Lippe R.

Sieg R.

Saar R.

Kaiserslautern

1663
3742
2533
3117

100 Miles
100 Kilometers

366

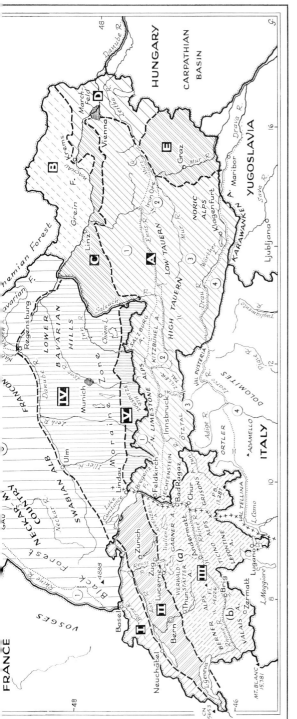

Fig. 6–1. Physiographic divisions of Central Europe.

GERMANY

I. North German Lowlands
  A. West of the Elbe
    1. East Frisian Islands
    2. Watten
    3. Marschen
    4. Geest
    5. Lower Rhine Plains
  B. East of the Elbe
    1. Schleswig-Holstein Marschen
    2. Schleswig-Holstein Geest
    3. Schleswig-Holstein Förden and Moraine Zone
    4. Moraine Zone
    5. Baltic Heights or Lake Plateau
    6. Glacial Valley Zone

II. Southern Transitional Borderlands
    1. Cologne Bay
    2. Münster Bay
    3. Lower Saxony Borderland
    4. Magdeburg Borderland
    5. Halle-Leipzig Bay

III. Central Uplands
    1. Upper Rhine Valley
    2. Rhenish Slate Mountains
    3. Thuringian and Hessian Depressions
    4. Saxon Uplands
    5. Bavarian Forest
    6. Scarplands of Swabia and Franconia

IV. Alpine Foreland
V. German Alps

SWITZERLAND

I. Jura
II. Swiss Plateau
III. Alps: a, Northern; b, Southern

AUSTRIA

A. Alps
    1. Northern Limestone Alps
       Northern Longitudinal Valley
    2. Slate and Shale Ranges
    3. Central Alps
       Southern Longitudinal Valley
    4. Southern Limestone Alps
B. Granite Uplands
C. Alpine Foreland
D. Inner and Outer Vienna Basin
E. Styrian Basin

367

tains, Weser hills, and other highlands. Subsequently, the ice movements across the Lowlands weakened. The various stages of glacial retreat are evidenced by moraines which give the region a hilly character. In its slow retreat northward, the ice sheet left two east-west-oriented depressions east of the Elbe River. These abandoned glacial-stream channels or spillways are called *Urstromtäler* by the Germans. Total yearly precipitation in the North German Lowlands decreases toward the east, except where influenced by relief. This is the only region where the full effect of maritime characteristics is felt (Fig. 1–14). Toward the east, seasonal contrasts become sharper.

The North German Lowlands are generally divided into two subregions, one west and one east of the Elbe River:

West of the Elbe. Between the North Sea coast and the East Frisian Islands, which at one time formed a continuous dune wall,

Fig. 6–2. Förden, Bodden, and Haff coasts.

there are tidal flats, or *Watten*, which are flooded at high tide. Reclaimed areas, called *Marschen*, border the seashore and the estuaries of the Elbe, Weser, and Ems rivers. This land, like the polders in the Netherlands, has been reclaimed by diking and draining. The soil is rich and very suitable for grazing. Some sugar beets and vegetables are also grown profitably. Between the *Marschen* and the adjacent zone of Pleistocene sandy soils known as geest there are usually extensive meadow moors (bogs), level, treeless, and covered with grasses. The geest is located between the Elbe and the Ems. Within it, a somewhat higher area extending from the Elbe to the Weser-Aller rivers is known as the Lüneburger Heath. Its highest point, the Wilseder Berg (1,663 feet), lies east of Bremen and has been made into a national park. The geest is of limited agricultural value. Grazing is only of local importance. The climate is maritime, with cool summers and mild winters, considerable precipitation especially in winter, and strong winds (Figs. 6–2 and 6–3).

The geest, particularly the part west of the Aller, is often interspersed with bogs. These bogs still cover a large area despite the

application of modern, Dutch-inspired methods of cutting and draining. Thanks to these methods, which in Germany are known as *Fehn*
or *Behn* cultivation, it is now possible to raise vegetables and cattle
here. New agricultural settlements in former bog country are called
fen colonies (*Fehnkolonie*). Papenburg, on the lower Ems, is such a
settlement. More recent methods have shown that cutting is unneces-
sary and that, with proper drainage and the addition of sand and clay,
bog soils can be made into valuable arable land. Peat is burned in
nearby power plants or used for domestic purposes. Since 1941,
petroleum has been found west of the Ems, in the southern part of
the Bourtanger Bog, and the wells of the so-called Emsland fields are
bringing a further change to the cultural landscape of this once unproductive land.

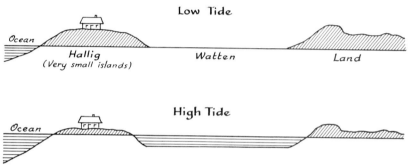

Fig. 6–3. Low and high tide, Wattenland.

East of the Elbe. The country east of the Elbe River has a history
of more recent glaciation; morainic ridges extend in several parallel
bands along the southern shore of the Baltic Sea. Going from north
to south the following subdivisions may be distinguished:

A ground moraine zone, consisting of glacial loams and forming
a fertile, rolling lowland belt. The many lakes in this zone are proof
of its recent glaciation. The coast is clearly divided into a western
and an eastern section, with the Oder River a distinctive boundary.
The whole coast line is drowned, and the German section has many
bays, gulfs, and islands. The western part of the Baltic coast line is
usually further subdivided into a *Bodden* coast (irregularly shaped
inlets behind irregular islands) between the Oder and Lübeck Bay in
Mecklenburg, and a *Förden* coast (long, steep-sided drowned valleys
formed by rivers underneath an ice sheet, similar to a fjord coast) so
typical of the Baltic coast of Schleswig-Holstein (Fig. 6–4 and Fig.
6–1). Climatic conditions along the Baltic are more continental than

to the west; low salinity and a very small tidal range allow the water to freeze over more readily. Stralsund was closed to traffic for over a month in 1947; most other ports are closed for at least two weeks.

South of this zone, extending 10 to 50 miles inland, is a strip of fertile lowlands covered with boulder clay. Crops such as sugar beets, rye, some wheat, and potatoes are grown here, and there are pastures for livestock.

Farther south, a zone of irregular hills marks a halt in the ice cap's last major retreat. This zone, commonly known as Baltic Heights or Baltic Lake Plateau (Fig. 6-1), is characterized by many lakes and undrained hollows, gravel, sand, boulder clay, and coniferous trees.

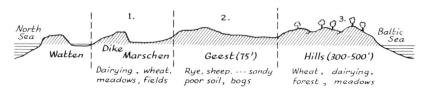

Fig. 6–4. Profile across Schleswig-Holstein.

Parallel to the main ridge of the Baltic Heights, a series of lower, more irregular, and less continuous terminal moraines marks the interruption of the slow retreat of the ice sheets.

Glacial Valley Zone. Between the morainal heights and the Central Uplands there is an extended plain of broad valleys (Fig. 6–1) alternating with somewhat higher ground consisting mainly of sandy soils. Here are the previously mentioned glacial spillways extending in an east-west direction and interconnected by diagonal valleys. These glacial spillways form broad and flat depressions now occupied in whole or in part by various rivers, such as the Havel and Spree near Berlin. Originally, the main drainage paralleled the front of the continental ice mass, but during the retreat of the ice many streams adopted a north-south course. The glacial spillways, however, are of great value in the construction of canals; the need for locks is almost obviated by the slight gradient from east to west. The southern boundary of the area of the glacial spillways is formed roughly by the upland zones of the Fläming and Lower Lusatia. It is here that the last ice sheet was halted by higher ground.

Originally the whole Glacial Valley was forested. German settlers after the twelfth century drained the swampy valleys, consisting largely of peat swamps and wooded or heath-covered sand dunes. Once drained, the alluvium itself offered more productive soil than that found in the sandy regions between the valleys.

II. Southern Transitional Borderlands. North of the Central Uplands and south of the glaciated lowlands lies a belt of thinly layered morainic material and highly fertile soil.

The width of this zone varies, but it broadens to include several bays (lowland embayments): (1) the Cologne Bay, which includes the Lower German Rhineland; (2) the Münster Bay; (3) the Lower Saxon Borderland; (4) the Magdeburg Borderland; and (5) the Halle-Leipzig bay.

This fertile belt consists of glacial soil covered by alluvial deposits which in turn are partially covered by loess. The whole belt has fertile brown forest and chernozem soils. Münster Bay has but a small area of loess near Soest. Situated between the dissected Central Uplands and the glaciated, moraine-covered lowlands, and cultivated since Neolithic times, this transitional belt is of outstanding importance to Germany and to the world.

Thanks to the natural quality of the land, to efficient crop rotation, and to the heavy application of fertilizer in less productive areas, this region has become a rich farm district in which wheat, sugar beets, barley, and vegetables predominate. The Transitional Borderlands also possess great mineral wealth, mainly bituminous-coal and lignite deposits in the Ruhr and the Rhineland, lignite in the Leipzig Bay, low-grade iron ore and petroleum in the Peine-Salzgitter area between Hanover (Hannover) and Brunswick, and potassium and common-salt deposits along the foothills of the Harz Mountains near Stassfurt and Halle.

This combination of great mineral wealth and valuable farm land supports a dense rural and urban population (500 to 600 per square mile). All the towns are old and have grown considerably in importance since the early Middle Ages. Situated for the most part at nodal points, where routes from the uplands fan out into the plain, these towns are also crossed by important east-west transportation arteries. The Midland Canal from the Ems to the Elbe is the most recent addition to the transport net; it provides a direct water connection between the Rhine, the Ruhr, Berlin, and the Oder.

III. Central Uplands. Between the North German Lowlands, the narrow belt of Transitional Borderlands, and the Alpine Foreland south of the Danube, there is a region of great diversity: rolling, dissected, and forested hills, granite massifs reduced by glacial action, old volcanoes, basins, plateaus, scarped limestone ridges, etc., all belonging to the Hercynian zone—the Central Uplands. The hilly and diversified character of this zone is the result of block movements, uplifts and subsidences, upwarpings and recessions, resulting from fractures and horizontal dislocations. Numerous horsts are char-

acteristic of this block landscape. Volcanic intrusions, which are
especially noticeable in the western part of the Uplands, are closely
connected with these movements. The heights near the center of the
Uplands escaped the ice cover for the most part, but the peripheral
valleys, particularly those in the north, were broadened by ice action.
Only the highest portions of the Uplands were covered by mountain
glaciers, as shown by the ridges and cirques of the Black Forest
(Schwarzwald), Bavarian Forest, and Ore Mountains.

The Central Uplands are not a climatic barrier. Rainfall increases
very rapidly with increasing altitude. This is well illustrated in the
Alb areas bordering the Alpine Foreland. Only during the winter,
when cloud banks are much lower than in summertime, do the summits show above the zone of maximum precipitation. The snow
cover in the Central Uplands is abundant and snowfalls continue as
late as March.

The Central Uplands may be divided into numerous topographical
units (Fig. 6–1):

Upper Rhine Valley. The Upper Rhine Valley, extending from
Basel to Frankfurt, has a length of more than 180 miles, but a width
of only about 25 miles. Flanked by mountains, it was formed by the
sinking of land between two roughly parallel faults in Late Tertiary
times. This is called a graben. The Rhine enters the valley above
Basel, at an elevation of 800 feet above sea level, and leaves it near
Bingen, 253 feet above sea level. The length of the regulated section
of the river is 224 miles. The surface of the valley consists of drained
alluvial land, dry gravels, and some loess deposits which have made
it into a very rich agricultural region (Fig. 6–5).

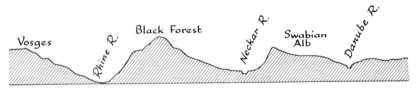

Fig. 6–5. Profile, Vosges to the Danube River.

The valley clearly forms a physical unit with its surrounding mountains. The Jura lies toward the south, the Rhenish Slate Mountains
to the north, the Vosges and the Hardt to the west, and the Black
Forest and Odenwald to the east. The mountains flanking the valley
in the east and in the west are part of a massif whose central section
was downfaulted. They are dissected by valleys and are heavily

forested. The Odenwald is separated from the Black Forest by a depression, the Kraichgau or Neckar Bergland. North of the Odenwald is the Frankfurt Basin, drained by the lower Main River. The highest summit in this mountain complex is the Feldberg (4,888 feet), located in the Black Forest. West of the Rhine, and linked to its upper valley by the depression of Kaiserslautern, lies the coal-rich Saar Basin.

The Upper Rhine Valley's equable climate permits a highly diversified agriculture including the cultivation of wheat, sugar beets, tobacco, hops, fruits, and grapes; vineyards occupy the foothills of the bordering mountains, especially between Karlsruhe and Darmstadt. Winters are very mild and July temperatures average about 70° F. The mountains have long winters and abundant precipitation.

Rhenish Slate Mountains. The Rhenish Slate Mountains form part of the Central Uplands, but in terms of regional geography they belong to the Rhine Valley.

The mountains (sometimes called the Rhine Plateau) are cut in two by the Middle Rhine River, which flows in a narrow, approximately 80-mile-long gorge from Bingen to Bonn. The surrounding heights rise to an average of 1,500 feet above the gorge. From Mainz the Rhine flows westward for some 15 miles, skirts the Taunus' as far as Bingen, and then continues northwestward through the gorge to Bonn and to the Lower Rhine Plains beyond. The course of the Rhine in this section is antecedent, the river having cut its channel at the same rate that the underlying peneplain was being uplifted (Fig. 6–6). The Rhine gorge is often very narrow, and rapids had to be eliminated in order to make the river more navigable. Vineyards cover the terraced lower slopes of the steep-sided Rhine gorge; they are also found in terraces along the tributary valleys, notably along the Moselle, Lahn, and Aare rivers. Today, the Rhine is not only a busy waterway for a great variety of craft but its gorge is also an important tourist attraction.

The upland areas of the Rhenish Slate Mountains extend from the Main to the Ruhr and from the Ardennes to the Thuringian and Hessian Depressions. The boundaries of the several subdivisions coincide with the courses of the Rhine's various tributaries. Severely weathered young volcanic deposits give the Westerwald better soils than are found in almost any other plateau region. In the Siegerland, whose mines and forests supplied Germany's first industries with iron ore and charcoal, some iron is still mined. North of the Sieg River, the plateau drops off to the Sauerland, beyond which the well-known industrial region of the Ruhr is located.

Fig. 6–6. The Rhine gorge at the Lorelei, famous in song and saga. Vine-yards line the terraced lower slopes of the gorge. Ships of many nations must carefully wind their way through the narrow and still-dangerous stretch of the Rhine. (Photo: Rotgans.)

Thuringian and Hessian Depressions. This region is bounded by the Rhenish Slate Mountains in the west, the Saxon Uplands in the east, and the fertile Transitional Borderlands in the north. The Main River forms the southern boundary. The region is a mass of basins, broad forested uplands, and narrow but fertile plains, disturbed by volcanic activity, faulting, and to the north by much folding. Two subdivisions are commonly recognized: the Hessian Depression toward the west and the Thuringian Basin and Forest. Hesse is characterized by many individual forested mountain sections, the broad fertile river valleys (depressions) of the Weser and the Fulda, with the important crossroad town of Kassel, and the dissected volcanic Vogelsberg (2,533 feet) and Rhön (3,117 feet) mountains north of the Main River. In the north, two low wooded ranges, the Teutoburg Forest and the Weser Hills, protrude toward the plains between Münster and Hanover.

Thuringia is composed of three distinct parts: The Harz Mountains, the Thuringian Forest, and the Thuringian Basin. These areas offer great contrasts. The Thuringian Forest is a densely populated, wooded mountain range, whose highly skilled inhabitants are engaged mainly in manufacture demanding great skill; there is only limited agriculture. In contrast, the Basin, which is drained by the Saale River and its tributaries, contains rich agricultural land, mainly degraded chernozem. The Harz Mountains are located between the Leine and the Saale and trend in a southeast-northwest direction. Their upper parts are still covered with forests, while elsewhere such crops as hay and potatoes are grown. The Brocken (3,742 feet) is the highest summit. Even today, the Harz Mountains remain a transportation bottleneck in an area of heavy traffic.

Saxon Uplands. South of the Halle-Leipzig bay, the forested Ore Mountains reach an altitude of over 4,000 feet. These mountains drop off abruptly on the Bohemian side and slope gradually toward the bay. Their slopes, known as the Saxon Foothills support some agriculture, but the real value of this area lies in its mineral wealth, which includes uranium and lignite. The Ore Mountains, which run in a southwest-northeast direction, are separated from the Sudeten, which trend in a northwest-southeast direction, by the Elbsandsteingebirge, an area of great scenic beauty. The Elbe River cuts through this sandstone range in a deep canyon formed by downfaulting and later filled by clays and sandstones.

Bavarian Forest. Between the German-Czechoslovak frontier and the Danube and Nab rivers lies a sparsely populated forested region. This region, which is underlaid by granite and gneiss, is known as the Bavarian Forest. The forest reaches deep into Bavaria; within Germany it is subdivided into a southern and a northern part, the depression drained by the upper Regen River serving as a dividing line. The southern part consists of long, high ridges with wide basins, while the northern part has an irregular knob-and-valley topography and is generally lower than the former. Precipitation is abundant, ranging from 47 to 55 inches at an elevation of 2,400 feet, and fogs are very frequent. Most of the region is occupied by forest, with beech, fir, and spruce dominant.

Scarplands of Swabia and Franconia. East of the Black Forest and the Odenwald, there is a region variously identified as scarplands, plateaus, and basins. Most of it is drained by the Neckar and Main rivers. The scarps of the region face mostly toward the northwest, and the older formations are usually clearly visible.

As we proceed northeastward from the Black Forest and the Odenwald, we encounter various geologic formations, each of which leaves a distinct mark on the landscape. The scarplands of the Swabian and the Franconian Alb are cut out of limestone which forms a plateau up to 1,200 feet high. The scarps extend in a southwest-northeast direction from the upper Rhine to the depression of the Ries, which divides the Swabian from the Franconian Alb; thence they trend from west to east until they veer northward toward the Main River.

Climatic conditions are influenced by elevation which varies from escarpment to escarpment. The Swabian and the Franconian Alb have considerably less precipitation (27 to 39 inches) than the escarpments farther west, while the leeward side facing the Danube receives less than 20 inches. Thanks to the latitude (48° N. to 50° N.) and to the protection afforded by the forested mountains on the west, the climate is well suited to the growing of cereals, tobacco, hops, and some hard fruits; even corn and vines do well on the plains. Except for deposits of lithographic stone found in the Franconian Alb, the region is almost lacking in economic minerals.

IV, V. THE ALPINE FORELAND AND THE GERMAN ALPS. The German part of the Alpine Foreland lies between the Swabian and the Franconian Alb in the north, the Bavarian Forest in the northeast, and the Alps in the south. It forms a northward-sloping plateau in continuation of the Swiss Plateau. Relief differences are between 1,000 and 3,000 feet, but the Foreland has the appearance of a broad plain, with its lowest point (915 feet above sea level) at the confluence of the Danube and Inn rivers. The Foreland's geologic structure is closely related to that of the Alps. There also exist similarities in fauna and flora, and the Alpine climate influences that of the Foreland.

Morainic deposits—gravels, sands, and huge boulders—cover wide areas of the Foreland, in testimony of the extent of Alpine glaciers (Fig. 6–7).

The northern part of the Foreland is covered by glacial outwash material, and therefore it is hillier and better suited for agriculture

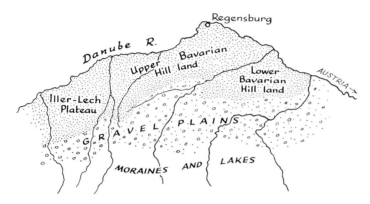

Fig. 6–7. Sketch of the Alpine Foreland.

(Fig. 6–8). There are numerous bogs in the higher southern parts of the Foreland. Finger lakes, at right angles to the trend of the moraines, are especially numerous east of the Lech River. All the rivers rise in the Alps and cross the Foreland in broad, marshy valleys. They are not navigable, because of the irregularity of their flow. The Danube Valley occupies a depression 15 to 30 miles wide. Although it has a moderate gradient, the Danube carries sufficient water for navigation to begin at Ulm.

The climate of the Foreland, noted for its cold winters, becomes more continental as one proceeds eastward. A comparison between Regensburg (1,125 feet) and Lindau on Lake Constance (1,329 feet) is of interest. The January temperature in Lindau averages 30° F., the July temperature 64.4° F., while the yearly mean is 48° F. In Regensburg, January temperature is 26.6° F., July 64° F., and the yearly mean 45.3° F. It should be added that the area has a milder climate, in part because of the influence of a large water body. Precipitation increases with elevation. The quantity of summer rainfall and of melting snow determines the rivers' summer volume.

Mixed forests, predominantly coniferous, are at higher altitudes; forests occur mostly in small patches in the Foreland. Soils are generally poor, so barley, oats, and rye are the chief cereal crops, and dairy grazing is widespread. A few special crops are grown on better soils along several streams.

Only a small part of the Alps falls within Germany. The international boundary runs through the outer zones of the Northern

Fig. 6–8. Vilshofen, Lower Bavaria, in the northern part of the Alpine Foreland. Patches of forest are interspersed among small agricultural holdings. (Amt für Landeskunde.)

Limestone Alps, from which rises Germany's highest mountain peak, the Zugspitze (9,711 feet).

German Rivers. The even distribution of precipitation and ample snow cover provide German rivers with sufficient water for navigation. Most of these rivers, for example, the Ems, Weser, Elbe, and Oder, flow from the Central Uplands (and from their extension into Poland and Czechoslovakia) toward the North and Baltic seas. As a result of structural differences, the Rhine and the Danube have a different drainage pattern and direction of flow. As late as the Middle Tertiary, the Upper Rhine Plains and the Alpine Foreland were still covered by vast seas. When the waters receded, the Foreland was drained eastward by the Danube and northward by the Rhine. However, the lower altitude of the Upper Rhine Plains and the very short distance to the North Sea enabled the Rhine to erode headward and to capture the drainage of the western Foreland and of the area around today's Lake Constance, which formerly fed into the Danube. This peculiar structural history also becomes apparent upon examination of the Rhine's course. The usual threefold division of rivers into upper, middle, and lower course is replaced in the case of the Rhine by a breakdown into five sections: Alpine Rhine (from its source to Lake Constance), high Rhine (to Basel), upper Rhine (to Bingen), middle Rhine (to Bonn), and lower Rhine.

Brief mention should also be made of the regimes of streams, i.e., the changes in the amount of flow and in the water level. The rivers which rise in the Central Uplands—the Ems, Weser, Elbe, Oder, the right tributaries of the Rhine, and the left tributaries of the Danube—reach high-water stage shortly after the melting of the snow, usually during the early spring; their low-water stage comes in July and August, largely because of increased evaporation. Typical mountain streams as well as parts of the Rhine and of the Danube reach their crest in the summer because of the late melting of snows in the high mountains and the heavy summer rains; their low-water stage occurs during the winter. On the other hand, the upper and middle Rhine receives a considerable volume of water from numerous tributaries rising in the Central Uplands, so the range between high and low water is reduced. The lower Rhine is characterized by an even regime, a factor of considerable importance for the river's economic usefulness.

Compared with their windward side, the leeward side of the Central Uplands has an abundance of rain. The waters of many mountain rivers are dammed and stored in reservoirs which provide protection against floods, storage for low-water periods, and water for industry and the generation of hydroelectric power. Most of these artificial lakes are within the Eifel, Sauerland, and the Bergischesland (south of the Ruhr).

The amount of ice cover on German rivers increases from west to east as expected, and impedes navigation. Great variations in the length of the winter freeze are characteristic. The Rhine at Cologne (Köln) is frozen over for an average of 20 days per year, the Ems for 27, the lower Weser for 37, the Elbe near Magdeburg for 45, and the Danube at Regensburg for an average of 37 days.

The Alps

Location and Size. The Alps are Europe's greatest folded mountain system in terms of both elevation and extent. The length of the Alps along the inner edge of the arc is approximately 470 miles, and about 810 miles along the outer edge. The chord of the arc is approximately 340 miles long. Their width ranges from 80 miles near the highest peak (Mont Blanc, 15,781 feet) to 150 miles north of Verona. They cover about 85,000 square miles, or an area somewhat larger than Kansas.[3]

The Alps extend in an arc from the Altare Pass on the Gulf of Genoa to a line which approximates the railroad line Vienna-Graz-Maribor-Ljubljana. Southeast of Altare Pass they connect with the Apennines. In France, near Lake Bourget (Lac du Bourget), the Jura Mountains detach themselves from the main body of the Alps, forming a separate spur. Lying between them and the Alps proper, the plateau extends from Lake Geneva to southern Germany.

The interior of the arc is occupied by the Po-Adriatic depression, toward which the Alps slope rather abruptly. Along the outer edge of the arc there are a number of old massifs against which the Alps had been pushed during the folding process. This Alpine arc has scores of peaks reaching above 10,000 feet, and several peaks in the Valais (Wallis) chain of Switzerland attain an elevation of 15,000 feet. Despite their relatively low latitude (43° N. to 48° N.), the Alps carry the most extensive glaciers found on the mainland of Europe.

Politically, the Alps extend into seven countries: Italy, France, Switzerland, Liechtenstein, Germany, Austria, and Yugoslavia. Of these, Switzerland, Liechtenstein, and Austria are referred to as "Alpine countries" in a true sense. This section of the chapter concerns itself chiefly with the Alpine countries.

Major Divisions. A line running south from Lake Constance, up the Rhine Valley, and across Splügen Pass (6,923 feet) to Lake Como divides the Alps into two parts of very different topographic characteristics. West of this line, the western Alps are narrower, more compact, and higher, with more and longer glaciers and more incised valleys. East of this line, the eastern Alps are broader and lower; their longitudinal valleys are wider and interconnected across low watersheds. The highest peak in the western Alps is Mont Blanc. Local

---

[3] As far as possible the Alps are discussed as a whole in this chapter, since they form a physiographic unit. Their southern slopes are also briefly discussed in the chapter on Southern Europe, and the French Alps in the chapter on Western Europe. The tectonic evolution and structural units of the Alpine orogeny are discussed in Chapter 1, pp. 30–37. For geological terms, see Appendix I.

relief, often exceeding 9,000 feet over a short horizontal distance, greatly contributes to the impressive picture confronting the visitor. The eastern Alps, with their highest elevation at Piz Bernina (13,287 feet) in Grisons (Graubünden) canton of Switzerland, have several levels of summits (*Gipfelfluren*), and only near the previously mentioned line of division do they reach heights comparable to those in the western Alps.[4]

Most of Switzerland falls within the western Alps. Only the mountains of the eastern part of Grisons canton are included among the eastern Alps. All of Austria lies in the eastern Alps.

The western Alps are further broken down into two divisions: the Franco-Italian Alps, which lie south and west of a line extending from the eastern end of Lake Geneva through the upper Rhone Valley, the Great St. Bernard Pass (8,110 feet), and the Dora Baltea Valley to the Piedmont lowlands and the upper Po River; and the Swiss Alps, which lie between the Great St. Bernard Pass and a line through Lake Constance-Rhine-Lake Como.

Germany's share of the Alps is limited to a narrow outer strip of the Northern Limestone Alps, between Lake Constance and Salzburg.

In addition to the transverse division described above, there are several parallel longitudinal zones separated by deep valleys and distinguished by differences in rock types. Thus the Alpine chains are broken up into several distinct groups.

Physiographic Divisions. As was pointed out in the introduction, the structure of the Alps is largely the result of the folding of sediments between the Eurasian forelands and the African land mass (see Chapter 1, pp. 31–33). Before this folding occurred, rivers had worn down the mountains of more ancient origin and carried the sediments into the adjacent seas. The mature surface thus created was very low and had little local relief, but during the later stages of the erosion cycle it was again uplifted and warped. Denudation and weathering have sculptured the mountains into the youthful forms we see today. These processes are much less evident in the eastern Alps than in the western Alps. During the Ice Age, the whole mountain system was repeatedly covered by ice and only certain regions in the southeast and the southwest, such as Styria, Carinthia, and Provence, escaped the effects of glaciation. Ice sheets cut and dug away large portions of mountains, and, as warmer temperatures returned, moraines, U-shaped valleys, Alpine cirques, and pyramidal

---

[4] The division of the Alps into two parts is widely accepted. The Italians, however, prefer a threefold division: (1) the *Alpi Occidentali*, with the Col du Ferret forming the boundary between it and (2) the *Alpi Centrali*, which in turn is separated by the furrow of the Brenner Pass from (3) the *Alpi Orientali*.

peaks were left as evidence of glacial action. Denudation by glaciers and streams is also responsible for such features as the broad, steep-walled hanging valleys (Fig. 6–9), polished and striated boulders, and the many tongue basins blocked by morainic deposits at their outward ends. Glacial action has been especially important in widening and deepening what had once been a small longitudinal hollow into the present important central depression between Martigny on the Rhone and Chur on the Rhine. This same depression can be traced south-westward from Martigny into the high Alps and the Pre-Alps of France.

The transverse subdivision of the Alps into a western and an east-ern part has already been described; more significant, however, is a division into several distinct longitudinal sectors along the deep val-leys mentioned earlier. In many ways the lithological zones which we shall briefly describe here correspond to these longitudinal sectors. It should also be pointed out, however, that only in the eastern Alps can the following division into longitudinal zones be clearly recog-nized. (See also the description of the six major structural units, in Chapter 1, pp. 33–36.)

The central Alps consist of resistant crystalline rocks (granite, gneiss, and schist), which form the principal chain of the Alps. These formations extend from the edge of the Carpathian Basin to the Pennine Alps just northwest of the Po Basin (Fig. 6–1). In the eastern Alps the zone of resistant rocks is interspersed with bands of shale and slate, which are more easily eroded and thus account for the gentler slopes.

North of the central Alps lies a belt of generally lower ranges con-sisting of sedimentary rocks, especially limestone, and characterized by a very jagged sky line and deeply incised valleys (Fig. 6–1). This belt is known as the Northern Limestone Alps. A southern limestone zone, which is not found in the western Alps, begins east of Lake Maggiore, increases in width, and extends clear across the Dinaric Ranges. It contains volcanic extrusions such as the reddish-black rocks of the peripheral plateau of Bolzano (see Chapter 7, pp. 480–81).

North of the Northern Limestone Alps are the rolling Foreland hills, a narrow and discontinuous zone (called Flysch zone), consist-ing mostly of slate, clay, and sandstone (see also pp. 36–37). This zone widens in Austria, where it forms an outer zone of the Northern Limestone Alps. In front of the Flysch zone, in the Alpine Foreland, there are stream-deposited beds of Molasse, which consist mostly of sandstone and conglomerates.

In order to clarify these differences and divisions, we shall list the main physiographic divisions and point out some of their distinctive features. For the sake of better identification, this presentation will follow existing political divisions which, with the exception of a slight overlap in Grisons canton of Switzerland, follow the widely recognized dividing line between eastern and western Alps.

Fig. 6–9. Wengen, overlooking the U-shaped Lauterbrunnen Valley (Switzerland). Some of the waterfalls have a vertical descent of close to 1,000 feet. The view is toward the Bernese Alps. (Swiss Tourist Office.)

Switzerland

Switzerland is normally divided into three distinct regions—the Jura, the Swiss Plateau,[5] and the Swiss Alps.

THE JURA. The Jura trends southwest-northeast from the Rhone to the Rhine and consists of several parallel limestone folds. The

[5] This region is also known as the Plains, the *Mittelland*, or the Alpine Foreland (*Alpenvorland*).

folds are well developed along the southeastern rim but flatten out toward the northwest and gradually merge into the undisturbed strata of the Swiss Plateau. The eastern slopes facing Switzerland are steepest and highest. The ridges run in the same direction as the axis of the folds and are separated from each other by longitudinal valleys. They become lower and narrower toward Basel and the Rhine and are therefore easier to cross in this area. The highest point, Crêt de la Neige (5,653 feet), is located in the southwestern part of the Jura, just inside France. The Jura's most important rivers are the Doubs, flowing almost entirely in France, and the Birse, which enters the Rhine near Basel. These rivers flow alternately in broad valleys and narrow gorges.

Thanks to abundant rainfall, the Jura's inhabitants practice dairying and lumbering and some wine growing on the southeastern slopes facing the Plateau. Because of the karstlike topography and underground drainage characteristic of the Jura's limestone formations, relatively few streams and lakes appear at the surface.

The Jura occupies 10 per cent of the total area of Switzerland and has 13.2 per cent of its population. Its real importance lies in the fact that it is the home of the watchmaking industry.

THE SWISS PLATEAU. The Swiss Plateau, an "uplifted depression" between the Alps and the Jura, extends for 180 miles in a southwest-northeast direction from Lake Geneva to Lake Constance; it is up to 30 miles wide. The Plateau was dissected by rivers and covered by ice. Its many small lakes attest to the former presence and movements of the ice sheet; their shape indicates the advance of various ice tongues. Other typical features of glaciation are terminal and ground moraines, huge boulders or erratics, drumlins, and deepened valley floors. The Plateau varies in elevation from 1,200 to 2,200 feet and has a mean altitude of 538 feet. It occupies 32 per cent of the total area of Switzerland but contains 67 per cent of the Swiss population.

The Plateau's climate is rather uniform; the mean January and July temperatures of Bern and Zurich are shown as examples:

	Mean January Temperature	Mean July Temperature
Bern, 1,870 feet	28.2° F.	63.7° F.
Zurich, 1,617 feet	29.5° F.	55.2° F.

Source: Marion I. Newbigin, *Southern Europe* (London: Methuen & Co., Ltd., 1949): p. 106.

Mist often covers the whole Plateau like a sea of clouds. Some localities have an average of 120 days of mist per year (see Fig. 1–10 and Chapter 1, pp. 48–49).

Precipitation ranges from 32 inches at Basel, 900 feet above sea level, to 46 inches at Lucerne (Luzern), 1,480 feet high, and to over 100 inches at Säntis, 8,202 feet high. However, only a small part of Switzerland has more than 47 inches of precipitation.

The Plateau is most suitable for dairying; it has excellent meadows and ample acreage on which forage crops are grown. In the southwest, there are sugar beet and tobacco fields, vineyards, and orchards.

The Swiss Plateau may be divided into three natural subregions of varying economic significance (Fig. 6–1): (1) the northeast from Lake Constance to a line from Baden to Zug, with wine growing on sunny slopes and considerable industry; (2) the center as far as a line through Solothurn-Bern-Thun-Brienz, largely agricultural; and (3) the southwest down to Lake Geneva, with specialized crops such as tobacco and sugar beets (Figs. 6–30 and 6–31).

THE SWISS ALPS. The Swiss Alps occupy 58 per cent of Switzerland, but only 18 per cent of its population resides there. The Alps have no clear-cut boundary either in the direction of the Swiss Plateau or the North Italian Plains. Toward the Plateau, they become gradually lower, are often called the Pre-Alps, and acquire a different land-use pattern; unproductive land is rare. The Rhone-Rhine longitudinal trough divides the Swiss Alps into the northern Alps and the southern Alps. The northern Alps may be divided as follows:

1. The Bernese Alps have the largest concentration of glaciers and reach their highest elevation (14,026 feet) in the Finsteraarhorn (Fig. 1–8), the principal chain, 68 miles long.

2. The Vierwaldstätter Alps, located between the Aare and the Reuss valleys.

3. The Garner Alps, located between the Reuss and the portion of the Rhine Valley below Chur.

4. The Appenzell Alps, situated between Wallensee and Lake Constance.

The southern Alps may also be divided into four main groups:

1. The Valais Alps, located between the Great St. Bernard and the Simplon passes, have many lateral valleys which give access to lofty peaks, notably the Matterhorn. The Simplon Tunnel (Fig. 6–12), which takes the Paris-Lausanne railroad line into Italy, is at the farthest end of the Valais Alps.

2. The Ticino Alps and the Lepontine Alps are pierced by the important St. Gotthard Tunnel on the Zurich-Milan railroad line. These mountains slope toward the Po Plain.

3. The Adula Alps, west of Splügen Pass, form the connecting link with the Grisons Alps.

4. The Grisons Alps, which cover most of the area of the canton of Grisons, are not as high as other Alpine summits, but the valleys are less accessible. Many important passes connect the Rhine and the Inn valleys with Austria and Italy.

Liechtenstein

The small, independent principality of Liechtenstein lies between Switzerland and Austria. Liechtenstein has been able to maintain its independence largely because of its favorable location controlling the Gap of Ragaz, which in turn controls the valleys and passes of Grisons and the easy Rhine crossing west of Vaduz.

Until 1719, it was ruled by the lords of Vaduz and Schellenberg, and since then it has been independent. Its customs and railroads are now controlled by Switzerland. In spite of its size, 67 square miles, it has a healthy economic foundation. The valleys are fertile, pastures plentiful, and vineyards highly developed. Cotton spinning and embroidering are of exceptional quality. Tourist trade is increasing and numerous small factories dot the landscape. Liechtenstein derives much of its revenue from the sale of postage stamps, of interest to stamp collectors.

Austria

Earlier in this chapter we discussed the more general aspects of the eastern Alps; both their geologic origin and lithologic divisions were described. Now we shall treat the various mountain groups and valley regions on the basis of their customary division into three longitudinal zones separated from each other by two longitudinal valley troughs. Following the standard works of Krebs, Sölch, and other geomorphologists, the country has been divided into regions, whose names describe their location and main characteristics (Fig. 6–1):

THE ALPS. The Northern Limestone Alps form a belt of varying width across the northern parts of the provinces of Vorarlberg, Tyrol, the central and southern part of Salzburg Province, and Upper Austria as far as the Vienna Woods. The outer zone, also called the Flysch zone, is characterized by rounded hills, gentle slopes, a very dense network of valleys, and many pastures. The limestone zone, which becomes wider toward the east, consists of many sharp peaks, barren high plateaus, fewer valleys, and much unproductive land.

The central Alps are separated from the limestone zone by the longitudinal valley depressions which run from Feldkirch and Vorarlberg over the Arlberg Pass, to the valleys of the Inn, Salzach, and

Enns, then along the diagonal route of the Schober Saddle to the Mürz Valley, and finally over the Semmering Pass to the Vienna Basin. Important transverse valleys open into this important east-west highway, which is dotted with settlements and also contains the largest city of the interior Alps, Innsbruck. The longitudinal valley varies in width from a hundred feet to one mile (Fig. 6–10).

At two places, slate and shale ranges are interposed between the Northern Limestone Alps and the central Alps. These mountains are located between the longitudinal valley depression described above and a second, wider but discontinuous, depression which runs from the Ziller Valley in Tyrol to the valleys of the Salzach and Enns rivers. Within these ranges are the Kitzbühel Alps and the rich ore mountains of the Eisenerz. The slate-shale mountains, whose rounded summits rise just over 6,500 feet, provide excellent pasture.

Between the Northern Longitudinal Valley, the southern edge of the slate-shale mountains, and the Southern Longitudinal Valley are the central Alps. They consist of many mountain chains of varying length. They run from the transverse line which divides the western and the eastern Alps, to the Noric Alps of eastern Austria. Included in the central Alps are the highest sections of the Austrian Alps, their numerous glaciated peaks rising over 10,000 feet. Routes across the central Alps are not numerous (Fig. 6–12).

The Southern Longitudinal Valley runs from Lake Como, along the upper Adda River (Val Tellina), over Tonale Pass, to the Bolzano-Adige-Isarco valley, to the Puster Valley (Pustertal), and thence along the Drau River. The Klagenfurt Basin, a highly cultivated depression filled in Late Tertiary times, lies between the central Alps and the Southern Limestone Alps. Frequent changes in rock composition make this zone a most picturesque one. Most of the mountains in this zone are located within Italy. The valleys of the Adige, Tagliamento, and Sava rivers offer the only through routes of any importance. With the exception of the South Tyrol, the entire zone is sparsely populated.

THE GRANITE UPLANDS. The Austrian Granite Uplands occupy the area between the Bavarian and the Bohemian border and the Danube, and also extend several spurs across the Danube. The Danube skirts the southern edge of the Bohemian Plateau and flows through a succession of narrows and basins. The river is swift and is now being harnessed in an ever-increasing amount for power (Fig. 6–36). Valleys are incised below rolling uplands covered by scattered dense forests and generally poor soils. The well-known Wachau is an example of such a valley. Water is abundant, and small farm

Fig. 6–10. The Inn Valley, in the Austrian Tyrol. The view is west and northwest to the Karwendel and Wetterstein ranges of the Northern Limestone Alps. Note the Innsbruck-Garmish-Partenkirchen railroad line incised on the flanks of the Wetterstein Range (right). (Stempfle, Innsbruck.)

patches are widely distributed. The eastern part of the Uplands has better farm land. The Uplands are situated between 1,300 and 2,400 feet above sea level.

THE ALPINE FORELAND. The Alpine Foreland is located between the Northern Limestone Alps and the Granite Uplands (Fig. 6–1). Both the southern and the northern boundary are sharp and distinct. Covered by sediments of the Great Ice Age, the Foreland consists of numerous low hills, steep scarps, and terraces. Numerous glacial lakes reach the Foreland and remind the visitor of similar lakes in the Pre-Alps in Switzerland and in the German Alpine Foreland. The Foreland has forests and excellent farm land; south of Linz and below Krems there is a cover of loess.

THE INNER AND THE OUTER VIENNA BASIN. Included in this area is the territory north of the Danube—the Marchfeld and its extension eastward to the international border—as well as the land south and west of the Danube to the first Alpine slopes. This region has a dry, warm climate, a long growing season which permits some grape cultivation, and sufficient rainfall for high agricultural yields. It is also Austria's main sugar-beet region.

Because of the open character of the country, this area has been of great economic and strategic value since ancient times, and strong fortifications were built to control it. Carnuntum (Petronell), built in 73 A.D., and, later, Vindobona (Vienna) were Roman legionary fortresses which guarded the many routes which converge here. It was protected in the northeast by the slopes of the Vienna Woods, and on all other sides by the Danube and its many arms and tributaries, prior to the regulation of the river. Throughout history, the Vienna Basin has retained its importance in the political geography of Central Europe. Both from an agricultural and from an industrial standpoint, it is the most important region of Austria.

THE STYRIAN BASIN. The Styrian Basin consists of important valleys and of rolling hills which flatten out toward the Carpathian Basin. The region also includes southern Burgenland. There are broad valleys with fertile meadows, cultivated fields on terraces and gentle slopes, orchards and vineyards on steeper slopes, and deciduous trees on shady slopes. Settlements are scattered in the hill lands, while the larger villages and the cities are located in the main valleys. The climate is very favorable, less extreme than that of the Vienna Basin and conducive to intensive land utilization. The Mur Valley, with the important city of Graz, is the center of this region.

Climate. The main trait of an Alpine climate is its great variability; it is influenced by the elevation, length, and width of the mountains.[6] Typical of mountain regions in general are local differences in exposure to the sun and length of shade; in the Alps, these are especially noticeable in the east-west longitudinal valleys. This factor is of great importance for the distribution of settlements and croplands on slopes: on sunny slopes settlements extend higher, while the colder, usually forested shady slopes are avoided by settlers. This pattern is particularly evident in the eastern Alps. The temperature-lapse rate amounts to approximately 3° F. per 1,000 feet elevation; it is somewhat lower in midwinter and higher in early summer. It is also higher along the southern slopes and edges of mountain ranges. Wide valleys are warmer in summer, but suffer from temperature inversion in winter and are therefore colder than nearby slopes. This phenomenon is especially noticeable in the Engadine (Grisons, Switzerland) and the Klagenfurt Basin (Carinthia, Austria). Only at elevations above 3,500 feet are winter temperatures on slopes as low as those of adjacent basins. In fact, slopes and terraces enjoy many more sunny, bright, and dry days than the valleys or basins they overlook, which frequently are filled with cold, heavy air and thick mist.

For all these reasons, Alpine settlements are usually located on slopes, terraces, and alluvial cones, for protection against low winter and night temperatures as well as flood danger. Temperature differences decrease and annual extremes are modified at increased altitudes largely because of exposure to sun, heating by insolation during the day, and earth radiation during the night, resulting in diurnal ranges of temperature. As a result, snow remains longer on the ground, August is often the warmest month, and late March the coldest month. The following table illustrates the foregoing statements:

I. Mountain Stations

	Alstätten	Gäbris	Rigi	Säntis	Sonnblick
Height in feet	1,509	4,100	5,873	8,202	10,171
January	−30°	−28.4°	−23.6°	−17.4°	−10° (Feb.)
July	64.6°	56.4°	49.5°	42.3°	34.3°

II. Valley Stations

	Locarno	Chur	Zermatt	Innsbruck	Graz	Bolzano (Bozen)
Height in feet	778	2,001	532	1,969	1,129	952
January	35.6°	29°	20.7°	26°	28°	32°
July	71.4°	63.7°	54.5°	64.1°	67.8°	72.5°

Source: Fritz Machatschek, *Länderkunde von Mitteleuropa* (Vienna: Franz Deuticke, 1925), p. 100.

[6] See climatic graphs, Appendix II.

Precipitation usually increases up to an altitude of 8,000 to 9,000 feet, and at times up to almost 10,000 feet, but decreases at higher elevations. Interior valleys are much drier, often receiving less than 30 inches of annual rainfall. Cases in point are the Valais (Switzerland) or the Inn Valley (Austria), where irrigation is practiced. Furthermore, along most mountain chains precipitation varies from the windward to the leeward side. In winter, precipitation occurs in the form of snow which covers most of the Alps for from three to five months, and areas above 6,000 feet for as long as six months. Snow depths of 30 feet have been recorded in places.

A whole series of local winds is characteristic of the Alps. In addition to being swept by the westerlies, most valleys have a regular alternation of up-slope and down-slope winds. These winds are especially strong in transverse valleys open toward the margin of the mountains. Between Geneva and Salzburg, those transverse valleys which open up toward the north or the northwest are under the influence of the warm, dry föhn (see Chapter 1, pp. 48–50, also Fig. 1–11). The föhn is responsible for the sudden melting of snow and for avalanches which endanger isolated mountain communities. It occurs both in midwinter and toward the end of the winter, when it usually heralds the coming of spring. It is accompanied by overcast skies, a sudden rise in temperature (40° F. within two hours is not unusual), and considerable dryness. High temperatures are due not only to the wind's southern origin, but also to the small loss of temperature incurred in rising to the summits and to the great increase in temperature resulting from the descent. Innsbruck has an average of 43 days of föhn. The föhn also accounts for the extension of agriculture into some high Alpine valleys. In the southern valleys of the Alps, one encounters a type of föhn which comes from the northern slopes. Its effect, however, is not as strongly felt as in the northern valleys.

Vegetation and Land Use. Alpine vegetation varies according to the climate of the different bordering regions. It is also characterized by vertical zoning. The central position of the Alps in relation to the different climatic types was noted in Chapter 1. As a result, surrounding climatic types extend their influences into lower altitudes. On the eastern slopes of the Alps, the black pine is common. In the hills of Styria one encounters alders and some true steppe plants. The greatest local differences are found along the upper Italian lakes and the northern shore of Lake Geneva, as well as in the southern French Alps, where drought-resistant shrubs replace forests and grasslands. Here the chestnut occurs up to 8,850 feet, while on the north side of the Alps this tree is found only in the warmer valleys and on the sunnier slopes. Other trees characteristic of this section are the olive, mulberry, and cypress.

Three vertical vegetation and land-use zones may be discerned (Fig. 6–11): (1) an arable zone, (2) a zone of forests, and (3) a zone of pastures. Above these zones is an area of rock debris and eternal snow. The exact width and succession of these belts depend not only upon elevation but also upon latitude, exposure to the sun, degree of slope, temperature, precipitation, and the acts of man.

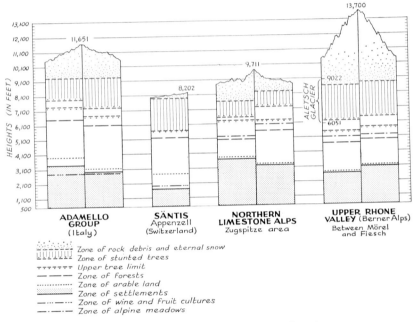

Fig. 6–11. Vegetation and land use in the Alps.

1. The arable zone reaches an elevation of approximately 4,200 feet, but considerable variations are found from place to place. Its upper limit is at lower elevations in the northern part of the Alps, and at 4,600 to 5,600 feet in the south. In the Northern Limestone Alps rye, oats, barley, potatoes, beets, and flax are limited to areas below 3,280 feet. In the interior these crops are found as high as 7,200 feet. In the eastern Alps the upper limit for cereals averages 5,100 feet, and it is somewhat higher in the western Alps. On low sunny slopes grapes are common.

2. The forest zone is made up of coniferous trees at higher elevations and of deciduous trees at lower elevations. As one proceeds upward, the species change from the common beech, oak, and birch

to spruce and fir, then to larch, and near the tree line to the stone pine. In the northern Alps (see pp. 386–87), the forests thin out at 5,200 to 5,900 feet; in the Valais, Engadine, and Ötztal Alps, they reach as high as 7,200 feet. In the eastern Alps, they seldom extend above 4,900 feet. The upper limit of trees is usually marked by a belt of stunted trees, such as the dwarf birch, dwarf pine, juniper, etc. In the limestone zone, the Grünerle and the rhododendron are especially numerous. The upper boundary of the forest zone is usually 2,600 to 2,900 feet below the snow line, which it parallels, but this distance is often increased by man in order to gain additional grazing land. This practice is rather common along the southern slopes of the Alps. Timber cutting and sawmilling are of great importance, especially in the more accessible parts of the Alps. Ancient conservation laws have played a vital role in the preservation of this "gold of the mountains."

3. Alpine meadows are of great economic significance. On them dairy cattle are grazed, and in some localities special breeds are raised for export. Transhumance, a typically Alpine form of cattle raising, is called *Senntenwirtschaft* or *Sennerei* here. Either the village or the individual farmers own pastures (each one provided with a hut) at different elevations; these are used in successive stages during the warm season. With the beginning of the colder season, the herdsman returns to the village. When the cattle are returned to their winter stables in the valley, they feed on hay cut from meadows located at lower altitudes. Cattle pastures generally extend 900 to 1,600 feet above the forest zone, while sheep pastures extend close to the snow's edge.

Various colorful Alpine flowers with creeping and grasslike stems and woody roots are found in great numbers in the upper reaches of the Alpine meadows and among the rock debris during the very short growing season. They include primroses, buttercups, gentian, monkshood, and edelweiss.

Glaciation and Hydrography. Precipitation, exposure to the sun, and latitude determine the extent of eternal snow in the Alps. The snow line ranges from 7,800 feet in the northern Swiss Alps to 10,500 feet in the central part of the Alps.

Precipitation in the mountains accumulates in the form of snow and ice, and is either quickly removed as dry or ground avalanches or more slowly as glaciers. Approximately 1,400 square miles, of which 600 are in the eastern Alps, are covered by glaciers. Because of its altitude, the central zone has most of the large glaciers, while the northern and southern limestone zones have small cirque glaciers for the most part. Compared with the extent of glaciation during the Great Ice Age, the area covered by present-day glaciers is small indeed. The longest Alpine glacier is the Aletsch Glacier (north of Brig, Switzerland) with a total length of 16 miles. The glacier which descends to the lowest elevation (3,500 feet above sea level) is the Lower Grindelwald Glacier in the Bernese Alps.

Alpine glaciers give rise to a great number of rivers. Many small torrents become mighty streams during the summer snow-melt season. Many Alpine rivers are regulated by lakes which they traverse and which keep their flow uniform. These lakes act as reservoirs, reduce the danger of floods, and contribute to the clearing of rivers by catching all the sediment carried in suspension. Among the largest lakes are Geneva, Neuchâtel, Thun-Brienz, Lucerne, and Zürich, all in Switzerland; Constance, divided between Switzerland, Germany, and Austria; Maggiore and Lugano in Switzerland and Italy; Como and Garda in northern Italy; Chiemsee in Germany; and Wörthersee in the Klagenfurt Basin of Austria. Numerous smaller lakes, mostly cirque lakes and lakes impounded by landslides, are scattered throughout the western and the eastern Alps.

Mention should also be made of the Alps' importance as a central watershed for several river systems which empty into four different seas. The Rhine rises in the southern Alps (see pp. 361–62) and flows northward into the North Sea; en route it is joined by several northward-flowing tributaries of Alpine origin. All the right tributaries of the upper and middle Danube, notably the Inn, Salzach, Enns, Mur, and Drave (Drau), rise in the Alps and ultimately find their way to the Black Sea. The southern slopes of the Alps feed the Po and other rivers emptying into the Adriatic. And finally, the Rhone River, which rises in the Bernese Alps not far from the headwaters of the Rhine, flows west and south into the Mediterranean Sea.

Alpine Communications. Despite the difficulties presented by the terrain, Alpine routes have been of great importance for transit traffic ever since prehistoric times. The few usable routes were first extensively traveled during the Roman period. Of the roads constructed at that time, some were not modernized until the late Middle Ages, and others not until the nineteenth century.

Three types of passageways, classified according to their orientation, may be distinguished in the Alps (Fig. 6–12):

1. Longitudinal furrows which run parallel to the main trend of the ranges and contribute so much to the accessibility of the Alps. Their continuity is preserved by the low, easily traversable divides

which separate one longitudinal river valley from another. Examples of such furrows are the valleys of the Inn, Salzach, and Enns rivers, which form almost a straight line from western Austria to the Danube; the Rienza and Drau valleys in southern Austria, which connect Italian South Tyrol with Yugoslavia; and the Mur and Mürz valley chain in central and eastern Austria. In the Swiss Alps the most important of such furrows follows the upper Rhone and upper Rhine valleys from Lake Geneva to Lake Constance. Railroads follow most of these valleys and in many places use tunnels to penetrate the divides. The Arlberg Tunnel, which connects Tyrol and Vorarlberg in Austria, is a case in point.

2. Many transverse valleys, now of greatest importance in the transit traffic, were once obstructed by gorges which inhibited direct traffic until the Middle Ages. Along the Brenner Pass, the gorge of the Chiusa (Klausen) in the Isarco (Eisack) defile route, for example, necessitated a traffic detour across the Passo di Monte Giovo (Jaufen Pass) north of Bolzano until the fourteenth century. Similarly, the St. Gotthard route was not opened until the thirteenth century, when a bridge was built across the Schöllenen gorge. Because the Alps are crossed by only a few direct north-south routes, these are of great significance. Several political units, notably Grisons and Tyrol, owe their existence to the establishment of pass routes. The Brenner Pass (4,495 feet) is the only Alpine crossing which a railroad can negotiate without the use of long tunnels. However, after it reaches the longitudinal valley of the Inn in Austria, one branch of the line uses several tunnels to pierce the ranges which bar access to southern Germany.

3. The diagonal routes are of lesser importance. One links the upper Inn Valley with Lake Como, via Maloja Pass; another, a proposed route, would lead from Chur on the Rhine over a series of passes to the upper Inn Valley and into the Val Venosta (Vintschgau) and Merano (Meran) in Italy. The diagonal line connecting the valleys of the Enns and Mur rivers via the Schober Pass in Styria is a link of some importance between the two Austrian cities of Innsbruck and Graz.

Today, railroads follow all the important old trans-Alpine routes, using tunnels to avoid difficult mountain stretches. It is now possible to cross any part of the Alps in less than four hours. Among the more important tunnels are the Mount Cenis (completed in 1871), which connects Genoa and Turin with Lyon and Paris; the Simplon and Lötschberg tunnels, which link Milan (Milano) with Bern; the 9.5-mile-long St. Gotthard Tunnel (completed in 1882), which connects Milan and the Po Valley of Italy with northern France and western Germany via Zurich and the valleys of the Reuss and the

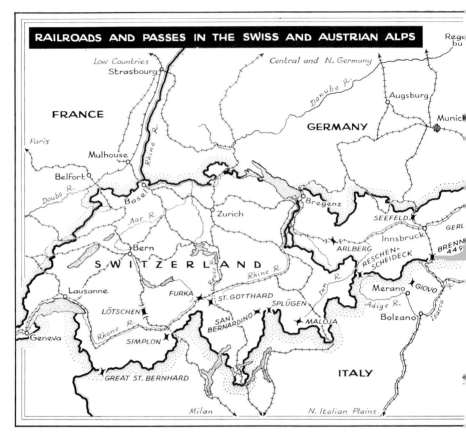

RAILROADS AND PASSES IN THE SWISS AND AUSTRIAN ALPS

Fig. 6–12. Railroads and pa

Ticino; the Tauern Tunnel for traffic between the Alpine Forelands and the Klagenfurt Basin; the Karawanken Tunnel for communication between the Klagenfurt Basin, Yugoslavia, and Trieste; and the Semmering Tunnel, which constitutes the main connection between Vienna and the south.

Although the roads are snowbound for several months each winter, the Alps have never presented a serious obstacle to travel. Thanks to the modern roads and to the numerous railroads built since the beginning of this century, the Alps have become much more accessible to the peoples of the adjacent plains. Today, they attract an ever-increasing tourist traffic which provides new means of livelihood for their inhabitants, but at the same time raises serious problems of road congestion. New superhighways are being built or planned, e.g., the St. Gotthard, Salzburg-Vienna, Semmering-Vienna, and Brenner

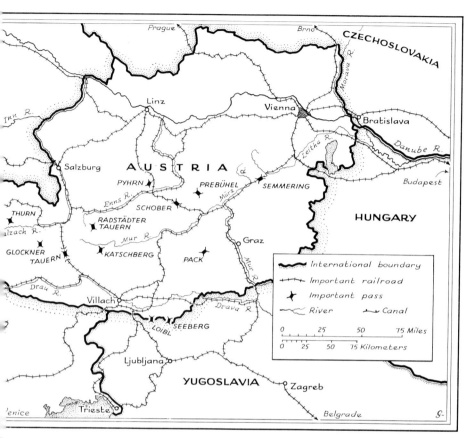

he Swiss and Austrian Alps.

Pass roads (Fig. 6–13). The latest engineering feat is the construction of a tunnel under Mont Blanc, providing a direct, year-round connection between Geneva, Alpine France, and the Po Valley of Italy (see Chapter 5, p. 330).

THE CULTURAL AND HISTORICAL BACKGROUND

The historical developments that are reflected in the changing political geography of Central Europe had in many areas certain broad trends in common. By following out these trends one may grasp the main characteristics of the historical geography of the region and gain as well a better understanding of its many present problems. The developments to be covered are: the migrations of the Germanic peoples following the decline of Rome; the establishment of the

Marches [7] to defend the main routes through the Danube Valley and
the North German Lowlands from encroachments from the east; the
growing independence of isolated regions, especially in the Alps, which

Fig. 6–13. The recently improved section of the northern St. Gotthard Pass
road in the gorge between Göschenen and Andermatt (canton of Uri), Switzerland. Above the road, which is kept open all year, the avalanche galleries of
the cog railway are visible. A few hundred feet below the surface is the St.
Gotthard Tunnel, 10 miles long. (Swiss Tourist Office.)

resulted in the founding of the Swiss Confederation; the growth and
decline of trade.

[7] A territorial border or frontier. The word is from the Old French word *marche*
and is of Teutonic origin.

The Decline of the Roman Empire
and the Age of Migration

Central Europe at the beginning of the Christian era was inhabited by various German-speaking peoples such as the Saxons, Frisians, Goths, Vandals, Franks, and Alemanni. There were Celts in the mountainous regions of the south, and also Ligurians, Etruscans, and Illyrians. The Rhine became the frontier of the Roman Empire in the west after Caesar's conquest of Gaul (57–51 B.C.). Thus, a corresponding advance farther east to the Danube was strategically desirable for Rome, to secure the eastern frontier and command important passes of the Alps. A Roman force advanced through the Adige (Etsch) Valley into Tyrol, and in 15 B.C. the province of Rhaetia was created. Shortly thereafter Noricum and Pannonia, both bounded by the Danube River and the crest of the southern Alps, were added. At one period the Romans tried to establish their frontier as far as the Elbe River, but were defeated by Germanic tribes. With Roman fortifications acting as a check to their westward and southward movement, Germanic tribes added an extensive agriculture to their primarily pastoral economy. This brought about increased population pressures, which contributed to the unification of various tribes into more powerful units, and to the natural desire for additional settlement space.

Much has been written and many reasons have been given for the decline of the Roman Empire. Certainly the constant drain on its resources for defense against the barbarians from the north was a major contributing factor. The breakdown of the Rhine-Limes-[8] Danube frontier zone during the fourth and fifth centuries allowed colonization by the various Germanic peoples, a process which had begun peacefully under sanctions of the emperors. The barbarian invasions brought new masters to Central Europe. The movement of the Germanic peoples toward the west and south also emptied wide stretches of land east of the Elbe, which soon were occupied by Slavic peoples from the east—an event of major historical importance in the relationship between Central and Eastern Europe.

The Germanic peoples were quick to follow the Roman withdrawal. Alemanni of Swabian stock proceeded from Brandenburg into central Germany. They crossed into southern and southwestern Germany, occupied the Rhine Valley, the Neckar lowlands, and the Swiss Plateau, and also settled in parts of mountainous Switzerland

[8] Outer defense wall from Danube near Castra Regina (Regensburg) to the Rhine near Confluentes (Coblenz).

and modern Austrian Vorarlberg. Saxons moved from the plains between the Ems and Weser rivers into Flanders and northern France; some even crossed to the southeast coast of England. Others moved in stages across the Thuringian Uplands and Plains to the Main and Danube rivers. Bavarians [9] occupied the Alpine Forelands of Germany and part of present Austria. Franks advanced from their original homes on the lower Rhine and in Westphalia across the Rhine into France and the southern part of the Low Countries. Other German tribes migrated beyond Central Europe. The Lombards traversed the Alps into the fertile Po Valley; the Vandals crossed into North Africa; the Goths settled in Iberia; and Burgundians in the valley of the Saône in France. Often these migrations were on a relatively small scale, with less than 25,000 people involved. One effect of this resettling of peoples was the establishment of many small political units. These were characteristic of medieval Central Europe and are still evident today in the political organization of the German Federal Republic.

The Marches: Austria and Prussia

On the eastern frontier of the Holy Roman Empire, a system of Marches was established between the lands of sedentary peoples and those of nomads to the east (Fig. 6–14). At first these Marches served only for defense, protecting the Empire against attack by peoples from the east, such as the Avars, Slavs, and Magyars. But once the eastern frontier became stabilized, the Marches served as bases for expansion. Constant fighting necessitated a large standing army, and the rulers of the Marches used their special privileges to further their own interests. Out of these Marches grew independent kingdoms, two of which were later to play a decisive role in the fortunes of the Empire and of all Europe. In the south was the Eastern March (Ostmark), later to be known as Ostarichi (Österreich-Austria). Its boundaries were slowly extended to include the fertile Vienna Basin (1041), the approaches to it, and several Marches to the south. The margraves made their headquarters at Vienna which, due to its location, soon assumed a leading position as "a potential capital of the whole Middle Danube region." [10]

After 200 years as the Eastern March of Bavaria, Austria became a duchy within the Holy Roman Empire. Its dukes were regularly

---

[9] As the name of the Bavarians—Baioarii or Bajuvarii—indicates, they once inhabited "Boiiland" (Bohemia).

[10] Derwent Whittlesey, *The Earth and the State* (New York: Henry Holt & Co., Inc., 1944), p. 218.

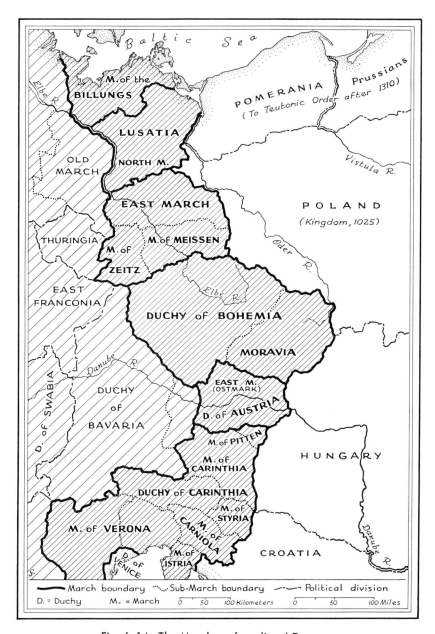

Fig. 6–14. The Marches of medieval Europe.

elected as emperors and dominated the area roughly comprised by modern Germany, until Prussia, which included the Brandenburg March in the north, gained supremacy in 1871. Making use of the strategic location of the Vienna Basin and of the resources of its incorporated territories, the Hapsburg rulers of Austria, through superior military strength and astute foreign policies, expanded toward Bohemia and Galicia (Poland) in the north and toward Italy in the south, defeated the Turks, and incorporated Hungary and parts of present-day Yugoslavia into a loose federation.

In the north, between the forested Ore Mountains and the Baltic coast, and the Elbe and Oder rivers, a series of Marches similar in origin and function to the East March was set up. The Old March (Altmark), in the vicinity of Magdeburg on the Elbe, was soon followed by the Middle March (Mittelmark) and the New March (Neumark), until territory given up by westward-moving Germanic peoples before 600 A.D. was reoccupied. In this way the Wendish territory of Brannibor (Brandenburg) was acquired. This expansion to the east, greatly aided by military religious orders (Teutonic Knights and Knights of the Sword), culminated after 400 years of slow but steady advances, and of intermittent warfare, in the occupation of Prussia [11] and of Livonia farther north, and in the re-establishment of the Vistula frontier. Only in 1410, at the battle of Tannenberg, were the advancing Germans stopped by the growing strength of Poland, a check to further expansion never since overcome. Germans also advanced along the Baltic coast but left the hinterland predominantly Slavic and under the control of the Polish crown, a factor of importance in the establishment of the Polish Corridor in 1919.

In their advances into the North German Lowlands and the Transitional Borderlands, the Germans occupied the area of Mecklenburg, Silesia, and present-day Saxony. The Slavs were absorbed, although some fled to the east, so with the exception of two small areas no vestige of Slavic culture remained. Names ending in old forms such as -ried (marsh), -hagen (fence), -schlag (fill), indicate the advances of the Teutonic pioneers. The March of Brandenburg, with its core area between the Elbe and Oder rivers, expanded in a series of acquisitions until in the seventeenth century it extended its influence across the North German Lowlands, from the Rhine to the Vistula. It is not possible in this brief summary to account in detail for the rise of Brandenburg from a March to the Kingdom of Prussia, but toward the end of the eighteenth century Prussia became the most powerful all-German state and was rivaled only by the former East

[11] Prussia at this time was a subdivision of Lithuania and its people spoke a language not unlike Lithuanian and Latvian. Their land was the former East Prussia, now divided between Poland and the U.S.S.R.

March of the south, which was ruled by the Hapsburgs of Austria, heirs to the imperial title. All other former Marches were now incorporated into these two, whose rise and decline show many similarities.

The "Passlands": Switzerland and Tyrol

Regional units, individual valleys, and such small administrative districts as the gau, canton, or ecclesiastical division make up the basis for the major political groupings in the Alpine regions of Central Europe. These units are often quite isolated and separated from each other by such barriers as high mountains, deeply incised valleys, or gorges. At various times several of these units were united, and if grouped around a pass controlling important routes were known as "passlands." The Swiss Confederation around the St. Gotthard, and the Tyrol around the Brenner are typical passlands of the Alps. Their origin and importance are now to be briefly analyzed.

The Swiss Federation. The area under modern federated Switzerland was once part of the Roman Empire and was afterward integrated into the Holy Roman Empire. The passes of the Swiss Alps, for example, Splügen, St. Gotthard, Great St. Bernard, and important valley routes such as those along the Rhine, Inn, and Reuss rivers connect Germany and Italy and gave the emperors easy access to Rome (Figs. 6–15 and 6–16).

In 1291 the inhabitants of the mountain valleys controlling the most important of the north-south routes, the St. Gotthard, combined to fight the ambitions of the Hapsburg emperors. In that year the three valleys around Lake Lucerne which control the entrance to the St. Gotthard, comprising the cantons of Uri, Schwyz, and Unterwalden, solemnly formed the first federation (Bund der Eidgenossen). The Federation gained allies and dependents in expanding from this core area along the St. Gotthard route to the North Italian Plain, and to the east and west. By hard fighting, the Federation asserted its independence within the Empire and soon received additional help from Lucerne and Bern in the west, Glarus in the east, and Zurich and Zug in the north. Swiss independence was acknowledged by the major European powers in 1648; its neutrality was guaranteed in 1815. Modern Switzerland consists of nineteen cantons and six half cantons. This complex organization is due to the complex relief of the country. And the fact that these units differ greatly from each other in area and size of population facilitated the addition of new cantons and also contributed to religious toleration. The constantly increasing trade across the Alps added to the economic well-being and the importance

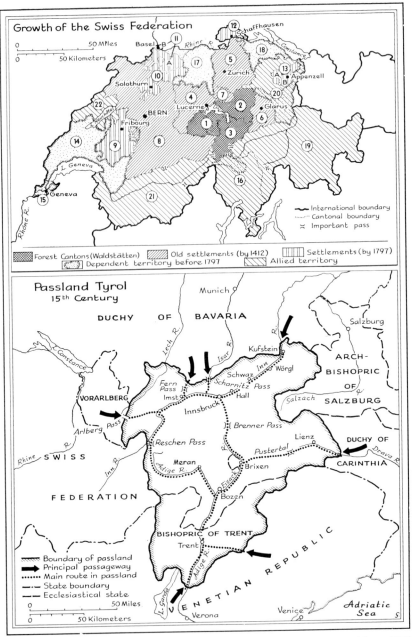

Fig. 6–15 (above). Growth of the Swiss Federation. (1) Unterwalden, 1291; (2) Schwyz, 1291; (3) Uri, 1291; (4) Lucerne, 1332; (5) Zurich, 1351; (6) Glarus, 1352; (7) Zug, 1352; (8) Bern, 1352; (9) Fribourg, 1481; (10) Solothurn, 1481; (11A) Basel (rural), (B) Basel (urban), 1501; (12) Schaffhausen, 1501; (13A) Appenzell—Outer Rhodes, (B) Inner Rhodes, 1513; (14) Vaud, 1803; (15) Geneva, 1815; (16) Ticino, 1813; (17) Aargau, 1805; (18) Thurgau, 1803; (19) Grisons, 1803; (20) Saint Gallen, 1803; (21) Valais, 1815; (22) Neuchâtel, 1815.

Fig. 6–16 (below). The passlands of the Tyrol.

of the Swiss passlands. Over the years cultural diffusion across passes, valleys, and gaps strengthened the unity of the Federation.

The Tyrol. The Tyrol, named for its first ruler, grew as a passland around the network of the Inn, Isarco, and Adige rivers, with the Brenner and Reschenscheideck passes serving as connecting links (Fig. 6–16). These routes were already extensively used by the Romans in their travel between the plains of Venetia and the Danube. The gorge of Finstermünz, on the Inn, and the Arlberg Pass are the exits to Switzerland and Vorarlberg. The two longitudinal valleys to Salzburg and along the Puster Valley to the Drau Valley are important routes toward the east, connecting with the rest of Austria. At the Inn ford, where the road from the Brenner meets the Inn River as well as the roads from Bavaria and Switzerland, a market place, Innsbruck, was founded in 1180. Through its control of this important north-south route, Innsbruck became one of the leading cities of the Alps.

As the result of a series of successful wars and agreements, the borders of this triangular area were pushed out from its important roads; by the second half of the fourteenth century all borders of the Tyrol were located at the high mountain crests or at the constrictions of valleys. In this way the important passland was kept under one rule until the end of World War I, when its southern part (South Tyrol) became Italian and the Alpine passes for the first time in history formed the border. This division also cut the direct connection between southern Austria (Carinthia) and the Inn Valley.

The Swiss passland was able to obtain independence early in the modern era; but the Tyrol was too closely bound to the Hapsburgs. However, its inhabitants received limited freedom early. For example, a Tyrolese assembly with full representation of the peasants was founded in 1342, and a deed (*Freiheitsbrief*, comparable to the Magna Carta) for its citizens' assembly (peasants and burghers) was also drawn up.

The Brenner and the St. Gotthard routes were the main north-south links between the German and the Italian parts of the Holy Roman Empire, and commerce along them brought considerable wealth. These routes, with their passlands, still play a vital role in the European transportation pattern.

Settlement Forms

The beginnings of modern settlement forms may be traced back to the period shortly after the beginning of the Christian era, when various Germanic tribes occupied land with little or no woodland, such as in the fertile zone of the Transitional Borderlands between the Cologne Bay and Silesia, the fertile river valleys, and the drier, sandy heath lands of the North German Lowlands.

The Central European cultural landscape is characterized by certain types of rural settlements: a nucleated village with the farm houses all centered on the village lands and the isolated farmstead surrounded by its own fields. Besides these two extreme examples many successions result from geographical, social, or economic influences which have shaped rural communities. The relief of the land, the fertility of the soil, and the original nature of the settlement (whether established by squatters or by well-knit groups) are among the factors which have determined the type of settlement evident today. Also significant are the type and layout of houses and the system of field ownership.

One of the best-known types of habitation is the typical Alpine single-unit house (Fig. 6–17). It is a wooden or frame structure built on a stone foundation, with two stories, a balcony on the first floor, small windows often protected by green shutters, and an overhanging roof permitting dry storage of wood.

In the Alpine Foreland, the Black Forest, and the Central Uplands, one encounters a second type of structure, the so-called Franconian house. Several units, the living quarters, stable, barn, storage facilities, etc., are grouped around a court closed off by a heavy wooden gate.

A third group of structures, known as the Saxon or lower-German unit house, is found predominantly in the North German Lowlands. It is similar to the Alpine single-unit house in its interior make-up, but has only one story, while the Alpine house has two stories. This building is normally built of timber with some brickwork; the latter is especially characteristic of the Frisian farms of the northern coastlands.

The isolated farmsteads and hamlets are probably the oldest known forms of settlement.[12] These farmsteads or hamlets consisted of one or several farm houses, surrounded by woodland, meadows, common pastures, and arable land. Upon the breakup of a farm community, these farmstead lands were divided into small elongated strips and arranged in irregular furlongs or Gewanne.[13] Thus a hamlet was

[12] For a detailed discussion and illustrations of German settlements, see Robert E. Dickinson, "Rural Settlements in German Lands," Annals of the Association of American Geographers 39 (December, 1949): 239–63.

[13] According to Eric Fischer and Francis E. Elliot, A German and English Glossary of Geographical Terms, Library Series No. 5 (New York: American Geographical Society, 1950), Gewann refers to the division of a village's communal lands into units of more or less uniform quality, enabling farmers to diversify their holdings by allowing each one to cultivate part of several Gewanne.

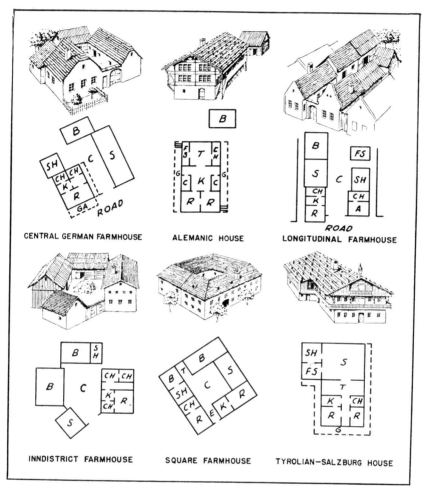

Fig. 6–17. Selected farmhouse types in Central Europe. (Hans Slanar, Öster-reichischer Mittelschul-Atlas.) B—barn, S—stable, C—court, SH—shed, CH—chamber, K—kitchen, R—room, FS—forage storage, T—threshing floor, G—gallery, A—separate house for retired farmer, E—entrance, GA—garden plot.

formed, a group of five to seven farmsteads, each with a number of such furlongs.

In the Southern Transitional Borderlands and in central and southern Germany, the hamlet has grown into a *Haufendorf*.[14] Here newly cleared land with better soils was added by additional clearings during the Middle Ages. This newly cleared land was divided into furlongs, and additional farms within the old hamlet were formed,

[14] *Ibid.*, a *Haufendorf* is a village in which the houses are irregularly clustered without any definite plan.

so a village soon had 15 to 25 farms. Near the end of the Middle Ages many such settlements disappeared again and their holdings were incorporated into existing settlements. In these ways larger, clustered villages were gradually developed.

Two more regular forms of settlement, the shoestring village with the longitudinal farm house (*Streckhof*) (Fig. 6–18), and the closely related roadside village, date from the twelfth and thirteenth centuries. Land for settlement had been originally donated by the large

Fig. 6–18. Wulkaprodersdorf, Burgenland, Austria. Main street with longitudinal farm houses.

landowner and was then divided evenly among the new owners so that each peasant received a single compact holding rather than a number of scattered strips.

Other regular types of settlements include a roadside village in which the road widens to enclose a centrally located common, large enough for a church; the *Runddorf*, in which a group of houses connected by a wall enclose a central courtyard with but one entrance; the *Marschhufendorf* in which a row of houses faces a dike in a tidal marsh and the strips of land run at right angles to the dike; and the *Waldhufendorf*, which extends along a wooded river bank, sometimes for several miles.

Relatively few new areas were brought under cultivation after the sixteenth century. East of the Elbe, marsh villages were founded in the glacial valleys and estates were organized by large landowners or *Junkers*, who concentrated on grain and dairy production. Earlier in this chapter, mention was made of the fen settlements which developed in the former peat bogs in the northwest. Some consolidation of holdings, particularly in mountainous areas, was accomplished, but has not progressed very far. Little alteration has taken place in the strip system of open fields. As Dickinson has pointed out, "The number of parcels was often reduced by the amalgamation of adjacent strips, but the strip system inside the arable land and the general grouping of the arable land, meadow, woodland and scrub invariably are the same today as they were hundreds of years ago." [15]

The Rise and Decline of Commerce in Central Europe

The importance of commerce in Europe and its main aspects are discussed in Chapter 10. The historical aspects of its development in the countries of Central Europe are briefly outlined here. As early as 1000 B.C. amber (a fossil resin), fur, leather, and other goods from the Baltic Sea area were carried to the Italian plains along the valleys of the Elbe, Oder, Morava, and Danube, and through the Inn and other valleys of the Tyrol. During Roman times a variety of Mediterranean products, such as wine, parchment, and olive oil, were exchanged for hides, flax, timber, pelts, salt, etc. The barbarians beyond the Roman wall at times traded actively with the Romans. Obviously, during the barbarian invasions and during times of war, trade was considerably limited. But by the end of the medieval period, as governments became more effective and towns more numerous, the exchange of goods increased in an unprecedented way. Many towns, for example, Munich, were founded at important junctions of inland trade routes; at outlets of passes, as Innsbruck; and on the North German coast, especially at the heads of navigation, such as Bremen, Hamburg, or Lübeck. Trade in various local minerals was also active in Central Europe. Commerce in gold, silver, copper, and salt gave added importance to the passland of the Tyrol. The Harz Mountains contributed lead, zinc, and copper, as did the Ore Mountains. While the total mineral trade was relatively small, it did affect several local communities. For example, it is estimated that nearly 30,000 men mined silver at Schwaz, and another 20,000 in other communities of the Tyrol.

Various parts of Central Europe participated in the ever-growing exchange of goods. Cities increased in population and importance. A canal system was started in the North German Lowlands; rivers

[15] Dickinson, "Rural Settlements," *op. cit.*, p. 259.

and coastal waters were used increasingly. Two major routes, both connecting the Alpine Forelands with the cities of the North German Lowlands and the Danubian lands, deserve special mention: (1) the Rhine, with its leading trading cities of Basel, Mainz, Cologne, etc., offered a direct route from the North Sea to the Alps; (2) the numerous navigable rivers of the North German Lowlands gave access to Vienna and the Danube by way of the Moravian Gate portage between the Oder and the Morava rivers.

Using the Baltic as its main route, the Hanseatic League was organized in 1256 as a loose association of about one hundred large trading towns of the North German Lowlands. The original aim of the League was to join forces in combating the pirates of the Baltic Sea, but it soon developed into a commercial and trade monopoly. Lübeck served as the League's headquarters, and during the three centuries of its hegemony trade flourished, roads and canals were built, and its trade spread westward and northward to British and Scandinavian ports and eastward as far as Novgorod in Russia. Its leading ports, many of which still retain the characteristic Hanseatic warehouses, are today among the ranking seaports and trade centers of Northern and Western Europe. The League declined and eventually broke up as a result of the discoveries in Africa and America which led to a reorientation of important trade routes, because of warfare with Denmark, the growth of British maritime power, and lastly because of internal dissension between strong-willed emperors and the League.

After the downfall of the Hanseatic League and a series of internal conflicts which culminated in the Wars of Religion, Germany played but a minor part in world trade for several centuries. Consequently, while Spain, Portugal, Holland, France, and England enriched themselves by trade with the newly won territories, the Holy Roman Empire was either torn by disunity or engaged in enlarging its southeastern holdings at the expense of the Turks. Not until the individual German states began to realize the importance of trade and undertook the formation of bilateral, then multilateral customs unions (*Zollverein*) after the Napoleonic Wars, did commerce once again play a more important role in Central Europe.

Disunity to Unity and Again to Disunity

The Holy Roman Empire was unable to control its constituent units, while they themselves were too small and powerless to make a decisive contribution to political or economic unity until late in the nineteenth century. Because of their location at Europe's invasion crossroads, and because of the dissected topography of the Central Uplands and the Alps, most political units remained small, often confining themselves to one small, narrow valley. The area occupied by these numerous powerless states stretched from the North German Lowlands to the Alps, and from the Rhineland to the Marches in the east.

While these small political units wrangled and fought each other, a number of strong leaders assigned to protect the Empire from newly organized borderlands (Marches) soon attained independence. Although the dukes of Austria had been the regularly elected emperors ever since 1273, the crown was meaningless and powerless in the face of opposition and the divergent aims of its many component states. Soon, therefore, disunity in Empire affairs was replaced by unity of purpose in the emperor's personal affairs, without regard to the welfare of the Empire as a whole. Religious disunity and foreign attachments by several political units added to the problems of the Empire. Meanwhile, the Marches of Austria and Prussia, both outgrowths of the Empire, began to fight for supremacy within it. They had expanded considerably from their original core, and each of them incorporated peoples of other language groups; in time each achieved some measure of national unity.

Only the threat of Napoleon brought the beginnings of unity to Central Europe. Almost two hundred minor political units disappeared, and for a time the Austrian Monarchy strove for greater centralization. Prussia incorporated many lesser German states, and the Swiss Federation received the promise of neutrality. By the end of the Napoleonic Wars, many rulers came to realize the need for greater unity, and various customs unions were established. This process was completed in 1844, when all German lands, with the exception of Austria and the free cities of Bremen, Hamburg, Lübeck, and Hanover, had joined the customs union.

Political unity, however, had to await the outcome of the contest for leadership between Austria and Prussia. The decision was reached in 1866, when Austria was defeated by Prussia on the battlefield. The cleavage between these two former Marches, ruled respectively by the Hapsburg and Hohenzollern dynasties, was too deep. Austria in general had nothing but contempt for Prussia, which in turn felt superior to Austria. When Prussia defeated France in 1871, all of the remaining German states joined it in proclaiming the modern German Empire (Deutsches Reich) with the king of Prussia as its emperor. Austria alone was not admitted.

Unity had finally been achieved in Germany, but not among Germans. During the centuries of disunity, political fragmentations, and conquests, many Germans had emigrated, especially to the frontier lands of Eastern Europe. Hand in hand with a revival of German nationalism, these Germans pledged their eternal loyalty to the fatherland and began to work for a Greater German Reich. World War I, 1914–18, followed. It ended in the defeat of Germany, in the loss of its recently acquired colonies, and in important territorial losses in Europe. Alsace, the Saar, a large part of the area between the Oder and the Vistula, and parts of Silesia were gone. And the Polish Corridor split East Prussia from the rest of Germany.

Austria, which had become a dual monarchy with Hungary in 1867, entered World War I on the side of Germany and lost all of the territorial acquisitions it had made almost from the time of its organization as a Marchland. Various members of the Austro-Hungarian Empire became independent. Austria proper, with a population of 7 million of whom over 2 million lived in Vienna, began a new life of independence, largely within the area of her former Alpine holdings.

A defeated but united Germany soon recovered from the havoc of World War I and, turning to a strictly centralized nationalistic regime, was determined once more to attain leadership in the world. After occupying Austria (1938), the Sudetenland and various smaller border areas of Czechoslovakia, and then its states of Bohemia-Moravia (1939), the German leader, Hitler, concluded an agreement with the Soviet Union to partition Poland. The German invasion of Poland, a few days later, brought about World War II (1939–45). This conflict ended in disaster for Nazi Germany and the world as a whole. Germany lost over 5 million people, many of its cities were destroyed, and its economy was entirely disrupted. Some aftereffects of this collapse are still visible. Germany has lost most of the eastern territory it had acquired since the beginning of its eastward movement in the eighth century. All the lands east of the Oder, including the Baltic port of Stettin, have gone to Poland, and East Prussia has been partitioned between Poland and the U.S.S.R. The German population of the lost territories and other parts of Eastern Europe either fled or were forced to flee into the reduced area of postwar Germany.

Austria, once-more independent after years of postwar occupation, considers itself a bridge between Western and Eastern Europe—others consider it a borderland against the latter. Thus her old function as a March is again being fulfilled.

We have now shown how Central Europe has gone through a full cycle from disunity to unity and again to disunity—from a conglomeration of numerous powerless states to a Germany split in two. Only

Switzerland, which succeeded in keeping apart from the main stream of events, escaped the upheavals of the last century. Thanks to its location and to its spirit of defiance in the face of major threats, Switzerland progressed in peace, while the world around it was dislocated by wars.

GERMANY

Population

In discussing the population of Germany, the student should be aware of the many changes brought about since 1939 by political developments. For one thing, the factor of migration has been brought to the forefront of the demographic picture as a result of World War II. Millions of German refugees from the lost territories in the east, and Germans from Eastern Europe, are crowding every one of the German states.

On June 16, 1933 (date of the last regular prewar census), the population of Germany, exclusive of the Saar, was 65,140,242, or approximately 355 people per square mile. On December 31, 1958, the population of a much smaller Germany amounted to about 71 million.[16] Present-day Germany consists of the German Federal Republic, divided into ten *Länder* (provinces) and West Berlin,[17] with an area of 95,733 square miles and a population density of 539 per square mile; and the German Democratic Republic, divided into 14 districts, not including East Berlin (Fig. 6–19), with an area of 41,646 square miles and a population density of 420 per square mile.

In this connection we must again recall that since 1945 all of the territory east of the Oder-Neisse line, including East Prussia, has been incorporated into Poland and the U.S.S.R., a loss of 24 per cent of Germany's 1937 territory and of 14 per cent of its population. While Germany's war losses amounted to more than 5 million people, this deficit has been more than made up by postwar immigration into a

---

[16] The last population census for the German Federal Republic was in 1950. A residential census was completed on September 25, 1956. East Germany had a census on January 1, 1958. All population figures used in this section have been taken from *Statistisches Jahrbuch fur die Bundesrepublik Deutschland: 1959.* The population figure of 71 million is estimated: the 1958 estimate for West Germany was 54.4 million including West Berlin, and the 1957 estimate for East Germany, including East Berlin, was 16.3 million.

[17] Until 1945, Berlin was the capital of the German Reich. Under the "Basic Law" of the German Federal Republic, West Berlin is a *Land* of the Federal Republic, but owing to the Four-Power agreement of 1945 it cannot belong *de jure* to the Federal Republic. Administratively, Berlin is divided into a West Berlin and an East Berlin administration.

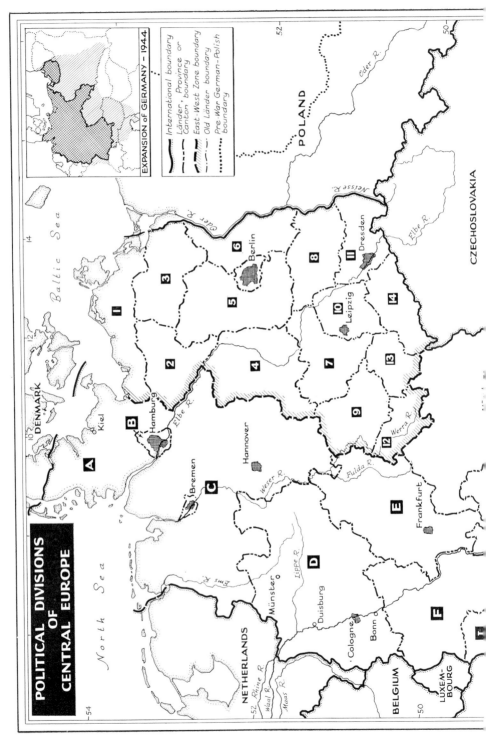

POLITICAL DIVISIONS
OF
CENTRAL EUROPE

EXPANSION of GERMANY – 1944

International boundary
Länder, Province or
Canton boundary
East-West Zone boundary
Old Länder boundary
Pre-War German-Polish
boundary

North Sea

Baltic Sea

DENMARK

Kiel

Hamburg

Bremen

Hannover

Weser R.

Elbe R.

Oder R.

Berlin

POLAND

Neisse R.

Dresden

Elbe R.

Leipzig

CZECHOSLOVAKIA

Fulda R.

Werra R.

Frankfurt

Münster

Lippe R.

Duisburg

Cologne

Bonn

Ems R.

Rhine R.

Waal R.

Maas R.

NETHERLANDS

BELGIUM

LUXEM-
BOURG

A B C D E F T
1 2 3 4 5 6 7 8 9 10 11 12 13 14

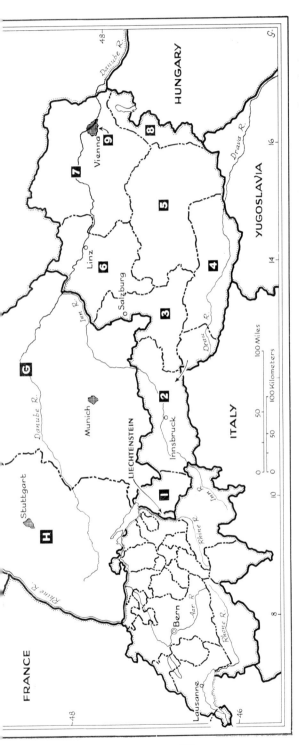

Fig. 6–19. Political divisions of Central Europe. *East Germany* (districts): (1) Rostock, (2) Schwerin, (3) Neubrandenburg, (4) Magdeburg, (5) Potsdam, (6) Frankfurt, (7) Halle, (8) Cottbus, (9) Erfurt, (10) Leipzig, (11) Dresden, (12) Suhl, (13) Gera, (14) Chemnitz. *West Germany* (*Länder*): (A) Schleswig-Holstein, (B) Hamburg, (C) Lower Saxony, (D) North Rhine-Westphalia, (E) Hesse, (F) Rhineland-Pfalz, (G) Bavaria, (H) Baden-Württemberg, (I) Saar. *Switzerland*: for canton names, see Fig. 6–29 and table on page 446. *Austria* (provinces): (1) Vorarlberg, (2) Tyrol, (3) Salzburg, (4) Carinthia, (5) Styria, (6) Upper Austria, (7) Lower Austria, (8) Burgenland, (9) Vienna.

smaller Germany. Today, there are about 12.1 million German-speaking refugees in West Germany, 21.9 per cent of the total population. They consist of *Reichsdeutsche*, i.e., former citizens of German territories lost to the U.S.S.R. and Poland, and *Volksdeutsche*, i.e., ethnic Germans expelled from Czechoslovakia and from other countries of Eastern Europe.[18] As a result of this immigration, both forced and voluntary, postwar Germany has to cope with a larger population, a complicating factor in the country's economic and political life. While the relative population distribution has changed but little during the last hundred years, the influx of the many refugees since 1945 has in many areas increased the population of what had been thinly settled rural areas (Figs. 6–20 and 6–21).

Migration has had an important effect on the population structure for almost a century. Overpopulation, wars, and religious and political persecution have been the chief causes of emigration. Close to 6 million people left Germany between 1830 and 1937; 5.4 million of these entered the United States during this period. Some returned to Germany, especially in the years immediately preceding World War II. There was also some immigration from other parts of Europe, notably between 1891 and 1911. After Germany's catastrophic defeat of 1945, population movements took place on an almost unprecedented scale. Over 600,000 refugees emigrated overseas between 1945 and 1957 (200,000 to the United States).

It goes without saying that two world wars, a major depression, and a brief period of artificial prosperity during which a pro-natal policy was being advocated—all within one generation—have left a deep mark on Germany's population structure. The natural increase (excess of births over deaths), which in 1910 stood at 13 per thousand, diminished steadily until in 1933 it reached a low of 3.5 per thousand. Recovery followed, and by 1957 the German Federal Republic recorded a natural increase of 5.7 per thousand. East Germany in the same year had a natural increase of 3.3 per thousand. Following a world-wide trend, rural areas have higher birth rates than urban areas. War losses have been made up, but the loss of employable males is being felt; in 1957, some 53 per cent of West Germany's economically active population consisted of women. More serious from the German point of view is the decline of the average-size family. In 1956, 18.2 per cent of all households consisted of one individual as against 8.4 per cent in 1933.

[18] Gabriel Wülker, Friedrich Edding, Elisabeth Pfeil, Werner Essen, *et al.*, *Europa und die Deutschen Flüchtlinge* (Frankfurt a. M.: Institut zur Förderung öffentlicher Angelegenheiten, 1952).

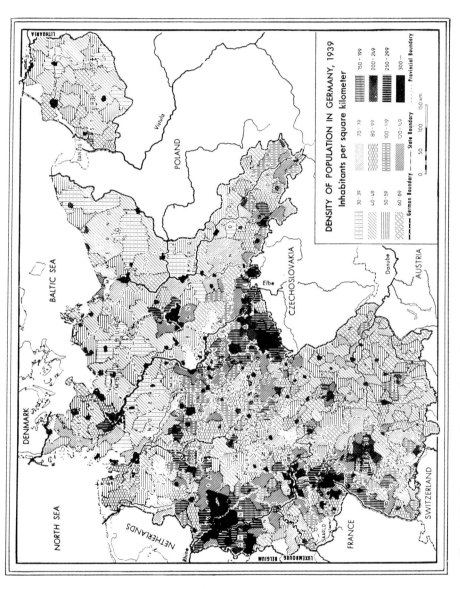

Fig. 6-20. Germany, density of population, 1939 (census of May 17, 1940). (From Werner Essen, modified by Chauncy D. Harris. By permission of the Institute für Raumforschung, Bonn.)

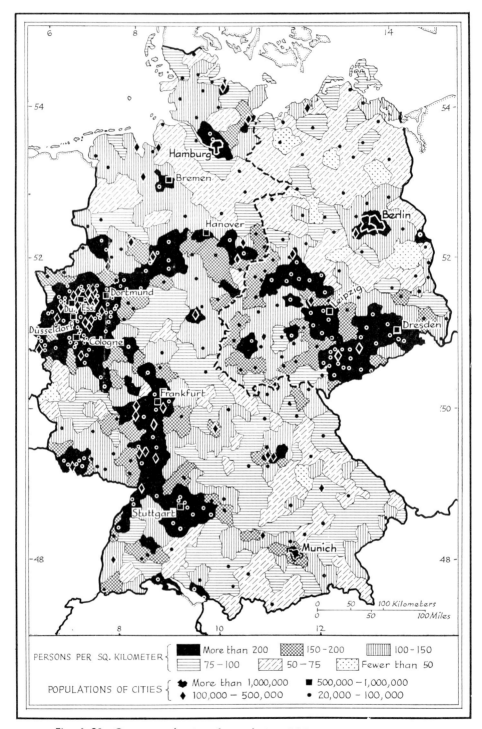

Fig. 6–21. Germany, density of population, 1955. (From *Diercke-Weltatlas,* 1957.)

In 1939, more than 31 per cent of Germany's population lived in cities of more than 100,000 inhabitants; the percentage figure for the territory of the present Federal Republic is 30. Germany's seven largest cities (1957 population) were Berlin (3,363,000), Hamburg (1,796,000), Munich (1,016,000), Essen (719,000), Cologne (719,-000), Düsseldorf (679,000), and Frankfurt on the Main (648,000).

If we compare the 1939 and 1957 population totals of Germany's larger cities, we realize that the country's population increase occurred chiefly in rural areas. Between 1939 and 1957, the population of villages with fewer than 5,000 inhabitants had increased by more than 29 per cent, whereas the larger cities have only now reached their prewar totals. These trends are contrary to those registered in other countries, but they will probably be reversed as soon as the housing shortage in large cities is alleviated.

German is spoken by the entire population, although in 1933 a small number of people reported their native language as being Polish, Wendish, Danish, or Dutch. German may be divided into the following groups:

Low German (*Niederdeutsch*)		High German (*Hochdeutsch*)	
Lower Frankish	Lower Saxon	Middle German	Upper German
Lower Rhenish		East Middle German	Bavarian
		West Middle German	Franconian-
			Alemannic

The distribution of religions is extremely complex. North Germany is predominantly Protestant; south Germany is predominantly Roman Catholic. In the rest of Germany the two religious groups are intermingled. For Germany as a whole, the 1933 census listed 60.8 per cent of the population as Protestant and 33.2 per cent as Catholic. With the loss of large territories in the east (where 66.6 per cent of the population had been Protestant and 30 per cent Catholic) and the postwar immigration of Germans, the 1950 proportion had shifted in favor of the Catholics: 50.1 per cent Protestant, 43.8 per cent Catholic.

While there are clear-cut differences of religion and of spoken dialects, there are no variations in the written language. Germans in Berlin, Cologne, and Munich, as well as those living in Zurich or Vienna, are united by the High German written language originated by Martin Luther. Illiteracy is negligible.

A few words should be added about the occupational distribution of the population. As Germany industrialized, more and more people, including women, entered the labor force. In 1957, the percentage of the population in the labor force was 50; the increase in women workers was especially spectacular. Between 1948 and 1957 it rose by 62.3 per cent. The most important conclusion to be drawn from employment figures is that there has been a relative decrease in stable agricultural employment over the last 50 years, while industry attracted most of the new recruits to the labor force. This development is characteristic of most industrialized countries.

In politics, the German population reflects great geographical disunity and diversity. While it would be an exaggeration to speak of a political cleavage between north and south Germany, there are unmistakable differences in character between the people of the North German Lowlands and those of the Alpine Foreland, between the inhabitants of the Rhineland and those of Saxony. Throughout history, these differences were reinforced by protracted feuds between ruling houses and by religious cleavages which originally followed lines of political division.

During the Hitler regime, every effort was made to obliterate these differences; the Nazis went so far as to change old established political units, laws, and customs. Since the end of World War II, regional differentiation and decentralization have been advocated by the states (*Länder*) of the German Federal Republic; this trend has also been backed by various foreign powers, especially France and the United Kingdom, which in this way hope to prevent a new dictator from assuming unlimited power over the German people. The government of the German Democratic Republic is highly centralized and in 1952 changed the administrative divisions of the area under its control. The German flair for militarism and their liking for discipline and organization have perhaps been subdued by the terrific destruction wrought by the last war, but no one can really be certain.

Germans are proud of their past, they are extremely hard workers, and they have highly scientific minds which qualify them as competent chemists, engineers, and physicists. Because Germany suffers from overpopulation and is heavily dependent upon vital raw-material imports, the Germans have constantly looked for additional living space, using various means to accomplish their aim. It has often been said that the middle position in Europe has its dangers as well as its temptations.

Present Economic Life of Germany

Germany went through the Industrial Revolution after its political unification in 1871. Although other European countries had thus gained a head start, Germany with its vast reservoir of human and material resources, its fertile soils capable of feeding a growing industrial population, and its central position, soon overtook its rivals in production and trade. Despite the defeat and the territorial losses of 1919, which for a time greatly slowed economic activity, Germany maintained its determination to achieve economic as well as political leadership. At the end of World War II, Germany's economic life was once more almost completely paralyzed. The countryside was scarred by bombed-out cities and destroyed industrial plants. The loss of territory resulted in the loss of important raw materials for industry. It is astonishing, therefore, how rapidly new life developed amidst the burned-out ruins and dismantled plants,[19] only a few years after the cessation of hostilities.

An analysis of the basis of Germany's economic strength will go far to explain this recuperative power, as well as her renewed importance in world affairs. The growth of agriculture and manufacturing after 1871 was made possible above all by the presence of domestic resources. Thanks to her pioneer efforts in applying scientific methods to agriculture, Germany greatly increased her wheat yields and attained world leadership in the production of sugar beets and potatoes. She also became the world's largest rye producer. By 1937, Germany produced close to 85 per cent of its food needs. This was an extraordinary accomplishment for one of Europe's most advanced industrialized countries. Industry, Germany's greatest asset, owed its rapid growth to the extensive coal deposits of the Ruhr, the Saar, and Upper Silesia. Plentiful coal was the basis of the iron and steel industry, which in turn supplied the basic materials for such vital industries as shipbuilding and the manufacture of rails, rolling stock, machines, tools, and armaments. Germany's other raw materials, including large potash and salt deposits for the fertilizer and chemical industry, also contributed to its leading position among Europe's principal manufacturing countries (Fig. 6–22).

Germany's present economic situation has undergone extensive changes from prewar days. Although the wartime loss of manpower has been largely offset by a great influx of immigrants, and German cities and industrial establishments are being rebuilt and improved, the territorial losses and resultant loss of important raw materials constituted a serious impediment to the restoration of normal economic life. Further obstacles to the country's rehabilitation lie in the

[19] According to the Potsdam Declaration of 1945, the four occupying powers—France, the United Kingdom, the United States, and the U.S.S.R.—were to dismantle many of Germany's industrial plants in order to reduce that country's war-making potential. By 1948, however, all four powers had discontinued this action. In fact, the United States, through the European Recovery Program, restored some key plants in order to increase Germany's productive capacity.

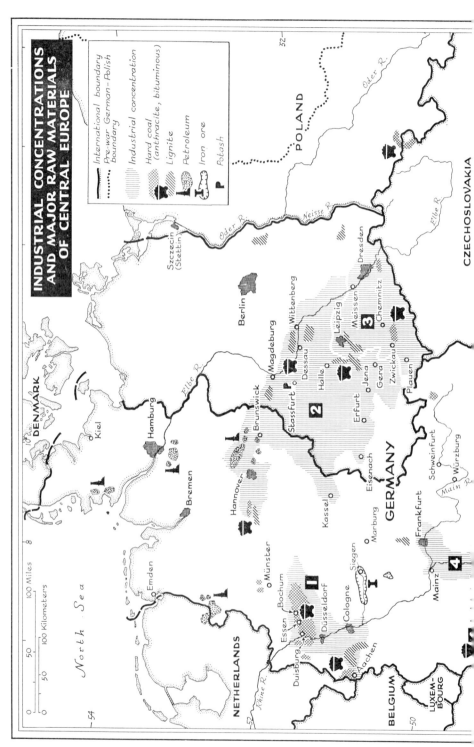

INDUSTRIAL CONCENTRATIONS AND MAJOR RAW MATERIALS OF CENTRAL EUROPE

International boundary
Pre-war German-Polish boundary
Industrial concentration
Hard coal (anthracite, bituminous)
Lignite
Petroleum
Iron ore
P Potash

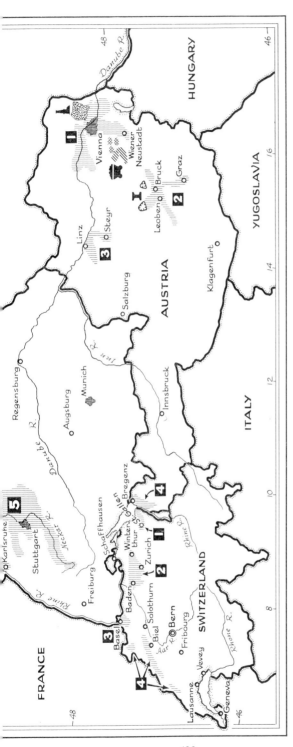

Fig. 6–22. Industrial concentrations of Central Europe. Germany: (1) Rhine-Ruhr, (2) Central German Industrial Region, (3) Saxony, (4) Upper Rhine, (5) Neckar Basin, (6) Saar. Switzerland: (1) St. Gallen, (2) Zurich-Winterthur-Baden, (3) Basel, (4) the Jura. Austria: (1) Vienna Basin, (2) Styria, (3) Upper Austria, (4) Vorarlberg.

fact that Germany is divided into two economic and political units and no peace treaty has yet been signed.

On the other hand, mention should be made of the considerable financial help which West Germany has derived from participation in the European Recovery Program (Marshall Plan). West Germany is also actively participating in many important European organizations (see Chapter 10), e.g., the European Coal and Steel Community (ECSC), the European Atomic Energy Community (EURATOM), and more recently in the European Economic Community (EEC). It is also a member of NATO, where its military contributions have greatly increased during the last few years. East Germany is a member of the Soviet-sponsored Council for Mutual Economic Aid (COMECON), and the counterpart of NATO, the Warsaw Pact.

In the following discussion we shall outline the facts of Germany's present economic life, but the reader should always be aware of the different economic developments and policies in the two parts of divided Germany.

Agriculture and Forestry.[20] Two noteworthy features marked German agriculture before World War II: (1) the high percentage of land under cultivation—61 to 63 per cent in 1939—and (2) the remarkably high crop yields. Both these characteristics contributed to the country's high degree of agricultural self-sufficiency; in average years Germany was 75 per cent self-sufficient, and in good years as much as 85 per cent. Since 1945, however, considerable changes have taken place. Territorial losses in the east, traditionally an agricultural-surplus area, have had important repercussions on Germany's postwar output. Of total prewar production, the lost territories had supplied the following percentages: rye, 33 plus; potatoes, 25; summer barley, 29; oats, 23; fodder, 25; sugar beets, 20; wheat, 15; horses, 25; pigs, 27; and cattle, 20. Today these territories ship almost no agricultural commodities westward. Furthermore, a Germany considerably reduced in area has to feed a much greater number of people. Besides, the normal flow of complementary interregional trade has been hindered by various interzonal restrictions and by the fact that East Germany has 55 per cent of the arable land and 48 per cent of the total agricultural land (based on 1937 figures), with only 24 per cent of the population.

One conclusion is evident: more than ever before, Germany—East and West—needs a large crop output, with high yields and intensive land use. By using additional fertilizer, machinery, and

[20] For statistical data, see Appendix III.

every available spare bit of land, prewar food consumption of about 3,000 calories per inhabitant has been maintained in West Germany. It took 15 years after World War II, however, to reach this level in East Germany. This, obviously, has not been accomplished from domestic production alone. On the average, the amount of food that West Germany must import amounts to 25 to 32 per cent of its total requirements. In spite of the difficulties, West Germany now produces roughly 99 per cent of its potatoes, 88 per cent of its butter, 81 per cent of its fruit, 70 per cent of its corn, 88 per cent of its meat, and 45 per cent of the nutritive fats it requires. Figures for East Germany are not available.

A combination of factors is responsible for the high percentage of productive land and the high yields. Among them are the relief of the country, the climate, the nature of the soils, the distribution of population, and the location of human activities. There are considerable regional differences in rainfall and temperature. But the diversified type of farming that is practiced yields a variety of products.

In Germany as a whole, the proportion of poor soil to total arable land is high (Figs. 6–23 and 6–24). However, by the consistent application of manure, commercial fertilizers, and various soil-conservation measures over the last 150 years, an exceptionally high crop yield has been achieved on these soils. A good part of Germany has grey-brown forest soils of various shades, mostly very light, leached, and acid, much like the soils found in New England. These soils can be used only for rye, oats, and potatoes, with oats cultivated only in the wetter areas. Loess soils (black and brown steppe soils) are found in patches, the largest of which is located between Brunswick and Leipzig (East Germany) in the zone of the Southern Transitional Borderlands. Although they have been in use since prehistoric times, these loess soils remain the most productive soils in Germany, thanks to careful cultivation, good conservation measures, and the regular application of fertilizers.

The amount of land under cultivation has remained rather stable. It averages about 58 per cent of the total land area of West Germany and 46 per cent of the total land area of East Germany.

The bread grains (oats, barley, rye, and wheat) and potatoes, of which Germany used to be the world's chief producer, constitute the base of Germany's diet. Rye, the most important cereal, is made into dark bread. Wheat is grown on heavier soils and in regions with warmer summer temperatures, predominantly in the Southern Transitional Borderlands. In addition to playing an important role in the human diet, potatoes are used as feed for pigs and as a source of

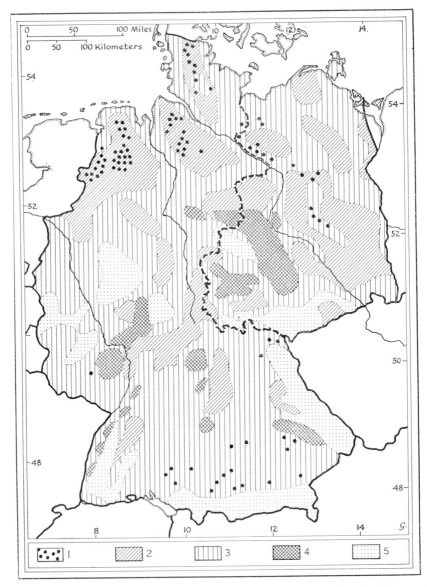

Fig. 6–23. Soil regions of Germany: (1) moor soils, (2) sandy soils, (3) mixed types ranging from sandy loams to clay, (4) black and brown steppe soils, (5) mountain soils. (After H. Niehaus, by permission of the American Geographical Society.)

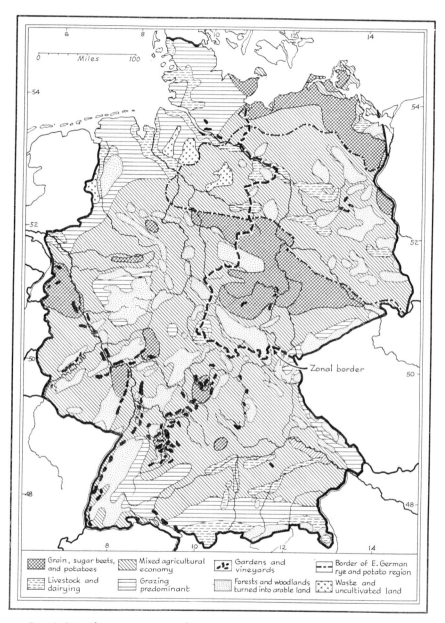

Fig. 6–24. The economic-productive structure of German agriculture. (After E. Otremba, *Die Deutsche Agrarlandschaft.*)

alcohol and starch. The distribution is similar to that of rye. Bread grains took 60 per cent of the planted area in West Germany in 1957, potatoes 24 per cent, fodder plants 13 per cent, and other plants 3 per cent. Barley, in special demand for beer brewing, is grown predominantly in southern Germany. Oats is the typical crop of the moist regions along the Baltic coast and the North Sea. The sugar beet, a source of sugar and fodder, is grown for the most part on loess soil at the foot of the Central Uplands; its distribution is similar to that of wheat. Various grasses, such as clover and alfalfa, are of special value for stock raising and dairying. Vegetable production is widespread. Industrial crops, such as hemp, flax, tobacco, hops, and rapeseed, have profitable uses. Soybeans are a relatively new crop, and corn is grown in only a few areas. Vineyards are located in the Rhine gorge and in the Neckar, Main, Moselle, and Nahe valleys. German wines (e.g., the Rhine wines) are of good quality and the production is not sufficient to meet domestic demand. Some of the warmer regions of southern Germany have extensive orchards, and in addition many roads throughout Germany are lined with fruit trees, especially apple trees. Cattle are reared in the vicinity of large urban concentrations and in the Alpine Foreland.

Before the outbreak of World War II, Germany was able to limit its agricultural imports to milk products and some grain. To keep food imports down, considerable attention is given to coastal and deep-sea fisheries in both West and East Germany. Fish are being used increasingly to supplement the diet of the people. In West Germany, in 1957, some 686,000 tons of fish, 40 per cent of them herring, were landed. The North Sea is the main fishing ground, where half of the catch is made. The rest is caught in the North Atlantic, mainly in Icelandic waters. Fishing grounds in the Baltic Sea are generally much poorer.

Germany has always had a large number of small farms. This is due partly to predominantly poor soil and partly to historical reasons. Larger holdings, e.g., farms with over 250 acres, were found chiefly in eastern Germany, in territories lost after World War II. The average-size farm in West Germany is approximately 17 acres. In some regions of West Germany, the farms are very much split up, because of traditional division among different heirs. Land consolidation, therefore, has top priority in West Germany, and it is hoped that this will increase productive capacity. Large farms, 50 acres and larger, occupy 36 per cent of the area of West Germany and are located mostly in the loess regions west of the Elbe. If we compare the prewar (1937) percentage of all farms under 5 acres with the postwar figure, we find almost no change in the general distribution pattern in the Federal Republic. Medium-size farms (5 to 50 acres) predominate in Bavaria and in the northwest, and comprise 60 per cent of the area. Small holdings of less than 5 acres are common in the south, in central Germany, and in the west, especially the Rhineland. They comprise 4.4 per cent of the total area. The Rhineland, with its great urban concentrations, is West Germany's largest food-deficit area.

As a result of the drastic agricultural reforms in East Germany, more than half of all agricultural land is now in farms of between 12 and 45 acres. Large farms (over 250 acres) which covered one-fifth of the total agricultural area in East Germany were confiscated and broken up after the war, as were many medium-size and small farms. Voluntary agricultural societies became the forerunners of collectivization, and, by mid-1960, over half of the total agricultural area was collectivized (including state farms).

In view of the importance of forests in Germany—28 per cent of the postwar area is covered with forests—a brief discussion is appropriate. During Roman times, large parts of present-day Germany were impassable, owing to the dense forest cover. The predominant forest types were distributed as follows: Scots pine and spruce in the northeast and in the glacial valleys, oak and beech in the Baltic hinterland, and beech, birch, and oak in northwestern Germany and in the middle Rhineland. Beech was dominant in the lower parts of the Central Uplands, and spruce at higher altitudes. Fir was commonly found in southern Germany.

Three main periods of forest clearing (*Rodung*) may be distinguished: sixth to ninth centuries (early German period), ninth to fifteenth centuries (clearing due to population pressure), and eighteenth century (clearing due to industrialization and timber exports). Following the second period of clearings, oak was replaced by beech and spruce and forest-conservation measures were initiated.

Thus, German forests in existence today differ widely from the virgin forests of Roman times. The great changes in the forest cover evident throughout Germany have been brought about largely by man. Once predominantly broadleaved, Germany's forests are now chiefly coniferous, the latter type having been found especially suitable for reforestation. One may generalize by saying that conifers are dominant in the east and southeast, while broadleaf species are more common in the west.

Plains originally covered by deciduous trees now have spruce or Scots pine and some oak. Riverine forests are predominantly alder, poplar, ash, and elm. A zone of larch, spruce, and Swiss stone pine is commonly found in the Alps; one of silver fir, beech, and some spruce, in the Alpine Foreland. Scots pine has been found useful in the reforestation of sandy areas (dunes, heaths, and steppes). Certain tree types, such as the linden, poplar, willow, ash, and maple, which are commonly associated with German forests, occur only in small woods.

Thanks to effective conservation measures, large tracts of forest have been preserved, the ratio of coniferous to broadleaf species being 70 to 30. In general, the percentage of forest area increases from north to south. Bavaria, North Rhine-Westphalia, and Lower Saxony are the most heavily wooded areas. Close to 42 per cent of the forested land is in private hands. German forests suffered from over-cutting, especially during the war and immediately thereafter, but between 1949 and 1957 more than one-fifth of the area under timber was replanted. There are no private forest holdings in East Germany.

Manufacturing. Germany is among the most important manu-facturing countries of Europe, next in rank to the U.S.S.R. and the United Kingdom. Despite two defeats in the span of a quarter century and the destruction of a large part of its industrial facilities, West Germany's industries have increased production above prewar figures. Her iron and steel, textile, chemical, optical, automotive, and precision industries are in full production. The postwar plans put forth by the occupying powers, for a "pastoral German economy" and a "transfer of her manufacturing facilities to other countries," were soon abandoned for increased German participation in industrial output. Generally speaking, German production has now reached prewar levels and in a number of items has exceeded them.

The industries of East Germany are dependent on the Soviet Union and several Eastern European countries for many vital raw materials (Polish coal, Hungarian bauxite, etc.) and are largely in-tegrated into the production pattern of the Soviet bloc (see Chapter 10, pp. 756–57). With increased specialization within the Soviet bloc, East Germany's industries are specializing in the output of chemicals, optical equipment, steel-mill equipment, passenger rail-way cars, trucks, and diesel engines. It should also be mentioned that many industries, especially those of high quality and world-wide repu-tation such as chemicals, photographic articles, printing, etc., have started new centers of production in West Germany (Fig. 6–25).

Germany's industrial achievements are due to a number of factors which will be discussed in the following pages.

THE RAW-MATERIAL FACTOR. Coal is Germany's basic mineral resource and accounted for much of the early success in industrializa-tion. Besides bituminous coal, sizable amounts of lignite, or brown coal, are mined. However, it should be realized that the heating value of lignite is considerably inferior to that of coal: about 4½ tons of lignite are needed to equal 1 ton of bituminous coal. Rich deposits of coking coal occur in three regions: in the Ruhr, in the Saar, and in Upper Silesia, now part of Poland. In 1937 the Ruhr accounted for 69 per cent of total production (127,750,000 tons), the Saar for 12 per cent, Silesia for 16 per cent, and a smaller field in Saxony for the rest.

Fig. 6–25. The world-famous Zeiss plant, relocated in Oberkochen, Württemberg, West Germany. The original plant is in Jena, East Germany. Most of the workmen and specialists fled from Jena and helped to establish this refugee industry in its new home. (Zeiss-Werkphoto.)

Lignite is widely distributed over Germany. It occurs in thick deposits close to the surface and is extracted mainly by open-pit workings. Its versatility gives it added value: for example, conversion into briquettes, electricity, and various chemical products. Through a difficult process called hydrogenation, coal is converted into liquid hydrocarbons (gasoline, petroleum) and into the raw materials for synthetic rubber. As may be gathered from Fig. 6–22, Germany's coal deposits are for the most part rather close to the country's frontiers. For strategic reasons and because of the tremendous fuel need in the prewar industrial-expansion program, lignite production was greatly expanded in the 1930's, and high transportation costs called for its utilization as close to the deposits as possible. With the post-war loss of important bituminous-coal mines, lignite has assumed an even more important position in the German industrial-fuel picture.

Germany in 1957 produced approximately 153 million metric tons of coal (anthracite and bituminous) and 310 million metric tons of lignite.[21] West Germany is the second-largest European coal producer, production in 1957 (including the Saar) contributing 54 per cent of the total produced by the six countries associated in the Coal and Steel Community. On the other hand, East Germany was almost completely dependent on imports, most of which came from Poland. Part of West Germany's production is exported to the coal-poor countries of Europe. West Germany's large supply of coal is thus an important reason for its key position in the European economy.

Despite the abundance of coal and the availability of potash, pro-duced from large salt deposits around Stassfurt, northeast of the Harz Mountains, Germany suffers from considerable raw-material shortages. One such shortage is in iron ore, which has been mined since 1850 southeast of Cologne in the Siegerland and in the Lahn and Harz regions. In 1937, all the iron ore mined within the present-day territory of the Federal Republic provided but one-fifth of total consumption. Even the tapping of poorer deposits could not supply the needs of the Ruhr industries. Imports today come from Sweden, Lorraine, Spain, and French North Africa and must provide 60 per cent of the needs of West Germany. The Democratic Republic imports about 44 per cent of its iron ores from the U.S.S.R. Other items which must be imported include lead, zinc, copper, tin, sulphur, and pyrites, as well as flax and silk for the textile industry. Germany became aware at an early date of the value of substitutes. Accord-ingly, many synthetic products and substitutes for essential natural resources were developed in Germany. Nevertheless, her dependence on key raw-material imports is an important economic handicap.

Waterpower is another important resource for German industries. It is concentrated in the Alps and in the valleys of the Central Up-lands (dammed lakes). Even though much progress has been made in enlarging electric power-generating facilities over the last 20 years, a great deal of electricity must be imported, some of it in exchange for Ruhr coal. In 1957, waterpower contributed 15 per cent of West Germany's electricity.

---

[21] It is estimated that 2.7 million metric tons of coal and 2.3 million metric tons of lignite came from the Soviet zone. The Saar contributed 16.4 million metric tons.

Of great importance is Germany's new petroleum production. Output increased from 230,000 tons in 1933 to nearly 4,440,000 tons in 1957. The Elmsland Field near the German-Dutch border is the newest of her productive fields, contributing almost 40 per cent of the country's total output. Oil has also been struck in the Aller River Valley, north of Hanover and Brunswick. There are minor fields in the western part of Schleswig-Holstein and in Baden-Württemberg. At the end of 1957, West Germany's production covered one-third of its requirements. Close to 80 per cent of the imported oil comes from the Middle East and 20 per cent from the Caribbean region; most of it is refined in the Ruhr and Hamburg areas. The capacity of the refineries will be doubled by 1964. In spite of surplus coal (14 million tons in 1959), West Germany's industries and households will follow the general trend of rapid conversion from coal to oil, but to slow this process a special tax has been put on oil. A new pipeline from Wilhelmshaven to the big refineries in the Ruhr was completed in 1960. Another is being built from the Mediterranean ports of Genoa and Marseille, which will take the petroleum from the newly developed fields of the French Sahara and of Libya to the industrial heart of Europe.

THE LOCATIONAL FACTOR. Many scholars have analyzed the locational aspects and the interregional relationships of Germany's industrial production. Among the more important factors of industrial location are: raw materials, transportation, manpower, and the proximity of agricultural land. German industrial concentrations are characterized by a combination of several of these factors. Most of Germany's industries are concentrated in six regions (Fig. 6–22). A belt of unequal width, extending from Aachen on the German-Belgian border to the Ore Mountains along the border of Czechoslovakia, includes (1) the Rhine-Ruhr region; (2) the Central German Industrial Region; (3) industrial Southern Saxony; (4) the upper part of the Rhine Valley, with chief centers at Karlsruhe, Mannheim-Ludwigshafen, Mainz, and Frankfurt; (5) the Neckar Basin, with Stuttgart as its industrial center; and (6) the Saar, with Saarbrücken as its chief center. Several minor industrial regions have grown in importance as a result of the war and the postwar division of Germany. Most of these are centered on large cities, including ports. Berlin is handicapped by its division into West Berlin and East Berlin. Among the industrial territories lost since the war, Upper Silesia used to play an important role, though not comparable to that of the Ruhr. While Silesia contributed less than one-sixth of Germany's over-all production before World War II, its contribution to Poland's economy is of major importance (see Chapter 8, pp. 584–86).

1. *The Rhine-Ruhr Region.* This region is most important for its coal and iron-ore mines and for the production of coke, steel, chemicals, and heavy machinery. The core of the Ruhr area extends about 45 miles eastward from the Rhine to Dortmund and has a north-south extent of less than 10 miles. A more recent expansion has taken place north of the core area, near the Münster coal mines. As may be seen from the following table, the Ruhr has been important for some time:

Ruhr Coal and Coke Production
(thousand metric tons)

Year	Coal	Coke	Year	Coal	Coke
1800	200	*	1929	123,600	34,200
1830	500	*	1932	73,275	15,323
1850	1,960	73	1937	127,750	31,600
1869	11,250	277	1939	130,500	36,000
1880	22,228	1,291	1942	131,183	35,000
1900	60,000	9,644	1945	33,380	5,338
1913	114,183	26,703	1948	81,106	18,920
1920	88,000	21,720	1958	132,582	39,580

* Not available.

Source: Wilhelm Helmrich, *Das Ruhrgebiet* (2d ed.; Stuttgart: Aschendorff, 1949) and official statistics.

In 1937, 70 per cent of the entire German output of steel originated in the Ruhr, a percentage which has barely changed despite altered postwar conditions. During the same year (1937), the Ruhr area produced over 25 per cent of Germany's electric power, 72 per cent of its coal tar, and 64 per cent of its crude benzene.

The importance of this region is due to its extensive, high-grade deposits of coking coal; its proximity to West Germany's only source of iron ore; the unrivaled natural artery of trade provided by the Rhine, and its tributaries, the Lippe and the Ruhr; and the dense network of canals which connects the Ruhr with most parts of Germany. Its location in the very heart of Europe's commerce and industry has consistently encouraged the expansion of its industries (Figs. 6–26 and 6–27).

This area is remarkable for its large concentration of cities, 23 of which have a population of over 100,000. Close to 7 million people, nearly all of whom are dependent upon Ruhr industries, live in a region which is about the size of Delaware. Its chief city is Essen. Other large cities are Dortmund, Bochum, Duisburg (Duisburg-Hamborn), and Gelsenkirchen. Duisburg, with a 1958 population of 495,000, is the leading Rhine port and the largest inland port of

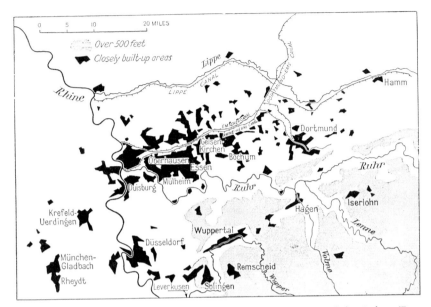

Fig. 6–26. Industrial and mining areas, and waterways, of the Ruhr. (From *Focus,* by permission of the American Geographical Society.)

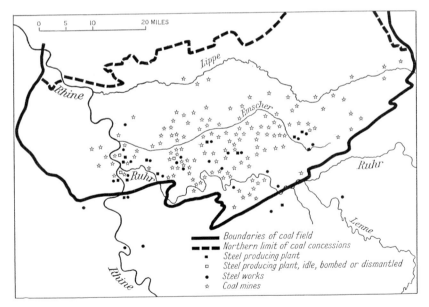

Fig. 6–27. Coal mines and steel works of the Ruhr. (From *Focus,* by permission of the American Geographical Society.)

Europe (Fig. 6–28). The Ruhr is dotted with iron and steel works, locomotive and chemical plants, and factories manufacturing equipment for mines and steel mills.

Important postwar political developments include the unification of the entire Rhine-Ruhr region into the province of North Rhine-Westphalia (Land Nordrhein-Westfalen) within the original British zone of occupation; the creation, in December, 1948, of the Ruhr

Fig. 6–28. Duisburg on the Rhine, looking upstream toward the Duisburg-Reinhausen bridge. Note the petroleum-storage tanks, thermal-power plant, copper foundry, and steel mill. The river teems with traffic, including many coal barges. (Deutsche Zentrale für Fremdenverkehr.)

International Authority to insure Germany's disarmament, to hasten German as well as European recovery by a steady return to the prewar structure (organization and ownership) of all Ruhr industries,[22] and,

[22] In the Potsdam agreement of 1945 the victorious Allied Powers committed themselves to "eliminate present excessive concentration of economic power" in Germany. Sweeping deconcentration and decartelization decrees were promulgated and enforced between 1947 and 1953. Deconcentration meant the creation of a new ownership pattern in the basic industries so that a few individuals, through interlocking directorships and holding companies could not dominate an entire industry. Decartelization stood for the breakup of a long-standing system of market sharing and price fixing whereby different companies protected themselves from competition. To avoid the pitfalls of the prewar period, the Bonn government in 1957 enacted anti-cartel laws similar to the United States anti-trust legislation. Also under the co-determination law, labor has a voice in company policy making, and one-man rule is thus no longer possible in the Ruhr.

finally, to promote closer integration of Germany's economic life with the Western world, thereby hoping to make the Ruhr a unique source of strength available to all the West. Heavy industry is now subject to the European Coal and Steel Community; thus, many Ruhr industries are now closely integrated into a larger economic framework.

2. *The Central German Industrial Region.* This extends eastward from the middle Weser River along the zone of the Southern Transitional Borderlands to the Elbe River, and south into the Central Uplands. Much of this region is in East Germany. Its various industries are largely based upon lignite and mineral salts. The combination of raw materials has made this the most important chemical-manufacturing region in all Germany. Lignite is the basic fuel for the production of electric power and for other energy uses. In the 1930's, the low-grade iron-ore deposits of the Peine-Salzgitter area near Brunswick attracted several heavy-manufacturing establishments which also used the dense river-and-canal transportation system for imports of coal and additional iron ore. During the war the region gained added importance when important industries from the Ruhr were relocated here. In addition to a large number of chemical and heavy-industrial establishments, there are many other industries dependent on the region's pool of skilled workers. The more important centers are Hanover (chemical and metallurgical industries), Salzgitter (steel mills, automobile and textile plants), Kassel (heavy machinery and locomotives), Magdeburg (chemicals), Dessau (aircraft center in the years before Germany was forbidden to build them), Halle (chemicals), and Erfurt and Jena (optical instruments, glass and chinaware, bicycles, typewriters, etc.).

3. *Industrial Southern Saxony.* The industries which developed in southern Saxony, on the northern slopes of the Ore Mountains, are largely based on lignite (formerly on minor bituminous-coal deposits) and on a wide range of metallic ores, many of which are now exhausted. Some of the mining and industrial activity goes back to the Middle Ages. Lignite is still available and forms the basic source of power. A large number of skilled workers are employed in the numerous textile plants and in the woodworking and tanning industries which have grown up here. This region generally ranks second among German industrial districts, with textiles predominating, and is wholly within East Germany. Important cities are Plauen (knitted goods, embroidery), Meissen and Dresden (porcelain), Chemnitz (general textiles), and Leipzig, a city of 600,000 people which is one of Europe's oldest trading centers. Before the war, Leipzig was a center of the fur trade and was also known for its publishing and

printing houses of high repute. Its famed international fair, while
handicapped by the postwar division of Germany, is still being held
annually. The Leipzig Bay is linked with other parts of Germany by a
network of canals, rivers (including the Elbe), and railroad lines.

4. *The Upper Part of the Rhine Valley.* This industrial region
extends along the Rhine from Mainz and Frankfurt-am-Main southward to Karlsruhe. The region's chief drawback is the lack of raw
materials. However, this disadvantage is overcome by its excellent
location, transportation-wise. The canalized Rhine and Main rivers
give easy access to the east and to the Rhine-Ruhr region to the north.
The region's industries manufacture precision instruments, tools, and
typewriters. The twin cities of Ludwigshafen-Mannheim produce
chemicals (dyes, fertilizer, nitrates, and pharmaceutical items).
Mainz and Frankfurt are important centers for the manufacture of
automobiles, railroad supplies, trucks, machines, and machine tools.
Mannheim and Mainz are also active river ports, while Frankfurt
was prewar Germany's leading commercial and financial center.

5. *The Neckar Basin.* The region's chief center is Stuttgart, and
its main transportation artery is the navigable Neckar River, which
enters the Rhine at Mannheim. Cement works, numerous wood
industries, textile plants, and precision-instrument and other metal industries dot the landscape. Automobile, machine, and shoe factories
make important contributions. Stuttgart (population 617,000) is one
of West Germany's important industrial centers.

6. *The Saar.* Situated along the German-French border, this region has changed hands several times in recent history. It owes its
industrial development to the presence of coal deposits in proximity
to the minette iron ores of Lorraine. Between 1871 and 1918, the
region was part of Germany and the output of its newly established
industries was shipped eastward on canals connecting it with the
main Rhine Valley. By the Treaty of Versailles, eastern Lorraine
was returned to France and the Saar was made an autonomous territory administered by France under League of Nations supervision,
but it reverted to Germany in 1935 as a result of a plebiscite. After
1945, the Saar was made autonomous once more and its economy
was closely tied to that of France. A semiautonomous "European"
status for the Saar was rejected by the Saarländers in October, 1955,
and in 1956 France and West Germany agreed on the Saar's political
incorporation into the Federal Republic on January 1, 1957, and on its
economic incorporation on January 1, 1960.

The rich deposits of Saar coal which form the basis of a powerful
iron and steel industry have made important contributions to the

flourishing economy of West Germany. The coal production during 1957 amounted to over 16 million tons, 12 per cent of West Germany's production. The overwhelming majority of the Saarländers are German by language and origin, and, obviously, this fact has always exerted a strong influence for the return to the German "motherland" of this 2,500-square-mile strategically located territory. Perhaps the integration of the Saar into the European Coal and Steel Community will reduce political tensions and insure the fair allocation of its resources to all member nations.

In addition to the six major manufacturing regions, numerous other industrial centers are scattered all over Germany. Most of them are in or near large cities. As pointed out by Dickinson,[23] a certain distribution pattern is clearly visible: rolling stock and manufactures and repair shops are located near railroad yards; the principal agricultural market areas attract industries producing agricultural implements—Düsseldorf is such a center for the lower Rhineland, Augsburg for the Alpine Foreland, Leipzig for the middle Elbe Basin, and Hanover for Lower Saxony. The electrical industry is represented in nearly all important cities, and above all Berlin, Cologne, and Munich.

West of Cologne, the rise of a number of industrial centers is closely linked to the coal basin extending from Belgium and the Netherlands into Germany. Aachen is the center of a diversified industry, producing hardware, textiles, steel, etc.

In Franconia, a great variety of manufactures is found in Nürnberg and its suburb Fürth, in Würzburg, and in Schweinfurt. The latter two cities have important engineering works. Nürnberg is noted for its metallurgical products (machinery, motorcars, bicycles), foods, and toys. It is also an important railway center.

Also, various industries are concentrated in the many cities of the Alpine Foreland. Munich makes automobiles, optical equipment, machines, beer, and luxury items. Regensburg, at the head of Danube River navigation, has several small shipbuilding works and machine and machine-tool industries.

Last but not least, there are important industrial concentrations in each of several German ports. Since June, 1945—when Germany lost a major portion of its Baltic coast line, and its main Baltic harbor, Stettin—the German ports on the Baltic have steadily declined. Hamburg, the easternmost North Sea port on the lower Elbe, has been hit hard by the loss of Czech transit trade which has been rerouted to Polish ports. Once a powerful member of the Hanseatic League, Hamburg has maintained to this day its position as a self-

[23] R. E. Dickinson, "The Economic Regions of Germany," *Geographical Review* 28 (October, 1938): 606–16.

governing city. Before World War II it handled over 70 per cent
of Germany's imports and 57 per cent of its exports. In 1957, 45
per cent of the total freight to and from West German ports
went through Hamburg. There are extensive shipbuilding yards and
machinery and tool plants in all German port cities, with the greatest
concentrations in Hamburg, Bremen, and Kiel. Each seaport has its
own trade pattern. Bremen is the major port for cotton imports
destined for Central and Eastern Europe. It is also Europe's leading importer of various tropical produce. Bremerhaven, its outer
harbor, carries much of the traffic. Emden, the third of Germany's
North Sea ports, was originally built to capture some of the trade
going to Rotterdam. Direct access to the Rhine-Ruhr industrial
region, via the Dortmund-Ems canal, has been an important factor
in Emden's growth, but comparatively few industries are located
within its port area. The port of Kiel is located on the Kiel Canal,
which connects the Baltic with the North Sea. It is the most important Baltic port of West Germany.

THE TRANSPORTATION FACTOR. Germany's industrial growth would
not have been possible without the development of an efficient,
highly integrated transportation system; although considerably damaged by the war, the transportation system has made important contributions to postwar rehabilitation.

Germany's principal waterways are the country's oldest transport
arteries. Four large, navigable rivers flow from south to north across
the North German Lowlands: the Rhine with the Dortmund-Ems
Canal extension to Emden, the Weser, the Elbe, and the Oder (now
part of the German-Polish border). The three east-west arteries are
the Danube and two canals, the Midland Canal and the Kiel Canal.
The Midland Canal links the Ems with the Elbe and is extended
eastward by various canals to the Oder. Completed in 1938, the
224-mile-long canal has a depth of 9 feet. Current political controversies between the occupying powers have reduced its usefulness as
a transit route, especially in and around Berlin. In order to prevent
interference with shipping, on the part of the Western powers, an
additional canal has been built to bypass the Western zone of Berlin
and thus afford a direct connection through the whole of the Soviet
zone.

The Rhine carries more passengers and freight than any other
German waterway. Since the mouth of the river is in foreign territory, Germany constructed the Dortmund-Ems Canal as a bypass
through German territory to the North Sea. However, because the
canal is too shallow and too narrow for modern barges, most of the

Rhine shipping continues to travel down the river into Dutch territory. The Rhine flows through Europe's greatest industrial concentrations. The upstream traffic is heaviest, with coal, coke, and grain the bulkiest commodities. Timber, potash, and iron ore are the main downstream cargoes. The Elbe provides a natural link between the North Sea and landlocked Czechoslovakia. The Oder is of lesser importance today, largely because of the loss of the Silesian coal fields and the port city of Stettin to Poland.

The Danube has always been of minor importance as an east-west artery, largely because of its isolation from other German waterways, the absence of a major industrial region along its banks, and the fact that it flows in the wrong direction, eastward. Many possibilities of connecting the Danube with Europe's other main rivers have been studied, but because of the high cost and technical difficulties little has been done so far. The only connection existing at present is the small Ludwig Canal which leads southward from the Main. The possibility of widening the existing river-canal system is again being considered and may ultimately come about.

The physiography of Germany presented no major obstacles to the development of a dense rail network connecting all important cities and industrial areas. Rail densities are highest in the Rhine-Ruhr region, the Central Industrial Region, and the vicinity of Berlin, Leipzig, and Mainz-Frankfurt. Only a small part of Germany's rail mileage is electrified, as compared with that of Switzerland and Austria.

Two general patterns of freight movement may be distinguished: (1) raw-material imports and overseas exports move from and to the North Sea ports and (2) raw materials and foodstuffs move from one region to another within the country and overland to other European countries.

Germany has excellent road communications. The density of the network is high, but with the exception of the superhighways (*Autobahnen*) the roads are no longer able to carry the traffic. In addition to ordinary roads, Germany built a number of superhighways since 1933. Although they were built primarily for strategic reasons—to facilitate troop movements—the superhighways are now used by an ever-increasing number of overland truck carriers. Of freight transported within West Germany in 1956, railways carried 55 per cent, inland waterways 29 per cent, and long-distance heavy trucks 16 per cent. With airlines again serving all important German cities (*Lufthansa*) and a further increase in the number of heavy trucks, the proportion transported by railways is still further declining. It should also be mentioned that *Lufthansa*, which started its postwar service in West Germany in 1956, has organized a dense flight network to many overseas areas, including North and South America.

Finally, it should be stressed that the various means of transport are interdependent. While rivers and canals are highly suited for bulk traffic, their limitations as carriers must always be borne in mind. In effect, considering the present importance of railroads and trucks, waterways supplement rather than compete with overland transport.

Foreign and Intrazonal Trade. The structure of West Germany's foreign trade, excluding intrazonal trade, resembles that of the German Reich before World War II. Imports of food comprise roughly 31 per cent of all imports, raw materials 30 per cent, semifinished goods 18 per cent, and finished goods 21 per cent. Since 1952, West Germany has enjoyed a net trade surplus and its total trade has reached the highest levels in Germany's history. As a matter of fact, West Germany is now an important financier in world business.

Over 80 per cent of West Germany's exports, by value, consist of industrial goods, chemicals, electrotechnical goods, etc. Semifinished goods contribute about 12 per cent, raw materials about 5 per cent, and the balance consists of food exports.

The countries of the European Payment Union (all European countries—with the exception of Finland, Yugoslavia, and the countries of Eastern Europe—plus their overseas territories and certain non-European members of the sterling area) supply about 60 per cent of West Germany's purchases and buy about 72 per cent of her exports. West Germany has also become the largest creditor in the Union. Its principal business partners are the United States, the Netherlands, Belgium, Luxembourg, Italy, France, Sweden, Switzerland, the United Kingdom, and Austria.

Before World War II, trade between western and eastern Germany was extremely heavy, but because no formal lines of division existed, no exact records were kept. Since the unified-currency area was divided in 1948, lists of goods have been drawn up annually in interzonal trade agreements. West Germany buys mostly lignite briquettes, mineral oils, chemical products, and textiles. It exports to East Germany machines, iron and various metal goods, and chemical products. Intrazonal trade has been on the increase since 1953, but its total amount is estimated as barely one-fourth of prewar trade.

Foreign trade in East Germany plays a much smaller role than in West Germany's economy. Over 80 per cent of East Germany's imports come from the Communist-bloc countries, and 85 per cent of its exports go to those countries. The Soviet Union, with its vital control of raw material and food imports, has a virtual monopoly on East German imports and exports. Raw materials comprise 18 per cent, metallurgical products 14 per cent, and food products 16 per cent of all imports. Chemical products and machines are the major export items.

SWITZERLAND

Population

The great diversity in the relief of Switzerland has been described earlier. A study of the origins of the Swiss state shows that it grew from an aggregation of autonomous units which combined to defend the important mountain passes against external attack. Siegfried wrote:

> . . . the homogeneity resides in the principle of political resistance entrenched in a natural fortress, but the diversity is everywhere. . . . We find that each canton is different from its neighbor, whilst the various geographical areas are of such marked individuality that their inhabitants are fully conscious of the differences. In each neatly circumscribed valley, corresponding to the boundaries of a canton (I am thinking of Glarus, for example), each citizen knows instinctively why he belongs to his particular valley, to his particular canton. This is the solid basis of a democracy which has its roots both in the soil and in men's hearts.[24]

Switzerland had an estimated population of 5,185,000 in December, 1958, concentrated in an area of less than 16,000 square miles—somewhat smaller than the combined areas of Massachusetts and New Hampshire.[25] There are about 320 people to the square mile, but when it is realized that only 54 per cent of the total area is permanently inhabited (22 per cent unsettled and the rest inhabited only during the summer months), the density of 370 per square mile of productive land becomes the more significant figure.

The distribution of the population is very uneven, whether measured by its altitudinal distribution or by the size of populated centers. Some 54 per cent of Switzerland's inhabitants live below 1,500 feet, while only 5 per cent live above 3,000 feet. More than a third (37.5 per cent) of the population is found in towns of 10,000 and over. Bern, Zurich, Basel, and Geneva are the four largest cities. Bern, with 853,000 inhabitants, is the most populous canton; Appenzell-Inner Rhodes half canton is the smallest unit of the Federation, with 13,500 inhabitants. Two-thirds of the people of Switzerland live on the Swiss Plateau, which comprises but one-third of the total area.

The population is increasing slowly, at the rate of about 1.1 to 1.4 per cent per annum. During the decade of the 1950's the birth rate

[24] André Siegfried, *Switzerland* (London: Jonathan Cape, Ltd., 1950), p. 25.
[25] The last Swiss census was in December, 1950. The figures quoted are taken from the *Statistisches Jahrbuch der Schweiz: 1958*.

stood at 17.2 per thousand; the death rate dropped to 9.9 per thousand during the same period. In 1958, some 160,000 Swiss citizens lived abroad, most of them in France and in the United States. Emigration has always played an important role in Swiss economic life, although the total has been far smaller on the average than that of most other European countries. On the other hand, many foreigners have immigrated to Switzerland. Many Swiss industries use foreign labor, largely of Italian origin.

Switzerland's unity, unlike that of many other nations, is not imperiled by the fact that people of different religions and languages live within the confines of one small country. The numerical ratio of the various religious groups has not changed significantly over the centuries: 56.3 per cent of the population is Protestant, 41.6 per cent Roman Catholic, and 2.1 per cent represents other faiths. Long-drawn-out religious controversies between several Swiss cities are recognized to have been extremely damaging to the country as a whole. Recognition of that fact, perhaps more than anything else, has convinced the Swiss people of the need for religious freedom.

The numerical language distribution is as follows: German dialects are spoken by 72 per cent of the population, French by 20.3, Italian by 5.9, and Romansh [26] by 1.0 per cent. The language boundary between the German- and the French-speaking parts of Switzerland runs in a north-south direction, diagonally from the Jura across the Plateau and the Alps. Italian is spoken in the canton of Ticino and to some extent in the adjacent areas of Grisons; Romansh is found exclusively in the valleys of Grisons. The linguistic line has changed hardly at all in the last century and does not follow cantonal boundaries. However, the dividing line is sharp. One village may be German-speaking, a nearby one French (Fig. 6–29). Romansh was recognized as one of Switzerland's official languages in 1941, when 46,400 Swiss citizens were given permission to use it on a par with the other three languages. It is the consensus of many Swiss people that recognition of the Romansh language came just in time to save it from extinction. Official recognition includes the authorization to teach Romansh in public schools, a basic factor in the continuance of its life.

In the light of such great diversity of religion and language it is interesting to study the country's political unity over the last century. Since 1848, Switzerland has been a confederation (*Bundesstaat*) of 19 cantons and 6 half cantons. Of special significance, perhaps, is the active participation of the people in legislative matters. Frequent

[26] A Rhaeto-Romanic language (Celto-Roman idiom) whose origin can be traced to the Romanization of Rhaetia.

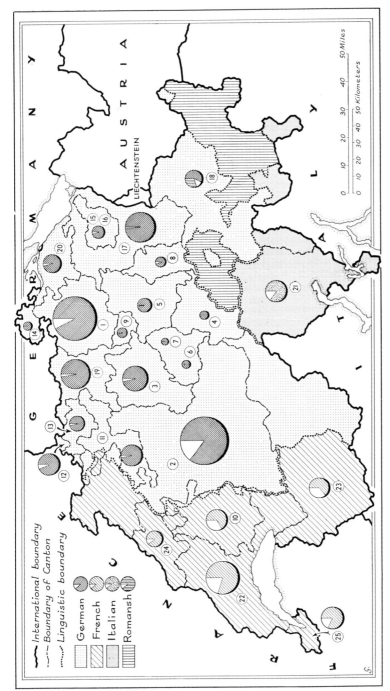

Fig. 6–29. The linguistic pattern of Switzerland. The size of the circle indicates the canton's population. For canton names, see the table on page 446.

referenda give the Swiss citizen the feeling of direct responsibility for the actions of his government. The three highest authorities are the federal assembly, federal executive council, and federal court. In many ways there is similarity between Swiss democratic organizations and those of the United States. Each representative who sits in the Lower House represents 22,000 constituents, and each canton, regardless of size, has two representatives in the Upper House. The two Houses in joint session elect the federal council which consists of seven members, the federal court, and, in case of war, the commanding general of the armed forces. At the head of the federal council is the president, elected from among its members for a term of one year. Bern is the seat of the federal assembly. The federal court, which acts on matters affecting the country as a whole, the cantons, or individuals, sits in Lausanne. Equality before the law, religious freedom, the right of assembly, of free speech, and the right to open a business are guaranteed in the constitution.

Switzerland, Linguistic Distribution, by Cantons *
(See Fig. 6–29.)

	Percentage Speaking				
	German	French	Italian	Romansh	Others
1. Zurich	91.2	5.11	3.4	0.2	–
2. Bern	83.7	15.4	0.6	0.1	0.3
3. Lucerne	97.6	0.6	1.3	0.1	0.4
4. Uri	99.5	0.2	0.3	–	–
5. Schwyz	99.5	0.2	0.3	–	–
6. Obwalden	99.5	0.1	0.2	0.2	–
7. Nidwalden	99.5	0.1	0.27	0.13	–
8. Glarus	95.5	0.65	3.6	0.25	–
9. Zug	99.4	0.2	0.4	–	–
10. Fribourg	33.2	66.6	0.1	–	0.1
11. Solothurn	99.8	0.1	0.1	–	–
12. Basel—Urban	94.0	3.6	1.1	0.1	0.5
13. Basel—Rural	96.6	1.5	0.8	0.13	2.0
14. Schaffhausen	99.8	0.1	0.1	–	–
15. Appenzell—Inner Rhodes	99.8	0.1	0.1	–	–
16. Appenzell—Outer Rhodes	99.9	0.1	–	–	–
17. St. Gallen	99.8	0.1	0.1	–	–
18. Grisons	55.0	–	12.7	37.3	–
19. Aargau	98.11	1.0	0.89	–	–
20. Thurgau	98.61	–	1.0	–	0.39
21. Ticino	8.15	1.5	85.1	3.0	2.25
22. Vaud	12.5	81.9	3.6	2.0	–
23. Valais	33.53	65.47	1.0	–	–
24. Neuchâtel	14.0	86.0	–	–	–
25. Geneva	13.56	80.58	2.45	3.41	–

* This compilation is based on the last Swiss census, December, 1950.

Limitations of space keep us from describing the great strength of this democracy in greater detail. A foreigner is surprised to see what great responsibilities are shouldered by the people. Cantonal governments are elected by direct popular vote. The famous outdoor plenary assemblies (*Landsgemeinden*) of Glarus are as old as the first settlements in this region. Education is compulsory. Swiss citizenship puts cantonal loyalty first and federal allegiance second. Perhaps the Swiss system of government is best epitomized by the expression "the Swiss Confederation administers; the canton governs."

Present Economic Life of Switzerland

General Characteristics. Switzerland is poor in raw materials. Oil and coal are totally lacking, and hydroelectric power is the only important source of energy. Nevertheless, 46.2 per cent of the economically active population is engaged in manufacturing, which is widely dispersed over the countryside and often found in remote valleys. The casual visitor will understand that this pattern is the result of an ample supply of water and of local manpower. Still, most of the larger industrial plants are concentrated in the Swiss Plateau, where communications are least difficult. The northern part of the Plateau is more densely settled and industrialized, the central and southern parts have many farmsteads and hamlets rather than rural agglomerations. Figures 6–30 and 6–31 illustrate the strong contrast in the landscape of the Plateau.

In general, Swiss industry is noted not so much for its methods as for its high-quality precision products which require skilled craftsmanship based on a long tradition, but yet are easily adaptable to modern techniques.

Only 16.6 per cent of the economically active population is engaged in agriculture. As would be expected, agricultural methods vary from canton to canton in response to soil conditions and custom. Switzerland imports most of the cereals she needs and directs her efforts toward improving her livestock breeds and farming techniques. Whenever wars have cut off her imports, Switzerland has increased her cereal production, but only enough to feed her population. Farmers generally wield great power and are able to protect both their technical and political interests. Farmers' associations, unions and cooperatives, agricultural schools, etc. play an important role in the rural scene.

Agriculture and Forestry. The 16.6 per cent of the population still employed in agriculture continues to be a vital economic force. Agriculture is a flourishing part of Switzerland's economy, despite

Fig. 6–30. A typical section of the densely settled, highly industrialized, and intensively farmed Swiss Plateau. Near the center, the Reuss and Limmat rivers join the Aare River, which flows 10 miles farther, through the Jura Mountains, to reach the Rhine River. (Photo: Swissair.)

Fig. 6–31. Emmental (canton of Bern) in the central part of the Swiss Plateau. Substantial farmsteads and hamlets, rather than rural agglomerations, characterize the landscape. In this valley the famous "Swiss" cheese (locally called "Emmentaler") was first made. Above the spruce forests in the background lie the Pre-Alpine pastures and the first chains of the limestone Alps. (Photo: Swissair.)

448

the severe handicap of poor soils and the large percentage of unproductive land.

The arable land is divided into medium- and small-size farms. Over 80 per cent of the farms occupy less than 25 acres each. Fewer than 15 per cent of all the farmers are tenants. The great pride the Swiss take in their homes and barns is reflected in the fact that farm buildings represent close to one-fourth of the entire capital investment of the farmer.

Relief, climate, and Swiss tradition combine to make the country outstanding in dairying. In a normal peacetime year dairying supplies about 50 per cent of the total value of the country's agricultural products. About two-thirds of the milk produced enters market channels; nearly one-half of the marketed milk is used in the manufacture of cheese, the rest in making butter, chocolate, etc. Such milk products as Emmental cheese (Fig. 6–31) and Suchard chocolate have acquired world-wide renown.

Stock feeding is normally second in importance to dairying. Cattle feeding and fattening is followed in terms of value by hog, goat, and sheep raising. Orchard products include apples, pears, cherries, and prunes. Grapes are grown in several areas which have exceptionally mild climatic conditions, for example, along the shores of Lake Geneva, in the upper Rhone Valley (Fig. 6–32), around the lakes of the Plateau, and in the sunny valleys of the Ticino.

Cereal production, though normally less than 5 per cent of the total agricultural output, has fluctuated greatly during the last few years. Since it is cheaper for Switzerland to purchase cereals abroad than to produce them, emphasis has been placed on such agricultural export items as dairy products. During the two world wars, however, cereals could no longer be imported and great efforts were made to attain self-sufficiency in order to avoid a serious food shortage. During World War II much hay and pasture land was plowed up for the production of staple crops, and grains assumed major importance; the dairying industry was greatly reduced; the acreage of land in cereals was doubled between 1937 and 1944, and the acreage in potatoes more than doubled. The prewar pattern has again been re-established. Of the various grain crops, wheat takes up the largest area, followed by oats and rye. The potato crop is usually large enough to satisfy domestic needs but sugar, tobacco, fruits, and vegetables must be imported.

The forests of Switzerland are 70 per cent coniferous and 30 per cent broadleaved; the spruce has the widest distribution. As would be expected, 55 per cent of the area of the Swiss Alps is forested, but only 20 per cent of the Jura and 25 per cent of the Plateau. While lumber production is considerable, the output is insufficient to meet demands.

Raw Materials and Industries. Switzerland's hydroelectric-power resources have played a very important part in the country's economic development. In 1958, Switzerland produced over 16.7 billion kwh of electricity in more than 6,000 hydroelectric-power plants. "White coal" supplies an ever-increasing share of the country's energy require-

Fig. 6–32. View of the wide glacial trough of the Rhone Valley near Sion, Switzerland. Irrigated fruit and truck gardens occupy the floodplain. The ter-raced south-facing slopes to the right are solidly covered by vineyards; on the opposite valley flank are grain and hay fields, forests, and summer pastures ("alps") above the timber line. Note the castle dominating the valley from the promontory in the left background.

ments. In 1938, coal, wood, and petroleum provided 83 per cent of the energy consumed; by 1957 this proportion had fallen to 70 per cent, the difference being accounted for by greater hydroelectric-power capacity.

Mineral resources are an almost negligible industrial factor (Fig. 6–23). Only 6,263 people were engaged in mining in 1957. Coal deposits are insignificant. Peat is the most plentiful solid fuel. Annual imports of coal vary between 2.4 and 3.3 million metric tons, which represent more than 98 per cent of the country's needs. Iron ore was mined at one time, but today this activity is unprofitable.

The ore is of very inferior quality—a considerable drawback in view of Switzerland's need for high-grade steel. Over 500,000 tons of ore—more than 80 per cent of industrial requirements—are imported annually. Some salt is found in the Rhine Valley, and small amounts of asphalt are recovered in the Val de Travers of the Jura.

Industry is an element of major importance in the prosperity of the country, even though Switzerland must import its raw materials and export its products in payment for its imports. Swiss industry is highly diversified and employs 46.2 per cent of the total labor force. Until the turn of the century the textile industry was in the lead. During the last half century, however, the engineering industries have risen to the dominant position. Today, the manufacture of machines, machine tools, and instruments outranks all other industries. Among the best-known Swiss-made products are electrical apparatus, textile machinery, engines of all types, locomotives, and agricultural machinery.

Watchmaking, which is centered in the Jura Mountains between Geneva and Schaffhausen, is the oldest branch of engineering. The cantons of Solothurn and Neuchâtel lead in the production of watches. Today, there are more than 400 factories, 65 of which manufacture watch parts. The industry is highly mechanized. Switzerland has almost a world monopoly because of the fame of its big-name watches, e.g., Longines. About 6.5 per cent of the country's industrial workers are employed in the watchmaking industry, 3 per cent of the total employed. The assembling of parts, which is the most important step in manufacturing, requires the great precision and technical skill characteristic of the Swiss workman.

Textiles, though a poor second in value to the output of the engineering industry, are nevertheless quite important. Many types of high-grade silks, ribbons, laces, knitted goods, and cottons are produced. The quality of the thread, the intricacy of the design, and the skill of the worker combine to give these textiles a highly competitive position on world markets. Eastern Switzerland, with St. Gallen, is the center of the textile industries (Fig. 6–22).

The substantial chemical industry has developed largely since 1929. The production of aniline dyes laid the basis for the industry. Today, production is varied and includes items such as plastics, dyes, insecticides, pharmaceuticals, cosmetics, and perfumes. The industry is centered at Basel, a key transportation hub.

The production of grease, oils, and soap, the shoe and leather industry, and the manufacture of chocolate and other food industries are also important but do not rank as high in terms of value added by manufacturing. The lumber and woodworking industry, which employs roughly 3 per cent of the industrial labor force, in saw-mills, paper mills, and woodworking establishments, deserves special mention. By rigid conservation measures and much scientific care this industry has operated on a sustained-yield basis for a long time.

In review, manufacturing in Switzerland is widely distributed. This is no handicap, in view of the country's size and its excellent transportation system. Highly trained workmen are found in nearly every Alpine valley, and the watchmakers of Le Locle and La Chaux-de-Fonds in the Jura, of Biel, Geneva, and Solothurn are world-famous.

In 1940, Switzerland began to build up her merchant marine; by 1958, the seagoing tonnage amounted to 109,000, with 23 ocean-going ships. Thus Switzerland moves one step closer to the raw materials she must import. With these raw materials, with her financial resources, industrial know-how, and excellent system of technical education, Switzerland has all the ingredients for the high-value type of industrial output which has set a world-wide standard of perfection.

Tourism. Switzerland is one country which can legitimately classify its natural charm and beauty as a financial asset, because the tourist trade furnishes a considerable part of the national income. Tourists have the choice of staying in one of the ultramodern or one of the many small- or medium-size hotels, inns, or private homes. Generally speaking, the Alpine regions of the Bernese Oberland, the Ticino, Zurich, Lucerne, and Interlaken are the most important centers of tourist trade. But it is not necessary to cite individual places. All of Switzerland offers scenic beauty, winter sports, and recreation to satisfy the tastes of any visitor. Today, Switzerland's hotel industry alone employs 81,000 people, but the economic benefits of the tourist industry are derived indirectly by a considerable part of the population. The tourist industry is well organized; there are a central tourist bureau, numerous travel agencies, many hotel-trade schools, and a school for restaurant personnel. The tourist industry in Switzerland is big business.

Transportation. In the face of very obvious topographical difficulties, the Swiss have built an excellent transportation system. Tunnels and bridges of world renown have been constructed. About 75 per cent of the railroad mileage is electrified, and most standard-gauge lines are state owned. Switzerland is famous for its many scenic mountain railways, some of which climb to heights exceeding 12,000 feet. The Swiss are world-famous as road builders. The recently improved St. Gotthard Pass road is an example par excellence (Fig. 6–13).

Basel is the major Rhine River port. It is located nearly 500 miles from the North Sea and in 1958 handled 4.8 million tons of freight. This is almost 35 per cent of Switzerland's international trade. Coal and coke from the Ruhr, oil from Dutch refineries, and wheat from the United States are the chief commodities carried upstream; industrial products, wines, and cheese move downstream to the world markets, a much less important traffic. With Basel as their home port, 364 vessels of Swiss registry ply the Rhine below Basel.

Foreign Trade. Switzerland's prospering economy and the high standard of living of its people are attributable to the large volume of foreign trade. The unfavorable trade balance—large import surpluses—is redressed by tourist income and international financial transactions. Switzerland's imports, in terms of value, consist of over 20 per cent food; 30 per cent fuels and raw materials for the chemical industries, cotton, and iron and steel goods; and roughly 50 per cent finished products. Her exports, in terms of value, are largely (91 per cent) finished products, aluminum goods, and chemicals. Watches and watch movements comprise 70 per cent of all exports. Over 70 per cent of Switzerland's purchases come from Europe, and about 65 per cent of her sales go to European countries. Germany, Italy, the United States, France, and the United Kingdom are Switzerland's most important trading partners. Because of its stable and prosperous economy, Switzerland for some time has been used as headquarters for international financial transactions (insurance, banking) which make important contributions to her trade balance. The Swiss currency is one of the world's most dependable international exchange media, and this has a favorable effect on her trade balance.

AUSTRIA

Population

Austria, with an area of 32,376 square miles, is somewhat smaller than the state of Maine. Its population totaled 7,021,500 in 1958, of which 1,652,400 lived in Vienna, the capital.[27] The country is divided into nine provinces, with an international border 1,646 miles long. Its greatest east-west extension is 360 miles, and the average width (from north to south) is 37 miles in the western and 170 miles in the eastern part of the country (Fig. 6–19).

The 1957 population density was 223 per square mile, a relatively low figure. However, if we consider the mountainous character of

[27] The last census was taken in June, 1951. All statistical data are taken from *Statistisches Handbuch für die Republik Oesterreich 1958,* and advanced data for 1958.

Austria and the relative scarcity of fertile land, the density per square mile of agricultural land becomes substantially higher.

Three regional density groupings may be distinguished in Austria, Vienna excepted: (1) the agricultural and industrial areas of Lower and Upper Austria, Styria, and the Burgenland are the most densely populated; (2) the valleys and scattered lowlands of Carinthia, Salzburg, Tyrol, and Vorarlberg belong in an in-between group; and (3) the mountainous parts of the latter provinces are either uninhabited or often populated during the summertime only. Villages and towns are concentrated in the plains, valleys, basins, and hill lands, while isolated settlements predominate in the higher regions. In recent years the population of the mountainous portion of Austria has increased considerably. Industries were relocated here during World War II, in search of protection from Allied bombers, and after the war, in flight from Soviet occupation forces in the eastern part of the country. Furthermore, most of the postwar immigrants from Eastern Europe (those who did not emigrate) settled in the western part of the country. Even the departure of Soviet forces has brought no rush to return to eastern Austria.

One-third of Austria's population live in cities of over 100,000; one-third in villages of less than 2,000. It is interesting to record that 35 per cent of the population of the Tyrol and 20 per cent of that of Salzburg live at altitudes above 2,400 feet. The upper limit of wheat cultivation varies from 2,900 feet to 5,200 feet. Numerous small settlements may be found even at these upper elevations.

While the uneven geographical distribution of the population is a considerable handicap to the development of a balanced economy, the occupational distribution of the working population (according to the 1951 census) is a great asset to the country's economic strength: 40 per cent of the working population were engaged in industry and handicrafts, 14 per cent in commerce and transportation, and 32 per cent in agriculture and forestry.

One of the great difficulties of the Austro-Hungarian Monarchy was its nationality problem. In contrast, the population of postwar Austria is predominantly German in character. Most of the non-Germans live in the frontier districts of Burgenland, Styria, Carinthia, and in Vienna. On the whole, the present ethnic composition gives strength to the country because the Republic is not beset by any language difficulties such as those which troubled the Monarchy. The Roman Catholic religion is dominant in Austria, claiming 90 per cent of the population.

Vienna is by far the largest city in Austria; it is about seven and one-half times as large as Graz, the second city in size. Linz, Salzburg, and Innsbruck are the other three large cities. Vienna has lost much of the glamour and importance it had under the Austro-Hungarian Monarchy. Today, it is merely the oversized capital of a small, impoverished country—a city only two hours' drive from foreign territory. Graz, a provincial capital, has always been a rather quiet city. Many of its citizens are retired people. The population of Linz has increased by more than 60 per cent over the prewar total. It is the center of important industries, many of which were established after 1940. Salzburg, center of Austria's cultural life and site of the world-famous Salzburg Festival, has also greatly added to its population. Innsbruck is the capital of the Tyrol and the largest city of the Austrian Alps; its university and beautiful surroundings are well known to the many tourists who visit the city every year.

The historical geography and past function of Vienna and Innsbruck deserve brief discussion. Vienna is mentioned in a record as old as 935 A.D. and in 1137 was cited as a city (*stadt*). In 1221 its citizens received the privilege of self-government. During the twelfth century, Vienna occupied no more than the site of a former Roman camp, protected on the northeast by the Danube and on the southeast and northwest by small rivers. There was no natural rampart to the southwest of the city. Situated at the crossing of important overland and river transportation routes, Vienna expanded rapidly through the years.

Beginning in 1438, the emperors of the Holy Roman Empire usually resided in Vienna. Thus, the function of imperial capital and permanent seat of the Hapsburg monarchy gave added impetus to Vienna's growth and importance (Fig. 6–33). Thousands of people moved to Vienna from all parts of the Empire, to participate in the city's political, economic, and cultural leadership. As recently as 1934, the census revealed that at least 24 per cent of the city's inhabitants had their birthplace beyond the borders of post-World War I Austria; the majority of these had come from what is now Czechoslovakia.

Innsbruck is located in the Northern Longitudinal Valley in western Austria. The Inn Valley had been first inhabited during the Neolithic and Bronze ages. The city was founded near an Inn River bridge which controlled a road leading to the west and northwest. Since the thirteenth century the city has expanded southward in the direction of the Brenner Pass, on the alluvial fan formed by the Sill River. In 1239, it received city status, and, as the route from Germany to Rome increased in importance, Innsbruck expanded rapidly. Situated at the natural focus of the whole North Tyrol, the city has always been a trading rather than an industrial center. Its population grew from 4,000 in 1600 to a 1951 population of more than 95,000.

Many of Austria's better-known towns of today owe their origin to a monastery. Examples are Melk, Klosterneuberg, and Krems, all on the Danube. Other towns date back to strategically placed medieval castles, e.g., Graz, Kufstein, Steyr. Several others, such as Linz, Wels, and Salzburg, began as Roman settlements. In Lower Austria

Fig. 6–33. The center of Vienna. The former fortified wall has been replaced by broad avenues. Rear, part of the Danube Canal; left foreground, the former imperial palace; in the center, St. Stephen's Cathedral. (Austrian State Tourist Office.)

a number of fortified towns such as Tulln or Ybbs grew up along the Danube; their location may have been determined by the routes of the salt trade or by the existence of fords. The border fortifications (*Burgen*) established along the rolling wooded hills of Lower Austria and Styria (later Burgenland) became villages, but none of them assumed any real importance. Thus, as early as the fourteenth century, the pattern of the population distribution and the location of Austrian cities had been fixed.

Present Economic Life of Austria [28]

When, in 1918, Austria emerged as one of the "succession states" of the former Austria-Hungary, serious administrative and economic problems had to be solved in order to provide a livelihood for her 6.5 million people, nearly one-third of whom lived in Vienna. The task of adjusting to a much smaller area was the major problem facing the government and the people of Austria between 1919 and 1938, when the country was incorporated into Germany. Thus, the new-born Republic of Austria had to struggle with problems of how to increase food production, reorganize the industrial structure, modernize and expand raw-material production, and establish a new basis for its foreign trade. It is generally agreed that Austria did succeed fairly well in re-establishing her economy, despite the serious economic and political crises of the interwar years.

In 1945, when Austria re-emerged as an independent country, after 7 years of occupation and complete absorption into the German war economy, it found itself in an entirely different situation, as compared with 1919. Although industrial capacity had increased, Austria's economy had been further unbalanced because most of the new facilities had been constructed to fit Germany's war needs. One favorable result was the fact that many new industries had been established in the western part of Austria and were thus beyond the reach of Soviet occupation forces after the war.

Starting once more from scratch, Austria's economy had to be completely rebuilt. The job in one respect was many times more difficult than after 1919; in another respect it was easier. Austria was occupied by four powers (the Soviet Union, the United States, the United Kingdom, and France), and this had an important effect on the rebuilding of the shattered economy. It made the future of Austria a direct concern of the United States. Austria became eligible for Marshall Plan aid in 1948 and received $1.3 million in United States aid, plus $386 million which it received before the start of the Marshall Plan, constituting a major contribution to the rebuilding of Austria's economy. Subsequent reconstruction of Western Europe revitalized its important foreign trade, transit, and tourist income. The conclusion of the State Treaty in 1955, while making heavy

---

[28] Material for this section is taken, by permission of the publishers, from various publications by the author: "The Survival of an Independent Austria," *Geographical Review* 41 (October, 1951): 606–21; "Austria," *Focus* (June 15, 1954); "Austria," *Funk & Wagnalls Universal Standard Encyclopedia* (New York: Standard Reference Works Publishing Co., Inc.), Vol. III, pp. 829–44.

demands on the Austrian economy in terms of cash reparation payments and long-term deliveries of goods (6 years) and petroleum (10 years) to the Soviet Union, on the other hand did return important assets to the country. And most important, after 17 years, Austria again was master of its own house.

Unfortunately for Austria, it occupies one of Europe's most strategic areas. No great power can afford to have it dominated by another power. That is why postwar Austria was occupied, divided into four zones, and, since 1955, has been neutralized.[29]

Agriculture and Forestry. When peace was restored in 1919, and an independent Austrian republic was organized, the new country found itself cut off from all its former sources of supply. Old trade channels within the Austro-Hungarian customs union and with the rest of Europe were severed, agricultural areas were cut in two by new international boundaries, and the new countries carved out of the former Empire were unwilling to export agricultural products except on a strict barter basis. Special attention was given to increased food production, but, in view of the climatic conditions and the generally poor soils in this mountainous country, there were sharp limitations to any plan for agricultural expansion. In the valleys, winter lasts three to four months; the higher parts of the Alps are covered by snow for six to nine months. The basins of the eastern and southern parts of the country are hot and dry during the summer. Forests cover about 37 per cent of the total area of Austria and about 47 per cent of its productive land. Nevertheless, agricultural production increased despite the lack of capital and the never-ending internal party strife. Before World War II, Austria had become about 75 per cent self-sufficient, an achievement which represented a new high in the country's agricultural economy.

World War II wiped out all the previous gains in Austria's food-producing capacity. Further shortages, loss of farm machinery, destruction wrought by moving armies, mass slaughter of livestock, and a shortage of manpower combined to bring about a situation similar to that experienced twenty-five years previously. Only the immediate postwar intervention of such international relief agencies as the United Nations Relief and Rehabilitation Administration and the aid given by private relief organizations and the occupation armies saved the Austrian population from malnutrition. Later, the Austrian government, in close cooperation with Marshall Plan aid, undertook to provide seeds and artificial fertilizer, initiated measures

[29] George W. Hoffman, "The Political Geography of a Neutral Austria," *Geographical Studies* 3 (London) (January, 1956): 12–32.

to control cattle tuberculosis, began a program of mechanization and electrification of farm equipment, and improved rural roads. Furthermore, laboratories and farm educational institutions were established. By the end of 1951, total agricultural production had risen to about 98 per cent of the 1937 level. Austria's chief crops are rye, wheat, oats, and barley, in that order of importance.

Austria's problem of self-sufficiency in food supply has already been touched upon. While food production increased steadily after reaching a low in 1946, consumption kept on exceeding these higher production levels. It is estimated that Austria had become 85 per cent self-sufficient by the end of 1958. Austria is self-sufficient in potatoes, sugar, dairy products, and meat; corresponding percentages for other agricultural products in 1957–58 were: fruit 90, wheat 76.5, rye 86, barley 98, oats 92, and maize 27. Nevertheless, with a population approximately 3.3 per cent larger than in 1934, and reduced American economic aid, Austria must constantly progress and solve the problem of how to increase acreage and agricultural output.

Various studies have been undertaken to determine how Austria's food-producing acreage might be increased. They have all come to the same conclusion: by improving existing acreage through reclamation and irrigation and putting greater emphasis on regional planning and the combining of the many small agricultural holdings,[30] enough new farm land can be brought under cultivation and put to a more rational use to make Austria nearly self-supporting; only the corn acreage cannot be expanded substantially, for climatic reasons. Since 1945, more than 60,000 acres have been reclaimed or brought under irrigation, and an additional 10,000 acres are marked for improvement.

Land holdings are, for the most part, of small or medium size. Of a total of 433,000 land holdings (19.3 million acres) nearly 50 per cent were holdings under 12.5 acres, and even the majority of the 6,278 land holdings over 250 acres were under 500 acres.

Forests, which cover 37 per cent of the country, are of special importance and are one of Austria's most valuable natural resources. A comprehensive reforestation and conservation program has been under way during the last few years, protecting the forests against continuation of the overcutting of war and postwar years. The two most important timber-trade regions are the Alpine regions and the slopes of the Böhmer Wald in Lower Austria. Spruce is the most important tree, with Scots pine and beech of secondary importance.

[30] George W. Hoffman, "Regional Planning in the Inn Valley of Austria," *Papers of the Michigan Academy of Science, Arts and Letters* 40 (1955): 181–89; "A Changing Cultural Landscape in the Middle Upper Inn Valley," *Southwestern Social Science Quarterly* 36 (June, 1955): 27–45.

Her forests make it possible for Austria to be one of the few European countries which export timber, paper, prefabricated houses, and cardboard. During 1957 these exports were valued at 16 per cent of the total exports. Forest holdings, like agricultural ones, are small, the average holding amounting to about 15 acres. Sawmills, forests, and industries associated with timber production employ about 120,000 people, with an additional 8,000 employed in paper production.

Fig. 6–34. The Erzberg (Ore Mountain) in Styria. Open-pit mining has been carried on here since Neolithic times. (Austrian State Tourist Office.)

Minerals. With the exception of coal, Austria is fortunate in having considerable mineral deposits: iron ore, salt, talc, gypsum, magnesite, and oil (Fig. 6–23). The iron-ore deposits of Styria are of excellent quality and suffice to meet domestic requirements (Fig. 6–34). Also mined in increasing quantities are antimony, bauxite, china clay, graphite, lead, and pyrite. Many of these minerals are exported, thereby contributing to Austria's growing foreign trade. The lack of adequate high-grade coal is a primary cause of many of the country's economic difficulties; 5 to 6 million tons must be imported annually. Production of lignite doubled between 1937 and 1957.

Waterpower. Austria is one of the most important sources of hydroelectric power in Europe. Its potential is estimated at more than 30 billion kwh annually, as compared with Switzerland's 20 billion kwh. In 1958, Austria produced a total of 13.5 billion kwh, an output 260 per cent above that of 1938. More than 15 per cent of this power is exported, principally to Germany. The present constant expansion of Austria's hydroelectric capacity (Fig. 6–35) assumes special importance in view of the country's coal shortage and increasing domestic demands.[31]

Fig. 6–35. Tauern power development at Kaprun, Salzburg, Austria. The Mooserboden Reservoir is in the foreground, with Mooser Dam (right), Drossen Dam (left), and Limberg Reservoir in the background. This development, completed in 1958, forms a part of the Glockner-Kaprun-Salzach system. (Austrian Information Service.)

One of the most ambitious projects is the development of the Danube River for hydroelectrical purposes. Along its 320-mile course in Austria, a total of 15 hydroelectric plants are planned.[32] Jochen-

[31] George W. Hoffman, "Toward Greater Integration in Europe: Transfer of Electric Power Across International Boundaries," *Journal of Geography* 55 (April, 1956): 165–76; also, *Die Österreichische Elektrizitäts-Wirtschaft 1947–1957* (Austria's Electricity Economy 1947–1957), Vienna: Bundesministerium für Verkehr und Eletrizitätswirtschaft, 1958; and annual reports by the Ministry.

[32] United Nations, Economic Commission for Europe, *Development of Hydro Power Stations on the Danube: Existing, Under Construction or Projected*, E/ECE/360, Geneva, 1959; Oskar Vas, "Geschichte und Tatsachen der Donaukraftnutzung in Österreich" (History and Facts of the Danube Power Utilization in Austria), *Wasser- und Energiewirtschaft* 5–6 (1956): 1–18.

stein, on the German-Austrian border, was completed in 1956. Ybbs-Persenbeug (Fig. 6–36) was completed in 1958. The even water regime of the Danube, together with the gradual sloping of the topography toward the mouth of the Danube into the Black Sea, guarantees a steady supply of power, satisfying the growing demands of the Austrian population, as well as those of some neighboring countries.

Fig. 6–36. The Ybbs-Persenbeug power development on the Danube River, looking upstream. On the left bank are the twin locks and the old castle of Persenbeug. (Photo: Osterr. Donaukraftwerke.)

Petroleum. Austria's most recent fuel discovery is petroleum, which takes its place, as a major source of energy, with hydroelectric power and imported coal. Most of Austria's petroleum and refining facilities are in the Zistersdorf area, 30 miles northeast of Vienna. Between 1937 and 1957, production increased from 32,000 metric tons to 3.1 million metric tons. Since minimum domestic needs are estimated at 2 million metric tons, a sizable export surplus could be available (under normal conditions), in exchange for coal imports. Unfortunately, the State Treaty obligates Austria to ship 1 million tons to the Soviet Union annually until 1965, and while the Soviet Union made some concessions in 1958, this obligation basically remains. In addition, new discoveries lag and some of the present wells already show a dangerous falling off in output. Petroleum production declined in 1958, as against 1957, by over 11 per cent. On the other hand, the output of natural gas has been greatly accelerated during the last few years. In 1953, gas contributed 6.3 per cent of Austria's energy consumption, oil 42.4, hydroelectric power 10.2, fuel wood 11.9, and coal 29. The contribution of natural gas has further increased since that year.

Industries. Austria's present and future industrial outlook is unquestionably more favorable than that of many other European countries. During World War II, the iron, steel, aluminum, and chemical industries were expanded, and, despite considerable bomb damage and destruction caused by early occupation excesses, the country's total industrial capacity is now much larger than it was in 1938. However, a large part of this expansion was for military needs, and many of the country's industrial plants which were unfortunate enough to be located in the Soviet zone of occupation were dismantled and shipped to the U.S.S.R. or forced to produce for the sole benefit of the Soviet Union during the 10 years of occupation. It is estimated that the equivalent of 12 per cent of Austria's prewar industrial capacity was removed by the Soviet Union. The Western powers, on the other hand, restored all the plants in their zones to Austria in 1946, and in addition (especially the United States) made major contributions to Austria's industrial rehabilitation.

Modernization since 1945 has made Austrian industries highly competitive. The geographical pattern of industrial production underwent important changes during and following the war, with the Linz-Wels-Steyr triangle in Upper Austria and its important steel (Voest in Linz) and chemical industries (Austrian Nitrogen Works in Linz) offering a completely new and modern addition to Austria's productive facilities. Also, many new medium-size and specialized industries were built in the western half of Austria since 1939, a fact which is partially responsible for the population growth of Austria's western provinces. Of the old industrial concentrations, those of middle Styria (steel and heavy machinery in the Eisenerz and middle Mur River Valley) were included in the modernization encouraged and financed with Marshall Plan funds. Those in the older industrial core, the Vienna Basin, were under Soviet control until 1955. They deteriorated and required much effort and investment following the departure of the Soviet troops. The importance of industry and manufacture in Austria is clearly shown by the facts that over 41 per cent of the labor force is engaged therein and that during 1957 manufacturing industries (including building and construction) accounted for 52 per cent of the gross national product (1937: 41 per cent).

Austria has also become the recipient of industries established by Germans who, before the war, had lived in the Czech Sudetenland, in Hungary, and in Yugoslavia. For example, the famous Gablonz glassware, formerly a noted export item of Czechoslovakia, is now produced in Salzburg and in Upper Austria and is a fillip to Austria's foreign trade.

Tourism. The tourist trade constitutes an important source of income for Austria. In this respect, Austria is in sharp competition with Switzerland although it does not have the latter's long experience in accommodating visitors. While the province of Styria has experienced the greatest influx of visitors, most of these have been Austrians; the Tyrol, Salzburg, Vorarlberg, and Carinthia have attracted more foreign visitors. The number of tourists visiting Austria since the war is constantly increasing, and contributes to the country's flourishing economy.

Transportation. Austria's strategic location involves a special responsibility for the upkeep and modernization of its transportation system. Both domestic traffic serving the important tourist trade and transit traffic serving the rest of Europe must be considered. Several important international rail lines cross the country, and their modernization goes hand in hand with the further electrification of Austrian lines. Here again competition with Switzerland is keen. Electrification of the main east-west line from Vorarlberg to Vienna has been completed, and many other lines have also been electrified. The improvement of the highway network is of equal importance to a country so dependent upon transit traffic and tourist trade. Most parts of Austria are accessible by modern roads, and up-to-date highways crisscross the country. Because of its mountainous character, the construction and maintenance of roads is not only difficult but costly. A new superhighway is now under construction between Salzburg and Vienna, and additional ones are planned.

The question of linking the Danube by canals with other European rivers has been discussed earlier in this chapter. Only when oil and surplus grains may be exchanged for the coal and machinery of the Ruhr and Silesia will the Danube become a traffic artery of major importance. However, such an exchange would have to be based on relatively free trade all over Europe. It is clear, however, that a link between the Danube and other trafficable waterways is as badly needed for Austria and for the rest of Europe today as it was in the seventeenth century, when Austrian and Bohemian merchants first proposed the Morava-Oder (Danube-Baltic) Canal.

With a certain amount of freedom of traffic again available on the full length of the Danube, Vienna is growing in importance as a port, both for Austria and as a transit station. The main products shipped on the Danube are coal and coke, iron ore, crude iron, petroleum products, and grain, which account for 68 per cent of the total tonnage. Linz is of greater importance to Austria as a river port than Vienna; it accounts for roughly 50 per cent of the total tonnage, while Vienna's share averaged 40 per cent of the total tonnage during the last few years.

Foreign Trade. Austria's foreign trade has greatly increased since the signing of the State Treaty, in 1955. The import deficit is largely redressed by the income from an increasing tourist trade. Exports have been increasing steadily, but, with the increased requirements of a constantly improving standard of living, imports have also increased. The economic stability during the last five years, largely brought about by United States aid and long-term credits, has resulted in improvements in the general trade balance. The import structure of food, fertilizers, and fodder (17 per cent); raw materials (27 per cent); semifinished goods (14 per cent); and finished goods (42 per cent) has varied little over the last few years. Exports are divided among finished products (46 per cent), raw materials (24 per cent), semifinished goods (26 per cent), and foods (4 per cent). Among the imports the following rank highest in terms of value: chemical raw materials and products, special machinery, and optical products. The main export items, in terms of value, include livestock, synthetic rubber, semifinished products such as textile goods, products of nonmetallic minerals, paper, wooden products, clothing, and products of the engineering and metallurgical industries, mostly of high quality.

Austria's foreign trade is chiefly with the countries of the OEEC (see Chapter 10). Eastern Europe supplies about 10 per cent of Austria's imports and buys about 12 per cent of her exports. The United States and Canada contribute about 11 per cent of Austria's imports and absorb about 6 per cent of her exports. Austria's most important trading partners are West Germany, the United States, Italy, the United Kingdom, and the Netherlands. Lately, increased emphasis has been put on expanding trade with the underdeveloped countries of Asia and Africa. The problem of credits for such an expanding trade has acted as a brake.

*　　*　　*

The problems of the individual countries of Central Europe vary greatly. Besides a common language and a common central position in Europe (excluding the territory of the Soviet Union), the four countries have little in common. Germany is divided and the component parts seem to go in different directions. East Germany is closely tied to the economic planning of the Soviet Union and its allies (73 per cent of its 1956 trade). West Germany is rapidly integrating her economy in a series of joint economic projects with the West, e.g., Coal and Steel Community, OEEC, and Common Market. The phenomenal growth of West Germany's economy during the 1950's resembles in many ways a similar growth during the late 1920's and the 1930's. It can only be hoped that this growth, tied as it is to other Western European countries, will benefit the Western world as a whole. Certainly, shortages of key raw materials and the need for vital food imports make West Germany's status anything but self-sufficient.

Neutral Switzerland and neutral Austria have greatly differing economic bases. In Switzerland, the absence of raw materials for many years has forced that country to rely upon vital imports of raw materials and semifinished products, and on exports of high-quality goods, including foodstuffs. Self-sufficiency in food supplies is neither desired nor possible. Still, Switzerland's neutral position during the two wars in this century made it an important financial center of the world and the headquarters of many international institutions. Switzerland's location dictated her joining OEEC and the Free Trade Area (The Outer Seven). The Swiss economy is one of the most stable in the world.

Austria, on the other hand, after tremendous war and postwar damages, including 10 years of occupation by Soviet troops, has greatly benefited from United States aid. This aid has enabled Austria to modernize and expand her raw-material and industrial capacity, modernize her agriculture, and prepare the basis for a prospering economy. With Austria included in OEEC and the Free Trade Area, in spite of its "neutral status," its economy is closely tied to the fortunes of the West. At the same time, Austria benefits from closer economic ties with the Soviet Union and other Eastern European countries, which are important for her trade balance and for a continuing high production of her numerous manufactured goods. In many ways, Austria is a more viable state today than at any time since it became independent in 1919.

BIBLIOGRAPHY

(Major references are asterisked.)

Books in English

BURGHARDT, ANDREW F. *The Political Geography of Burgenland.* Foreign Field Research Program, Office of Naval Research, Report No. 2. Washington: National Academy of Science–National Research Council, 1958. Publication 587.

*DICKINSON, ROBERT E. *Germany: A General and Regional Geography.* London: Methuen & Co., Ltd., 1953.

MAYER, KURT B. *The Population of Switzerland.* New York: Columbia University Press, 1952.

OESCHLI, WILHELM. *History of Switzerland: 1499–1914.* London: Cambridge University Press, 1922.

PARTSCH, JOSEF. *Central Europe.* New York: Appleton-Century-Crofts, Inc., 1903.

*POUNDS, NORMAN J. G. *The Ruhr.* London: Faber & Faber, Ltd., 1952.

RUSSELL, FRANK M. *The Saar: Battleground and Pawn.* Stanford, Calif.: Stanford University Press, 1951.

WISKEMANN, ELIZABETH. *Germany's Eastern Neighbors.* London: Oxford University Press, 1956.

Books in Foreign Languages

*BLANCHARD, RAOUL. *Les Alpes Occidentales* (The Western Alps). Tours: Arrault et Cie, 1938–45.

*DOPSCH, HANS. *Die Ältere Wirtschafts und Sozialgeschichte der Bauern in den Alpenländern Österreichs* (The Early Economic and Social History of the Farmers in the Alpine Provinces of Austria). Oslo: Aschehoug (Nygaard), 1930.

FRÜH, JACOB. *Geographie der Schweiz* (Geography of Switzerland). St. Gallen: Fehr, 1929–45.

GSTEU, HERMANN. *Länderkunde Österreichs* (Regional Geography of Austria). Innsbruck: Tyrolia Verlag, 1948.

*GUTERSOHN, HEINRICH. *Landschaften der Schweiz* (Regions of Switzerland). Zürich: Büchergilde Gutenberg, 1950.

*HAEFKE, FRITZ. *Physische Geographie Deutschlands* (Physical Geography of Germany). Berlin: VEB Deutscher Verlag der Wissenschaften, 1959.

*HAUSHOFER, ALBRECHT. *Pass-Staaten in den Alpen* (Passlands in the Alps). Berlin: K. Vowinckel, 1928.

KOBER, LEOPOLD. *Bau und Entstehung der Alpen* (Structure and Origin of the Alps). Berlin: Gebrüder Bornträger, 1923.

KREBS, NORBERT (ed.). *Landeskunde von Deutschland* (Regional Geography of Germany), 3 parts. Leipzig and Berlin: B. G. Teubner, 1931–35.

*KREBS, NORBERT. *Die Ostalpen und das heutige Österreich* (The Eastern Alps and Today's Austria). Stuttgart: J. Engelhorn's Nachfolger, 1928.

LEITMEIER, HANS (ed.). *Die Österreichischen Alpen* (The Austrian Alps). Vienna: F. Deuticke, 1928.

MACHATSCHEK, FRITZ. *Länderkunde von Mitteleuropa* (Regional Geography of Central Europe). Enzyklopädie der Erdkunde, ed. O. Kende. Vienna: F. Deuticke, 1925.

OTREMBA, ERICH. *Die Deutsche Agrarlandschaft* (The German Agriculture). Wiesbaden: Steiner Verlag, 1956.

Zehn Jahre ERP in Österreich 1948/58. Vienna: Verlag der Österreichischen Staatsdruckerei, 1958.

Articles

*BOBEK, HANS. "Schlüsselstellung in Europa" (Key Position in Europe), Spectrum Austriae, Otto Schulmeister, ed. (Vienna: Verlag Herder, 1957): 21–49.

CAROL, HANS VON, and SENN, ULRICH. "Jura, Mittelland und Alpen: Ihr Anteil an Fläche und Bevölkerung der Schweiz" (Jura, Mittelland, and Alps: Their Share in the Area and Population of Switzerland), Geographica Helvetica 5 (1950): 129–36.

DICKINSON, ROBERT E. "Economic Regions of Germany," Geographical Review 28 (1938): 609–26.

———. "Rural Settlements in the German Lands," Annals of the Association of American Geographers 39 (1949): 239–63.

FISCHER, ERIC. "The Passing of Mitteleuropa," The Changing World, W. Gordon East and A. E. Moodie, eds. (Yonkers, N.Y.: World Book Co., 1956): 60–79.

GARNETT, ALICE. "The Loess Region in Central Europe in Prehistoric Times," Geographical Journal 106 (1945): 132–43.

*GRADMANN, NORBERT. "Das mitteleuropäische Landschaftsbild nach seiner geschichtlichen Entwicklung" (The Central European Landscape in Its Historical Development), Geographische Zeitschrift 7 (1901): 361–77, 435–47.

*HASSINGER, HUGO. "Boden und Lage Wiens" (Site and Situation of Vienna), Mitteilungen der Geographischen Gesellschaft in Wien 84 (1941): 359–84.

HELD, COLBERT C. "The New Saarland," Geographical Review 41 (1951): 590–605.

HOFFMAN, GEORGE W. "A Changing Cultural Landscape in the Middle Upper Inn Valley," Southwestern Social Science Quarterly 36 (June, 1955): 27–45.

*———. "The Political Geography of a Neutral Austria," Geographical Studies 3 (January, 1956): 12–32.

———. "Regional Planning in the Inn Valley of Austria," Papers of the Michigan Academy of Science, Arts and Letters 40 (1955): 181–89.

———. "The Survival of Independent Austria," Geographical Review 41 (1951): 605–21.

KUEHNELT-LEDDIHN, ERIK M. R. VON. "The Southern Boundaries of Austria," Journal of Central European Affairs 5 (1945): 243–59.

KULIGOWSKI, JOACHIM. "Die Seehäfen des österreichischen Aussenhandels" (The Seaports of Austria's Foreign Trade), Wiener Geographische Schriften 1 (1957).

MAYER, KURT. "Recent Demographic Developments in Switzerland," Social Research 24 (1957): 331–53.

NIEHAUS, HEINRICH. "Agricultural Conditions and Regions in Germany," Geographical Review 23 (1933): 23–47.

PFANNSCHMIDT, MARTIN. "Probleme der Weltstadt Berlin" (Problems of the World City Berlin), Zum Problem der Weltstadt (To the Problem of the World City), Joachim H. Schultze, ed. (Berlin: Gruyter & Co., 1959): 1–16.

PLATT, ROBERT S. "A Geographical Study of the Dutch-German Border," Landeskundliche Karten und Hefte der Geographischen Kommission für Westfalen, Reihe Siedlung: Landschaft in Westfalen 3, 1958.

POUNDS, NORMAN J. G. "The Ruhr Area: A Problem in Definition," Geography 36 (1951): 165–78.

ROBINSON, G. W. S. "West Berlin: The Geography of an Exclave," Geographical Review 42 (1953): 540–57.

SÖLCH, JOHANN. "The Brenner Region," Sociological Review 19 (1927): 318–34.

WINKLER, ERHART. "Österreich und die Schweiz" (Austria and Switzerland), Festzeitschrift zur Hundertjahrfeier der Geographischen Gesellschaft in Wien: 1856–1956, Konrad Winkler, ed. (Vienna: Geographische Gesellschaft, 1956): 209–35.

WOPFNER, HANS. "Die Besiedlung unserer Hochalpentäler" (The Settlement of Our Alpine Valleys), Zeitschrift des deutsch-österreichischen Alpenvereins 51 (1920): 25–86.

7

Southern Europe

This chapter deals with the area within the present political boundaries of Turkey, Greece, Italy, Spain, and Portugal, as well as with
several minor political units closely connected with them such as the
republic of San Marino, the Vatican state, the island of Malta, Gibraltar, the republic of Andorra, and the new republic of Cyprus. This is,
obviously, an arbitrary definition. However, a short review of all
possible and actually proposed delimitations of Southern Europe
will show that all are arbitrary, whether they are based on topographic or hydrographic features, on climate or vegetation, on
language or cultural traits. Using any one of these criteria, several
different boundaries can be justified. A grouping based on a combination of several features would result in showing a boundary belt instead of a line, a concept which has many merits but is impractical
for our purpose. Political boundaries have the advantages of being
definite and of coinciding for long stretches with linguistic and cultural boundary lines. They often coincide with climatic and vegetation boundaries and sometimes even follow orographic and religious
boundaries.

THE PHYSICAL LANDSCAPE

Southern Europe with Turkey consists of four separate peninsulas
(Fig. 7–1). Regarded as the northern half of a circum-Mediterranean
region, it has many unifying and characteristic features which stand
out clearly. Only once in history, during the Roman period, did the
whole area form a political unit, although its essential unifying traits
of climate, vegetation, and way of life have persisted. At other periods,

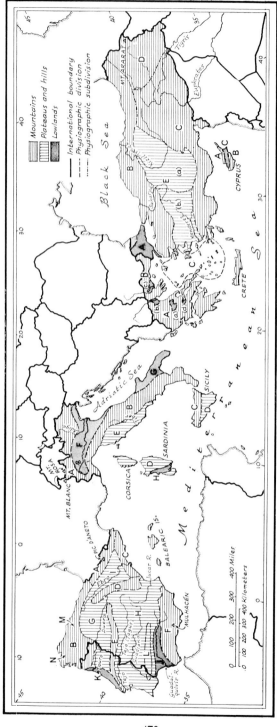

Fig. 7-1. Major physiographic divisions.

African states extended over parts of the opposite European shores, or European countries reached into Africa. When the enmity between Christianity and Islam disrupted this unity most completely, the disruption was felt as something unnatural and both parties tried to correct the situation, though, of course, each acted in its own interest.

Location. Peninsular location means that some of the Southern European countries have a land boundary in common with no more than one neighbor (Portugal, Gibraltar, Vatican City, and San Marino) or with two (Andorra). On the other hand, very short distances across the sea separate most of these nations from several other territorial units. It is less than 100 miles from Italy to Albania, Greece, Malta, Tunisia, or French Corsica, or from Spain to Morocco and Algeria. And it is less than 250 miles from Portugal to Morocco; between the Spanish Balearic Islands and Italian Sardinia; between Sardinia and Algeria; and between Greece and Cyrenaica, Egypt, or Cyprus. Add to this the fact that the Greek and Turkish coasts, as well as those of Italy and Yugoslavia, face each other across narrow seas for much greater distances than the length of their land boundary. All these factors illustrate the intimate interpenetration of land and sea in Southern Europe.

The longitudinal extent of this region is rather wide, namely 2,200 miles from the Atlantic coast of Portugal to the Dodecanese Islands. That is almost as far as from New York to Hoover Dam or from San Francisco to Detroit. When it is noon at Rhodes (Rhodos) it is 9:30 in the morning in Lisbon. The north-south distances are much shorter. From Malta to the Brenner Pass on the northern border of the Italian Tyrol is roughly 800 miles, the distance from Atlanta to Detroit. Crete's southern coast is still farther to the south, but the distance thence to the northern frontier of Greece is only about 450 miles.

The maritime character of Southern Europe is pronounced. It explains why, despite the distances involved, the land area is only somewhat larger than that of Texas and New Mexico combined. Of this area, more than 75 per cent is peninsular, eight per cent is insular, and another 15 per cent belongs to the mainland of Europe.

Land and Sea. The inland point located farthest from a coast (230 miles) lies in the Iberian Peninsula, roughly 50 miles southwest of Madrid. This fact is a good indication of the general character of the region. Though land and sea interpenetrate over the whole area, this is least true of the Iberian Peninsula and most true of Greece. Only on the plateaus of Spain do people live largely unconscious of the sea and its life. Everywhere else the proximity of the sea is felt in some subtle way. The Mediterranean Sea with its deep, clear, blue waters; its unending variety of bays, forelands, and islands; its fishing boats with their triangular white sails; its small, white towns surrounded by cordons of single trees or small groves in a bare mountain landscape—all this belongs to the typical picture of Southern Europe. The peculiar coloring of the countryside is largely a result of the prevailing dryness of the air throughout a great number of sunny days. The azure color of the sea is a reflection of the sky in a sea of high salt content.

Like the sea, the mountains belong to the landscape and typify the region. There are hardly any coastal points where mountains are not visible at some distance inland, nor is the view of mountains absent in the largest lowlands, the North Italian Plain. For the most part, hills and mountains come quite close to the coast, with small towns overlooking the sea from some summit. In northern Italy the famous lakes repeat the general character of the Mediterranean, their ultramarine expanses surrounded by oases of Mediterranean vegetation. The vivid clear colors, together with the exquisite shapes of the mountains rising out of the sea, helped to stimulate the early development of the artistic sense in many of the Mediterranean peoples. The distinctive way in which they developed established a tradition to which we are heirs.

Turkey

The Turkish republic has a rather regular, rectangular shape. It extends 970 miles from east to west, and its north-south width varies only between 280 and 380 miles. It occupies the peninsula of Asia Minor and extends eastward into the Armenian Highland. By a narrow extension along the eastern coast of the Mediterranean Sea, it cuts northern Syria from direct access to the sea. The northwestern corner of Turkey is in Europe. This part, Eastern Thrace, comprises 3 per cent of the total area of 296,185 square miles, which is somewhat larger than Texas.

The following physiographic regions can easily be recognized (Fig. 7–1):

The Turkish Straits. In a geographical sense, European and Asiatic sides of the straits formed by the Bosporus, the Sea of Marmara, and the Dardanelles cannot be treated separately. The Bosporus is only 800 yards wide at its narrowest part and the Dardanelles not much over one mile. Both are flanked by steep hills, and a strong surface current flows through them from the Black Sea to the Aegean

Sea. They were river valleys in the geological past, and like a river valley they unite their banks rather than separate them (Fig. 7–2). The character of the landscape is the same on both sides.

Coastal Regions of Asia Minor. The straits connect two seas of different character. The highly saline, deeply blue, quiet Mediterranean Sea loses water by evaporation and maintains its level mainly by the influx of water from the Atlantic Ocean. The darker, stormy

Fig. 7–2. The Bosporus, looking from the Anatolian side to European Turkey. This narrow strait has all the characteristics of a river. (Turkish Information Office.)

Black Sea has only slightly saline surface water, and in its depths is stagnant water with only little oxygen, supporting no life. Despite the short intervening distance, not only are the seas different but also the adjacent coastal regions. Almost directly from the Black Sea rise the Pontic Mountains, a part of the Tertiary folded mountain belt. The narrow strip between the mountains and the coast has warm, moist summers, and cool, rainy winters, especially in its eastern part. Here are the only large forests of Turkey, deciduous mixed with evergreen trees. Sugar beets and tobacco are widespread, but the cold winds blowing across the Black Sea from the southern Russian steppe preclude full development of a typical Mediterranean vegetation.

Fig. 7–3. Land use in Southern Europe.

Mediterranean orchards
Grains
Semidesert
Deciduous forest (prevailingly evergreen)
Coniferous forest (mostly pines)
Vineyards
Steppe
Dry savanna
Rice
Steppe with dry plowing
River oasis

Black Sea

Mediterranean Sea

Adriatic Sea

Lisbon
Madrid
Rome
Athens
Istanbul
Ankara

0   100   200   300   400 Miles
0   100   200   300   400 Kilometers

Mediterranean vegetation is characteristic of Asia Minor's west and south coasts. In the mild, moderately moist winters and hot, dry summers, olives can grow as far north as the straits, and vineyards and orchards of citrus, figs, and almonds flourish along the Aegean and the southern coast. In the protected southeasternmost corner, the plain of Adana, cotton is the predominant crop. The southern coast, especially the Plains of Antalya, is effectively cut off from the interior by rugged, treeless, almost-uninhabited mountains, the Taurus Ranges. They are another link of the great Alpine Tertiary Ranges [1] leading west to the Greek islands. These mountains protect the south coast from the cold air masses which accumulate on the central Anatolian Plateau in winter. The eastern parts of these mountains, the Taurus and the Antitaurus, continue into the core of Asia, and separate Anatolia from the plains of Iraq.

Anatolian Plateau. In its western part, the Anatolian Plateau is an old Palaeozoic block between the folded mountains to the north and south. It is fairly well dissected by rivers flowing to the Aegean Sea. Farther east the older structures are buried beneath a rather level surface formed by material brought from the surrounding mountains. The Anatolian Plateau has a harsh continental climate, very cold in winter, burning hot in summer, and very dry throughout the year. By nature it is a steppe; but meadows and pastures predominate today, as they did presumably in antiquity. On its cultivated fields, primarily wheat and the subtropical species of barley are grown. While several rivers in the west and two large rivers in the north reach the sea, none reaches it in the south. Several small rivers end in saline lakes which have no outlet.

In the easternmost part of Turkey the Pontic and the Taurus (Toro) mountains, especially the Antitaurus, converge in the Armenian Highlands. They culminate in the highest mountain of Turkey, Mount Ararat (16,945 feet).

Greece

The Kingdom of Greece has its center on a very irregularly shaped peninsula of the much larger and more regular southeast European peninsula. It extends into the main peninsula northeastward through Macedonia and Western Thrace along the northern coast of the Aegean Sea. Almost a quarter of the Greek territory is islands, most of them small and scattered over the Aegean Sea. The largest island, Crete, separates the Aegean from the Mediterranean Sea. Greece has an area of 51,246 square miles, approximately the size of Alabama.

[1] For geological terms, see Appendix I.

Pindus System. In the eastern Alps a southern chain of limestone mountains is well discernible and is generally regarded as the beginning of the Dinaric Ranges which trend southeastward along the eastern shore of the Adriatic Sea, through Yugoslavia and Albania into Greece, culminating in the Pindus Mountains. In Greece, smaller ranges fork from the parent chain, most of them swerving eastward in arcs open toward the north. These arcs have been cut into many isolated parts by large-scale faulting and subsidence. Thus, parts of the chains are often below the level of the Aegean Sea, whose islands are the lofty peaks of submarine ranges. The main chain can be traced through Kythera, Crete, Karpathos, and Rhodes (Rhodos). This interpenetration of sea and land has helped to make the Aegean coasts and islands of Greece one of the earliest centers of mutual cultural contacts. In sharp contrast are her western coasts, parallel to the axis of the mountains, and difficult of access. Along the coast trend the Ionian Islands, of which Corfu (Kerkira) is the largest, and Ithaca (Ithaki) the most famous. Like their Aegean counterparts, they prospered in ancient times and prosper again at present, in strong contrast to the physical and cultural bareness of the adjacent mainland. Many of the mountains of Greece rise almost isolated from the sea, thus appearing very high and impressive. Yet they would be little known were it not for the ancient writers and poets who peopled them with gods and heroes.

Many ranges of the eastern Italian Alps and virtually all the young mountains of Greece are made of limestone. Limestone mountains are poor. They have no mineralization and water tends to sink rapidly underground so that little is left on the surface. If deforestation occurs, and it did occur at one time or another in highly civilized, densely populated countries, the shallow soil is easily washed away and the typical limestone or karst phenomenon of *lapiés* becomes apparent. In the central Peloponnesos many rivers disappear in sinkholes, to reappear at some distant point, occasionally at the other side of a range as a strong spring. All over Greece are karst lakes without visible outlets. Many of them dry up in summer, leaving fertile, formerly malarious plains. At other periods, the sinkholes become blocked and their lakes flood the surrounding country. Some, like Copais Lake in Boeotia, have been drained to reclaim land for agriculture.

Old Blocks. The Thracian block, an area of old structures, culminates in the Rhodope Massif. It occupies central and eastern Macedonia and Thrace. This block is broken by numerous fault lines, and though some parts are raised, others are depressed and either have been buried under recent alluvial deposits or have subsided below sea level in the deep northern part of the Aegean Sea. The northernmost islands and the finger-like forelands of the Chalcidice (Khalkidhiki) Peninsula, especially the steep, dark heights of Samothrace (Samothraki) and Mt. Athos (6,349 feet), rise sheer out of the azure sea, in striking contrast to the dazzling white limestone plateau of the nearby island of Lemnos, in the folded zone. A second group are the Cycladic islands (Kikladhes) and small parts of Boeotia, Attica, and the island of Euboea (Evvoia).

Between these components the land has subsided relatively little to form the shallow central part of the Aegean Sea. Fault lines have extended from this area and have also broken the Tertiary ranges into numerous small uplands and basins. Many basins, such as that of Thessaly, have been filled in and are now small lowlands. They are especially frequent in the inner corners of bays, where short streams enter the sea. A famous example is the Gulf of Lamia. Here the Sperkhios River has advanced its mouth approximately 10 miles since historical time began (Fig. 7–4). The walls of the mountains which once made the few hundred feet of narrow Thermopylae an easily guarded pass, today face the deltaic plain. Less well known but more critical for navigation is the problem of the Gulf of Salonika.

The Cyclades group ends in the south at a fault line marked by active volcanoes and severe earthquakes. In historical times, only the volcanoes of Methana and Santorin (Thera) have erupted. The latter island is the remainder of the outer rim of a tremendous explosion crater, with steep walls facing the interior. The sea has broken through this wall and now occupies the interior crater (Fig. 7–5). In recent times, submarine eruptions have occurred within the crater, thereby creating two small islands.

Italy

The Italian republic occupies the elongated Apennine peninsula between the Adriatic and the Tyrrhenian Sea in the center of the Mediterranean Sea. In the north it extends with a broad base into the mainland of Europe. From the northernmost point in the Alps to the southernmost tip, Cape Spartivento, is a distance of 660 miles. The peninsula itself is nowhere wider than 140 miles, but the broad base extends 320 miles from east to west. Sicily and Sardinia, the two largest Mediterranean islands, and a few small islets belong to Italy. The area of 116,260 square miles is slightly larger than that of Arizona.

Two small political units which are physically within the Italian republic must also be mentioned: Vatican City and the Republic of San Marino. Vatican City is the smallest sovereign state of the world,

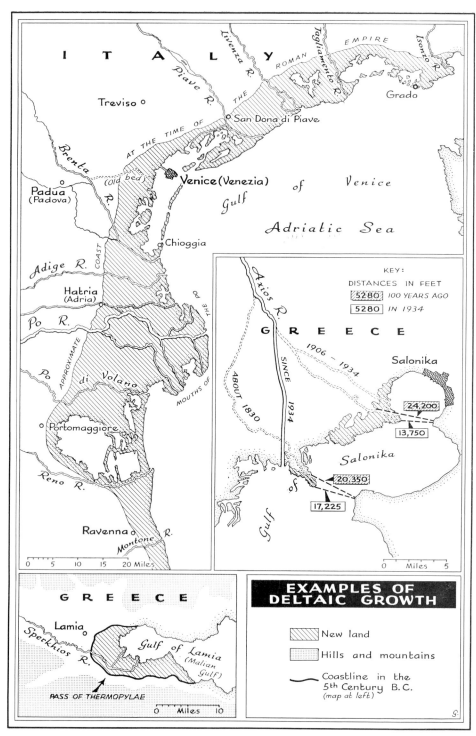

Fig. 7–4. Examples of deltaic growth.

478

occupying 108.7 acres within the confines of the city of Rome. The Republic of San Marino is near the coast of the Adriatic Sea, in the northeastern part of the Apennine peninsula.

Fig. 7–5. Santorin (Thera), an island of volcanic origin. The precipitous slopes (note the severe grade of the zigzag road) are the inner walls of an old crater. (Greek Government, Press Department.)

Areas of Faulted Structure. Remnants of a large old structural block are found in the western Mediterranean. Under the tremendous stresses and pressures of the Tertiary folding, the block was broken into many small pieces, and many of the fragments were submerged. Others, such as the high and rugged islands of Sardinia, Corsica, and Elba, and some of the hill country in western Tuscany, are characteristic areas of faulted structure. On the border between the Tuscan fault-block remnant and the Apennines is a structural line of extinct volcanoes which trends from northern Tuscany southward to quite-active Vesuvius, which was thought to be extinct until it erupted in 79 A.D. The ashes of this famous first explosion buried and preserved the city of Pompeii for posterity. At present, the volcanic activity of Vesuvius is centered in a cone which was built within the central caldera.[2] Still farther south is Stromboli, one of the few known constantly active volcanoes. Etna in Sicily erupts mostly through parasitic cones on its slopes. The lava flows have frequently destroyed orchards and towns but have also produced some good soils. Some cities, like Messina in 1908, have been victims of severe earthquakes connected with volcanic activity.

The Alps. Only parts of the Alps, primarily their southern slopes, belong to Southern Europe (Fig. 7–1, also Figs. 1–3 and 1–7). During the glacial period they were completely buried by ice, and stream erosion since that time has not been able to obliterate the glacial features. Many valleys are lined by terraces where villages and fields have more security from floods than at the broad valley bottoms. Because of the proximity of the sea, base level[3] for erosion is everywhere near. Gradients are steep and immature, offering many good sites for hydroelectrical installations, but poor living conditions amid splendid beauty.

The boundary of Italy encloses most of the drainage basin of the Po and its tributaries, following the divide more or less closely. The tributary valleys allow Mediterranean vegetation, climate, and crops, and Italian language and cultural habits, to penetrate deep into the Alps. The same sort of penetration occurs in the French Alps to the west. These features are especially visible in the broad longitudinal valleys such as those of the Dora Baltea, Adda, Adige, Rienza, Durance, and Isère rivers. Valleys which bear names different from those of their streams, such as Val d'Aosta, Val Tellina, Val Venosta, and Val Pusteria (Pustertal), preserve names of very ancient tribes. These valleys lead to easy passes, some used since prehistoric times. They have helped to minimize the barrier function of the Alps and have been the routes of numerous invasions from the north.

Valleys and passes break up the Alps into numerous well-defined groups. In the west they are mostly bare, steep, jagged mountains with relatively small glaciers. They form two closely connected arcs, whose convex side faces France. They are highest at Mont Blanc

---

[2] A caldera is a large basin (calderon) resulting from volcanic activity.
[3] Base level is the level to which erosion is tending to lower the surface. If the interval in altitude between the base level and the source of the river is great and the horizontal distance small, erosion is very strong.

(15,781 feet), the highest part of which is totally in France. A group of passes, of which Mont Cenis is the best known, provide the main connection between France and Italy. The Alps curve eastward from the Great St. Bernard Pass to the Simplon Pass. On this stretch is the highest peak of southern Europe, Monte Rosa (15,271 feet), rising directly on the Swiss-Italian border. But the larger glaciers of this border chain face northward on Swiss soil, and the tremendous Italian precipices are largely bare rock.

East of the Simplon the glaciers have carved deep furrows which cup the blue waters of Lago Maggiore, Lago Lugano, Lago di Como, and Lago di Garda. Eastward from Lago di Garda a separate zone of limestone mountains constitutes the inner arc of the Alps. Among these, the Dolomites are the most widely known group because of their bizarre towers and crags, their white-and-pink walls standing above the green Alpine meadows, and the afterglow of their summits at sunset. Other limestone groups form bare, karstic plateaus with steep walls neighboring fertile valleys. In between are old volcanic extrusions such as the reddish-black rocks of the porphyry plateau of Bolzano. Farther in the interior, crystalline schists, similar to those of the western Alps, form dark, high, glaciated massifs. Their highest peaks, however, do not attain the elevations of the western Alps.

The Apennines. The Apennines are the southeastern continuation of the western Alps, the two forming a semicircle around the western end of the North Italian Plain. The Apennines run through the entire Italian peninsula, in a bow-shaped chain. They first hug the shore of the Gulf of Genoa in Liguria, the famous Italian Riviera (Fig. 7–6), and then cross the peninsula and sweep close to the shore of the Adriatic Sea. Continuing farther, they form the toe of the Italian boot, the peninsula of Calabria, and reappear in northern Sicily.

Throughout their length, the Apennines are a rather narrow and rugged mountain chain, though of moderate height. Limestone and sandstone formations are prevalent, and this explains the lack of water in the higher parts. Where the Apennines recede from the Adriatic coast, extremely dry limestone plateaus of nearly horizontal strata form the spur of Mount Gargano and the plain of Apulia. They resemble the karst plateau of Yugoslavia, across the Adriatic Sea, of which they are virtually a part in their geological structure. Along the eastern Italian coast a straight, almost harborless coast line has developed.

The Apennines are the longest—though by far not the highest—of the south-European folded mountain chains, extending approximately 600 miles from the group of low passes north and northwest of Genoa, which mark the boundary between the Apennines and the Alps. Another 175 miles of mountain ranges stretch across Sicily and continue as the Atlas Mountains in northern Africa.

The Apennine peninsula and Sicily are occasionally subjected to warm, moist, and, even if weak, very oppressive south winds, the sirocco, which interrupt the normal course of the Mediterranean climate. Sicily—and rarely Sardinia—are also reached by infrequent sandstorms from the Sahara.

Fig. 7–6. Air photo of Cape Mortola, on the Italian Riviera. Note the characteristic promontories, the semicircular bays, and the sparse vegetation cover. (Touring Club of Italy.)

North Italian Plain. Different from the structures so-far discussed is the northern third of the Adriatic Sea, which is a zone of downwarping between the uplifted folded zones of the Apennines and the Dinaric system of Yugoslavia. The Adriatic Sea once extended farther inland. Sediments brought by rivers from the Alps and the Apennines filled in this upper part and created the North Italian Plain. This process is still going on at the combined delta of the Po, Brenta, and Adige, at the pace of almost 30 feet per year (Fig. 7–4). The northern part of the North Italian Plain was later buried under the moraines and outwash plains of the great Alpine glaciers of the Ice Age. Rivers cut into this unconsolidated material, lowering thereby the groundwater table. It emerges in a line of springs (*fontanili*) at the border of the morainic, dry, unfertile zone and the alluvial materials (Fig. 7–7). The Po meanders in the floodplain, confined by natural and man-made levees.

Both the eastern part of the plain and the northern Adriatic Sea and its coasts are subject to a strong cold wind from the northeast, the *bora*. It starts rather suddenly when cold air accumulates on the limestone plateaus of Yugoslavia and breaks down into the warmer lowlands.

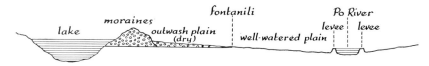

Fig. 7–7. The location of *fontanili* on the North Italian Plain.

The practically enclosed basin of the North Italian Plain has continental climate. In winter, cold air sinks to the bottom and stagnates for prolonged periods. Temperature inversion develops; the plain is then covered with fog, although the surrounding hills may be bathed in sun in the slightly warmer air layers above the cold air.

Iberian Peninsula

Spain occupies almost five-sixths of the Iberian Peninsula, a roughly quadrangular appendage of the European mainland. It extends approximately 500 miles from north to south and 640 miles from east to west. With an area of 194,433 square miles, Spain is the third-largest country in Europe, about the size of the combined states of Arizona and Utah.

The Republic of Andorra lies in a high valley of the eastern Pyrenees between France and Spain. Its area of 179.5 square miles constitutes Europe's fourth-smallest sovereign state. The crown colony of Gibraltar is located on a small extension of the Iberian Peninsula, facing Africa across a narrow strait. Its area is only 2.25 square miles.

The Republic of Portugal, on the western side of the Iberian Peninsula, forms an elongated quadrangle. In the north and east it borders Spain, in the south and west it faces the Atlantic Ocean. Its area of 35,419 square miles is slightly smaller than that of Indiana.

The Old Structural Elements. The western and central part of the Iberian Peninsula took its form essentially during the Hercynian revolution. The wide plateaus were uplifted during the Alpine orogeny, and consequently the main rivers, Duero, Tagus (Tajo), and Minho, cut deep gorges near the Spanish-Portuguese border. Only on the northern margin in the Cantabrian Mountains were the

Fig. 7–8. The treeless, flat Meseta. The village of Vico di Segovia is sheltered in a small valley. No dispersed settlements exist in this part of Spain. (Spanish Tourist Office.)

Hercynian masses involved in the Tertiary folding of the Pyrenees. The evidence of this folding process becomes less and less pronounced toward the west in the mountains of Asturias. The old Iberian massif was, however, broken by later tectonic movements into many smaller blocks. The two largest pieces constitute the northern and southern Meseta. They form wide uniform plateaus, largely dry and treeless, a landscape with African affinities (Fig. 7–8). The southern Meseta is somewhat lower and slightly tilted toward the southwest, where the transition to the Portuguese coastal plain is rather gradual. The northern Meseta is higher (on the average, 2,500 feet above sea level) and almost completely surrounded by rugged land. In the northwestern corner of the peninsula, erosion by numerous small rivers draining into the Atlantic Ocean has completely destroyed the original level surface. Galicia is a country of bold hills and meandering valleys. Stream erosion also played a great role in the dissection of the Cantabrian Mountains.

Numerous smaller blocks were lifted high above the surface of the Meseta. For the most part these segments are narrow and arranged in elongated rows. Thus they form the long ranges of the Central Sierras between the northern and southern parts of the Meseta, the Sierra Morena, at its southern rim, and the shorter ranges of the Montes de Toledo and their western continuation. As they are not a single chain of mountains, there are many low passes between the individual ranges. Fluvial and, in the higher parts, glacial erosion has almost completely destroyed the original plateau surface. As their name, *sierras* (saws), indicates, they appear as saw-toothed ridges. The least passable are the Iberian Ranges. They can be bypassed through the gap of Burgos, between the Cantabrian Mountains and the Iberian Ranges. The eastern part of the Meseta is buried beneath horizontal layers of Tertiary material, and there is no visible break between the Tertiary deposits and the old structural surface.

The Meseta is sufficiently large to cause an independent air circulation. During the winter a stable anticyclone develops there, causing low temperatures and light winds blowing outward from the center of the peninsula. In summer, the Meseta is much more heated than any other part of the Mediterranean lands. Oppressive temperatures and dryness develop, which place the interior of Spain in summer on a climatic par with parts of North Africa.

The triangular Ebro Lowlands are presumably a depressed block buried beneath deeply dissected Tertiary deposits (Fig. 7–9). Its western, innermost corner is a dissected hill country; only in the eastern part does the Ebro Valley merge with a somewhat extended plain.

Least conspicuous of the sierras is the Sierra Morena, at least when viewed from the Meseta. In the south, the Sierra Morena fronts the Andalusian Lowland along a straight fault line several hundred miles long. Thus it appears from the Andalusian side as a formidable mountain chain. At its foot is another triangular area of subsidence, which in its innermost corner is a country of low hills, but otherwise is an alluvial plain wide open toward the Atlantic Ocean.

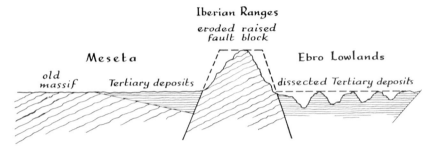

Fig. 7–9. A west-east geomorphic profile of the Meseta and the Ebro Lowlands.

Folded Mountains. There are three Tertiary mountain chains on the Iberian Peninsula, two of them of almost equal and considerable height. The Mulhacén Peak in the Baetic Cordillera rises to 11,240 feet, the Pico de Aneto in the Pyrenees to 11,169 feet. The third chain, the Catalonian Ranges, are much lower. Because of their trend parallel to the coast they nevertheless constitute an important orographic feature, isolating the coastal area from the enclosed, subhumid Ebro Basin. This coastal strip, the *costa brava*, is reached by the mistral, a cold strong wind from the plateaus of southern France, moving down to the Mediterranean Sea. However, a lasting cooling effect is precluded by the high temperature of the enclosed Mediterranean Sea (57° F. in winter). Though more characteristic of the southeastern coast, the *leveche*, a humid southern wind, occasionally reaches the Catalonian coast.

The Pyrenees are for most of their length a fairly uniform mountain range, crossed by high, difficult passes. The central part is the highest and only near the ends are passes which have been used frequently. Railroads had to use the narrow space between the mountains and the sea on both ends until some twenty years ago, when engineers pierced these ramparts with two tunnels. The western end of the Pyrenees is accompanied by a lower parallel chain. Here a few longitudinal valleys exist. Elsewhere, short transverse valleys descend in grandiose steps from the glacial cirques near the main crests. The valleys of the southern and northern flank rarely originate on opposite sides of the same mountain and this explains the lack of good passes. Most valleys end against a steep towering wall. Because of their steepness and lower altitude, the Pyrenees were not as heavily glaciated in the Pleistocene period as were the Alps, and lack the many beautiful lakes of the latter.

The Baetic Cordillera has a similarly complicated structure, broken into numerous individual groups separated by transverse and longitudinal valleys (Fig. 7–10). In a central depression, irrigated gardening and cities such as Granada have developed. The settlement pattern, therefore, resembles the Alps rather than any of the other folded mountain ranges. The highest group of the Baetic Cordillera is the Sierra Nevada (the snowy crest). In the northeast, the higher parts of a submarine continuation emerge from the sea to form the Balearic Islands. In the west, the Baetic Cordillera comes close to the Rif Mountains of northern Morocco at the Straits of Gibraltar. The Straits have been regarded by some as a low, flooded pass in a recurving chain. However, they seem rather to be a structural depression parallel to the trend of the mountains.

Malta and Cyprus

Malta is a British possession whose status is in flux at the moment. It is located at the very center of the Mediterranean Sea, south of Sicily, and includes, besides the main island, two smaller islands; all three, however, have a total area of only 121.8 square miles. Malta, the main island, consists of several limestone plateaus, separated from each other by low but steep escarpments. Drainage is generally subsurface.

The territory of the youngest European republic, Cyprus, comprises the island of the same name. The diamond-shaped island, with an area of 3,572 square miles (about half the size of New Jersey), lies in the Mediterranean Sea, 50 miles south of the Turkish coast. The surface configuration of the island somewhat resembles a bowl: a central plain fringed by two arcuate chains which repeat the trend of the mountains along the south coast of Turkey. The northern chain is lower but very narrow, and the crest has very steep, even precipitous, slopes.

THE CULTURAL AND HISTORICAL BACKGROUND

Despite obvious differences, the countries of Southern Europe have been influenced time and again by a common set of geographical factors: their location on the same landlocked sea, their connection

Fig. 7–10. Pass in the Baetic Cordillera, between Murcia and Cartagena. Sparse vegetation is found only in a few protected spots. (Spanish Tourist Office.)

with the European continent, and their relationship to Africa and Asia. There were periods when none of these factors exerted a decisive influence and each peninsula could develop autonomously. We shall discuss these autonomous developments by individual countries.

The Mediterranean Sea as a Unifying Factor

The Mediterranean Sea exerted its unifying influence very early, when seafaring nations, the Minoan Cretans, Phoenicians, and Greeks, founded trading posts and colonies around its shores. Owing to the difficulties of land travel, the foundation of trading posts meant the economic domination of the hinterland by the sea power. Where such trading posts were closely spaced a whole empire developed, centered around one or the other of the various basins of the Mediterranean. Thus the Minoan Cretans apparently ruled effectively the area around the Aegean Sea, and the Phoenician settlers of Carthage the western-Mediterranean basin. The Athenians established their rule around the Aegean Sea; Corinth and its colony Syracuse, around the Ionian Sea. The oldest urban settlements in Southern Europe have grown from protected centers of some small landscape, such as Athens or Rome, or from the outposts of these trading empires, such as Cadiz, Malaga, or Palermo. Many Greek tribal centers developed into merchant cities, and colonies such as Salonika (Thessaloniki), Syracuse, and Naples were founded.

These older mercantile empires were replaced by the Roman Empire. The contemporaneous attempt of the Carthaginians to build an empire around the western-Mediterranean basin did not succeed. The Romans based their rule on the sea, but at the same time penetrated inland, building roads and cities as military strongholds and bases of colonization. Some of these Roman roads have survived and served as main lines of communication up to the age of the railroads. Several bridges still stand and are used (Fig. 7–11), and many railroads follow rather closely the alignment of Roman roads. It is almost unique that no modern road follows the trace of the Roman road from Durazzo (Durrës) to Salonika.

Most Roman cities have survived. While many of the Greek cities such as Paestum, Emporium, Cnossus, and Phaestus were destroyed or at best left their names to small villages, this fate befell hardly any of the larger Roman cities. Some Roman cities replaced older fortified towns and tribal centers in Italy and the Iberian Peninsula, such as Toledo, Lisbon, Bologna, Florence (Firenze). Most cities dating from Roman times are inland. On the coasts the Romans took over Greek and Phoenician cities, Genoa and Trieste being exceptions.

Fig. 7–11. This Roman bridge near Salamanca is still in use. (Spanish Tourist Office.)

No later empire succeeded in duplicating the Roman feat, although the Arabs in the ninth and the Turks in the sixteenth century almost did. In the nineteenth century, Great Britain virtually dominated the Mediterranean Sea from her bases at Gibraltar (1704), Malta (1815), the Ionian Islands (1815–64), Cyprus (1878), and Egypt (1882–1924), but it can hardly be said that she ruled over the adjacent countries. Other attempts were on a less ambitious scale. The Turks did succeed in making the eastern Mediterranean a Turkish sea; Venice ruled the Adriatic and Aegean seas; Spain dominated the western Mediterranean for a short time. The Greek attempt to convert the Aegean Sea into a Greek sea was defeated by the Turks in 1922. The Italians succeeded in making the Adriatic Sea their *mare nostro* in 1919, but later met defeat when they strove to rule the whole Mediterranean.

The Spread of Civilization

History tells us that our civilization originated in the Near East, in Egypt and Mesopotamia. From here it spread, first very slowly, and reached Asia Minor about 4,000 years ago. Here the Hittite Empire emerged and, at about the same time, the Minoan civilization on Crete. From these early centers civilization spread westward in Europe, but for approximately 2,000 years remained confined to the southern peninsulas. After Asia Minor and Crete, Greece became the home of literature, arts, ideas, and democratic government. Slowly, also, parts of Italy, including Sicily and Tuscany, became foci of culture and civilization. The next period saw Rome's political ascendancy followed by a concentration of cultural activities. Rome brought higher civilization to other Mediterranean countries, also to the Iberian Peninsula, where it competed with the Punic civilization which had arrived somewhat earlier. As the centers of civilization shifted westward, the older centers went into relative decline. Nevertheless, all of Southern Europe, including Asia Minor, was highly civilized since the first centuries B.C., in striking contrast to the barbaric or semibarbaric parts of the continent.

The civilization of Europe, later accompanied and often led by Christianization, was a long and gradual process. For many centuries, however, Southern Europe remained superior in civilization, although Greco-Roman civilization began a protracted decline. During this period, Greco-Roman civilization split, with an eastern center in Byzantium-Constantinople and a western center in Rome. Each molded in its own image that portion of the European continent north of its domain. This break has never been completely healed. During the early Middle Ages, the Iberian Peninsula under Arab rule was a highly developed center of civilization, but because of its Islamic character its influence upon the rest of Europe remained relatively weak.

For a short period during the Renaissance, Italy again became the center of European cultural life. At the same time, Turkish conquests eliminated Greece and Asia Minor as cultural centers for eastern

Europe. When western Europe definitely took over cultural leadership, culture spread in the Mediterranean from west to east, the same road it had taken in the opposite direction in antiquity. Greece re-entered the Western cultural community in the nineteenth century, and Turkey followed suit only about 40 years ago.

The Southern European Peninsulas and the Continent

Cultural eminence does not necessarily go together with political and military domination. When Italian cultural influence in the Renaissance was at its peak, French kings invaded the peninsula. This was part of an oft-repeated pattern. Time and again, attempts have been made to rule peninsular Southern Europe from a broad continental basis. Time and again, German kings crossed the Alps to gain the coveted imperial crown in Rome. They established a firm hold over the North Italian Plain and parts of central Italy for long periods, but only at the peak of their might over the south. Later the French kings, Napoleon, and finally the Austrian Hapsburgs repeated these attempts. The French succeeded in dominating Spain for much shorter periods by installing a relative of their rulers on the Spanish throne. Culturally more significant are the positions French monastic orders held in northern Spain in the wars against the Mohammedans. But in general the Pyrenees proved to be a better protection than the Alps with their deeply indented passes.

Greece, too, was annexed to northern empires for some short periods. Philip of Macedonia and Dushan of Serbia are the most famous conquerors from the north. On the other hand, there is no clear instance of any of the peninsulas serving as the basis for a dominion over the adjacent parts of the continent. The Romans established such a dominion only after they had founded their circum-Mediterranean empire. The Spanish attempt could succeed for a short while, only because of the dynastic connection with the Austrian Hapsburgs.

The domination of the Southern European peninsulas from the continent should not be confused with their use as land bridges between Europe and Asia or between Europe and Africa. They have served as such from prehistoric times, when people from North Africa took advantage of the disappearance of the ice from Europe to push northward. In the last war, the Germans first used Italy as a bridge to Tunisia and Libya. The Americans and British, starting from Tunisia, fought their way through Sicily and then crossed to Italy. In the many centuries of recorded history there were many such movements in both directions. Some peoples merely moved through these countries. The Vandals, when they migrated across Spain into North Africa, left ruins but little else, as did Celtic tribes in Greece on their way to Asia Minor. Other peoples, such as the Turks in their advance to Central Europe, stayed on to rule over Greece for centuries. Still others, blocked in their advance, settled down as did some Celtic tribes in the North Italian Plain and other Celtic tribes in the Iberian Peninsula. Langobards and Visigoths are later examples. The Arabs passed through Spain into France, were finally thrown back, but remained in the Iberian Peninsula from the eighth to the end of the fifteenth century.

TURKEY

Historical Geography [4]

Turkey of today is the national state of the Turkish people and in many respects a state totally different from historical Turkey, which rightly should be called the Ottoman Empire. Though a Turkish tribe from inner Asia founded and ruled the Ottoman Empire, it was not a Turkish state but essentially a supranational Islamic Empire. When it had gradually disintegrated and finally collapsed in the holocaust of World War I, the Turks under the leadership of Kemal Atatürk founded the present republic. Atatürk succeeded in freeing Turkey from Western political domination, by making her a Western state in culture and organization.

In its present boundaries Turkey has no exact historical predecessor, although the Greek-speaking Byzantine Empire, during part of its period of decline, had similar boundaries in Asia and during another period had boundaries in Europe similar to the present ones. At present the European part of Turkey, Eastern Thrace, is no more than a bridgehead protecting the Turkish straits.

During the period of antiquity many peoples and tribes moved into Asia Minor in successive waves, from both Europe and inner Asia. They all contributed to the racial medley, and some of them left important ruins and written documents. The Hittites founded an empire with the center at Boghazköi, east of Ankara. Later Ankara, ancient Angora, was the capital of Galatia. Most important of all ancient invaders were the Greeks, though for a long time they settled only along the coast. From the west coast, Greek civilization and language spread up the wide valleys to the Anatolian Plateau. This

---

[4] Owing to the great differences in the historical geography of the individual countries in Southern Europe, separate discussions of the historical background are included in the discussions of every country.

process was accelerated after the conquest of the Persian Empire by Alexander of Macedonia in the fourth century B.C. Under the Roman Empire and its successor, the Byzantine Empire, Greek language completed the conquest. It—and Christianity—remained dominant until the conquest by the Turks in 1453. The conquering Turks found here a country similar to their original inner-Asian home and many settled on the Anatolian Plateau and made it the base for their conquests in three continents. The illiterate mass of the indigenous peasants and herdsmen first quickly adopted Islam, the religion of the conquerors, and then gradually adopted the Turkish language. In contrast, the educated population of the coastal towns, and the peasantry in the vicinity, remained largely Christian and retained their Greek language. Their descendants were expelled in the aftermath of the Greco-Turkish War of 1922.

The Turkish Straits. This area deserves a short separate discussion. Since very early times peoples and empires extended over both banks: the Persian Empire, some of the Hellenistic states, Rome, Byzantium, the Latin Empire of the Crusaders, and the Ottoman Empire. Also, the population on both sides of the straits was uniform most of the time. It is again uniform, the Greeks of the coastal towns and of Thrace having been expelled and replaced by Turks from Macedonia and Bulgaria.

The importance of the straits lies in their function as the most important gateway through the great Eurasian mountain belt east of Marseille. Even the relatively easy mountain passes cannot rival them in importance. Routes from inner Asia have used this gateway. From antiquity to the Bolshevik Revolution in Russia, the Black Sea's northern borderlands, the Ukraine of today, exported their grain to the deficit areas around the Mediterranean Sea. Thus, since prehistoric times, cities have been founded to guard this pass. The oldest was Troy. When the Arabs besieged Constantinople they were prompted as much by the desire to open the trade route to the Black Sea as by a desire to expand Islam.

There have been interruptions in this Black Sea–Mediterranean Sea trade, either at times when the south-Russian plains were invaded by barbarian hordes from the east, or when order and civilization broke down in the Mediterranean Basin in the Dark Ages. More insidious were such interruptions when war and trouble on the straits closed them and jeopardized the interests of both the Black Sea and Mediterranean partners. Fortunately such periods never lasted long, because of the desire of the rulers of the straits to profit from the passing traffic. Sometimes it meant only the replacement of one trading power by another. Venetians and Genoese alternated with the change of the rulers, Byzantines, Latin emperors, and Turks.

The situation changed when the Russians reached the north shore of the Black Sea. The Russians were well aware that their quest for the open sea was thwarted as long as they depended on the good will of the Turks for an exit from the Black Sea. There have been various legal arrangements in the last hundred years to safeguard free transit through the straits. None of them has proved satisfactory either for Russia or Turkey. As a consequence, the problem of the straits continues to disturb the relations in this part of the world, though it may be shelved for shorter or longer periods.

The Crossroads City. Several cities rose to prominence and disappeared, from the fall of Troy to the selection of Byzantium by the Roman Emperor Constantine as the new capital of the Roman Empire in 330 A.D. The advantages of Istanbul—this nationalistic Turkish name is a corruption of the Greek *eis tan polin* (into the city)—over its competitors are local: a deep protected harbor, the drowned valley of the Golden Horn, which together with the Bosporus and Sea of Marmara surrounds a peninsula which could easily be defended. Since the establishment of Constantinople as capital and guardian of the crossroads, all other cities in this area have dwindled to insignificance. Today Ankara, Turkey's capital in Asia Minor, outshines Istanbul politically, and traffic between the Black Sea areas and the outer world is at a low ebb. The Near East–Central European trade route, which has suffered many ups and downs during history, is virtually dead at the moment. The Berlin-Baghdad railroad, which had been launched with high expectations, was completed during the last war but never functioned as an effective link between northwestern Europe and the Near East. The nearby Turkish-Bulgarian boundary has indeed become the frontier between two worlds.

Population

The present linguistic uniformity of Turkey is of recent origin, a result of the population exchange with Greece after the war of 1922. Turkey is now about 90 per cent Turkish speaking. The largest minority is the Kurdish group in the southeastern corner of the state, and the Kurds pose the only serious minority problem. (They share the Islamic faith with the Turks.) The number of Greeks is still decreasing. Although the Greek population of Istanbul was exempted from the population exchange between Greece and Turkey, many left. When Istanbul ceased to be the center of a multinational state, many

Serbs, Bulgars, Albanians, and Arabs also left. Government agencies and foreign embassies moved to Ankara, and banks, shipping concerns, and great business firms closed their Istanbul offices. The decline of its population was speeded by an appallingly high death rate in the unsanitary older sections of the city. Although conditions have improved, there is not sufficient immigration to replace the deficit of deaths over births, because Istanbul's European hinterland is lost to the Balkan countries and the Asiatic hinterland to the new capital of Ankara. Some smaller waves of emigration have also affected the city, such as the return of Armenians to Soviet Armenia and the Jewish migration to Israel. The majority of its White Russian refugees have also moved on.

After the main migrations had ceased, smaller ones continued, the largest being that of Turkish expellees from Bulgaria between 1951 and 1953.

The migrations of the early 1920's, whether voluntary or not, left many areas and cities depopulated. Since then, they have again filled up by natural increase as well as by immigration. Armenia, however, is an exception. During World War I, the Christian Armenians of the northeastern mountain areas had been practically exterminated, but few Turks cared to move into its empty inhospitable valleys. Turkish Armenia remains sparsely populated today, threatened from across the border by the Soviet Union and its constituent Armenian Soviet Republic.

Present Economic Life

As has its political center, the economic center of Turkey is also gradually shifting to Asia Minor. In the period between the two world wars the few foreign-owned railroad lines were taken over by the government and expanded into a network, but in the last decade railroad building has largely given way to road construction. In many fields lack of private capital has led to state intervention. Thus, the main commercial and investment banks were founded with government capital.

Turkey has a great variety of minerals (Fig. 7–12), but most of them are only moderately exploited. Prospecting, however, is going on and has led recently to the discovery of oil in southeastern Turkey. In export value, chromite is first. Internally, the coal of Zonguldak east of Istanbul and several iron-ore deposits in central Anatolia are most important. They made possible the founding of a large steel mill in Karabuk, a strategically but not economically well-selected site because it is far from the sources of coal, iron ore, and skilled labor.

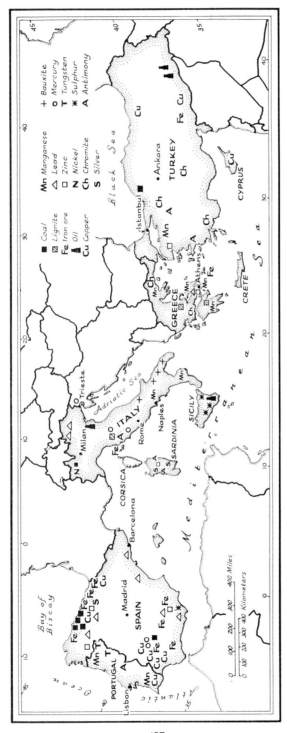

Fig. 7–12. Mineral resources.

497

Other industries, such as textiles, cement, and food processing, are developing. They blossomed first in those cities where, after the expulsion of the Greeks, suitable buildings were empty and available along with a small nucleus of skilled labor, e.g., in Istanbul, Izmir, and Bursa. Industrial development in cities on the Anatolian Plateau, such as Eskishehir, Ankara, and Kayseri, followed later.

Istanbul, though no longer the great port with world-wide connections, is still the main harbor for Turkey and the home port for most of its merchant shipping. The Turkish merchant marine, owned and manned largely by Turks, is slowly increasing. This new fleet has replaced foreign bottoms in much of the traffic with ports of the eastern Mediterranean. Internally it has also replaced the vessels which used to fly the Ottoman flag but which were owned and manned almost exclusively by Greeks.

Turkey is still predominantly an agricultural country with 80 per cent of its population occupied in agriculture and forestry (Fig. 7–3). Forestry, however, is of minor importance. Most of the cultivated land is farmed by owners of moderate-size farms. There is much land still to be reclaimed by modern methods of dry farming and irrigation, and progress in this direction is steady. The wave of expellees, mostly peasants from Bulgaria in the early 1950's, settled largely on unoccupied land with good soils. However, soils are only part of the problem, for crops in inner Anatolia depend much on the vagaries of a marginal climate. In good years Turkey is an important wheat exporter. About twice the area put to crops is in meadows and pasture. Of the products of animal husbandry, the most valuable is the hair of the Angora goat, called mohair. Much more variegated are the exportable products of the Mediterranean coastal areas, among which dried olives, figs, grapes, and tobacco are foremost. Important also are products for domestic consumption. They include cotton, sugar, and vegetable oil from a great variety of plants such as sesame and hazelnut.

GREECE

Historical Geography

Greece in Ancient Times. The most important geographical factor in Greek history is the interpenetration of sea and land. Inland areas more than a few miles away from the coast remained backward and without recorded history into late antiquity. The oldest civilization rose on Crete and the Cycladic islands. It is almost certain that the earliest inhabitants spoke a non-Indo-European language related to languages spoken in southeastern Asia Minor. When the Greek tribes moved into the peninsula and on to the islands they developed a high civilization but never succeeded in creating a unified state. The separation of the various cultural nuclei by arms of the sea or by difficult mountain terrain contributed to this development. The small city states on the peninsula were virtually more isolated than the island states. The areas least favored by access to the sea, primarily in the west, remained the most backward, a development which is duplicated in modern Greece.

Fig. 7–13. One of the fortified monasteries on Mount Athos. Throughout the period of Turkish suzerainty over Greece, these monasteries preserved their autonomous status as an ecclesiastic republic. (Greek Government, Press Department.)

Greece Under Foreign Rule. When unification came, it was the result of foreign domination. From the fourth century B.C. onward Greece was a part of the Macedonian, Roman, Byzantine, and Turkish empires. Some of its islands were ruled by Arabs, Crusaders, Genoese, Venetians, British, and Italians. These foreign rulers have left surprisingly few vestiges, except negatively by the destruction of old monuments. A few Byzantine churches and monasteries, and Crusaders' and Venetian castles, mostly in northern Greece and on the islands, recall their rule (Fig. 7–13). It has been surmised that the neglect of drainage and the consequent spread of malaria had something to do with the decline and depopulation which took place in Roman times. In the long war of liberation from Turkey (1821–28) Greece won liberty for only a small part of its former area, but this time was unified as a nation. Ancient Greece had been a land of cities. In 1821 virtually all of them were faint memories, at best small villages. Only a few have regained the status of cities. The ancient Greeks had built their cities on protected sites, isolated steep hills, or slopes, looking inland but at the same time not far from the sea. No bay, only a sandy beach, was needed as a harbor. Now such sites are no longer sufficient, and the cities of modern Greece are often successors of latecomers among the ancient cities, such as Patras (Patrai) or Salonika. In the case of Athens historical tradition was strong enough to insure its victory over rival Nauplia in the bay of Argolis, and Hermoupolis on the island of Syros (Siros).

Modern Greece. Greece owed its independence to the valor of its people, and to external aid given by the liberal movements of the period. So the Greek constitution was fashioned after liberal patterns. Despite these liberal ideas, the heritage of subjection by the Turks and the long years of guerrilla war resulted in personal feuds, assassinations, revolutions, and civil wars. A number of external wars had to be fought before the whole Greek-speaking area was liberated (Fig. 7–14). Only Cyprus, though about 80 per cent Greek speaking, is outside the national boundaries. After several years of bloody struggle against British rule and Turkish claims for a division, a compromise was reached and Cyprus became an independent binational republic. As we have noted, western Asia Minor lost its Greek character by expulsion of its Greek population, as a result of the Turkish defeat of the Greek forces in Anatolia, in 1922.

The development of the new state started from the well-protected islands and deeply indented parts of the peninsula and has absorbed parts of the continental southeastern peninsula and some islands on the fringes. Athens is more than ever the geographical center. The ecclesiastical center, however, has remained in Constantinople, as the Greeks still call Turkish Istanbul.

Population

The demographic development of Greece has been radically upset by the political events of the last decades. In the early 1920's, when Greece had only 5 million people, it had to accept 1,220,000 Greek refugees expelled from Turkey and Bulgaria, while only 430,000 Turks and Bulgars left the country. With the help of the Nansen committee of the League of Nations, health and nutrition conditions improved rapidly and by 1940 the population had increased to 7,344,000. The losses of World War II amounted to the tremendous figure of approximately 870,000, i.e., at least 12 per cent of the prewar population. However, Greece has one of the highest birth rates in Europe, and a falling death rate. This high net increase, and to a minor degree the incorporation of the Dodecanese, explains why the population reached

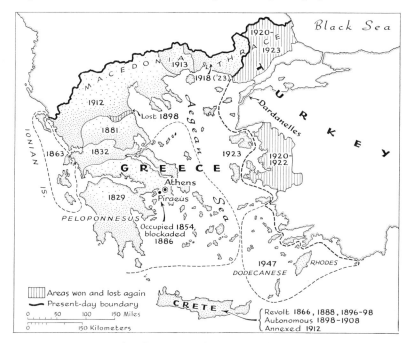

Fig. 7–14. The changing political boundaries of Greece.

over 8 million, in 1956. This meant a density of 157 persons per square mile, a very high figure for a mountainous, by no means fertile, little-industrialized country. Foreign and civil wars have contributed to keep people very poor and the living standard very low, especially in the rural districts. Low living standards are the result, but also the cause, of the use of primitive tools and implements, small and often unsanitary houses, and primitive means of transportation. Food is simple, consisting largely of fish, vegetables, and cheese. The cooking is done with olive oil. Lamb is the meat most frequently eaten, and wine is the common drink, partly because of the lack of good water.

In 1940, 64 per cent of the population lived in rural communities of less than 5,000 and 52 per cent were employed in agriculture and stock raising. Only 27 per cent of the area was under cultivation in 1956—an area that had been doubled between 1923 and 1947, but may now almost have reached the possible limit.

The density of population for the cultivated area amounts to 796 per square mile. Under these circumstances emigration has always played a great role, both by actually diminishing population pressure and through remittances. At present, outlets for emigration exist for small numbers only. Another remarkable by-product of this rapid population increase is the fact that about 65 per cent of the population is in the productive age group of 15 to 60 years.

Illiteracy is still widespread. However, this is rapidly changing thanks to the higher literacy of the children. Despite these handicaps the average Greek is quick and open-minded. Politics is the burning interest even in the most remote village. Political strife is bitter between the numerous parties. Newspapers and discussions in public places and inns play a great role in daily life. Coffee houses and inns have their tables and chairs outside the houses and are frequented mostly by men. Women have equal legal status, but custom makes the man predominant in all public places and affairs. In the villages women often do the hard work while men look on or direct. Work pauses during the noon hours, even the work in the fields. Shops, banks, and offices reopen at 3 or 4 o'clock and business and life go on far into the night. Streets and squares in cities and villages are noisy and vivid, accentuating the natural vivacity of the landscape, its bright colors, and entrancing shapes. Everywhere the deep blue of sky and sea, the white of bare limestone, the silvery green of olives, the darker green of other trees, and the red hollow bricks of the roofs blend with the manifold forms of mountains and hills, the curving bays and beaches, and the skyward-pointing cypresses and pines. Man almost disappears in this landscape, except where he puts his monuments on dominating heights, such as the Acropolis of Athens, the St. George's monastery of Lycabettos, the temple to Poseidon on Cape Sounion, the Crusaders' castles of Mytilene, or the Venetian fortresses at the entrance of Corfu harbor. Towns are frequently built on slopes, but disappear into the landscape because the houses of native stone blend with the rocks. Villages are usually large, hamlets or dispersed settlements existing only in a few sections of northern Greece. The scarcity of water has forced people to live around the wells; centuries of insecurity have contributed to the habit of gathering on protected sites. Many of the war-ravaged villages are now being rebuilt, often more sanitary though less beautiful, and on less spectacular sites in the valleys near the fields and roads (Fig. 7–15).

It is impossible to speak of a Greek racial type, as we know how many elements have been absorbed throughout historical times. Nevertheless, a swarthy type, of moderate height, often rather heavy-set, and having a round face, is frequently found. Anthropologists

Fig. 7–15. Arachova, a rebuilt mountainside village. Note the isolated bell tower, the antique style of the public building in the background, the tile-covered roofs, and the olive trees on the steep slopes. (Greek Government, Press Department.)

have classified the majority as belonging to the Mediterranean subrace of the white race.

Greek is an Indo-European language, but without any close relationship to other languages of this group. The Greek written language has changed surprisingly little in historical times, though Homer's speech would be unintelligible today. There are a number of dialects, and there is a struggle going on between those who adhere to a language patterned after classical Greek and those whose speech is more popular.

There have been periods when immigration was more important to Greece than emigration. From the sixth century on, almost all of continental Greece had a Slavic-speaking population. At one period, many islands and harbor towns were largely Italian speaking and Albanians settled in the regions devastated in the struggles against the Turks. Spanish-speaking Jews, as well as Turks, Rumanian nomadic herdsmen, Russian Tsarist refugees, and Armenian refugees came in smaller groups. Greek civilization succeeded in assimilating most of these groups, especially those belonging to the Greek Orthodox Church. The population exchange with Turkey and Bulgaria removed other minorities. The Rumanians are linguistically Hellenized and are recognizable by their way of life and descendants of Italians by their Roman Catholic religion.

In their 1940 census, 93 per cent of the Greeks recorded Greek as their mother tongue, and, in 1951, 98 per cent were members of the Greek Orthodox church. Nevertheless, the small Macedo-Slavic group proved to be a source of trouble, associating itself first with the Bulgarians and later with the Communists. Today most of them are gone and with them a group of Mohammedan Albanians. The Spanish-speaking Jewish community of Salonika was destroyed by the Germans. Many Armenians followed the call of the Soviet Union to return.

Present Economic Life

There is no part of the Greek economy which has not suffered from the last war and its aftermath. Whole villages and towns were destroyed; men were drafted into the army, fled abroad, or were deported; cities were bombed; ships were sunk; and fishing equipment deteriorated from non-use. Recovery was much delayed by the Communist rebellion and civil war. British and, later, American aid was necessary. The economy is now on its way back, and many segments must now be considered healthy and even modernized.

Agriculture. Unfortunately for Greece, bare rocks and thorny brush constitute 55 per cent of the surface of the land. The cultivated land is badly exhausted, and the poor owners for the most part are unable to procure needed fertilizer. There are no large estates, and the prevalence of small owners, though socially preferable, is an obstacle to efficient management. Agriculture is confined to the river valleys, delta plains, and few intermontane basins. Level areas are not very extensive and are often swampy and malarial. Drainage work has been going on, more vigorously since the middle 1920's, primarily in the plains of the Axios (Vardar) and Strimon (Struma), in Macedonia. Flood control played a great role in this work. Malaria has been fought successfully, and new land for the expellees from Asia Minor was won. The Axios Delta has been converted into a densely settled, well-drained, and well-cared-for landscape. The mouth of the Axios was shifted so that it no longer threatens to bar the entrance

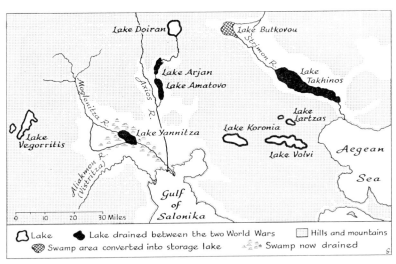

Fig. 7–16. Lakes of southern (Grecian) Macedonia.

to the Gulf of Salonika. The bed of the Strimon was shortened, and its flood waters are now stored in Lake Butkovou, formerly a swamp area. The Takhinos lake in its course, and several other lakes such as Lake Yannitza, west of Salonika, and Lake Copais in Boeotia have been drained and their area utilized for tobacco, corn, barley, and some cotton (Fig. 7–16). There are numerous other swamps and shallow or periodical lake areas which can and will be drained.

The main products of Greek agriculture are cereals, olives, grapes, and tobacco—in that order. However, the restricted size of the plains is not sufficient to provide Greece with both exportable cash crops and the needed food. Thus the greater part of the arable land is devoted to cash crops. The harvests of cotton, tobacco, and wheat are three times those at prewar levels, and those of rice more than twenty times. Corn yields are back to prewar levels and are steadily improving. However, the partial loss of the United States market and that of Germany is threatening the basic tobacco industry. Tobacco is the main export of Greece, furnishing as much as 45 per cent of the value of all exports.

Many of the tree crops serve to produce exports. The silver-grey leaves and knotted trunks of the olive trees are a characteristic sight, as are the terraces of the vineyards. Exported are seedless currants (Corinthian raisins) from the western Peloponnesos, as well as raisins and wine, mainly products of the islands. The wine of the mainland is used for home consumption only. Currants and raisins amounted to 12 per cent of the value of the prewar exports. Seldom are large areas all under the same crop. Thus citrus fruits, mulberry groves, orchards of fig trees, peaches, almonds, etc. alternate frequently. There is less variety in the more continental area of northern Greece, where tobacco, grains, and some cotton replace the typical Mediterranean products, and fields quite generally take the place of gardens and orchards. In these northern areas agricultural machinery is slowly replacing animal and man power.

Forestry. Less than a fifth of Greece is in forests, of which the state owns two-thirds. This is only a small remnant of the woods which covered the land and were destroyed in antiquity. During the last war, 30 per cent of the remaining forests were cut down, a loss hard to replace. Many of the preserved forest areas are in the dissected Pindus Mountains. Reforestation is still in its beginnings and is much hampered by the goat, an animal which is almost indispensable to the poor peasant.

Animal Husbandry and Fishing. There is no large-scale animal husbandry. However, because of the little mechanized agriculture and the condition of the roads, asses, horses, and mules are still numerous. Oxen and the water buffalo are primarily work animals. In numbers, work animals have recovered from wartime depletion far less than have pigs, sheep, and goats. In the remote mountain districts, a few shepherds still migrate between winter and summer villages. They used to roam far into the Balkan Peninsula in Turkish times and a few groups managed to do so until the last war. The closing of the frontiers and the increasing utilization of much winter pasture land for agriculture have sharply curtailed their way of life.

The resources of fish should not be overestimated. As everywhere in the Mediterranean, there is a great variety of fish, but few types in great numbers. Fishing is done on a small scale, by many small craft. Tunny fishing is the most important. It is done at night, the fish being attracted by open fires on board the boats, and caught with nets or speared. A few modern vessels have been acquired in recent years. The only marine product for export are sponges obtained by divers from clear shallow waters.

Merchant Marine and Commerce. The poor natural endowment of most of Greece, the existence of many sheltered bays, and the short distances between the islands and across the bays have always made seafaring important. However, Greece is no longer on one of the highways of world traffic, and only a few of the Greek harbors are visited by the great ship lines. In spite of this basic handicap and the fact that much shipping was destroyed during the war, the Greek merchant marine surpasses its prewar tonnage. A large proportion of the Greek merchant marine consists of cargo vessels and tankers, which, in tramp shipping, have an important share of the world's maritime commerce. The Greek fishing fleet is larger and better equipped than it was before the war. Furthermore, in the present air age, Athens has become a convenient stopping point on the way from Western Europe to the Near East and from Eastern Europe to Egypt.

Among the Greek harbors that of Piraeus, the harbor of Athens, is foremost. Its modern development and importance date from the growth of Athens. The main harbor of northern Greece is Salonika. Located at the southern end of an easy corridor through the Balkan Peninsula, it once served an extended hinterland. Political conflicts, however, have restricted its trade area to Greek Macedonia. The latter's increased settlement and production make up partially for loss of the tributary area. Patras, at the western exit of the Gulf of Corinth, is the main export harbor for currants and is the port of call for ships going into the Adriatic Sea. Traffic between the east and west, in small- and medium-size vessels, is greatly helped by the existence of the Canal of Corinth. Some harbors are specialized, such as Kavalla for tobacco, or serve particular areas or islands, such as Corfu on the island of Corfu, Canea (Khania) on Crete, Rhodes on the island of the same name, and Volos on the plains of Thessaly.

Throughout all its history as an independent nation, Greece has been in a difficult economic situation. Wars and revolutions occurred frequently and interrupted recovery every time it showed some prospects. Thus Greece had to rely on invisible imports, first of all remittances from abroad by its emigrants, merchants, and seamen, many of them serving under foreign flags. Many rich communities contributed generously, either as communities or as individuals. Another source of income has been tourist traffic. Tourists come primarily to see the relics of classical antiquity; some come to enjoy the pleasant climate.

Land Transportation. The Greek network of railroads and roads is not well developed. Railroads over the mountains cannot compete with shipping around the deeply indented gulfs and inlets and, obviously, the islands have to rely on shipping. Even Epirus is without a railroad and the Peloponnesian and other railroads are narrow gauge. There is a single main line from Piraeus-Athens to Salonika, connecting through the Vardar Valley with Central and Eastern Europe, and east to Istanbul. The total road-net mileage is given as eight times that of the railroads, but only one-third is hard surfaced. Obviously inadequate, the roads of Greece are now being considerably improved, with an increased mileage of hard-surfaced roads.

Industry and Mining. It has been estimated that about 13 per cent of the Greeks are industrial workers and their dependents, and that an equal percentage are handicraftsmen and their dependents. This gives some measure of the slight development of mining and industry in Greece. Most manufactured products come from small artisans' shops. Much is connected with processing of agricultural products, such as the pressing of olive oil, the curing of tobacco, and the manufacture of wine. However, there are also some larger industries, many started by the refugees from Asia Minor, such as weaving of the famous Smyrna rugs. However, the leading products are chemicals, textiles, cement, and pottery. Except for Piraeus-Athens, hardly a city can be considered industrialized.

Mining, too, is on a small scale. There is a great variety of minerals (Fig. 7–12), but almost all deposits are small, either by nature or because they have been exploited for many centuries. Greece has little indigenous fuel; moderate-quality lignite, the only one available, is found in small mines in Thessaly and the Peloponnesos. Its production has considerably surpassed prewar figures. Of some slight importance are the lead and zinc mines near Athens, the magnesite on Euboea, and the molybdenite and chromite deposits in northern Greece.

ITALY

Historical Geography

Unity and Diversity. Unlike Greece, the middle peninsula of the Mediterranean has many places where human settlement could develop without recourse to the sea. Indeed, both coasts stretch hundreds of miles without harbors, made still less favorable for human habitation by malarial swamps, while a few miles inland fertile basins provide the basis for self-contained development. Only in southern Italy and Sicily do small secluded plains look toward the sea, offering a habitat comparable to that of Greece. They provided points of access for Phoenicians and Greeks, and later for Arabs, Norsemen, and Spaniards. All these nations have left their impress upon the landscape, some mainly in names, more in ruins and buildings, and all in the character of the people.

Throughout much of its history Italy was split into many states. The mountainous nature and long narrow shape of the peninsula account for it. However, the obstacles to unification are less rigid than in Greece. Tuscany, ancient Etruria, was split into city states, which were united in the 12-city federation of the Etruscans, and, since the Renaissance, under Florence. Other regions emerged as political units, such as Latium and Umbria, to break up again under certain historical conditions into minute units. The largest natural unit of the peninsula, the North Italian Plain, achieved unity only when it was imposed from the outside.

Cultural Unification. In spite of the geographical obstacles to unification, and in contrast to the persistence of numerous political units far into the nineteenth century, cultural and linguistic unification came early. This was an accompaniment of the first political unification of Italy, under the Romans, and later foreign invasions did not change this fact. This cultural and linguistic unification is the more remarkable because the Romans conquered people of different origin, civilization, and language. The Etruscans, Sards, Ligurians, and Sikels spoke non-Indo-European languages of unknown origin. But only the Etruscans had advanced culturally. Other languages encountered by the Romans were Indo-European, Greek in the south, Celtic in the north, Illyric (the predecessor of Albanian) in the northeast and southeast, and languages related to their own Latin language in the rest of the peninsula. Most of these languages disappeared from Italy in ancient times. Greek was spoken in a few places until recently, and there are still a few Albanian-speaking villages. The map of Italy shows the variegated story of naming the geographical features, from Ligurian Genoa, Illyrian Venice, and Celtic Bologna in the north to Greek Syracuse, Phoenician Palermo, and prehistoric Sicily and Sardinia in the south.

Italy entered the Renaissance period with a common written language, which had been given its final literary form by Dante. During this period city states gave place to somewhat larger political units. Two of the tiny medieval states, however, have survived to the present day—San Marino and Monaco. In many places, the boundaries established at that time survive as internal boundaries. The greatest obstacles to further unification were the States of the Church, ruled by the Pope and separating northern from southern Italy. Rome became the seat of the Pope when it was the center of the Roman Empire. The Papacy survived the empire, inheriting the central location and prestige of ancient Rome. The French Revolution gave a decisive impulse to unification, which was accomplished in 1871 despite temporary reverses. From 1871 to the rise of Fascism, Italy was a constitutional monarchy; today, Italy is a republic.

After 1871 the remaining national problem was the northern boundary. The linguistic, historical, and physiographic boundaries nowhere coincided. The result was the irredentist movement, born of the desire to unite all Italian-speaking areas. In the northwest the physiographic boundary of high Alpine ridges against France was maintained, sacrificing Savoy, historically a part of Italy, and Nice, linguistically Italian (1859). Some tiny districts were ceded to France in 1947, and the French-speaking Val d'Aosta was given restricted autonomy. The main struggle developed in the northeast. World War I brought Italy a boundary which, for strategic and economic reasons, was largely drawn through German-, Slovene-, or Croat-speaking areas. Italianization was pushed into the German-speaking Alto Adige (southern Tyrol) region. The emigration of Germans, agreed upon with Hitler, was only partially carried out. The peace treaty of 1946 left the area with Italy and provided for a restricted autonomy. Although the artificial boundary of 1919 has become a reality in many respects, complaints have nevertheless been heard time and again from the German-speaking inhabitants of Alto Adige that they do not get their due, especially that they are outnumbered by the inclusion of Italian-speaking Trentino in the autonomous region. After World War II, Italy had to yield to Yugoslavia her Dalmatian and Istrian acquisitions of 1919, among them cities such as Pola. Trieste, after a transitional period, was annexed to Italy in 1954.

Italian irredentism has also claimed Corsica and Malta. The first is Italian speaking and belonged to Pisa and Genoa for several centuries until it was annexed by France in 1768. Today it is closely integrated with France. Malta belonged to Sicily only from the end of the eleventh to the beginning of the sixteenth century, otherwise it was independent or belonged to African states, until it became British in 1800. It was a main anchor of the British "lifeline" to India through World War II. Its population is Roman Catholic. The language, however, is basically Arabic although the vocabulary has many Italian words.

Urban Development. Dispersed settlement is to be found in northern Italy and even predominates in Tuscany, Umbria, and parts of the Emilia. In most parts of Italy, however, large agglomerations are characteristic and the peasant often has to walk several miles to his fields. The scarcity of springs and (formerly) adequate protection (Fig. 7–17) is probably as much responsible as the gregarious nature of the people for these large agglomerations. Italians, even those who are illiterate, are much more aware of their glorious history than are most other people, which could hardly be otherwise in a country where the monuments of the past are everywhere present. There is hardly a village where the church or the palace of the lord does not remind one of the past; few are the churches which do not possess a picture, a statue, or some votive piece by some great master. Thus, an understanding of artistic values is widespread, though often unconscious. Many Italians have great appreciation for dramatic performances, for example, a good speech. Therefore, they are apt to applaud a political speaker for his oratorical performance rather than the content of his speech.

The history of most cities goes back to antiquity. A few of the ancient sites have been deserted, such as Greek Sybaris and the famous victim of a volcanic eruption, Pompeii. Ancient ruins are still the great attraction, foremost in Rome and Ravenna. Few new sites have been added since Roman times. Towns were added as adjuncts to ecclesiastical institutions, e.g., Monte Cassino or Loretto, but they are exceptional. Leghorn and Venice were founded on the growing deltas. There were shifts in importance. Naples, a minor Greek colony, became the seat of a kingdom and is the third city of Italy today. Merchant emporia such as Amalfi and Pisa won prominence and lost it again, Amalfi for lack of hinterland and Pisa because it is now cut off from the sea by the growth of the Arno Delta. Venice is struggling hard to maintain its position in the lagoon, which is threatened by the deposits of the Brenta, Adige, and Po rivers.

Of the great medieval maritime cities Genoa alone has maintained its importance, due to its deep harbor and easy access over low passes to the main Italian industrial area. The Renaissance palaces and churches of Siena, Perugia, Urbino, and many other cities are witnesses of a greater past as independent cities or capitals of petty states. Others such as Florence, Milan, Verona, and Bologna would be interesting cities even without such relics, because they became industrial and administrative centers or crossroads towns. There are, however, a few cities which make a thoroughly modern impression, such as Turin, Novara, or Leghorn, though they, too, are old urban sites.

Fig. 7–17. Scilla, north of Reggio di Calabria. The old castle atop the hill overlooks the town on the slopes and the narrow beach. (Photo: Enit Roma.)

Rome has again become the largest city of Italy, largely because of its political and religious position.

Population

Many racial strains and languages have contributed to the making of the Italian people and to the growth of a rather uniform nation. Small, dark, stout types prevail in the south; taller lighter ones in the north. But numerous local and individual variations also occur.

The Roman Catholic creed is professed by the great majority of the people (99.6 per cent), though many pay only lip service. Roman Catholicism is the state religion and is taught in the public schools. Hardly less impressive is the linguistic uniformity. The Val d'Aosta, with its French-speaking population, and Alto Adige, with its German majority, are the only areas where minority problems exist, and the republic has granted to these areas autonomous status and bilingual administration. The small group of Romansh-speaking Ladins in Alto Adige has allied itself closely to the Germans. The small groups of Albanians in scattered villages of Apulia and Catalans in a corner of Sardinia are insignificant.

Although there is one Italian written language, there are many widely differing spoken dialects. An illiterate peasant from Sicily is unable to communicate with a man from Piedmont, and the latter may not be able to understand the dialect of Friuli, the area northeast of Venice. With the spread of literacy, these dialect differences, tied to historical traditions, are decreasing as a menace to unity. Illiteracy is still widespread in southern Italy, where obligatory school attendance is difficult to enforce. While northern Italy has virtually no illiteracy, the over-all average was still around 20 per cent in 1953, with a slightly better showing for the male population. In many southern areas the increase in population outruns the supply of teachers and classrooms, which results in increased illiteracy. The difference in educational standards and the great poverty of the predominantly rural south have kept alive the lingering antagonism between northern and southern Italians.

It is difficult to give examples of national characteristics which apply to all Italians. Foreigners are apt to take the mentality of guides and other people catering to tourists as typical, and most Italians resent such a generalization. A definite trait is the general frugality, which is partly a result of poverty. Meals from wheat, such as macaroni and spaghetti, or corn, such as polenta in northern Italy, and dried rice in some regions, constitute the main food. Vegetables, fish, and cheese are often added. Until recently, light, cheap wine was the only unpolluted drink available in many areas. The food is usually cooked with olive oil. The one-sided nutrition, especially in the corn- and rice-eating areas gave rise to many deficiency diseases, such as pellagra, and lowered resistance to other diseases, such as tuberculosis.

Italy has a very high birth rate, which declined rapidly in prewar years. While it stood at an average of 36.9 per thousand during the years 1866 to 1872, it sank to approximately 18.3 per thousand in 1957. However, the death rate declined still faster, from 29.7 to 9.8 during the same period. Infant mortality is still very high, 103 per thousand just before the war, and about 53 per thousand in 1954. These rates mean a net increase of approximately 350,000 persons each year, a difficult burden for a relatively small country. Italy is unique in postwar Europe, for despite its apparent prosperity the number of its unemployed has diminished very slowly. The govern- ment has concluded agreements, for supported emigration, with Argentina, Venezuela, Brazil, Australia, and Canada. Agreements for seasonal emigration exist with Belgium, France, and Switzerland. The number of persons covered by these plans, however, is entirely inadequate. In 1956, total emigration was 135,000 persons.

Present Economic Life

When the unified Italian kingdom came into being it was primarily an agricultural country. Numerous cities had degenerated into local market centers. Only a few administrative centers (Turin, Venice, Milan, Parma, Florence, Rome, Naples, Palermo) and university towns (Padua, Bologna) had survived as cities. Tourist trade took the place of manufacture and export of products of high artisanship, because of both the unfavorable political conditions and the com- petition from Western European industry. Modern industry had hardly started.

Agriculture. By far the most numerous group of Italy's population is employed in agriculture, as in other less industrialized Southern European countries. There are many people on farms who are not needed and yet stay on with the family because they have no other choice. This "hidden unemployment" is especially characteristic of the backward areas of southern Italy. The result is a heavy concen- tration in the countryside of about 400 people per square mile.

Another characteristic of Italian agriculture is the extended use of manpower. Much agriculture is only gardening, partly because of the traditional attitudes which originated in the natural conditions of agriculture in a mountainous country of Mediterranean climate. Plains have been, and some still are, malarial. They are also exposed to cold winds in winter and do not allow the planting of the typical Mediterranean plants, while the summer drought makes it difficult to grow other products. Therefore unirrigated cereal production is restricted to certain regions. Where the land needs irrigation a network of narrowly spaced ditches requires much manual work. The same is true of work on the terraces and on the small plots wrung from stony slopes. On the other hand, the mild winters allow and require work the year round, though it never results in peak work loads such as harvesting within a short period.

Fig. 7–18. Farms in the Maremma, the drained coastal area in Tuscany. It was formerly dreaded because of malaria. (Italian Tourist Office.)

The prevalence and natural advantages of intensive cultivation of small plots contrast with the low yield of the great estates (*latifundi*) of southern Italy and Sicily. This is caused partly by the well-known evils of absentee ownership. The situation is worsened by the use of at least part of the land for crops needing intensive care, which cannot be expected from scarcely supervised landless laborers and sharecropping tenants. Under land-reform measures, these large estates are disappearing gradually as they are divided among small owners (Fig. 7–18). Cooperatives organized by these small owners are designed to retain the advantages of potential mechanization on large areas. There is yet another problem. Many small or medium-size farms are owned by the petty bourgeoisie of the small towns, who operate them as absentee landowners, but do not qualify as large landowners.

Among the fruit trees, olives and figs are best adapted to the climatic conditions as, likewise, are the grapevines which grow to considerable height and are often trained on stone pillars over which beams are laid. Trees and vines are planted at considerable distances, leaving space for other crops which thus receive enough light and sufficient protection from the direct sun. Occasionally three different crops are planted simultaneously on the same plot, and in the compass of two years a succession of as many as five crops may be grown. Vegetables and grains are equally important for such intercropping. Among industrial crops sugar beets, flax, and hemp are important. Italy is the only European rice-producing country of any importance, although its production is hardly one-half of one per cent of the world crop. The average yield per acre, however, is by far the highest in the world, more than one-third higher than that of Japan, its next competitor for rank in yield. In most of the North Italian Plain corn and rice need irrigation, but they can be grown without it along the lower Po and in the Roman Campagna. These growing conditions influence the distribution of the grain areas. Rice and corn are most abundant in the North Italian Plain, while wheat is grown in the drier parts of the Plain and in the dry limestone areas of southern Italy and Sicily.

Except for olive and fig trees, most fruit trees, especially the citrus fruits, need irrigation or special protection from the winter cold. They are outside their natural habitat in many cases and, like the oranges of the Riviera, are cultivated more for the tourist trade than because of their crop value. Their market has been endangered recently, because refrigerator service permits shipment from more-distant countries.

Other Non-industrial Resources. Like all countries of Mediterranean climate, the Italy of the Apennine peninsula has few forests. Many so-called forests are of the maqui type, which at best furnish wood for charcoal only. Fortunately, Italy possesses some good forests in the Alps, though timber still must be imported.

Animal husbandry plays a minor role in Italian economy. However, on the irrigated meadows of the Lombardy plain, cattle are abundant. This is the only area where milk and butter replace olive oil in general consumption. Most Italian cheese, such as gorgonzola or parmesan, is exported.

In Alto Adige, transhumance is the usual mode of cattle raising. Transhumance with large sheep and goat herds also occurs between the summer dry plains of southern Italy and the Apennines. Advancing irrigation and reclamation, however, continuously narrow the area available for transhumance. As in all Mediterranean countries, donkeys and mules are widely used, and horses are used in the North Italian Plain. The small plots and the location of fields on terraced slopes give these domestic animals a good chance to compete with mechanized equipment.

Fishing is carried on all along the Italian coast. For the most part, small boats are used and the haul is of moderate size, for reasons discussed on page 506. Only the small Italian sardines are caught in large numbers. Fish is an important ingredient of Italian food supply because of the scarcity of meat and the strict observance of the Catholic fast days. Meat and fish combined, however, constitute a minor portion of the food.

Commerce and Communications. At unification, Italy lowered its tariff walls. Though this proved a handicap for the agricultural southern provinces, Italian industry and commerce developed rapidly. At the same time, the Suez Canal was opened. Naples and Genoa rose to become important harbors on one of the world routes; Trieste, still Austrian at the time, Venice, and—as a passenger-embarkation point—Brindisi profited too. Genoa had the advantage of easy access to the rapidly developing industrial centers of northern Italy and even of Switzerland and southern Germany. Naples and Palermo became embarkation points for the increasing emigration; Venice and Trieste were rivals for the commerce of their overlapping hinterlands. Until 1914, Trieste profited from its political attachment to the Austro-Hungarian monarchy. Venice was threatened by the silting of the shallow lagoon, but favored by shorter routes to the Italian hinterland. Trieste and Genoa became the seats of the large shipping companies of Austria and Italy. Trieste, now handicapped by the closeness of the border with Yugoslavia, has lost its geographic hinterland in the countries of the Iron Curtain, and is losing ground in Austria by the competition with the North Sea ports.

The Italian railroad net, and somewhat later the road net, was expanded and improved after unification. Because of the shape of the peninsula, no one center arose. The railway lines crossing the Alps focus on Turin, Milan, and Bologna. The route from southern France follows the coast of the Riviera, although many tunnels are needed. From Genoa it runs parallel to the coast to Rome and Naples. The important lines from the north join it either at Genoa or from Bologna, via Florence, at Rome. From Turin an important route follows the outer edge of the Apennines, through Bologna, along the Roman Way, and along the Adriatic coast to Bari and Brindisi. Before the air age this was part of the shortest route from western Europe to India. Another important international route crosses the North Italian Plain via Milan, Verona, Padua, and Venice to Trieste and the Balkans. Many Italian railroads are electrified, especially in the north, close to the waterpower from the Alpine rivers. Italian roads are among the best in Europe, partly because of the skill of the Italian road worker. An interesting route will be added when the Mont Blanc tunnel is finished.

Power, Mining, and Heavy Industry. Coal-poor Italy is among the leading nations in the development of waterpower. Between 1938

Fig. 7–19. Overhead electric cable across the Strait of Messina, here about 3 miles wide. The view is from the Calabrian side, toward Sicily.

and 1957, electric-power output, mainly hydroelectric, nearly tripled and numerous transmission lines were constructed (Fig. 7–19). The main area of waterpower is in the western, Trentino, and Alto Adige sections of the Alps, where more than 50 per cent of the potential sites have been developed. Those which are still undeveloped require more complex engineering and greater capital investment. There are a few coal mines in Sardinia and Val d'Aosta and lignite deposits in Tuscany (Fig. 7–12). In the last few years, however, the production of these mines has declined, and coal is being imported in increasing volume. Today, the United States is Italy's main source of coal, providing the fuel which formerly came from England, the German Ruhr, and Polish Silesia.

Intensive prospecting has led to the discovery of oil both on the northern Adriatic coast not far from Ravenna and in Sicily near Ragusa. In explorations for oil, large sources of natural gas were discovered along the southern rim of the North Italian Plain. The production of natural gas and oil, however, does not begin to satisfy Italy's needs. The extreme shortage of power and fuel resources led Italy to pioneer in the use of volcanic steam, at Larderello in Tuscany.

There are a few iron-ore mines on the island of Elba and in Tuscany in the Catena Metallifera (the name means ore-bearing range), but their output is low. The need to import iron ore has caused much of Italy's heavy industry to locate near Genoa and the neighboring harbor Savona. Shipbuilding is important here, and also in Trieste and vicinity. The great wharves of Monfalcone, a few miles northwest of Trieste, are still on the Italian side of the border. Another branch of the metal industry is the production of automobiles. The Fiat factory in Turin is one of the leading European firms in this field. Italian heavy industry has specialized in a few lines requiring little raw material. Ball bearings are an excellent example.

A few minerals are abundant and can be exported. Foremost among them is sulphur, from Tuscany and especially Sicily, where the small port Agrigento specializes in it. American competition, however, threatens to ruin the sulphur trade. Another export product is mercury, coming from mines in Tuscany. Bauxite is found on Monte Gargano and in the southern projection of Apulia, both in the limestone areas closely related to that of the Dinaric system. All other mineral output, such as that of manganese, lead, and zinc, is insignificant.

Other Industries. Because the lack of coal and iron has hampered the development of Italian heavy industry, other industries took the lead. Foremost has been the textile industry in most of its branches, especially silk and rayon products. This industry is centered in the Lombardy center of the North Italian Plain, in the cities of Milan, Como, Brescia, and Bergamo, and many others of less importance. Here hydroelectric power and skilled workers are available. The division of the land into tiny parcels, and the large number of children in the family, forces many members, frequently the father, to earn money outside the farm. The basis of silk fabrication, the silkworm, is tended in all parts of Italy. Mulberry trees are especially frequent in northern Italy.

Cotton and wool industries are only a little less important than silk weaving. More recently, the chemical industry has also come into prominence, especially the manufacture of sulphuric acid and copper sulphate, which could draw on the native resources just at the moment when the external market for these mining products was shrinking because of American competition. Among the food-processing industries, sugar refineries and fish canning should be mentioned.

Though Italian industry gives work to a substantial number of workers—more than 6 million, one-third of them in large concerns— the possibilities for further expansion of most industries seem definitely limited because of the lack of raw materials. Imported raw materials can be used for the internal market but can be used in competition in the export market only when wages are kept at a starvation level. Italy's attempt to create a protected market overseas through acquisition of colonies ended in failure. The Italian colonists still remaining in Eritrea and Libya can, however, be relied upon to buy as much as possible in the Italian market.

Trade Balance. Italy is comprised of some small but very productive and several poor regions. Therefore, in all periods of progress, population quickly outran domestic supply, in Roman as well as in modern times. The present population density of nearly 900 per square mile of cultivable land is one of the highest known in Europe. The handicaps which the nation faces in its development of large-scale industries are also responsible for the inability to pay for food imports by exports. In prewar times, the Italian economy was sustained by remittances from Italians abroad, the savings of the returning emigrants, the earnings of the merchant marine, and the earnings of some Italian insurance companies which had branches all over Europe and the Near East. The restrictions on emigration have caused the first two sources to dwindle in importance. But the steadily increasing tonnage of the merchant marine is making important contributions to a better trade balance.

Post-World War II Trends. World War II put a heavy stress on the Italian economy, although actual destruction by bombing was less severe than in many other European countries, and some of the famous historical sites, notably Rome, were spared. At the end of the war, industrial output had sunk to 40 per cent of the prewar level, but it reached the prewar level again in 1949. Since then the rise has been steady, but the output is still low when compared to Italy's augmented population and the great need to improve the living standard in many of its regions. Best progress has been made in northern Italy, in areas which had been the most advanced economically before the war. Progress in southern Italy has been made also, but not enough to close or even to narrow the gap with the north.

Very promising is the progress made in the reclamation of swampy, malarial areas. The program was begun, though overadvertised, under

Mussolini. The most spectacular results are to be seen in Sardinia, where the Campidano has been drained and the Flumendosa River has been harnessed to produce hydroelectric power. These two developments may well make possible the settlement in Sardinia not only of the island's landless rural workers but also of landless persons from the mainland. The population of Sardinia could double within a few years. Land reform in southern Italy and Sicily started slowly, but it is gaining momentum. The reforestation and industrialization taking place should also assist in improving the economy. A public agency, the Cassa per il Mezzogiorno, founded in 1950, has allocated considerable funds to a 12-year program for developing the south.

The Former Colonies. Italian Somaliland was restored to Italian trusteeship for a period of 10 years, ending in 1960. Now called Somalia, it is a small semidesert strip whose economy must continue to be supported by Italy. Eritrea (now in a federal union with Ethiopia), Libya (which has become independent), and even Ethiopia still have some economic and cultural contact with Italy, partly through the settlers who have remained after those nations regained their independence. Their number, however, is dwindling.

THE IBERIAN PENINSULA

Historical Geography

Interior and Fringe. The fact that the interior uplands tower above the narrow coastal lowlands has played a great role in Spanish history. The Civil War showed again how difficult it is to defend these lowlands. On the other hand, a strong sea power such as Great Britain could hold on to a part of the fringe, the isolated rock of Gibraltar. British sea power was also a major factor in helping Portugal preserve its independence from Spain. Portugal's face is turned seaward even more than that of other marginal regions of Europe. It has, with one exception, the only rivers of the peninsula which can be entered from the sea, and its territory extends as far inland as the head of river navigation, beyond which deep gorges hinder further river communication. The boundary between Portugal and Spain passes through some of the most thinly settled parts of the peninsula. Portugal conquered the area south of the Tagus River long before Castile penetrated as far south, acquiring in war a distinct national consciousness which became indestructible in the great age of discoveries. Portugal's interest overseas took quite a different turn from that of Spain. Its colonial empire was genuinely based on sea power and never became another overseas continental empire. The Portuguese language became an established literary language through the influence of the poems of Camoëns, "the Dante of Portugal."

When the Spanish Christians gradually recovered from the Arab conquest of the eighth century they formed a number of small states in the northern mountains. These states became united under the crown of Castile from the time they expanded onto the plateau, which made unity feasible and also imperative in order to resist Arab pressure. From this center Castile imposed unity upon the coastal lowlands as ancient Rome had forced it upon Italy, not from a national feeling of community. The coastal regions, however, have retained their peculiarities, either in dialect and character, as the Gallegos of Galicia, the Asturians, and the Andalusians, or in the political separatism of the Catalans and Basques.

Roman and Arabic Influences. Many peoples and cultures have influenced Spain and Portugal. Many names, sites of cities, racial peculiarities, and the Basque language of the western Pyrenees survive from the prehistoric and the early Celtic and Iberian population. Along the coast Phoenician and Carthaginian colonies left their imprint. Some institutions and a few buildings can be traced to the Vandal, Visigothic, and Suevian invaders of the fifth century.

The strongest and most lasting influences, in this respect, came from the Romans and Arabs. The most impressive monuments of Rome's rule are the Spanish and Portuguese languages. The Romans built roads around their main centers, Caesarea Augusta (Saragossa), Asturica (Astorga, north of Valladolid), Emerita (Mérida), Hispalis (Seville), and Olisipo (Lisbon). The Roman provincial capital, Tarraco (Tarragona, southwest of Barcelona); the pre-Roman center, Saguntum; and the Carthaginian capital, Carthago Nova (Cartagena), were connected by a coastal road. Some of the paved roads and arched stone bridges are still usable. Scarcely a city of any importance in Roman times has disappeared from the map. Of much later foundation are the fortress cities of the Christian-Islamic wars—Castile is the land of castles—religious centers such as Santiago di Compostela, and administrative centers such as Madrid.

The Romans also brought some of the cultivated plants to Spain, for example, several fruit trees. Far more important, however, was the contribution of the Arabic-Moorish period. In the coastal areas citrus fruits, sugar cane, and cotton are outstanding contributions, closely connected with an elaborate system of irrigation. Water rights are still administered according to Moorish customs, while in every other respect Roman law prevails. Many of the Moorish castles and mosques still stand, the latter converted into churches. Christian artisans, trained under Moorish rule, influenced Spanish architectural styles decisively.

More difficult to trace is the racial mixture, undoubtedly strong, but hard to separate from earlier Phoenician and Jewish admixture. Arabic names are most frequent in southern Spain and southern and central Portugal, but appear occasionally in both countries as far as north of the Douro. Examples are, among rivers, Guadalquivir (Wadi al kabir, "the great river"), among mountains, Mulhacén (Mulay Hassan), among regions, Algarve (al gharb, "the west"), among settlements, Gibraltar (gebel al Tariq, "rock of Tariq"). A less fortunate inheritance is the survival of large estates bestowed by the conquerors upon knights, religious orders, and bishoprics.

The eight centuries of war against the Mohammedan Moors also molded the character of the Spanish and to a lesser degree the Portuguese people. Religious fanaticism, intolerance, and the idealization of the fighting life characterized certain periods of the history of all European nations, but nowhere with such lasting effect. The Roman Catholic Church became so intimately connected with national liberation that it could survive the crisis of the Reformation with comparative ease.

The Colonies. The two Iberian countries led in geographical discoveries and became the first truly colonial powers. The waxing and waning of their colonial empires have historical as well as geographical causes. The discoveries were, in their first phase, virtually the continuation of the struggles of the reconquista.[5] After having reached the southern coast, the Portuguese crossed into Morocco and continued along the west-African coast. The Iberian Peninsula was the most advanced vantage point of Europe toward the southwest, either on the route to India or to the Antilles. It had a seafaring tradition because of its Mediterranean coast, and Catalonia participated in the great period of Italian shipping and expansion to the east, in the late Middle Ages. The peninsula also had an Atlantic front, and both Seville and Lisbon became leading European ports for a while. However, conquest, emigration, and the expulsion of the Moors and the Jews sapped the manpower of both Spain and Portugal. The decline of Spain's national vigor was accelerated by her close connection with the Catholic Church, a connection which involved the nation in unproductive European wars. The easy influx of American gold accustomed people to look down on arduous, less rewarding

[5] The period in Iberian history when the Christians reconquered the country from the Moors.

work. Finally, the mountain barrier of the Pyrenees made the peninsula difficult to reach from most of Europe, and hence unfit to serve as a permanent base for overseas shipping. The national-liberation movement in the Americas overthrew the weakened colonial empires.

The Atlantic island possessions of both Spain and Portugal, and the Portuguese colonies of Goa, Diu, and Daman in India, Macao on the Chinese coast, and half of the island of Timor in Indonesia, are the only relics of this great period, together with a few coastal way stations and fortified points. Based on the latter, Portugal was able to win and hold new African colonies in Guinea, Mozambique, and Angola in the nineteenth century. Spain did the same in northern Morocco (now lost to the kingdom of Morocco), Ifni, Rio de Oro, and Guinea.

Constitutional Development. The rule of one province over others seems best assured by a central absolute power. On the peninsula, Castile occupied such a central geographical position. Thus many Castilians came to uphold absolutism both in its traditional form and as modern dictatorship. Liberal ideas are mainly French importations, brought to literary circles in the eighteenth century, and to the masses by the armies of Napoleon. But in this respect Spain, behind the barrier of the Pyrenees, seems rather remote from Europe, more so than countries not contiguous to France.

Portugal, with her face to the Atlantic Ocean, maintained closer contacts with France and England, and was somewhat more influenced by Western European thought. After a protracted struggle, it became a republic in 1910. At present it is governed by an attenuated form of dictatorship, based on a social program developed by the Catholic Church.

Urban Developments. The distribution of Iberian cities is strongly determined by the position of the central highlands. Most large cities are located on the periphery. Of these peripheral cities the most important is Barcelona, the Spanish thriving industrial capital. The dominating center has concentrated all functions in its only large city, Madrid, which has replaced the older, similarly central city of Toledo as the capital. Toledo, located on a detached part of the plateau, surrounded on three sides by the deep and steep-sided Tagus Valley, was an excellent site as long as defense was imperative. When the Moorish wars ceased the disadvantages of cramped space and obstructed communications became obvious. Some cities of the northern Meseta, such as León, Burgos, Valladolid, and Salamanca played their part at a time when a frontier crossed the high plateau, and since have stagnated.

All Iberian cities show the influence of past history in their architecture. French Romanesque and Gothic style came with feudal knights and fighting orders to the northern half of the peninsula. All along the pilgrims' road to Santiago di Compostela are the splendid churches of this period. Other cities, too, have grown around ecclesiastical foundations. Arabic architecture contributed splendid monuments in the south from the Alhambra ("the red one") of Granada to the mosque churches of Córdoba and Seville and the Alcazár ("the castle") of Toledo. The wealth of the Indies made possible the erection of famous works of Renaissance and Baroque architecture all over the peninsula.

In most areas the climate permits many activities to go on outdoors, and most Spaniards seem to enjoy the crowd. However, less loud and vivacious talk is heard than in Italy or Greece. Traditions still have a firm hold on many groups of the population. It is often difficult to find people who are willing to do certain necessary but lowly work. They do not regard it as beneath their dignity to live from charity. The lag in mining development, and of industry in some areas, is partly due to this reluctance to do manual work (aside from agriculture) because it is regarded as socially degrading.

Spanish houses show oriental influence, especially in the south. Designed to keep women secluded, the enclosed yards and walls with few windows are reminiscent of Mohammedan cities. The patios of the more pretentious houses have gardens and fountains. The custom of having iron lattice work in the windows is found far into northern Spain, and many of the lattices are true works of art. Flat roofs, on which to spend the cooler hours, are confined to the south. Elsewhere in Spain, the round tiles of Roman derivation are used to cover gently sloping roofs (Fig. 7–20). Stone and brick houses prevail in most parts of the country, except in the northern mountainous region where native wood is available. The bricks are often unbaked, of the type called adobe. Walls are frequently whitewashed, and the lime kiln is a characteristic adjunct of the town.

In the drier parts of the Meseta, windmills are another characteristic feature of the landscape. Towns and cities of northern Spain frequently have enclosed squares, which are entered through passages and which give the feeling of an enlarged patio. Balconies and arcades are much used in town houses. Outside the closely built towns there are few buildings except for the amphitheater used for bullfighting. The older parts of cities and towns are irregular and narrow, although sections built up since the Renaissance show rectangular patterns. There is scarcely a Spanish city which does not harbor architectural treasures from the Moorish, Romanesque, Gothic, or Baroque period, more rarely from the Roman or Renaissance period, hardly any from the Carthaginian or Visigothic era.

Each coastal region has its own well-developed center. The importance of some of these centers dates back to Phoenician times with Cádiz and Cartagena; to Roman days with Saragossa, Pamplona, and Seville; or to the early Middle Ages with Barcelona and Valencia. Some cities, though much older, have acquired real importance only

Fig. 7–20. Pedraza, a small village near Segovia. Note the characteristic architecture, the barren slopes in the background, and the lack of women in the dusty courtyard. (Spanish Tourist Office.)

with modern industry and mining, such as Bilbao, Santandér, and Oviedo, and their harbors Gijón and Portugalete. In Portugal only Lisbon and Oporto became large cities. The old university town of Coimbra has remained small, and Setúbal, a specialized fishing port.

Portuguese farm houses are often several storied, the first story serving as a barn. There are a great variety of house types in this small country. They are adapted to the various local building materials, ranging from granite and limestone to sun-baked clay. In some areas walled-in small plots (*quintas*) are characteristic. They enclose the house, orchard, fields, and a small pasture. Only Lisbon and Oporto should be called modern cities. Although monasteries and churches are not conspicuous in the landscape, buildings of ancient architecture are numerous, though less so than in Spain. Ruins of castles are frequent north of the Tagus, where the war with the Moors lasted longer than in quickly overrun southern Portugal.

SPAIN

Population

It has been stressed in the historical section that the apparent uniformity of the Spanish people covers many differences. Dialects differ widely and regional consciousness is very strong. The Gallego dialect of Galicia is closer to Portuguese than to Castilian, Catalan is claimed to be a separate language, and Castilian is used as the official language only. There is only one undisputed linguistic minority, the Basques, living in three small provinces off the Bay of Biscay. Spain's religious uniformity is even more pronounced, Roman Catholicism being not only the state religion but in fact the creed of an overwhelming majority. Tensions result, however, from anticlerical attitudes of both workers and intellectuals.

Like that of all Southern European nations, the Spanish population is increasing rapidly. However, because the birth rate and the death rate are falling at the same pace, the proportion of increase has not changed much. Spanish vital statistics are generally somewhat more favorable than Italian figures, but still reflect the social problem of a backward, largely illiterate peasantry. School attendance is obligatory and illiteracy among the younger generation is definitely decreasing.

Population density varies. The whole interior, with the exception of the urban agglomeration around Madrid, is very thinly populated, most sparsely on the steppe of the upper Ebro Basin and of La Mancha southeast of Madrid. In contrast, several coastal regions have very high densities. This is the case in the mining and industrial areas of Catalonia and the Basque provinces, and somewhat less in Asturias. Areas of intensive irrigation around Valencia and Murcia and the coastal strip from Málaga to Almería show a high concentration of population. None of these favorable conditions, however, can explain the equally high densities of preponderantly rural Galicia and Andalusia. The unhealthy overpopulation in these areas has led to continual emigration. Most of the emigration to the Americas originates here, although many emigrants are from the Basque provinces. Argentina and Cuba are the main countries of destination. However, emigration does not play as important a role in Spain as it does in other Southern European countries.

Most Spaniards are very conscious of the past glory of their country. The memory of the fight against Islam, as well as the golden age (*siglo de oro*), is very vivid. The century-old state of affairs has fostered a widespread feeling of resentment and suspicion of foreign nations. Together with the actual remoteness from the rest of western Europe, this has contributed to the peculiar Spanish brand of isolationism.

Present Economic Life

Mediterranean landforms and climate are ideally suited to a garden economy based on manual work and irrigation. Such an economy, however, is very susceptible to disturbances from outside. In addition, only part of Spain is truly Mediterranean. Spain was not involved in World War II, but it had its own Civil War in 1936–39, and the devastation was so severe that its industry could not profit from World War II as those of other neutrals did. The general stagnation of the Spanish economy dates back to the exhausting accomplishments of the sixteenth century. Since the seventeenth century, Spain has been economically behind other European countries.

Agriculture and Fishing. Despite the potentialities of industrial development, agriculture is and will probably remain Spain's main economic activity. It has unexploited possibilities. Though the number of animals and the volume of some minor crops have increased, the harvests of the key crops, barley, corn, and wheat, are still below the pre-Civil War level. Wheat is the main crop of the better soils of the dry northern Meseta, while the shallow soils and still-greater aridity of the southern Meseta permit the cultivation of barley only. Moist northwestern Spain is a land of corn and pastures. Most of the cattle of Spain are found in Galicia, Asturias, and the Pyrenees. The southern half of the country is characterized by olive groves (Fig. 7–21), vineyards, and orange groves. Spain is the world's greatest producer of olive oil and the largest exporter of oranges (Fig. 7–22). The orange groves are closely confined to the southern and eastern coasts, although the olive tree is also found inland. Other Mediterranean fruit trees, such as almonds, pomegranates, and figs, are found in the same general area, and also tropical ones, such as carobs and date palms. The date palm, though it grows in a wider area, bears fruit only in the famous groves of Elche, near Murcia. All these tropical and subtropical products need irrigation and are most plentiful in areas where the old Moorish irrigation installations are well preserved, around Valencia, Murcia, Almería, Málaga, and inland in the mountain valley of Granada and the plains of the Ebro and

Guadalquivir. The intensively cultivated oases in semiarid surround-ings are called *huertas*, where two crops are harvested, or the Arabic equivalent, *vegas*, where only one crop is possible. From these areas western Europe receives its early spring vegetables. The products of the vineyards are exported either as grapes and raisins or as wine. Sherry received its name from the town of Jerez de la Frontera. Inter-cropping is less frequent than in Italy, though it occurs, especially in

Fig. 7–21. An old olive grove in Andalusia. (Spanish Tourist Office.)

the open olive groves. Recently rice has become important in Anda-lusia, in the Ebro Basin, and along the east coast.

A few other products, of secondary importance, are interesting for one reason or another, some because of their importance in Moorish times. Examples are cotton, sugar cane, the mulberry tree, and the cork oak, which grows along the border of Spain and Portugal. Until recently, these two countries had a monopoly of its products, but North Africa has become a serious competitor in the last two decades.

It is still questioned whether the steppe of the interior upland is natural or is a product of the destruction by man and his animals at an early period. One argument for the existence of a genuine steppe is that the Meseta shares the esparto grass, a coarse bunch grass, with the North African steppe. It is used for mats, baskets, braided shoes, etc. Great herds of sheep and goats are kept in these areas. The merino sheep is a native of Spain, though the best merino wool no longer comes from this country. In summer the flocks have to be brought to the sierras. The wide tracks of these migrations are char-

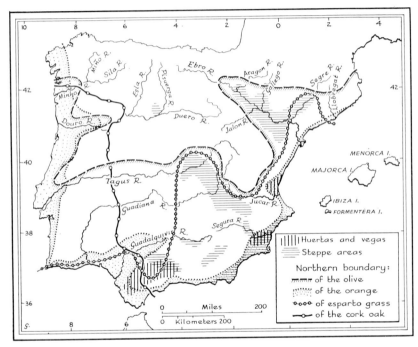

Fig. 7–22. Mediterranean products of the Iberian Peninsula.

acteristic of many parts of Spain, and the strife between the *Mesta*, the organization of the big sheepowners, and the peasants fills many pages of Spanish history. In this instance modern technology has brought beneficial changes to Spain. Today, the animals are shipped by railroad and much land can be reclaimed for agriculture. On the other hand, the goat is still unrestrained from damaging tree growth, more so than in any other Mediterranean country.

Another reason for the backwardness of Spanish agriculture is the large estates owned by absentee landlords, created in the later phases of the reconquista. Several attempts at land reform have been undertaken, yet nothing decisive has been accomplished against the opposition of the large landowners, including the Church. In the Badajoz region a test project was launched recently which shows promise of success. Northern Spain, however, remains a land of small land-owners. By progressive division some of the farms have become so small that they hardly can be called viable. The situation is worst in Galicia, where practically all farms have been divided into minute parts.

In the Basque provinces and Galicia, Spain has a coastal popula-tion with a long maritime tradition. They have been engaged mainly in fishing, the only economic activity not significantly interrupted by the Civil War. The volume of catch is constantly increasing. The livestock destruction which occurred during the Civil War may have had something to do with the replacement of meat by fish in the general diet.

Communications. A great obstacle to the development of industry in Spain is the peripheral distribution of the main population centers. Shipping around the coasts is inexpensive but slow. Railroad and truck traffic are both undeveloped. Spanish railroads are slow and the trains are infrequent. There is a well-developed road-and-railroad net on the map, but its efficiency is very low, and the meshes of the grid are rather large. This is partly because of the mountains which must be crossed and partly because of the broad gauge. Prompted by her fear of invasion, Spain chose a very broad gauge in the early years of railroad building. This necessitates great curves and makes con-struction of tunnels and bridges very expensive. Therefore, seldom can more than one track be laid. Because of the high costs, about a quarter of the tracks were laid in narrow gauge. Some of these lines, once regarded as feeder lines, could do better today if through service could be given. All these factors make railway traffic slow and expensive.

Although it has numerous good natural harbors, Spain has a mer-chant marine which totals only a little more than 1.25 million tons, most of them fishing vessels and small coastal steamers. The bulk of the traffic to other countries is carried in foreign bottoms.

Mining. In many respects, Spain possesses a better basis for a modern economy than any other Southern European country. Its power basis is assured by rich coal deposits, and the large rivers, even in the dry south, are a permanent source of waterpower. The iron ores of the Cantabrian Mountains (Fig. 7–12) are among the best in Europe—41 to 57 per cent iron—and are exported from Bilbao to several countries. Those of Asturias are located close to coal mines.

Little smelting is done in Spain itself. This is partly because the mines are owned by foreign, mostly English, capital, and partly because of the precapitalistic psychology of many Spaniards; the rich aristocrats are not ready to invest money in anything other than land. Oviedo, Bilbao, and Santander are the main centers of the northern Spanish mining districts. Other mining districts are the Sierra Morena, where mercury, copper, and lead are the main products, and the Baetic Cordillera, which has a great variety of products. Almadén is one of the world's richest mercury mines. Despite centuries-old exploitation, Spain still produces more than a fourth of the world's mercury. In other metals, such as gold, silver, lead, and copper, Spain lost its leading position either in late antiquity or as late as the nineteenth century, and its resources of zinc, tin, and tungsten have never played a very important role. Recently pyrites, oil shale, and potash have grown in importance. It is surprising how little this mineral wealth contributes to Spain's economy. However, there has been a steady though slow increase in coal and iron-ore production, which more than doubled between 1951 and 1957.

Industry. The main center of Spanish industry, including heavy industry, is Catalonia and its capital Barcelona, rather remote from the mining districts. This industrial vigor is commonly attributed to the different psychological attitude of the Catalans. Coal from northern Spain must be shipped around the peninsula, so a number of the hydroelectric plants and imported coal furnish most of the power for Catalonian industry. Textile industries lead, with many small-scale light industries following.

Madrid is growing in importance as an industrial center. The metal industry in the northern part of Spain, and to a lesser degree textiles in Andalusia and in the larger cities along the Mediterranean coast, are the only other industries worth mentioning. The greatest handicap to the development of a healthy Spanish industry is the lack of a domestic market among the desperately poor peasantry and the underpaid workers.

Overseas Spain. The small Spanish overseas empire has little economic value. The most important possession is the Canary Islands, officially a part of metropolitan Spain. Their products are similar to those of Mediterranean Spain. They are a frequented tourist resort and have a certain importance as a halfway station on the route to South America. The islands in the Gulf of Guinea produce cocoa and coffee. The enclave of Ifni and the Spanish Sahara are of strategic and prestige value rather than an economic asset.

PORTUGAL

Population

The people of Portugal have attained uniformity of religion and of language unequaled elsewhere. The religion of Portugal is overwhelmingly Roman Catholic. Portuguese is a separate Romance language, with an ancient and valuable literature. It may be true that Portuguese is more closely related to Castilian than is Catalan, but it certainly cannot be regarded as a Spanish dialect. Within Portugal, dialect differences are insignificant. The linguistic boundary between Portugal and Spain coincides very closely with the political boundary, a natural consequence of the fact that the political boundary antedates the written fixation of both Spanish and Portuguese. The political boundary is one of the most stable in the world. Except for one small correction, it has not been changed since the thirteenth century.

The Portuguese birth rate and death rate are both high. Though the latter has shown a considerable decline lately, it is still the highest in Southern Europe. The high mortality does not begin to offset the far higher number of births, and hence Portugal has one of the highest known net reproduction rates.

This overpopulation has led to a large emigration. Though Portuguese statistics are rather unsatisfactory, it appears that proportionally more Portuguese have emigrated during the last decades than have emigrants from any other country except Ireland. The bulk of the emigration has gone to Portuguese-speaking Brazil. As there is considerable unauthorized emigration, available figures tell only part of the story. Some of the successful emigrants return later with their savings. It is not without significance that literacy among these emigrants was higher than the average of the country. Thus, emigration takes away from the country a higher proportion of its better-educated and presumably more ambitious and more intelligent elements. It is obvious that the center of cultural activity in the Portuguese language is no longer Portugal but Brazil. Illiteracy in Portugal is high (59.6 per cent in 1950), and is higher among women than among men. Even among boys from 10 to 14 years of age about 33 per cent are illiterate. Among women of 60 years and over the percentage is 71.5.

The population is unequally distributed. Northern Portugal is a land of dense population on small holdings. In the south, in the area of large estates, low density prevails. Only the extreme south, Algarve, is a land of small proprietors. About 17.5 per cent of the whole territory is in the hands of large landowners. The density of population decreases in most regions from the coastal plain toward the interior upland. The international boundary, as we have noted, runs through a very thinly inhabited area.

The Portuguese resemble the Spaniards physically, and on an average are only slightly taller. There are also more individuals of Near Eastern type. How much this is due to Phoenician colonization and how much to later Arabic and Jewish admixture is unknown. Likewise, it is debated whether the Negroid features of many individuals should be traced to a prehistoric Negro population or to the influx of slaves in the age of discovery.

The Portuguese have many traits in common with their Castilian-Spanish cousins. They are a proud, sensitive people, given to vainglorious daydreaming, and are easily discouraged by obstacles. The weight of tradition is felt in Portugal even more strongly than in Spain, especially among the illiterate peasants, who are reluctant to accept improvements. The Portuguese, however, are gayer and more accommodating than the Castilians. The conservative nature of the country is seen among other things in the retention of many costumes, or at least parts of them, such as the strawbraided raincoats, the leather apron worn to protect the legs in the thorny maqui, and the colorful woolen caps or felt hats. Agricultural tools are often primitive, unchanged for centuries. No other European country has among its fishing boats such a large proportion of sailing vessels and rowboats. These often have high bows and sterns and are gaudily painted.

Present Economic Life

Portugal is a poor country. The great age of discovery exhausted its material and population resources and was followed by a period of dependence on Spain (1580–1640). Portugal has never recovered from the losses suffered during this period. It profited in a moderate way from its neutrality during both the Spanish Civil War and World War II. The dictatorial regime has maintained rigid economic controls and secured a surplus of revenues over expenditures since the war. The economic situation has improved, but has not changed basically.

Agriculture. Of all the countries of Southern Europe, Portugal is the most uniform, not so much because of its small size as because it belongs entirely to the western fringe of the Iberian Peninsula. There is a gradual transition from the typical Mediterranean climate in the south to the Atlantic humid climate of Galicia. Most of the important Mediterranean products such as olives, grapes, oranges, cork oaks, and fig trees grow in low-lying parts of the country (Fig. 7–22). Cork oaks and olive trees are planted in open stands, and between the olive trees vegetables and occasionally grain are grown. Vines are trained on trellises in the northern part of the country; elsewhere, they are kept continuously trimmed as low bushes. Wine and cork are among the three main exports, fish being the most important. Port wine is so called because its export is legally restricted to the port of Oporto. Madeira wines also find a good market abroad. Other significant products are turpentine and resin, from the large pine forests in the sand dunes. Other forests are mostly maqui, which furnish only some wood for domestic fuel. Portugal is, however, one of the few countries where reforestation has a rather lengthy record.

Grains are widely planted, corn in the wetter north on small terrace plots and wheat on the large estates of southern Portugal. Irrigation is slowly spreading and with it the cultivation of rice. Only in northern Portugal can the spring flood of the rivers be used for rice cultivation. The grain crops, however, are not sufficient for the needs of the growing population, and more has to be imported. Neither the cultivation by small landowners working without capital and with antiquated methods nor that by tenants on large estates of absentee landowners produces good results. The per-acre yields are the lowest in all of Europe except Greece, and nearly the lowest known anywhere. About half of the cultivated area is left fallow every year. Other areas could be drained or improved. Taken all together, Portugal could increase its agricultural production considerably.

The small area of Algarve, between the south coast and the Sierra de Monchique, the last spur of the Sierra Morena, is the orchard of Portugal. Mediterranean and some tropical fruit trees, such as bananas and date palms, are grown here in well-tended small plots. The agriculture of Madeira and the Azores is of similar character; the latter specialize in pineapples, the cultivation of which occupies 60 to 70 per cent of the population.

Fishing. Portugal is dependent for part of its food and for much of its export revenue on the products of its fishing industry. Among the fish, sardines occupy the first place. When the shoals of sardines did not appear along the Portuguese coast in the 1948 and 1949 seasons, it caused a serious crisis in the entire economy. The importance of the fishing season for the Portuguese economy may be judged by the fact that, according to value, an average of 83 per cent of the entire production of the country is agricultural, and 4 per cent products of the sea, but for exports the figures are 60 and 20 per cent, respectively. The ancient participation of Portuguese trawlers on the Newfoundland Banks is declining and codfish is now imported.

Mining and Industry. There are many small mines in Portugal (Fig. 7–12). Only wolframite, the mother ore of tungsten, is important, and probably the dependence of both the Axis and the Allies on this metal helped to keep Portugal out of World War II. Coal and iron ore are mined in some quantity, but this is not sufficient. Though little coal is needed for heating or industry, and charcoal is used for cooking in the villages, coal has to be imported, mostly for the railroads. Most of the industry is on a small scale, and is concentrated in Lisbon and Oporto. But even in these two cities workers constitute only a small proportion of the population. Portuguese industry is beginning to supply part of the needs of the colonies, which repay primarily in badly needed foodstuffs.

Communications. Although much work has been done to improve roads, the dirt road is still predominant in Portugal. Two-wheeled wooden carts are still in use. In many mountainous sections donkeys and mules on bridle paths are the only means of transportation. The railroad net is sparse. Portugal uses the Spanish broad gauge, and the two nets are connected by six lines. On these lines only a few trains cross the boundary in each direction each day. The only railway line used to any extent is that connecting Lisbon and Oporto.

Colonies. Portugal was able to save some parts of its colonial empire, and in the nineteenth century extended its rule inland from the coasts of Angola and Mozambique. Portugal has not been able to invest much capital in the development of these colonies. As we have seen, their foodstuffs and other products contribute in a modest way to the economy of the metropolitan country. On the other hand, Portugal has had little part in the commerce of its smaller colonies in Asia, and in that of Guinea and the Cape Verde Islands. The most prosperous possessions are the two islands of São Tomé (St. Thomas) and Principe in the Gulf of Guinea, and Madeira and the Azores in the Atlantic. The latter two groups are regarded officially as parts of European Portugal. Both their population and their products are similar to those of the mainland.

*   *   *

There are certain problems which trouble all the countries of Southern Europe, with the partial exception of Turkey. Underlying most of these troubles is the rapid increase in population, which threatens to outrun any possible increase in productivity. Industrialization, though widely recommended, is hampered by lack of basic minerals, especially in Greece and Italy, and by lack of capital. Only in Turkey can more land be easily put under cultivation. Mechanization of agriculture has definite limitations, too, especially on the small plots and narrow terraces used for tree culture. Some staple products of Southern Europe, such as citrus fruit, Greek tobacco, Spanish and Portuguese cork, and even wine, face increasing competition from countries which can produce under more economical conditions and have become competitive through development of modern means of transportation. However difficult some of these problems may be, and despite the handicaps inherent in the social and political conditions of several of the Southern European countries, all these countries strive for industrialization and improved agricultural conditions, though with different degrees of vigor and with varying success.

BIBLIOGRAPHY

(Major references are asterisked.)

Books in English

AMERICAN GEOGRAPHICAL SOCIETY. *Readings in the Geography of the Mediterranean Region.* Reprint series 2. Contributions by various authors. New York: American Geographical Society, 1943.

*DICKINSON, ROBERT E. *The Population Problem of Southern Italy.* Syracuse, N. Y.: Syracuse University Press, 1955.

GRINDROD, MURIEL. *The Rebuilding of Italy.* London: Royal Institute of International Affairs, 1955.

McNEILL, WILLIAM HANDY. *Greece: American Aid in Action 1947–1956.* New York: The Twentieth Century Fund, 1957.

NEWBIGIN, MARION I. *The Mediterranean Lands,* 3d ed. New York: Alfred A. Knopf (a division of Random House, Inc.), 1948.

*SEMPLE, ELLEN CHURCHILL. *Geography of the Mediterranean.* New York: Henry Holt & Co., Inc., 1931.

THORNBURG, MAX WESTON, SPRY, GRAHAM, and SOULE, GEORGE. *Turkey: An Economic Appraisal.* New York: The Twentieth Century Fund, 1949.

Books in Foreign Languages

AMORIM, GIRÃO A. DE. *Geografia de Portugal* (Geography of Portugal). Pôrto: Portucalense Editora, 1941.

BIROT, PIERRE, and DRESCH, JEAN. *La Méditerranée Occidentale* (The Western Mediterranean). Vol. I. Paris: Presses Universitaires de la France, 1956.

DANTIN-CERECEDA, J. *Regiones naturales de España* (Natural Regions of Spain). Madrid: J. Cosano, 1922.

ECHEVERRIA, MARTIN L. *España: el pais y los habitantes* (Spain: The Country and Its Population). Mexico City: Ed. Atlante, 1940.

KRUEGER, KARL. *Die Türkei* (Turkey). Berlin: Safari Verlag, 1951.

*PHILIPPSON, ALFRED. *Das Mittelmeergebiet: seine geographische und kulturelle Eigenart* (The Mediterranean: Its Geographic and Cultural Character), 4th ed. Leipzig: B. G. Teubner, 1931.

*————. *Die Griechischen Landschaften* (The Regions of Greece). Vol. I. Frankfurt am Main: V. Klostermann, 1952.

*TOURING CLUB ITALIANO. *Attraverso l'Italia* (Across Italy). Milan: Touring Club of Italy, 1927–55.

Articles

DOBBY, E. H. G. "Agrarian Problems in Spain," *Geographical Review* 26 (1936): 177–89.

DOZIER, CRAIG L. "Establishing a Framework for Development in Sardinia: The Campidano," *Geographical Review* 47 (1957): 490–506.

FELS, EDWIN. "Landgewinnung in Griechenland" (Land Reclamation in Greece), *Petermanns Mitteilungen* 242, 1944.

FOOD AND AGRICULTURAL ORGANIZATION, UNITED NATIONS. *Mediterranean Development Project: Greece.* FAO/57/10/7078.

GIUSTI, UGO. "Lo spopolamento montano in Italia" (The Depopulation of the Italian Mountains), *Studi e Monografie* 16 (Rome: Istituto Nazionale di Economia Agraria, 1938).

HOFFMAN, GEORGE W. "South Tyrol: Borderland Rights vs. World Politics," *Journal of Central European Affairs* 7 (1947): 285–306.

HOUSTON, J. M. "Irrigation as a Solution to Agrarian Problems in Modern Spain," *Geographical Journal* 116 (1950): 55–63.

KISH, GEORGE. "The *Marine* of Southern Italy," *Geographical Review* 43 (1953): 495–506.

KOSTANICK, HUEY L. "Turkish Resettlement of Bulgarian Turks: 1950–1953," *University of California Publications in Geography* 8 (1957).

*LAUTENSACH, HERMANN. "Portugal auf Grund eigener Reisen und der Literatur" (Portugal: A Description Based on Own Travel and Literature), *Petermanns Mitteilungen* 46 (1932), 50 (1937).

NAYLON, JOHN. "Land Consolidation in Spain," *Annals of the Association of American Geographers* 49 (December, 1959): 361–73.

OGLIVIE, ALAN G. "Physiography and Settlement in Southern Macedonia," *Geographical Review* 9 (1921): 172–97.

PATTERSON, ROSINA M. "The Balearic Islands," *Journal of Geography* 45 (1946): 153–56.

WEIGEND, GUIDO G. "Effects of Boundary Changes in the South Tyrol," *Geographical Review* 40 (1950): 364–75.

8

Eastern Europe

Between Central Europe and the Soviet Union, bordered by three seas—the Baltic, Black, and Adriatic—are located seven countries: Poland, Czechoslovakia, Hungary, Rumania, Bulgaria, Albania, and Yugoslavia. This group of countries is usually arbitrarily grouped, because of its general location in relation to other areas within Europe, as Eastern Europe, East Europe, East Central Europe, or Mid-Europe. It has been given specific names such as the "Shatter Belt" or the "Devil's Belt," which characterize its fragmentation into many political and cultural units, and the instability and resultant insecurity of its people. Lastly, the group of countries bears names which express its political function or position: the "Eastern Marchlands," the "*Cordon Sanitaire*" of the interwar period, the "Iron Curtain" of the postwar period, or simply "satellite" or "captive" countries (with Yugoslavia excluded from the last two expressions).[1] Eastern Europe as defined here covers about 449,000 square miles, is roughly the size of Colorado, New Mexico, and Texas combined, and has a total population of about 96 million. The importance of this region has often been underlined. Sir Halford Mackinder[2] spoke of the importance of the "tier of independent states between Germany and Russia." Others mention its importance for Europe's balance of power.[3]

---

[1] Certain material presented in this chapter has been taken, by permission, from a study by the author, which covers some of the problems of this area: "Eastern Europe: A Study in Political Geography," *Texas Quarterly* 2 (Autumn, 1959): 57–88.

[2] *Democratic Ideals and Reality* (New York: Henry Holt & Co., Inc., 1919, 1942), pp. 158 ff. He also refers to them as "middle states of East Europe."

[3] Henry L. Roberts, "Eastern Europe and the Balance of Power," in Norman J. G. Pounds and Nicolas Spulber (eds.), *Resources and Planning in Eastern Europe*, Slavic and East European Series, Vol. IV (Bloomington, Ind.: Indiana University Press, 1957): 1–11.

Moodie [4] drew attention to "the reduction of the north-south extent of Europe between the Baltic and the Adriatic" and to the fact that this 500-mile-wide thoroughfare has been essential for the "movements of peoples, goods, and ideas between the Russian realm, on the one hand, and Central and Western Europe, on the other." Location is paramount in any explanation of the importance of this region with its seven political units. Eastern Europe is an area of transition, instability, and diversification, and this is clearly expressed in its physical as well as its cultural-political characteristics.

Physically, Eastern Europe consists of many well-defined and highly diversified regions. This variance of landforms is easily seen when comparing the many structural units analyzed later in this chapter (Fig. 8–1). Its mountains and other highlands never have been barriers to the movement of peoples. As a matter of fact, many easily accessible passes, gates, and river valleys, and most of all the Danube River, have acted as unifying factors. These important transportation links have played a significant role in the geography of Eastern Europe, inasmuch as they were often the reason for conflict over control of routes into the fertile basin areas. For example, the Polish Uplands served as an important routeway between western Europe and northwestern and central Russia (Slavic and Germanic settlers had their first encounter here); the Morava-Vardar corridor assisted the Ottoman Turks in their easy penetration to the gates of Vienna; and control of important passes, gates, and basins facilitated the control of important lands to the western slopes of the Carpathian Mountains and beyond by the Hapsburg rulers of Austria.

The transitional character of Eastern Europe is also expressed by the great variety of climates, e.g., from the typical Mediterranean climates along the Adriatic littoral of Yugoslavia (with the bordering Karst Mountains precluding any inland penetration) to the semiarid steppe conditions along the lower Danube in the Dobruja. This variety of climatic conditions is shown in the great complexity of soils and the diversity of vegetation adding another variance to an already complex area.

The importance of the approximately 500-mile-long thoroughfare has been pointed out. Different peoples have used this thoroughfare since the dawn of European history, and it is not surprising that for many the Danube corridor became their permanent home. The settlements nowhere coincided with the many complex and well-defined geographic regions. The peoples had to adapt themselves to the physical conditions they found. The major groups settling in this

[4] A. E. Moodie, *The Changing World* (Yonkers, N. Y.: World Book Co., 1956), p. 111.

region were the Poles, Czechs, Magyars, Germans, Rumanians, Bulgars, the various Slavic people of today's Yugoslavia (meaning Land of the Southern Slavs), etc. They brought with them different customs and beliefs. As a result of these movements, this area was occupied by people of many different cultures, and this fragmentation in turn contributed to the lack of a stable political-territorial framework.

Eastern Europe is rich in natural resources. Even though agricultural activities by a large rural population still dominate—a fact giving the region a certain amount of unity—increased industrial activity in nearly every one of the countries, often based on important local raw materials, is rapidly changing the economic structure of the area. In addition, six of the countries—excluding Yugoslavia—are closely integrated into the Soviet Union's economy (East Germany's contribution to the Soviet bloc is discussed in Chapter 6).

THE PHYSICAL LANDSCAPE

Location, Size, and Configuration

Approximately 96 million people live in Eastern Europe, an area of 449,000 square miles extending from the Baltic to the Black, Aegean, and Adriatic seas. Eastern Europe is somewhat larger than the combined areas of Central and Western Europe. Its east-west distance varies from 650 miles between the Adriatic and the Black Sea, to 240 miles between the Vienna Basin and the nearest border of the Soviet Union, and 400 miles between the western and eastern boundary of Poland. The longest north-south distance, i.e., from the Baltic to the Ionian Sea, is 1,000 miles. Its most northern point, near Gdynia (Gulf of Gdansk, on the Baltic)—55° N.—has the same latitude as the southern tip of the Alaskan Panhandle, while its southern border along the Albania-Greece border, at roughly 39° N., is located on the same latitude as Cincinnati, Ohio.

The Soviet Union has a common border with every one of the Eastern European countries with the exception of Yugoslavia and Albania (it borders Bulgaria via the Black Sea). Germany, Austria, and Italy border Eastern Europe on the west, Turkey and Greece on the south. The countries of the region vary greatly in size and population: Poland, with 120,000 square miles and over 28 million people, is the largest, and Albania, with 11,096 square miles and 1.4 million people is the smallest political unit. The region is centrally located on the European peninsula, and its transitional character is exemplified by its varied physiographic and cultural characteristics.

Main Physiographic Divisions

Diversity of structure is characteristic of the whole region. Owing to its location, the region participates in a great variety of structural and tectonic elements (Fig. 8–1), already mentioned in Chapter 1.

Fig. 8–1. Structural divisions.

The structural elements in the region can be divided into several units: those which form part of the Alpine mountain system, e.g., the Alps, the Carpathians, Balkan ranges, Dinaric ranges; Caledonian [5]

[5] For geological terms, see Appendix I.

structures which extend from the western Baltic to the Polish Uplands; and the Hercynian remains, including the Bohemian Massif,
the Sudeten and Lysa Gora mountains and plateaus, the Dobruja,
parts of the Rhodope Massif, and various structural islands in the
Carpathian Basin. The Alpine mountain system also encloses several
Tertiary and Quaternary depressions, of which the best known are
the Hungarian and Transylvanian basins (joint name: Carpathian or
Pannonian Basin).

In spite of the great structural diversity, it is possible to distinguish
four major physiographic regions in Eastern Europe: (1) the North
Polish Lowlands; (2) the Polish and Bohemian Uplands, covering
parts of Poland and Czechoslovakia; (3) the Carpathian Ranges and
Basin, the Wallachian Plain and Moldavian Hill Lands, which cover
parts or all of Czechoslovakia, Poland, Hungary, Rumania, and Yugoslavia; and (4) the Southeast European Highlands, in, Yugoslavia,
Albania, and Bulgaria. In addition, mention should be made of two
narrow transitional zones, the Southern Moraine Zone, which changes
gradually to the south, leading into the Silesian Plain, and a rolling
fertile zone of hills, the Carpathian Forelands.

North Polish Lowlands. The North Polish Lowlands, in geo-
morphological structure, are a continuation of the North German
Lowlands discussed in Chapter 6 (pp. 365–70). Two clear-cut
divisions can be made: the Baltic Coastal Zone and Heights (sometimes referred to as the Baltic Moraine Zone) and the Polish Lowlands.

Baltic Coastal Zone and Heights. Poland's coast line, since
1945, has increased from 85 miles to 315 miles and now extends from
the estuary of the Odra (Oder) to the Bay of Gdansk. On the whole,
the coast line is flat and sandy and long sand bars brought about by
strong sea currents enclose the depressions of the low coastal platform. This shore line has few good ports: Gdansk, the former Danzig;
Gdynia, which was built after 1919 to give Poland an independent
ocean outlet; and Szczecin, the former important German port of
Stettin, on the mouth of the Odra. Szczecin today serves Poland as
the outlet for the exports and imports of the Silesian industrial region
—particularly coal exports and iron-ore imports.

South of the narrow coast line are high dune ridges which have
been shifted inland by the onshore winds. Southward, a broad, un-
dulating-ground moraine zone paralleling the shore line reaches an
average height of 150 feet. These moraines indicate a stable stage
of the last ice sheet and reach nearly 1,100 feet southwest of Gdansk.
The steeper slopes of the terminal moraines and sandy outwash plains
are covered by coniferous forests. Cultivated land is found on the

boulder clay of the gentler slopes. Lakes are plentiful in the valleys between the moraines and especially in the Masurian lake area of former East Prussia, in which they fill hollows thought to have been created by subglacial streams. These lakes and some marshes extend on both sides of the lower Vistula (Wisla). Large flat sections are absent in this irregular land surface, and gullies and creeks abound in the typical glacial till. The whole region is sparsely settled, with minerals lacking, agriculture poorly developed, an absence of good harbors, and only a few small and scattered urban concentrations.

GLACIAL VALLEY ZONE. Terminal moraines extending in an east-west direction form the southern boundary of the Baltic Heights. South of these moraines, extending all across Poland, are the Polish Lowlands, a belt of glacial valleys (*pradoliny*, comparable to the German *Urstromtaeler*—primeval valleys of streams) which have a strong influence in the present drainage pattern of the Odra, Warta, and Vistula rivers. These rivers use part of the *pradoliny*, and their entries or departures are clearly indicated by the sharp bends of the rivers. Similar to the North German Lowlands, the glacial valleys offer excellent opportunities for connecting Poland's river systems. Two of the important ones are the Odra-Warta-Notec-Vistula-Bug and the Warta-Bzura-Vistula-Bug farther south. The first has a canal connecting the Notec with the Vistula at Bydgoszcz (Fig. 8–2). The Polish Lowlands, including the glacial valleys, present a generally flat and monotonous plain. The valleys, which are slightly below the level of the plain, have loamy soil scattered with moraines, rocks, dunes, and sand flats. Most of the lowlands were originally covered by forests, but only an area east of the Nisa (Neisse) River, stretching toward the middle Odra, is still heavily forested. The Vistula River, which occupies a dominant position in the lowlands, flows generally in a north-south direction through a broad valley. Originally the valley was marshy, and floods are still common. While the Vistula is navigable, it plays a much smaller role in transport than the Rhine River in Germany, or even the Odra River.

SOUTHERN MORAINE ZONE AND SILESIAN PLAIN. Transitional between the Polish Lowlands and Uplands, characterized by the dissected character of its surface, caused by postglacial erosion, lies the Southern Moraine Zone. In the valley of the Odra, the zone extends southward, known as the Silesian Plain. The Silesian Plain is limited on the southwest by the foothills of the Sudeten and on the east by the Hercynian Uplands of the Silesian Plateau.

Polish and Bohemian Uplands. Between the Southern Moraine Zone and the Carpathian Mountains stretches a zone of uplands, consisting of low plateaus and basins. The only exception is found in a brief extension of the lowlands along the valley of the upper Odra (the Silesian Plain). The upland zone is divided into two clearly defined sections, the Polish Uplands and the Bohemian Massif (also called Bohemian Plateau) and surrounding heights. South of the

Fig. 8–2. Main railways and navigable waterways.

Polish Uplands and east of the Bohemian Massif are the rolling hills of the Carpathian Forelands and the valleys which lead to the Carpathian Ranges.

POLISH UPLANDS. The Polish Uplands consist of five clear-cut subregions (Fig. 8–1) which were intermittently covered with fertile loess deposited during the Ice Age by winds carrying loose surface material from areas that had been denuded of vegetation. (1) The Sudeten Mountains, largely composed of old rocks, are west of the Odra River, an area covered with loess, and an important cereal-growing region. (2) The Hercynian Uplands of the Silesian Plateau, east of the Odra River and overlooking the Silesian Plains, contain one of Europe's largest coal fields as well as other minerals. The plateau's earlier role as an important frontier region is indicated by its many old castle ruins. (3) The incline eastward from the Silesian Plateau up to the Little Polish Plateau is slight. The high plateau consists of Cretaceous limestones, with some of the area covered by loess. The old rocks of this area contain some copper and iron ores. (4) Between the upper valleys of the Vistula and San rivers lies an important triangular depression: Crakow-Sandomierz-Przemysl. This depression is made up of alluvial deposits coming from the Carpathian slopes and on its southern margin is covered with fertile loess. (5) East of the Vistula and San rivers and south of Lublin is the Plateau of Lublin, consisting mainly of limestone covered with a heavy layer of loess. This is a treeless region, with wheat and sugar beets the main crops.

BOHEMIAN MASSIF AND SURROUNDING HEIGHTS. The very ancient structures of the Bohemian Massif consist of a series of wooded mountains with a few peaks over 4,000 feet, several longitudinal depressions in the southwest and east, some basaltic uplands in the northwest, and a very fertile loess-covered intermontane basin (Bohemian Basin). The Bohemian Forest forms the boundary in the southwest, the Czecho-Moravian Uplands toward the east; toward the northeast heavily eroded, horst-type mountains (crystalline nuclei, surrounded by gneiss, slates, and limestones) of the Sudeten with its highest elevation 5,200 feet in its northwestern part which also includes the headwaters of the Labe (Elbe) River. The lower eastern part of the Sudeten contains the headwaters of the Odra and Morava rivers and ends abruptly at the Moravian Gate (930 feet); toward the northwest are the crystalline Ore Mountains where important uranium ore (pitchblende) is found near Jáchymov. The Labe River divides the Ore Mountains from the Sudeten. In addition, the Massif contains a number of depressions which are often rich in Tertiary lignite, mineral springs, and other important raw materials, e.g., the springs and kaolin of Marianske Lazne and Karlovy Varý, lignite of Replice, and iron ore in the Berounka Basin. These resources are the basis for an old and flourishing industry.

CARPATHIAN FORELANDS. South of the Polish Uplands and east of the Bohemian Massif is another transitional zone, a rolling zone of hills. This region is important agriculturally, and where loess is not present forests abound. The Moravian depression, between the Danube River (Vienna Basin) and the low gap of the Moravian Gate near Moravska Ostrava, forms part of the Carpathian Forelands. The Czecho-Moravian Uplands border the fertile longitudinal Mora-vian depression toward the west, and the Carpathian Mountains toward the east. The depression is one of Europe's important routes, connecting the North European plains with the Danube Valley, the Baltic, and the Black Sea drainage. Agriculture, encouraged by mild winters, warm summers, and sufficient rainfall, is dominant in the depression, with sugar beets, wheat, and maize most widely distributed.

Carpathian Ranges and Basin, Wallachian Plain, and Moldavian Hill Lands. The third of the major physiographic regions of Eastern Europe is characterized by its great uniformity. The Carpathians, together with their forelands, are usually subdivided into four separate physical regions based on characteristics of relief and general landscape. Extending from the east and south are the Moldavian Hill Lands and the Wallachian Plain. Within the Carpathian Ranges is the Carpathian Basin, sometimes referred to as the Pannonian Basin. Through the whole length of this region flows the Danube River, cutting the Basin into unequal sections.

CARPATHIAN RANGES. The arc of the Carpathian Ranges and their forelands extends from the Vienna Basin to the Iron Gate for a distance of over 1,000 miles. This is about the length of the Alps, but the Carpathians reach only an elevation of 8,700 feet in the High Tatry located in the western Carpathians. The Ranges have a continuous outer sandstone belt of Tertiary rock and a discontinuous central zone of crystalline rocks and limestone. Toward the basin of the central zone there is a volcanic inner belt. Within the Carpathian Ranges various divisions are possible; for the purpose of our discussion four subdivisions are briefly analyzed: northwestern, central, eastern, and southern.

1. The northwestern Carpathians extend from the Danube and Morava rivers to Dukla Pass, at 1,640 feet elevation near the headwaters of the San and Hornád rivers in eastern Czechoslovakia. The Carpathians are widest here and are penetrated by several longitudinal rivers which facilitate transportation and settlement. The most important is the Vah River, which separates the High from the Low Tatry and offers a most valuable connection between western and eastern Slovakia. The High Tatry is located south of the main chain of the western Carpathians. It is a zone composed of crystalline rocks which was glaciated during the Ice Age. Its many cirques, arêtes,

waterfalls, and crest-shaped peaks are typical and similar to those of the high Alps. The mountains of the High Tatry average 6,000 to 8,000 feet, with Stalin Peak (8,737 feet) the highest elevation in the Carpathian Range. South of the High Tatry are the Low Tatry, composed of gneiss and granite. South toward the Carpathian Basin are a series of young volcanic intrusions. The range is known as the Slovakian Ore Mountains. These stretch toward the Hornárd River and contain small deposits of iron ore, copper, gold, and silver. The area between the Tatry and the Dukla Pass has many deep valleys and small intermontane basins, and is heavily forested. Kosiče on the Hornárd River is the most important town of eastern Slovakia, located on important north-south and east-west routes. The basins and valleys of the western Carpathians, on the whole, are well cultivated, with the greatest densities on the southern slopes of the Ranges.

2. The central Carpathians (also called Forest Carpathians) extend west from Dukla Pass, but their eastern border is poorly defined and is variously considered as between the sources of the Tisza River near Tartars Pass and as farther south. Here the mountain width is about 60 miles, with a number of low passes offering easy access between the Carpathian Basin and the upper Dniester. This is the former territory of Carpatho-Ukraine, which was part of Czechoslovakia and since 1945 has been part of the Ukrainian S.S.R.

3. The eastern Carpathians, located entirely within Rumania, extend southward from Tartars Pass to Orașul Stalin (Brasov). These mountains may also be divided into three zones: parallel ridges of the eastern sandstone belt, a central limestone and crystalline zone, and a western zone made up of young volcanic material. Rounded mountain tops, the result of weathering of the crystalline schists, is common. Peaks have a height of from 5,000 to 7,000 feet and glaciation has had only minor effects. The lower slopes are heavily forested with deciduous trees (beech predominant) and coniferous forests on the higher slopes, deep valleys and gorgelike passes, and numerous pastures.

4. The Transylvanian Alps or southern Carpathians extend from Orașul Stalin to the Kazan Gorge of the Danube (the Iron Gate being the narrowest part of the gorge) at a point where the mountains curve south and southeastward, and later take an eastward direction as the Balkan Ranges. The Transylvanian Alps also continue as the Banat Mountains west of the Timisul River. Porta Orientalis offers easy access, including a railroad line between the Carpathian Basin and the Wallachian Plain. The numerous peaks of the Transylvanian Alps exceed 8,000 feet, and the various glacial features gave the name "Alps" to these ranges. Only a central limestone and

crystalline zone and the foreland are represented. Typical features of this region are flat-topped plateaus and terraces, as well as numerous longitudinal depressions containing rivers. The present relief is largely the result of uplifting and warping and later stream erosion. Several important routes traverse the Transylvanian Alps at low altitudes, connecting the interior Basin with the Plains; all these routes are of long-standing historical importance: the Predeal Pass (3,400 feet), Turnul Roşu (1,155 feet), and the Vulcan Pass (5,000 feet). Mention should also be made of the Bihor Mountains in the eastern portion of the Carpathian Basin, which are part of the main chain of the Carpathians and are extremely rich in minerals. The eastern forelands form a continuous belt with important petroleum deposits in the Prahova district and minor ones near Bacau in Moldavia.

WALLACHIAN PLAIN AND MOLDAVIAN HILL LANDS. The Wallachian Plain, or "The Plains of the Lower Danube" as it is so often called, is a depression which in the Tertiary was a gulf of the Black Sea, but which by now has been entirely filled by river deposits from the Transylvanian Alps. The whole depression has been uplifted and is now about 150 feet above sea level. The Plain extends from the southern foothills of the Transylvanian Alps through the piedmont plateau of the Balkan Ranges to the Dobruja. The steppe plateau of the Dobruja blocks the straight course of the Danube and forces it into a northward direction. The Moldavian Hill Lands form the northern boundary of the Wallachian Plain. Navigation on the Danube, especially during floods, is extremely difficult because of the sluggish course of the river. Its many braided channels were formed by its alluvial deposits. These channels have cut broad valleys below the general level. Bordering the floodplains on both the Rumanian and the Bulgarian side, cliffs rise as much as 300 feet above the marshes on the latter side.

The Moldavian Hill Lands lie between the Siret and Prut rivers, with hills, especially in the central part, reaching an elevation of over 1,300 feet. The whole area consists of sedimentary rocks of the Tertiary age. With the exception of a central plateau, the entire region is a hilly steppe. The hills are loess covered with fertile chernozem soils. Recurrent and disastrous droughts do much damage.

CARPATHIAN BASIN. This depression is enclosed by the arc of the Carpathian Ranges, the Eastern Alps, and the Dinaric Ranges. The Basin itself, with an area of over 100,000 square miles with centripetal drainage, is not uniform in relief. It is divided into minor basins, hill lands, and mountains. Much of the Basin was covered by an inland sea until rivers from the surrounding mountains filled it with alluvial deposits. The division of the Carpathian Basin is as follows: the Little Alföld, the Transdanubian Hill Lands, the Croatian Hill Lands, the Great Alföld, the Bihor Mountains, and the Transylvanian Basin. The Little Alföld [6] extends from the foothills of the Alps to the southeast slopes of the Bakony Mountains and north across the Danube to the foothills of the western Carpathians. The central portion of the Little Alföld is located southeast of Bratislava and consists of a large alluvial fan of gravel and silt. Neusiedler Lake, at the Austro-Hungarian border, is surrounded by swamps and mud flats and is one of the remnants of the inland sea.

South and west of the Little Alföld are the rolling hill lands of Transdanubia. They are covered by loess and have a general northeast-southwest alignment. Their greatest height is reached at about 3,300 feet. This subdivision is bordered on the east by the Danube and on the south by the Drava River. Lake Balaton, with a maximum depth of only 35 feet, is another of the shallow fresh-water lakes remaining from the inland sea. Between Lake Balaton and the Drava and Danube rivers is a low, dissected, very productive plateau covered with loess. The city of Pécs is in the center.

Between the Drava, the Danube, the Sava, and the foothills of the Slovenian Alps are the Croatian Hill Lands. These are very fertile loess-covered lowlands interspersed with limestone and crystalline hills. Patches of forest cover alternate with densely cultivated lands.

The Great Alföld stretches irregularly east and north of the Danube to the foothills and volcanic belts of the western and central Carpathians and the Banat and Bihor mountains. The Alföld is a perpetually settling block which has been covered by Tertiary and Quaternary strata and is dissected by the meandering Tisza River. The western part is an elongated, partly sand-covered region often referred to as "Mesopotamia." [7] Southeast of Kecskemét is the *puszta* (waste), a region of soil saturated with salt. Near Debrecen is Hortobágy, a steppe region covered with sand which has a high soda content. Most of the Banat between the Tisza and the Transylvanian Alps is covered with fertile black soil.

[6] *Al*—low, *föld*—land.

[7] As a result of Sumerian-Magyar affiliations in early historical time the Magyars, when occupying the Carpathian Basin in the ninth century, called it the Mesopotamian region between the Danube and Tisza rivers (Duna-Tisza-Köze: Mid-Danube-Tisza, or Danube-Tisza-Mesopotamia) and, based on the old tradition, regarded this area as the center of their country. The region east of the Tisza was named Tiszántúl (Trans-Tisza, or Transtisia), while the area west of the Danube was called Dunántúl (Transdanubia). This explanation will clear up some of the errors and misunderstandings of these terms in various works. Hungarian (Magyar) verbiage, customs, and place names reflect, even at present, a strong Sumerian affinity.

The Transylvanian Basin, east of the Great Alföld and the Bihor Mountains, consists of Tertiary clay strata reaching an elevation of up to 2,000 feet. It also was once a sea basin which filled with river deposits, but it is now high and hilly, having been uplifted and dissected. The Basin also has quantities of natural gas and salt and is heavily forested at higher elevations.

The Carpathian Basin is transitional with regard to climatic conditions, which in this region are typical in many ways of the contrasts in parts of Eastern Europe. All four basic climatic types prevail, with the greatest transitions in the Hungarian part of the Basin. Rainfall declines from west to east, as, for example, between Bratislava and Szeged (total precipitation 28 inches in Bratislava and 22 inches in Szeged). Most of the rain falls in early summer, with smaller but still sufficient amounts in the latter part of the summer. October rains are important, especially for southwestern Hungary. Unfortunately, the summer rain occurs during a period of high temperatures and high evaporation which lessen the effectiveness of the precipitation. Temperature differences between summer and winter are considerable, but by no means extreme. Bratislava, for example, has an average January temperature of 30° F., Budapest of 28°, and Debrecen, in the eastern part of the Great Alföld, of 25°; the average July temperatures of these locations are 70°, 71°, and 71°, respectively. Temperatures are higher in the southern cities of the Great Alföld, e.g., Szeged has a January temperature of 30° and a July temperature of 75°. The nearby mountain ranges act as a climatic barrier and often limit oceanic influences. Certain changes indicate a progressive continental condition, e.g., the daily ranges vary from 30° in Bratislava to 40° in the eastern part of the Great Alföld.

Southeast European Highlands. Five physiographic regions can clearly be defined within the Highlands: the Alps; the Dinaric Ranges, including the Adriatic littoral; the Transitional and Basin Lands of the Morava and Vardar; the Rhodope Massif and depressions; and the Balkan Ranges. The structure and relief of these Highlands is extremely complicated and diverse, and the lithic composition varies from calcareous to the more resistant crystalline rocks. Volcanic intrusions indicate that the Highlands are an area of instability. Steep mountains and small intermontane basins and heavy erosion, especially in the southern Highlands, are typical. A large part of the Highlands is composed of karst, containing all characteristic karst features.

THE ALPS. The Karawanken chain of the Eastern Alps forms the northern boundary of the Southeast European Highlands. The limestone Julian Alps have their continuation in the Dinaric Ranges. The valleys are heavily forested, but the limestone rocks support only poor agriculture. The Ljubljana Basin is partly enclosed by the Julian Alps and the Karawanken chain. Between the Alps and the Dinaric Ranges an arm of the Pannonian Plain approaches the Adriatic to within a distance of 75 miles. This gap was important as an early route connecting the Baltic with the Mediterranean, and modern highways emphasize its importance as a routeway. The climate varies from extreme cold in the Alpine region, through somewhat higher annual average temperatures (53–56°) in the middle Drava and Sava valleys, to typical continental conditions farther east in the Croatian Hill Lands.

DINARIC RANGES. These Ranges, folded in the mid-Tertiary period, trend southeast from the Ljubljana Basin and the Sava-Kupa Valley in the northeast to the Morava-Vardar passage. The width of the ranges varies from 60 to 100 miles, and the average elevation varies from 4,000 to 6,000 feet. Great diversity, ranging from the barren, dissected, and waterless High Karst in the west to a series of parallel forested mountains and hill lands in the north and northeast, characterizes this region. Commonly, the Dinaric Ranges are divided into three parts:

1. The narrow coastal zone, the Adriatic littoral, with its many islands and arms of the Adriatic Sea, presents a most picturesque landscape. The coastal zone and the terraced hillsides have only a limited amount of soil, and Mediterranean crops such as olives, vines, and figs, and limited pasture land and cereal acreage, together with fishing, are important sources of income for the rural population.

2. Access to the interior is blocked by the High Karst, part of the Dinaric massif, a barren, mainly Mesozoic limestone zone which extends from northwest to southeast for 350 miles, and has a maximum width of 50 miles and an elevation averaging 8,000 feet. The relief gives this region its fortress-like characteristics (Fig. 8–3). The river valleys are very short and widely spaced because precipitation falling upon these limestone rocks sinks underground where it continues to flow. Rivers flow in deeply dissected valleys or through gorges which are difficult to traverse. They carry varying quantities of water and have considerable elevation differences between source and mouth. Their use for hydroelectric projects is now under way or planned. The whole region consists of a series of barren, rocky plateaus with a series of flat ridges, the so-called *planine*; longitudinal troughs, *polja* (meaning fields), which were formed from subsiding hollows and subsequently enlarged when rain water and rivers dissolved the calcareous rocks; dolinas, small round depressions also formed by the solution of calcareous rocks; and *uvale* (larger dolinas—600 feet in

Fig. 8–3. View of the Dinaric massif, between Dalmatia and Bosnia. During Pleistocene times limestone detritus filled the karstic hollow, now the plain of Suho Polje. Sheep and goats have destroyed all but small areas of the forest cover (the black patches in the middle distance). Suho Polje is now a state plantation of almonds and other nut trees.

diameter). These *polja*, dolinas, and *uvale* are covered with alluvial deposits and/or red earth (terra rossa), a relatively fertile soil formed by the non-soluble material in the limestone (Fig. 8–4). Karst *polja* often are surrounded by peneplains (formed during the late Tertiary). Mention should also be made of the important subterranean caves, typical for certain calcareous areas.

3. The inner part of the Dinaric Ranges, inner Bosnia and western Serbia, is less barren and rugged. Sandstone and limestone predominate in a few places and crystalline rocks of Pre-Cambrian origin are visible. Narrow and open valleys are interspersed and extensive mining and logging activities are carried on throughout the countryside. The slopes toward the Sava lowlands are the most densely settled areas of the region.

The Dinaric Ranges extend through all of Albania. One of them, the Prokletije Range, reaches over 7,000 feet astride the Albano-Yugoslav border. South of this range, a series of parallel ranges extends southward to merge with the Albanian Epirus Ranges. Between the coast and the Dinaric Ranges are hilly lowlands. The coast line does not have the characteristics of the Adriatic littoral of Yugoslavia, and

Fig. 8–4. Dolinas under cultivation in Montenegro. Stone walls protect the terraces from erosion. The white (light) part of the lowest dolina is extremely sandy.

it alternates between swampy depressions, marshy deltas, and sand bars, which enclose numerous shallow lagoons. The limestone hills are covered with maqui and offer few opportunities for agriculture. Grazing and mountain agriculture are the main occupations of its people.

TRANSITIONAL AND BASIN LANDS OF THE MORAVA AND VARDAR. A region of great diversity is located south of the Danube, including the Morava-Vardar depression, with its many tectonic basins which originated in mid-Tertiary times. This depression affords a short route (about 300 miles) between the lowlands of the north and the Aegean Sea and its head port of Salonika. West of the depression are the foothills of the southeastern Dinaric Ranges, which consist of detached mountain blocks and basins connected by narrow passages.

RHODOPE MASSIF. Crossing the Transitional and Basin Lands of the Morava and Vardar depression, in an easterly direction, is the relatively narrow Rhodope Massif. It broadens southeastward and falls gradually toward the east into a series of uplands and dissected hills, which are broken by the Maritsa River northwest of Edirne. Toward the north, the Rhodope Massif and the Balkan Ranges enclose the Rumelian Basin (also called Maritsa Basin), which is drained by the Maritsa River.

The highest part of the Rhodope Massif is in the Rila Planina, an area of volcanic origin, containing the headwaters of the Maritsa River. Mount Stalin (9,596 feet), in the Rila Planina, is the highest mountain in Bulgaria. With the exception of some fertile basins (e.g., Skoplje, Stip), the whole Rhodope Massif is highly unproductive. Toward the central part, forested areas alternate with grasslands where grazing is prevalent.

BALKAN RANGES. Between the Wallachian Plain in the north, the Rumelian Basin in the south, and the Rhodope Massif in the south and southwest, the arc of the Balkan Ranges forms a continuation of the Carpathian Ranges. The part south of the Danube to the Timok River is known as the Northeast Serbian Mountains and forms a link between the Carpathians and the Stara Planina (old mountains). This region reaches altitudes between 3,700 and 5,100 feet and is characterized by poor lines of communication, by karstic relief, and by valuable mineral resources.

The northern portions of the Balkan Ranges slope gradually to the Danube, where they fall off rather abruptly about 300 feet, in a wall of limestone and loess. This area is known as the Danube or Bulgarian Plateau. The plateau is extremely fertile, covered by loess, but dissected by deep and broad valleys. The contrast in relief and climate between the fertile valley plains and the plateau is great. The valleys have abundant water supply and are protected from the cold, dusty winter winds blowing across the plateau from the Wallachian Plain. The Danube Plateau reaches the steppelike plateau of the Dobruja, with its eastern and northern border formed by the marshlands of the Danube. The Balkan Ranges are easily crossed by two north-south railways, via the Isker Valley to Sofiya and via the Shipka Pass, connecting the Danube port of Giurgiu (on the railroad to Bucharest) with the Maritsa Valley. The Ranges gradually become lower toward the east and, together with the Plateau on the north, enclose the small Stalin (Varna) Basin, which opens toward the Black Sea.

South of the main range of the Balkan Ranges are a number of significant depressions. The Tundzha depression, which results from a downfaulting of the land, is characterized by numerous hot springs and the widespread cultivation of roses. This specialization, which began many years ago, is responsible for the name "Valley of the Roses," by which this valley is known. The Anti-Balkan Range, with deeply cut valleys, extends south of this depression which in turn rather abruptly slopes to the depression of the Rumelian Basin. Another depression is that of Sofiya, the southern border of which is formed by a branch of the Balkan Ranges extending in a southeastern direction from the Pirot Basin in Yugoslavia toward the main range of the Rhodope Massif near Rila Planina. The basin has an elevation of 1,800 feet and is easily accessible through several river valleys. The largest depression is drained by the Maritsa River and opens toward the Aegean Sea. The fertile alluvial soil and abundance of water permit the growing of a great variety of crops, especially tobacco, cotton, rice, vines, and hardy fruits.

THE CULTURAL AND HISTORICAL BACKGROUND

In the Introduction, Eastern Europe was described as a zone of transition, a zone of clash and instability, a Shatter Belt for some and a cordon or curtain for others. The objective here is to describe in broad outlines the peopling of these lands, the settlements and social structure of the people, the political-territorial framework of the present countries, and finally the economic development of the new post-World War I national states. At times the discussions include developments in the whole area, at times it will be necessary to refer to individual peoples or countries. At the same time, the close relationship between developments in this area and the main stream of European history must constantly be kept in mind. The location of the area between the main body of the Slavic people in Russia and the Germanic people in Central Europe; the settling of the numerically few Magyars and Rumanians in the centrally located Pannonian Basin, thus dividing the Slavic people into a northern and a southern group; as well as the deep penetration of the Ottoman Turks over so many centuries have left important marks on the people and their institutions.

The Peopling of Eastern Europe

Before answering the question of who the people of Eastern Europe are, it is of interest to locate the main routes of the ancestors who established their present homes. People moved along certain well-defined routeways and easily penetrable passes, preferring grasslands and plateaus to forests and marshes. Inasmuch as these movements were not always the rapid invasion of raiders, it was important for the migrants with their herds constantly to seek fertile soils and pasture lands as they moved along. As a result of these limitations, the routes were few in number. On the basis of a reconstruction of the early vegetation and hydrographic pattern, and with the assistance of archaeological evidence, it is possible to trace in a general way the major routes by which these primitive people entered the area.

The lands of origin of many of these primitive people are still not exactly determined, but three source regions from which migrations came can definitely be established: the grasslands of western central Asia, the lowlands between the Odra and the Vistula, and the plateaus and basins of the Polish Uplands. Generally speaking, we can distinguish six routes or groups of routes leading to and within Eastern Europe:

1. The most northerly route led from the middle Vistula along the swamps and forests of the Baltic and made good use of the various river systems north of the Pripet Marshes. This was a part of the old Amber route.

2. A route led from the loess-covered plateau region (Lublin Plateau) south of the Pripet Marshes, along the northern slopes of the Volhyno-Podolian Uplands, to the Dniester Valley.

3. Another route led from the Polish lowlands to the upper Odra, the Moravian Gate, using the easily crossed low watershed between the Odra and Morava [8] valleys, to the Danube and the Pannonian Basin.

4. Several routes cross the Carpathian arc from the northeast, e.g., Dukla Pass and Tartars Pass, affording an easy crossing from the Dniester Valley into the Pannonian Basin.

5. The important Vardar-Morava depression offered a relatively easy route both from the coastal plains of Thrace and from the Aegean Sea to the Danube Valley and the Pannonian Basin.

6. An important route led from the Adriatic Sea, through the valleys of the Kupa and Sava, to the Pannonian Basin.

Overpopulation and the search for new and better lands were the main reasons for the movements of so many people in the first millennium. Before the period of large-scale folk-wanderings got under way in the fifth century A.D., small groups had already established themselves within Eastern Europe. For example, the Romans, ancestors of the present Rumanians, in their conquest of the lower Danube made contact with the Dacians in the lower Danube Basin; the Illyrians, first reported by Herodotus as living in the western half of the Balkan Peninsula, north of present-day Greece, are today repre-

[8] Note that there are two Morava rivers in Eastern Europe, one in Moravia (Czechoslovakia) and another in Serbia (Yugoslavia). The name Morava means "frontier," and both rivers have played a great role in the history of migration in two key transitional lands of Eastern Europe.

sented by the Albanians, the name of an Illyric tribe. Throughout the third and fourth centuries A.D., people from the central-Asian steppes, known as Huns and Avars, crossed the Carpathian passes into the Carpathian Basin. Various Nordic people, also, appeared at diverse times.

Various Slavic people began to leave their original homelands during the first and second centuries and owing to their greater numbers easily slavicized the few settlers they found. These Slavs first settled the broad river valleys and fertile rolling plains of the Vistula, Morava, Danube, and Morava-Vardar rivers, but, as more and more moved through and settled along the well-established routes, some settled on land well beyond these easily accessible routes (Fig. 8–5). The Poles, whose original homeland is believed to have been in the Vistula Basin, spread to the Odra and beyond, and east to the Pripet Marshes;[9] the Czechs settled the valley of the Morava (Moravian depression) and in the Bohemian Basin; the Slovaks moved into the southern valleys of the western Carpathians; the Ruthenians settled most of the central Carpathians; and Slavic settlements in the territory of today's Yugoslavia commenced during the sixth century A.D. and occupied three geographically well-defined regions. In the north, the Slavs settled the southern part of the old Roman province of Pannonia, especially the valleys extending north and south of the Sava River; in the south, they occupied the watershed region of Raška, and the basins of the Drin River, in Albania. The Slavic settlements remained permanently in the first two regions only. Raška played a very important historical role inasmuch as it became the ancient center of the first Serbian state.[10] The various South Slavs, Serbs, Montenegrins, Macedonians, Croats, and Slovenes slowly spread over most of the area of today's Yugoslavia. The Bulgars (today's Bulgarians), of Asiatic origin with Finno-Ugric and Turkic affinities of race and language, first settled in Bessarabia, but during the seventh century moved across the Danube to the Danube Plateau and the Maritsa Basin. They quickly became slavicized and lost their Finno-Ugric language. The Rumanians, who made their homes mainly in

[9] There is ample proof that the Poles were not the first occupants of the Vistula Basin. Being one of Europe's important migratory regions, it is obvious that these lands were the home of a succession of people with different racial history. But the fact remains that, in spite of Germanic pressures, the rural areas of the lower Vistula remained Polish.

[10] According to Jovan Cvijić, La Péninsule Balkanique (Paris: Librairie Armand Colin, 1918), p. 278, differences in physical appearance and emotional characteristics among the various South Slavic people appeared because of the isolation and inaccessibility of their settlements. Cvijić believes that the main differences between the people of the Balkan Peninsula are to be found in their physical characteristics and not in their language and religion.

the foothills of the Carpathians and later moved into the Wallachian Plain, also were under Slavic pressure, but they retained the language of Imperial Rome.

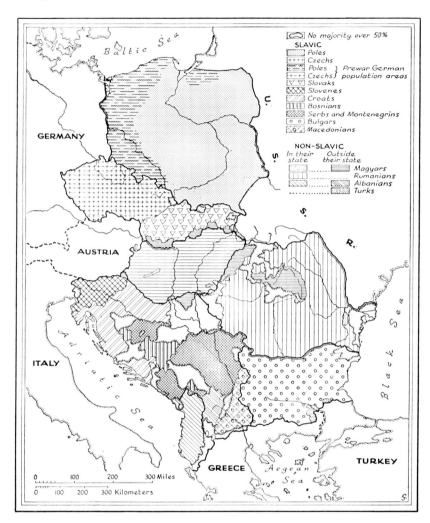

Fig. 8–5. Ethnographic patterns of Eastern Europe. Majorities over 50 per cent are represented, on the basis of censuses taken since 1945 and unofficial data concerning German resettlement.

Another people of Asiatic origin, the Ural-Altaic-speaking Magyars, crossed the passes of the eastern Carpathians during the ninth century. Retaining many nomadic traits, and after a series of deep penetrations into the west by the year 1000, they occupied the dry grasslands of the Great Alföld. The few people living in the grasslands were either absorbed, as were the Avars, or forced to retreat into the bordering mountains, as were the Slovaks in the north and the South Slavs in the south. The settlement of the Magyars thus contributed to the permanently established wedge between the Slavic people, dividing them into a northern Slavic group—Poles, Czechs, and Slovaks—and a southern Slavic group—Serbs, Macedonians, Bulgars, Croats, and Slovenes. At the same time it must be pointed out that, without a dependable reinforcement, the Magyars probably could not have held out alone against the numerically stronger Slavic people. And that brings us to the third element in this transitional zone, the Germans. Inasmuch as the movements of the various Germanic tribes already were traced in some detail in Chapter 6 (pp. 400–03), only those aspects of Germanic settlement having to do with extension into Eastern Europe are discussed here.

Germanic penetrations extended along the whole east front from the middle Elbe and the Saale, its tributary (its eastern boundary until about 1200), to the southern Marches of Styria and Carniola (Fig. 6–15). Generally speaking, Germanic eastward movements commenced after the general pattern of Slavic and Magyar settlements had been well established. These eastward movements were brought about, in part, as a reaction to Slavic and Magyar penetration into the west; in part, for simple military conquest and territorial increases; in part, by missionary and trading activities; and, in part, by the need of various Slavonic and Magyar rulers for craftsmen and skilled artisans. The Magyars' need, in the thirteenth century, for additional settlers to protect their eastern boundary in Transylvania against recurrent Mongol forays and conquests is connected with the well-known settlements of the Saxons.[11] These German settlements— most of them ceased to exist after the changes brought about during and following World War II—were distributed among nearly all of the Eastern European countries, extended as far east as the middle Volga River, and for centuries played an important role as a powerful cultural minority.

Germanic movements across the northern lowlands resulted in the acquisition of territory between the Elbe and Odra, the so-called *Mittelmark* (later Brandenburg), in the early thirteenth century. At the same time the Order of the Teutonic Knights moved along the Baltic coast, conquering lands northeast to the Nieman River, part of which became Prussia (later East Prussia). During the beginning

---

[11] Saxon is the general name applied to German settlers. The numerical superiority of the Slavs surrounding Magyar territory, and possible intrusions from the east, were constant sources of fear for this country.

of the fourteenth century, land east of and along the upper part of the Odra came under the authority of the Holy Roman Empire. But, with the growth of Polish power at the end of the fourteenth century, Germanic conquests were halted, and even reversed in the territory east of the Odra, which resulted in the destruction of the Teutonic Order and the incorporation of conquered territory into the Polish-Lithuanian state. German settlers were permitted to remain, but colonization was not renewed until the eighteenth century. It reached its greatest extent after the partition of Poland at the end of that century. The demand for German craftsmen continued all through the period of Polish strength, and many Polish cities in the Uplands were founded by Germans, substantial numbers of whom remained until the end of World War II.

German settlements within the Bohemian Basin are all connected with the movements of craftsmen, artisans, woodsmen, peasants, and miners and started as early as the late twelfth century and the beginning of the thirteenth. They were largely confined to the towns and countryside along the inner rim of the Ore Mountains and were encouraged by the Czech nobility. German penetrations into the Pannonian Basin included both agricultural settlers and those interested in establishing cities. Again German craftsmen, artisans, and miners were called into the country, together with general settlers assisting the defense of the country, and the earlier-mentioned Saxons settled in parts of Transylvania. German penetrations south, among the Slovenes, were peaceful missionary and trading missions, but they brought to a halt and often reversed the northward movements of the Slovenes. Slovene settlements north of the southern Alps, in Carinthia (Austria), are a reminder of those times.

There were other movements into this transitional zone, both military and peaceful, e.g., Swedes into the Baltic areas and Italians, especially Venetian traders, along the Adriatic littoral, while Jews from Western Europe came as tradesmen, hoping for freedom from religious persecution. It is thought that nearly half of the world's Jews lived in the Kingdom of Poland at the end of the Middle Ages. But none of these later penetrations left as deep an impact as that of the Ottoman Turks. Turkish conquest and control between the fifteenth and eighteenth centuries extended as far as the gates of Vienna and included in its furthest expansion most of the Carpathian Basin and southeast Europe, and the only South Slavic people who escaped this destructive control were the Slovenes and some of the Croats and mountain-dwelling Montenegrins. The Magyar homelands were controlled for a comparatively short period, about 150 years, but during that time their numbers were reduced by half from the original estimated population of five million. Among the South Slavs the Serbs, Macedonians, and earlier-slavicized Bulgars, Vlachs (Wallachians and Rumanians), and Albanians were completely suppressed under Turkish rule. With the slow retreat of the Turkish armies toward Serbia and the southern Dinaric Ranges, brought about by the victorious Austrian army comprised of soldiers from many lands, these devastated countries were resettled. The settlements along the so-called Austrian-Turkish military border north of the Danube and along the Sava and Kupa rivers became a mirror of all the lands under the Hapsburg control. This is one reason why the new state of Yugoslavia, after its founding in 1918, had such large minorities of Germans, Slovaks, Magyars, Czechs, Italians, etc. The last time territory was freed from Turkish control was at the beginning of the twentieth century, following the first Balkan War in 1912.

These folk-wanderings, military conquests, pioneering efforts, forced settlings, missionary efforts, and trading ventures brought about a great instability, backwardness, and oppression in this whole region. This was further accentuated by divisions of a religious nature and of class structure inherent in the prevalent system of land ownership. Christianization came from two centers, Rome and Constantinople. Often these two centers worked at cross-purposes. The religious boundary between Roman Catholicism and Eastern Orthodoxy extends north and south through all of Eastern Europe,[12] separating the Poles and the Lithuanians from the Russians, the Rumanians from the Magyars, and the Slovenes and Croats from the Macedonians and Serbs. This religious boundary has its greatest import where it divides a single political unit such as Yugoslavia, where it results in deep differences between the Croats and the Serbs. The religious division also influenced the outlook of the individual countries, toward Western or Eastern European culture, and had a lasting impact on the social and political organizations of this area. An additional element of instability resulted from the occupation of Constantinople by the Moslem Turks and the conversion to Islamic faith of many people living within Turkish-controlled territory. The division of the Christian Church in Western and Central Europe, the growth of Protestantism, especially among the various Germanic peoples, and their

---

[12] It should, however, be pointed out here that the first Czech state, the Moravian Kingdom of the ninth century, was Byzantine, and not Roman in its religious orientation. Two missionaries from Constantinople, Cyril and Methodius, were responsible for the spread of Byzantine culture and creed. When the Magyars penetrated into this important transitional area, the Czech and Slovak people were forced to flee into the surrounding, better-protected territories of the western Carpathians and the Bohemian Basin. One of the consequences was their change in orientation to a Western European and Roman culture.

struggle during the fifteenth and sixteenth centuries, left deep marks of further division among some of the people of Eastern Europe, e.g., in the northern lowlands, but also among the Czechs and Magyars. The Poles remained faithful to the authority of Rome, and the Church closely identified itself with the struggle for national survival, against German Protestantism and Eastern Russian Orthodoxy.

Social Structure and Settlements

The different people settling the lands of Eastern Europe had certain preferences and aptitudes which usually became the mark of their civilization. The Slavic people were land tillers, hunters, stockbreeders, and fishermen and at first preferred to settle in lowlands. They cut virgin forests and some of them practiced seasonal pasturage. They raised cattle, pigs, and horses, and traded in timber and later in minerals. The Rumans (Rumanians) and Bulgars, too, were land tillers and preferred open grasslands or plateaus and hill lands. The Albanians and Montenegrins survived in the mountainous areas into which they had been pushed. The Magyars, finding a great similarity with their original physical environment, found in the dry grasslands of the Great Alföld the ideal conditions for a nomadic way of life, emphasizing pastoralism and despising tillage.[13] Germans settled in uplands and along rivers. They liked to alter the surroundings and are also well known as tradesmen, skilled artisans, and city builders.

The shelters built by these people and the settlements developed through the ages depended on existing materials, on military pressures exerted against the people, on their occupations, and on their location. Tent dwellings, typical for a nomad society, were common for the Magyars; clay houses were typical for the plains; wooden houses for mountains; and stone houses for the karst lands and the Adriatic littoral, and combinations thereof could be found in most borderland regions. Long narrow houses as well as small flat-roofed ones are usually found in lowlands; mountainous regions have everything from one-story, one-room houses to the high quadrangular buildings typical for the South Slavs and the Mediterranean people. Many houses have fortress-like characteristics. Typical for the North Slavs living in the upland areas is the one-story, so-called smoking-room house, with open fire in the living room, small, partially covered entrance hall, and stables, all under one roof. Only the more wealthy peasants could afford a second room. Variations of this type are common in the mountainous areas south of the Danube. A variation common among

[13] Only in the nineteenth century was a wheat economy substituted for the horse and the sheep.

the Magyars and lowland Slovaks is a one- to two-story house with a partially covered pillared entrance hall along the full length of the house, opened toward the yard. Still another variation, common among the Croats, is the one-story house with a wide overhanging roof covered with straw. Two rooms are customary, a kitchen-living room and a bedroom. Considerable storage space for winter feeding of the animals is provided in the attic. Livestock have a place nearby (Fig. 8–6). Mention should also be made of the custom of white-

Fig. 8–6. Farm house in the Zagorje (Croatia). It consists of two rooms and is painted blue.

washing the outside. Sometimes the outsides of the houses are painted in different colors (blue being very popular). Obviously, the great intermixture of people, especially in those areas resettled after the Turkish wars, makes it difficult to establish a definite pattern. Migrants adjusted their original forms of shelter to existing conditions.

Urbanization was slow in coming. In the Carpathian Basin, to protect the croplands against constant pillages, villages developed, the so-called "village towns" or "peasant villages" (Fig. 8–7), with outlying houses occupied only during harvest times. Scattered hamlets with stone houses on steep slopes are typical for some of the southern Dinaric regions of Montenegro and Albania. These hamlets, too,

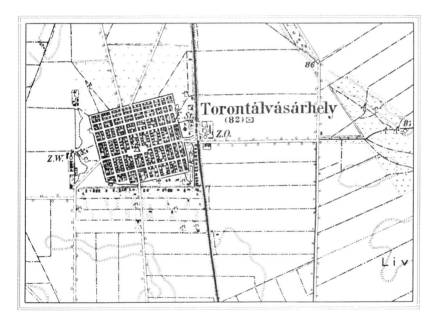

Fig. 8–7. Two characteristic settlement types of the Carpathian Basin: (*above*) a circular rural town established in the Middle Ages, for defensive purposes; (*below*) a square modern village laid out by engineers.

were defensive in character and purpose. The layout of settlements depended upon local relief. In agricultural regions, both the closely patterned nucleated village (Fig. 8–7, bottom) and the so-called "shoestring" village were typical; in forested areas there were round-patterned villages permitting an easy expansion where timberland was brought under cultivation. Dispersed settlements, found in mountain areas all over Eastern Europe, were typical for people following pastoral or lumbering occupations or in regions of poor soil. Closely packed villages with narrow streets are common in the mining communities of Bohemia and the western Carpathians, and in the coastal towns along the Dalmatian littoral. German influence usually can be traced to many of the market centers in the Bohemian and Polish Uplands, and in the closely built towns of Transylvania—houses two and three stories high and decoratively ornamented, administrative buildings with the church in the center, and a well-laid-out market place with streets radiating to the town's edges. Many towns in the Carpathian Basin are relatively new. They had to be rebuilt after the region was reoccupied following the Turkish military defeats in the seventeenth and eighteenth centuries and therefore consist largely of one-story whitewashed stone buildings with tile roofs, with all of the wide tree-lined streets leading to a central square.

Turkish occupation, on the whole, did not result in new settlements, but towns are characterized by houses which are closed toward the street and opened toward the interior. Sometimes a high wall with a heavy gate encloses a yard. In the center of the towns is the famous oriental bazaar, a place for trade and commerce which is the center of activities. The Turkish settlements usually were divided into a quiet living district and the business quarters. The houses of tradesmen, artisans—metal and armament industries, silk and gold embroidery—were usually concentrated in the center of the towns. On the whole, areas long under Turkish occupation developed fewer and smaller urban concentrations. Belgrade, at the northern end of the Morava-Vardar depression on the confluence of the Sava and Danube rivers, and Skopje, located where the routes to Niš divide, were the only two larger settlements in the Slavic-settled regions under Turkish control. Towns within the Hapsburg Empire, the Prussian state, and Poland developed along important trade routes and/or near strategic cities. Good examples are Cracow on the upper Vistula River, one of Europe's leading trading cities for roughly 300 years; Prague, roughly in the center of the Bohemian Basin; Buda, on the high, western bank of the Danube River; and Pest, the commercial town on the low, eastern part, located where the Danube is easy to bridge, before it reaches the marshy course it takes through the plains to the south

(Fig. 8–8). While the location of the city is extremely favorable geographically, it never was able to rival Vienna, its neighbor to the west, in terms of trade and strategic location.

During the nineteenth century railways were built to link important commercial and strategic centers. The Danube, at the Iron Gate, was made navigable. With transportation of goods over longer distances becoming easier and more abundant, thousands of agricultural workers moved into the rapidly expanding towns. By the end of the

Fig. 8–8. Budapest, on the Danube River. The view is from Buda, the higher and older part of the city, toward Pest, on the left bank. (Photo: MTI, Hungarian News Agency.)

nineteenth century Bucharest, Prague, Lodz, Breslau (Wroclaw), and Warsaw had become cities with a population of over 100,000, Budapest over half a million. Industrialization came later and much more slowly to the countries of Eastern Europe. Their first function was to supply raw materials to the newly expanding industries of Western and Central Europe, and only slowly did heavy industry move in. Industrialization was still slower in the former territory of the Turkish Empire and did not start until after World War II.

A brief reference has been made to the importance of and the implication of the class structure on the people of this region. Obviously, it would be too difficult to trace this structure back to the first settlers, but for a clear understanding of the tremendous changes in society during the last 15–20 years it is important to summarize briefly the basic structure as it existed at the onset of World War I.

Generally speaking, two structures existed in Eastern Europe: (1) that of the North Slavs, Magyars, and those areas of the South Slavs under control of the Austro-Hungarian Empire; and (2) that of those areas south of the Danube and Sava rivers formerly controlled by the Turkish Empire, especially the territory of the Serbs, Montenegrins, and Albanians, and the mountainous parts of Bulgaria. The first group, the northern region, consisted of a number of feudal states—Prussia, Poland, Bohemia, Hungary, etc.—where the landed gentry was the leading class and the mass of the peasants were either serfs (in most regions until 1848, in the Russian part of Poland until 1867) or half free. This landed nobility, together with the high clergy, had a dominant influence on the central government. Often these central governments were weak and indecisive. Ever since the Middle Ages, and closely related to the growing importance of trade and commerce, a small but growing middle class living in towns and villages exerted an increasing influence.

The picture in the southern areas was quite different. Both the landed nobility and the middle class were largely non-existent in the Turkish-dominated lands There the dominant class included Turkish officials, military leaders, and large landowners. Trade was in the hands of the Greeks and Jews. The original Serbian feudal state of the fourteenth century, with its landowners, high and low nobility, clergy, and dependent peasantry,[14] had been completely destroyed by the Turkish conquerors. Peasant families lived in groups which were referred to as zadrugas or joint family units.[15] Their origin goes back to the tribal organizations of the southern Slavic peoples. Many of the people who could escape from the Turks fled into the impassable mountains, mainly Montenegro, where their ancestors had incessantly carried on guerrilla warfare for generations. Among the people living in the mountains, especially the Montenegrins and Albanians, clan rivalry played an important role. The constant struggle for freedom from foreign oppressors became part of the daily life. These struggles

[14] Eastern Europeans generally consider a "peasant" to be someone who is a self-sufficient farmer, who produces primarily for home consumption. He differs from the so-called "farmer," who produces primarily for the market.

[15] The zadruga was a consuming and producing collective on which several families lived and farmed in common. With the change from an autarchic to a competitive economy, the zadrugas became disorganized and large-scale emigration to towns and overseas led to their gradual dismemberment. See the authoritative discussions by Jozo Tomasevich, *Peasants, Politics and Economic Change in Yugoslavia* (Stanford, Calif.: Stanford University Press, 1955), pp. 178–202.

were led by local leaders and were encouraged by the Orthodox Church, which during the national struggle for survival played an important role in preserving the Serbian state idea. The few intellectuals in the Eastern European countries came largely from the middle class and frequently had to fight to uphold their beliefs, and often were forced to emigrate. With the Industrial Revolution hardly affecting the masses, long-established modes of life remained unchanged in Eastern Europe for a longer time than in nearly any other part of Europe.

The Political-territorial Framework

No discussion of the cultural and historical background would be complete without briefly analyzing the major origins and characteristics of the present political-territorial framework of the countries of Eastern Europe. It can be traced to four major nineteenth-century developments which led to World War I: (1) the steadily growing power and imperialistic ambitions of a united Germany; (2) the declining position and power of the Austro-Hungarian Monarchy, brought about partially by the desire of its many national groups for independence; (3) the disintegration of the Ottoman (Turkish) Empire, resulting in the emergence of a number of small, weak independent states in southeastern Europe—Rumania, Bulgaria, Serbia, Montenegro, and Albania; and (4) the growing antagonism between the Austro-Hungarian Monarchy and the Russian Empire, especially after 1878 when both openly competed for influence in the newly created independent states of southeastern Europe.

World War I resulted in a complete redrawing of the map of Eastern Europe. Poland, Czechoslovakia, and Yugoslavia were each created from land formerly part of at least one of the three empires. Yugoslavia, since 1919, included the formerly independent states of Montenegro and Serbia. Rumania's territorial expansion was at the expense of Austria, Hungary, and Russia, and its new boundaries penetrated deep into the Carpathian Basin. Bulgaria lost two areas to Greece and Yugoslavia. The effects of this changed map were far-reaching. The principle of "self-determination" which was applied to this fragmented region (both physically and culturally) was based on a concept which was too idealistic, and insufficient attention was paid to the creation of really viable states. The power vacuum caused by the almost simultaneous disappearance of the three empires was certainly not filled by the creation of these small, economically and politically weak new independent states. In addition, boundary disputes between nearly all of these new states; the early withdrawal of the United States, sponsor of the principle of "self-determination," from active participation in world affairs; and the unexpected early re-emergence of a powerful Germany and later of the Soviet Union all contributed to a continued instability in this region. Eastern Europe, potentially rich in resources, but underdeveloped (except for a few areas), was suddenly left to itself, inexperienced in governing, a highly diverse population without a strong *raison d'être*. Discontent was obvious. This, naturally, was an open invitation to the powers of Europe to intervene. Between the two wars, some efforts for regional cooperation, such as the Little Entente or the Balkan Entente, either faltered because of the absence of a common policy or were connected with motives of little value to the Eastern European countries themselves.

In addition, Germany's phenomenal reassertion of her power after 1936, and the appeasement policies of the West, left deep impressions of varying degrees on every one of the Eastern European countries. All through the 1930's, sound economic and social planning was replaced by economic self-sufficiency, the development of which would meet the needs of future wars. In other words, "economic nationalism" and "small-power imperialism" became the guiding motives of these countries. Anti-Semitic movements, often supported by Nazi Germany, and a constant round of changing governments, in certain countries semi-dictatorial governments for the most part strongly anti-Russian and in heavy German debt, usually lost contact with the broad mass of the people who seldom understood the intricacies of government. Czechoslovakia, generally considered the citadel of Western democracy, was undermined by a strong German minority, and the Czech majority in turn had difficulty with its Slovak brethren. After Austria's incorporation into Germany (March, 1938), the strategic position of Czechoslovakia became untenable, and shortly thereafter it, too, lost its independence after less than 20 years of precarious statehood. Disunity among the Allied Powers, and the emergence of the Soviet Union as a powerful factor in world affairs, influenced and lessened the importance of Eastern Europe as the so-called *Cordon Sanitaire* between the West and the East. The Soviet-German agreement of August, 1939, spelled the end of Poland and brought about her "fourth partition." The end of the independent states of Eastern Europe had arrived, and, within months after the Russian-German agreement and the beginning of World War II, the map of this region was again completely redrawn.

Pressures previously unknown in modern history forced over 20 million [16] people of Eastern Europe to leave their homes in the wake

[16] Malcolm J. Proudfoot, *European Refugees* (London: Faber & Faber, Ltd., 1957).

of German and Russian armies. Boundaries were completely redrawn between 1939 and the end of the war. Territories were exchanged like pieces of property by Germany, the Soviet Union, and Italy—and also by the countries of Eastern Europe themselves.

The collapse of Nazi Germany found the Soviet Union in control of most of Eastern Europe. American troops had advanced close to Prague and deep into what is now East Germany but, honoring an earlier agreement on occupation zones, had withdrawn, and their place was immediately taken by Soviet troops. Most of Yugoslavia was freed by local partisan soldiers under the leadership of Marshal Tito, a long-time Communist from Croatia, a feat which assumed great importance in the years that followed.

The defeat of Germany and Italy in World War II, disagreement between the United States and the United Kingdom on a postwar policy with regard to the future of Eastern Europe, and, perhaps mainly, the geography of the region gave the victorious Soviet armies nearby a preponderance of power and a strong voice in the future of Eastern Europe.

Disagreement between the Allies and the Soviet Union made territorial settlements in Eastern Europe difficult, and in some instances impossible. The problem was further complicated inasmuch as Poland, Czechoslovakia, and Yugoslavia had been associated with the Allied Powers, while Hungary, Rumania, and Bulgaria had been classed as enemy states, having been associated with Germany, even though under heavy pressure. The three Baltic states, Lithuania, Estonia, and Latvia, already had been incorporated into the Soviet Union during the war, a fact still not recognized by the United States. After considerable difficulty, peace treaties were signed with Hungary, Rumania, and Bulgaria, all recognizing the *de facto* influence of the U.S.S.R., which gained 56,700 square miles of land from Poland, Czechoslovakia, and Rumania.

A number of important territorial changes took place within the area. The most important affected Poland, even though this change has not yet legally been recognized. Poland's boundary was shifted westward from the 1939 location to the Odra and Nisa rivers, giving her the former German ports of Stettin and Danzig, the important rich Upper Silesian industrial area, and valuable farmlands. Over 7 million Germans from this region fled to Germany, mostly to the western part. The disputed area of western Tešín was returned to Czechoslovakia (it had been seized from Czechoslovakia in 1938). From its eastern territories, Poland lost to the Soviet Union farm and forest land and most of its oil reserves. About 4 million people lived in this area, but many returned later to Poland. This westward push of its borders forced Poland to rely on the Soviet Union, inasmuch as the security of Poland against a re-emergence of a strong Germany depends upon friendly relations with the Soviet Union. Despite resentment against Soviet domination, openly expressed in 1956, this basic political dependence certainly has an overriding influence.

Three other boundary changes have more than local importance: (1) the transfer of the Julian March (Istria) from Italy to Yugoslavia—the so-called statute of the Free Territory of Trieste never operated and, in October, 1954, the future of this area was amicably settled; (2) the forced cession of Czechoslovakia's Ruthenia (Carpatho-Ukraine) to the Soviet Union shortly after the war; and (3) the loss of three areas by Rumania. With the acquisition of Bessarabia and northern Bucovina, the Soviet Union again gained a dominant position on the lower Danube. Also, the earlier transfer of southern Dobruja to Bulgaria (1941) was confirmed. Other minor territorial changes occurred between Czechoslovakia and Hungary.

With the exceptions of Yugoslavia and Albania, every one of the Eastern European countries now has a common border with the Soviet Union (Bulgaria with the Black Sea), permitting the Soviet Union easy entrance into its satellite countries. In addition, all of them (again with the exception of Yugoslavia) are militarily tied to the Soviet Union under the Warsaw Pact. The boundaries drawn after World War II have by no means solved all the territorial problems of the countries involved. The situation is dormant for the moment and as long as Soviet authority is maintained no changes are to be expected. On the other hand, it must be stated that the mass transfer of minorities from nearly every country has solved a number of possible territorial disputes.

Economic Development

The Economic Foundation of the New National States. Most of the countries of Eastern Europe were economically backward before World War I. With the exceptions of some mineral exploitation and the establishment of a few industries, especially in Bohemia, Slovenia, and Upper Silesia, the area was predominantly agricultural. The exploited minerals for the most part were shipped to the industries located in the Vienna Basin or to some foreign countries in exchange for needed manufactured goods. Urban settlements, with few exceptions, were small in size and far between, and the rural population comprised between 70 and 90 per cent of the population in all regions except Bohemia, Upper Silesia, and parts of Hungary. Agriculture consisted mostly of large private and church estates, often owned by absentee landlords, and there was little opportunity for the land-hungry peasantry to obtain property. Communications tied regional centers with Vienna and to a lesser degree with Budapest, Berlin, and Leningrad, and usually were based on the strategic necessities of the Monarchy and the German and Russian empires. Generally speaking, the Russian and German interests in Eastern Europe were largely strategic. The interests of the Austro-Hungarian Monarchy have been summarized by Teleki as follows:

> The economic well-being of the old Austro-Hungarian empire lay in the regional character of its economic organizations, which depended mostly on a coordinated internal market and a natural division of labor between the component parts of the empire. Although it was a social and cultural mosaic, the empire was organized in such a manner as to take advantage of the regional distribution of natural resources and the differing skills of the various populations.[17]

An opportunity for basic economic and social changes was offered by the breakdown of the empires of Russia, Germany, and Austria in 1918, the incorporation of some of the small independent states of the southeast into newly organized larger units, and the emergence of seven independent states. Agriculture, the basis of the economy for every one of the newly independent countries, did increase in output between 1919 and 1938, but, in spite of various land reforms, the land hunger of the peasants could not be satisfied. Peasants, on the whole, were highly taxed, had to pay high interest rates, and were frequently caught in the price squeeze between industrial and agricultural prices. In addition, agriculture in Eastern Europe was influenced by the competition from overseas. All during the interwar period, a large percentage of the population was dependent upon agriculture for their income. The population was rapidly expanding, roughly three times as fast as in Western Europe, and agriculture was characterized by large surpluses and a low per-capita per-acre productivity.

With the exception of Czechoslovakia, the newly created states lacked a satisfactory basis for the development of industries, even though individual plants which later laid the foundation for a more concentrated industrialization did exist in Poland, Hungary, and Slovenia (Yugoslavia). Many of the new industries built were often operated on unsound principles. Often, local raw materials, which could have been the foundation for a prospering industry, were sold abroad and finished products were purchased at a high price. Foreign capital for fresh investments was scarce, and available funds usually found their way into extractive industries only. The exploitation of

---

[17] Geza Teleki, "Industrial and Social Policies Between Wars," *Challenge in Eastern Europe*, C. E. Black, ed. (New Brunswick, N. J.: Rutgers University Press, 1954), p. 137.

raw materials was largely in the hands of foreign investors. In Yugoslavia, for example, all of the capital in the copper mines at Bor (French concession), the lead mines at Trepca (English concession), and the manganese and bauxite mines was from foreign lands. Very little attention was given to the possibility of developing consumer goods from local raw materials such as agricultural products, timber, etc. Industries often produced goods for export only, without any thought of developing a domestic market. It was therefore not surprising that the world depression of 1929, the aftereffects of which were felt all through the 1930's, had a devastating impact on the whole economy of these countries. The few foreign investments which had ventured into this region for the most part dried up. Power competition encouraged a drive for autocracy, and what little economic reasoning was originally manifest in the development of the economy was clouded by divergent nationalistic aspirations.

Except in Czechoslovakia and, to a lesser degree, in Poland, the pattern of trade consisted of export of agricultural and raw materials (ores, oil) and import of manufactured goods. Eastern Europe served as the only European market from which to secure grain. The total trading volume during the interwar period was small, less than 7 per cent of Europe's imports and less than 10 per cent of its exports.

Looking back on the social and economic developments of the interwar years, it is rather surprising to see how much progress was made. Actually this region had only about ten years of peaceful, independent development, from 1919 to the outbreak of the world depression. This depression found the Eastern European countries still in the middle of making adjustments and major decisions based on their newly created independence. While the height of the depression was passed by 1934, its repercussions were felt to the beginning of World War II.

Postwar Economic Changes in Eastern Europe. The changes in the political geography of Eastern Europe have been manifested in economic developments also. These developments have varied from country to country and have depended upon the degree of Communist control (Yugoslavia's developments after 1949 have been completely outside the Soviet bloc). The period before 1948 consisted of a mixture of private enterprise, state capitalism, and various other types of economic structure. Particularly on the farms, private enterprises such as the many small peasant holdings were confirmed and collectivization was seldom mentioned. Agricultural investments received a low priority. At the same time, the states acquired considerable land holdings through expulsion or voluntary withdrawal of foreign landowners, and various restrictions as to the size of private holdings. Poland and Hungary, where large estates survived, and Czechoslovakia, where over 3 million Germans were expelled, showed the largest figures for confiscated property; the figures for Yugoslavia, Rumania, and Bulgaria, where small peasant holdings predominated, were far lower. Planning was selective and was certainly not coordinated either with the other countries of Eastern Europe or with the Soviet Union. Trade with the Soviet Union was still of only minor importance, and trade between Eastern European countries and the West was still much valued.[18] Rehabilitation from the effects of the war had first priority. The drive for greater industrialization through investments in heavy industries received early attention. Many ambitious schemes were planned and dismantling on a gigantic scale went on throughout all of this period in East Germany.

The years after 1948 were marked by important changes in every one of the Eastern European countries. East Germany rapidly assumed an important position within the whole framework of the Soviet satellites and is therefore briefly mentioned in the following discussions. Spulber [19] defines three phases in the economic development since 1948:

1. The period to 1953, ending approximately with Stalin's death, was characterized by the entrance of East Germany into the planning of the Soviet bloc, by increased trade with the Soviet Union, and by detailed planning affecting every aspect of life in the People's Democratic Republics.

2. The period from 1953 to 1955 resulted in a general slowing down of the rate of economic expansion. Long-term plans embarked upon earlier were revised, and a new look was taken at agriculture, in a state of crisis in every country of Eastern Europe and the Soviet Union.

3. The present phase started with Malenkov's replacement by Nikita Khrushchev, in 1956. The beginning of this last phase was deeply affected by the upheavals in Poland and Hungary, when the whole Communist control of the satellite countries suddenly became precarious. While many policies initiated earlier had to be held in check, the basic pattern was nowhere drastically altered. Even in Poland, where upheavals in the fall of 1956 for a short time caused profound internal changes, location and history predetermined its basic geopolitical relationships.

[18] For statistical data, see Appendix III.
[19] Nicolas Spulber, *The Economics of Communist Eastern Europe* (New York: Technology Press of MIT and John Wiley & Sons, Inc., 1957).

What are the fundamental changes that have evolved over the last few years? Briefly, they can be summarized as follows:

1. Planned industrialization is the core of the economic development of the Eastern European countries. In this process main attention has been given to heavy industries and increased mining activities, while consumer industries have received lower priorities. The emphasis on heavy industries has taken an important part of the available investment funds. This development followed along the lines of the Soviet Union and was the first step in bringing the economies of Eastern Europe closer to the level of that of the U.S.S.R. The location and huge capacity of the iron and steel mills in Hungary and the capacity of the Polish steel industry are classical examples. Bituminous coal in Poland, and to a lesser degree in Czechoslovakia and Rumania, and lignite in East Germany are ample for all demands (Fig. 8–9). Poland plays a key role with its bituminous coal mines in Silesia. Its output of iron ore, however, is small and the reserves are very restricted. This places the huge iron and steel mills of Poland, East Germany, Czechoslovakia, and Hungary in complete dependence on outside, largely Soviet supplies. Barter agreements between Sweden and Poland (iron ore for coal) are in force, but most of the iron ore is shipped long distances from Krivoi Rog in the Ukraine. Although minor low-grade iron-ore deposits are being utilized, present plans call for even greater dependence upon the high-grade Soviet ore supplies, in this way reducing the demand for metallurgical coke. Petroleum and natural-gas reserves and actual production are insignificant, except in Rumania and Albania. To step up the supply for her rapidly increasing needs, the Soviet Union is building a pipeline from its oil fields in the western Urals across Poland to the Odra River and a branch line to Hungary.

Other raw materials mined in Eastern Europe include manganese and chromium in Rumania and Hungary, chromium in Albania, nickel (in small quantities) in East Germany and Poland, and lead and zinc in East Germany, Poland, and Bulgaria, with the bulk of zinc found in Poland. One of the most important minerals of Eastern Europe is bauxite in Hungary, with minor reserves in Rumania. Mention should also be made of the important potash deposits in East Germany, which account for more than one-third of the world's reserves, and of the world's largest graphite mines, in Czechoslovakia. It is clear from the availability of raw materials that much of the industrial production can depend on a sufficient supply of raw materials from either the region itself or the Soviet Union. This industrial production, without question, has made great strides

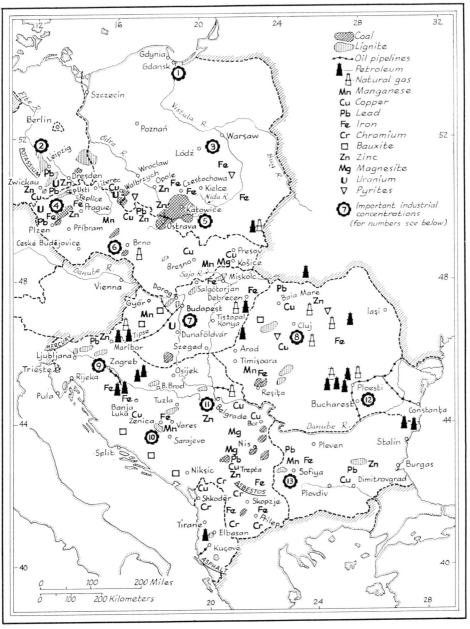

IMPORTANT INDUSTRIAL CONCENTRATIONS

1 Gdynia-Gdansk: shipbuilding, machinery
2 Leipzig-Zwickau-Dresden: textiles, machinery, metallurgy, automobiles, electrical equipment, chemicals
3 Warsaw-Lódź: textiles, machinery, chemicals, paper, food
4 Prague-Plzen: metallurgy, machinery, chemicals, electrical equipment, textiles, paper, glass, leather, food
5 Polish-Czech (Katowice-Ostrava): metallurgy, machinery, chemicals

6 Brno: metallurgy, machinery, chemicals
7 Budapest: metallurgy, machinery, food, textiles, leather, paper
8 Cluj: chemicals, lumber, leather
9 Zagreb: machinery, food, glass, textiles
10 Sarajevo-Zenica: metallurgy, machinery, leather
11 Belgrade: machinery, food, leather, textiles
12 Bucharest-Ploesti: metallurgy, machinery, food, glass, wood and paper, chemicals
13 Sofiya: machinery, food, leather, textiles

Fig. 8–9. Raw materials and industrial concentrations in Eastern Europe.

and has basically changed the prewar agricultural structure of the region.

2. The proportion of agricultural land to the total territory is relatively high, varying from 42 per cent in Albania to 65 per cent in

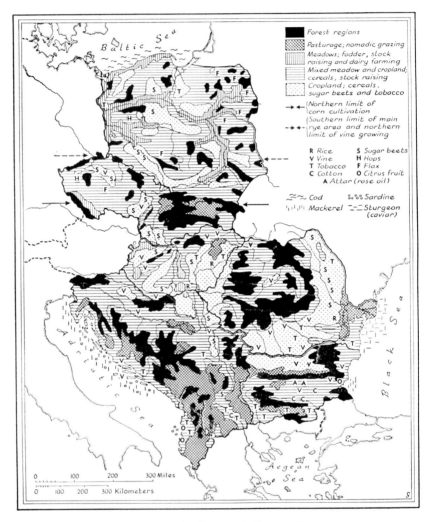

Fig. 8–10. Land utilization in Eastern Europe.

Poland (Fig. 8–10). The agrarian economy is predominantly based on cereal production, with most emphasis on bread grains. Before World War II, Eastern Europe had one-third of Europe's (excluding the U.S.S.R.) wheat area, 55 per cent of its rye area, and 65 per cent of its maize (corn) area. This produced roughly 25 per cent of

Europe's wheat, 50 per cent of its rye, and 70 per cent of its corn. This pattern has changed little in the postwar period, even though industrial crops have recently received added attention. This is especially true for sugar beets, with Eastern Europe now producing one-third of Europe's total production. During normal years, when there is no drought, Eastern European countries are self-sufficient in potatoes, grains, and sugar. The great change from prewar years is the decline of exportable grains and livestock, brought about by the stagnation of yields of crops and animal products and the various land reforms which in turn brought instability to the farmer, as well as greater and changing demands in Eastern Europe (population increase, increased urbanization). Increased cooperation and integration in agriculture has begun, e.g., Bulgaria has agreed to reduce its grain acreage and increase production of tobacco, vegetables, and fruits for export to the other countries of the Soviet bloc. Large capital investments and a basic change in the philosophy with regard to the peasant are needed to increase yields and raise the standard of farming. The success in raising agricultural production in Yugoslavia, which completely abandoned collectivization in 1953, is proof of this truth. And while greater attention has been given to improved farming methods in different degrees in different countries of Eastern Europe, the drive for collectivization (except in Poland) has never been completely abandoned. As a matter of fact, it has been greatly accelerated during the last year or two.

3. Before 1954, contacts among the countries of Eastern Europe and the Soviet Union were largely on a bilateral basis, e.g., the organization of joint companies, arrangements for special low-priced sales of certain products, delivery of certain raw materials in return for finished products, agreements on some specialization in production, etc. (see the discussion in Chapter 10). These contacts tied individual countries closer to the Soviet Union and certainly benefited the Soviet Union, but on the whole contributed little to the integration of the region. The problem of economic cooperation, and especially of regional integration, has received increased attention since 1955. This is expressed in some synchronization of joint plans, greater exchange of goods, joint financing of important projects of value to the whole region or to the Soviet Union, establishment of long-term trade agreements, cooperation in technical assistance, and division of labor for the production and distribution of certain goods. Plans are now closely timed to fit in with those of the Soviet Union, which has a new seven-year plan which will run to 1965. There is every reason to assume that it will be important in the 1960's to include in Soviet Russia's economic potential the increased contributions of Eastern Europe, including East Germany.

POLAND

Population

At the end of World War II Poland was re-established as an independent nation after having been partitioned between Germany and the Soviet Union. Even though its western boundaries have not been permanently decided by treaty, it may be assumed that they will persist. Earlier, the western shift of the whole Polish territory was briefly mentioned—loss of territory in the east to the U.S.S.R. and gain of former German territory in the west and north along the Baltic coast. It must be stressed that this westward push of its borders has, on the whole, created a more viable Poland. The mass exodus and exchange of population certainly settled for the time being the problem of her ethnic minorities.[20] Poland has a total population of more than 28 ✓ million in an area of roughly 120,000 square miles (approximately the size of New Mexico), giving an average density of 237 per square mile. Administratively, Poland is divided into 19 provinces (voivodeships), including the cities of Warsaw and Lodz, and those 19 are subdivided into rural and urban counties (*powiaty*) and rural district settlements (*gromada*). The capital, located on the Vistula River, is Warsaw (Warszawa), a city with over 1 million people. Poland's most densely inhabited regions are in the Polish Uplands from the Silesian Plain, the industrial region of Upper Silesia, across the Carpathian Foreland, to the upper San Valley. In this region densities of between 600 and 800 per square mile are common, with average densities of 200 the norm. Twenty Polish cities now have populations of over 100,000, with Warsaw, Lódź, Wroclaw, and Poznań the largest. The important industrial region of Upper Silesia (Katowice Voivodeship) has the largest concentration of cities with over 50,000 people. As a result of the many territorial and demographic changes, the urban percentage of the population has changed from 26 (in 1939) to 47 per cent

[20] One of the most amazing migrations in the history of mankind took place in the territory of Poland between 1939 and 1949. Close to 10 million people either fled, were expelled, or voluntarily changed their residence. Over 90 per cent of the Jewish population was killed. Statistics indicate that close to 8 million people who lived in Poland in 1939 are now living elsewhere and roughly 1.8 million people who are now living in Poland lived elsewhere in 1939. Of those 8 million people now living outside Poland, close to 7 million are ethnic Germans who either fled or were expelled after 1945. Of those, 5.9 million came from former German territory now administered by Poland (the "Western Territories"). Former Polish citizens now in Western countries are largely in the United States, Israel, and Canada. People now living in Poland who lived elsewhere before 1939 came largely from territories ceded to the U.S.S.R. War losses of the Polish population are estimated at 6 million people killed.

(in 1958). The former German territory now administered by Poland is of great political and economic importance, and it is noteworthy that its population has reached roughly 85 per cent of the prewar population figure. It should be clearly understood, however, that the present population is no longer German but is ethnically almost entirely Polish.

Poland's population is ethnically unified, with only small, dispersed minorities of Czechs, Jews, Germans, and Ukrainians. A large majority of the people are Roman Catholic, but, as is common in Communist countries, a religious census is not part of the official census. The population structure is typical for countries with heavy war losses. Forty-eight per cent of the population in 1956 were 24 years of age or under, 34 per cent were in the age group of 25 to 49 years. Birth rates in Poland have been among the highest in Europe, giving Poland a natural increase of 19.5 per thousand in 1956. Much emphasis has been given to raising the educational level of the population: 76 institutions of higher learning are distributed among twenty cities in Poland. Forty-two per cent of those enrolled during 1956–57 were in technical work, 21 per cent in medicine, and 10 per cent in agricultural sciences. The illiteracy rate in 1951 amounted to 6.1 per cent of the population 10 years of age or older, but compulsory instruction, according to official reports, has reduced this figure.

The occupational distribution has undergone many changes since the war. In 1956, industry, construction, and mining employed 27 per cent of the population and agriculture, forestry, and fishing 52 per cent, a drop from 65 per cent in 1937.

Present Economic Life

Poland's economic structure has undergone basic changes from the prewar period. With the addition of the German part of the highly industrialized Silesian area, together with the great emphasis on industrialization during the whole postwar period, and the loss of 46 per cent of her prewar area to the Soviet Union, an area which contained more than half of Poland's cultivated land, the prewar agricultural emphasis of the economy has basically changed.[21] The addition of the two important Baltic ports of Stettin (Szczecin) and Danzig (Gdańsk) and full control of the Odra and Vistula rivers have greatly improved the country's river and ocean transport system. Erratic plan-

[21] Eleanor T. Brzenk, "Poland, East of the Curzon Line," in Malcolm Jarvis Proudfoot Memorial Volume, *Northwestern University Studies in Geography* 2 (March, 1957): 61. It should be stressed here that yields in this area were lower than in the western part of the country.

ning, as expressed by the many changing goals, has caused much waste and internal difficulty. Poland's whole economic development is today closely integrated with the plans of the Soviet bloc, discussed earlier in this chapter and in Chapter 10.

Agriculture, Fishing, and Forestry. Sixty-five per cent of the total land area of Poland is classified as agricultural, with a little over half arable land (Fig. 8–10). Twenty-four per cent is in forests and 11 per cent is classified as waste and fallow land. The southern river valleys and the glacial valleys (Fig. 8–11) have the highest percentage

Fig. 8–11. The farming village of Wolbórz in the Polish lowlands.

of arable land, and the Polish Uplands and Forelands have the best pastures and meadows. Sixty per cent of the total area cultivated is in cereals, rye being by far the most important, followed by oats, wheat, and barley. Rye and oats are grown all over the country; the Silesian Plain, the Polish Uplands, and the lower Vistula Valley are the dominant wheat areas; and barley predominates in former German Silesia and the Polish Uplands. Potatoes occupy 18 per cent of the cultivated land and are well distributed throughout the country because they are a basic item in the people's diet. Sugar beets are the predominant industrial crop; others are flax, hemp, hops, and chicory. Other crops include fodder plants, legumes, vegetables, rapeseed, linseed, and hemp. Corn, wine grapes, and even tobacco acreages are restricted by climate. Yields of most crops have reached the prewar average, and mechanization and the use of fertilizers are slowly increasing, but important shortages remain. Substantial quantities of grain must still be imported each year (43 per cent from the Soviet Union in 1958).

Losses in livestock between 1939 and 1945 were close to two-thirds of the cattle, pigs, and horses. Horses and cattle have still not quite reached their prewar numbers, but the number of pigs is 20 per cent larger than in prewar times. The horse is still the main draft animal and horses are well distributed throughout the country, with the greatest densities in the central parts of Poland. Efforts are now under way to reduce the number of horses, inasmuch as they consume more bread grains than the entire urban population. The Bialystok and Poznań voivodeships account for more than 20 per cent of the sheep population, although sheep and goats are also widespread in the Carpathian mountain valleys. Milk production has increased from prewar times, and the production of eggs increased by over one-third between 1938 and 1956. Fishing has increased in importance, thanks to the greater length of the Baltic coast line of postwar Poland, with cod and mackerel the chief catches. The 85,000 tons of fish landed play an important role in the proper food balance of the population. Polish trawlers are now also in offshore waters catching cod and herring in the North Sea.

Forests as a natural resource are of major importance to Poland, but great wartime damage and the loss of important reserves of hardwood (oak, beech, birch, and aspen) in the east have forced Poland completely to discontinue its former large exports. As a matter of fact, war damage to forests and to the lumber and wood industry was the single most important damage inflicted on any branch of Poland's economy. Coniferous forests occupy roughly 87 per cent of the present forest area of approximately 18 million acres over 80 per cent of which are state forests. Since the war, wood pulp, plywood, and lumber production has been encouraged, and various by-products, e.g., ship supplies and tanning extracts, are now produced within the country.

Land ownership, too, has undergone basic changes from the prewar period, but especially since the 1956 upheavals. Collective farms have greatly decreased in number and in area, and most of those which remain are in the former German-owned territories. At the end of 1958, 85 per cent of the agricultural land was in private hands, producing 82 per cent of the total production. The average size of private holdings amounted to 15 acres. State farms cover 12.4 per cent of the total arable land. Agricultural production is increased mainly by means of the so-called voluntary cooperatives, "agricultural circles," whose origin goes back to the nineteenth century. They were discontinued after the war, but many thousands have been organized since the fall of 1956. Compulsory delivery quotas were abolished for most farm products after 1956, and general production has increased rapidly ever since. Livestock production has shown the least improvement.

Mining and Manufacturing. Poland's mineral balance, except with regard to coal, has not greatly changed from prewar years. Raw materials other than coal, lead, and zinc are insufficient for the increased industrial requirements and must be imported (Fig. 8–9). Among Poland's minerals, coal assumes the dominant position. With the acquisition of the former German coal mines, coal production has greatly increased from prewar years. Twenty-nine per cent of Poland's 1958 production of 93 million tons came from mines located in former German territories. Poland ranks third in Europe in coal production, and coal is both the principal source of energy for industry and the most important raw material for the expanding chemical and metallurgical industries. Poland's coal production has been fluctuating since the war, with labor shortages, poor housing conditions, and insufficient modern mining machinery the greatest obstacles. The most important bituminous mines are located around Katowice and near the Czech border, the so-called Upper Silesian fields. These form part of the great though discontinuous coal belt extending from the British Isles across Germany. Seams with a maximum thickness of 555 feet are among the thickest in Europe, and the working depth (1,300 to 2,600 feet) is much more favorable for mining than in the Ruhr or British deposits. Reserves are estimated at 100 billion tons, or approximately two per cent of the world's reserves. The quality of the bituminous coal is regarded as very high. Lignite production also has increased from the deposits located on the right bank of the Nisa River, between the Warta and Odra rivers, and south of Czestochowa.

Most of the iron-ore deposits are of poor quality (metal content between 30 and 35 per cent) and mining costs are high. The main deposits are located in the Kielce-Radom district, and near Czestochowa. Poland's mills must import as much as 84 per cent of its iron ore. As we have mentioned, iron ore is imported from the Soviet Union (Krivoi Rog), Sweden, and China in exchange for Polish coal.

Poland is short of nearly all ferrous metals. It has a sufficient supply of non-ferrous metals such as zinc and lead, located near Kielce in central Poland and in Upper and Lower Silesia. Sulphur and sulphuric acid are valuable by-products of the processing of lead and zinc ores. Arsenite ores, mined south of Wroclaw, are of importance. Low-grade pitchblende (uranium) deposits are located near Walbrzych and Jelina Gora. Deposits of salt, gypsum, and lime are plentiful and supply the growing chemical industry. Low-grade copper deposits from Silesia are now used to produce electrolytic copper, important for domestic requirements. Some potash is located west of Lublin, but most of the important deposits are in territory ceded to the Soviet Union.

Poland's most important petroleum fields were also located in the Galician area ceded to the Soviet Union. Her present production comes from fields southeast of Sarnok in the Carpathian Forelands, but supplies only 25 per cent of her domestic requirements. Natural gas has increased in importance and is brought by pipeline from the old Polish fields, now mostly in the U.S.S.R., to Kielce, Cracow, Katowice, and Warsaw. The production of electric power is based largely on thermal (coal and lignite) production, and plans call for greatly expanded production.

The greatest industrial expansion has taken place in machinery and metal goods, chemicals, and shipbuilding. Industrial production did increase during the interwar years, e.g., rolling stock, machine tools, engines, boilers, farm machinery, textiles, chemicals, and food processing, but the addition of German minerals and industries added roughly one-third to the Polish iron and steel capacity. The core of Polish manufacturing today is located in the 786-square-mile coal-rich area of Upper Silesia stretching between Katowice and the former German city of Oppeln (Opole). If the newly built and expanded steel mills near Cracow and the mills at Czestochowa are added, 88 per cent of the output of steel and rolled products in Poland are accounted for. Plans call for a 1960 production roughly four times that of the prewar period. The steel industries employed 6 per cent of the industrial labor force and contributed roughly 7 per cent to the value of Poland's industrial production. On the other hand, supplying the raw materials needed for the metal-processing industries employed 22 per cent of the industrial labor force in 1955.[22] Other important steel and iron works are located at Szczecin, Poland's most important port, and at Warsaw. These industries not only supply Polish domestic demands but also serve as an important supplier for all the countries of the Soviet bloc, including Communist China. As a matter of fact, iron-ore deliveries from the Soviet Union must be repaid in various

[22] John M. Montias, "The Polish Iron and Steel Industry," *The American Slavic and East European Review* 16 (October, 1957): 300–22; Norman J. G. Pounds, "The Industrial Geography of Modern Poland," *Economic Geography* 36 (July, 1960): 231–53; also "Iron and Steel," *Polish Perspectives* 6 (October, 1958): 46–50.

steel products, and rolled steel constitutes over 15 per cent of Poland's total exports.

The iron and steel industries are by no means Poland's only industries of importance. Textile manufacturing has an old and important tradition, and Lódź is often called the "Polish Manchester." Owing to its location, the city is an important manufacturing center for chemical, metallurgical, electrotechnical, food-processing, and other miscellaneous industries. Also, important industries are concentrated in Warsaw, Cracow, Kielce, Czestochowa, Wroclaw, Szczecin, and other cities. Expansion in manufacturing has continued throughout the various three-, five-, and six-year plans. Shipbuilding facilities, which became Polish property with the acquisition of the most important Baltic ports of Szczecin and Gdańsk, have been modernized and expanded. Traditional glass production is carried on mostly in Silesia and has been greatly enlarged at Walbrzych. A new chemical plant producing fertilizers and chlorine has been completed at Kedzierzyn. In the area between Warsaw, Lublin, Radom, Lódź, Poznań, and Bydgoszcz are concentrated a scattering of small and medium-size plants, e.g., sugar refineries, food canneries, breweries, and flour mills. Southward, in the uplands and the valleys of the Carpathians, are woodworking plants and paper mills.

A word should also be said about the over-all importance of the so-called "Western Territories" to Polish manufacturing. These newly acquired territories, which comprise roughly one-third of Poland's total area, contribute a third of the total power production, more than a fourth of the coal, and nearly a fourth of the steel. Of the total number of those employed in industry and handicrafts in the country, one in four work in the "Western Territories." [23]

Communications. Poland's transport network largely reflects the country's historical development (Fig. 8–2). The part east of the Vistula has few rail connections, while rails are densest in the former German and Austrian territories. Inasmuch as both the old and newly built industries are located in these territories, as well as in the upland regions, the transport network satisfies most industrial needs and moves about 96 per cent of all freight traffic (a third of it being coal and coke). This network was in a deplorable condition following the end of World War II. Besides repairs, a few connecting lines and changes from narrow to standard gauge have been completed since 1945. Poland's most important railroads are the two north-south lines: from Gdańsk to Katowice, and from Szczecin to Wroclaw; and

[23] Maria Horowitz, "The Rise of the Western Territories," *Polish Perspectives* 6 (October, 1958): 50–55.

two west-east lines: from Frankfurt on the Odra via Warsaw to Brest, and the industrially important line from Wroclaw to Jaroslaw. Other lines connect Warsaw with various southern cities. Passenger traffic has tripled, freight loadings have increased by two and one-half times since 1938, but rolling stock has not kept up with demand. These increases are due to the industrialization of the country since the war, to the greater postwar mobility, especially in increased commuting between rural and urban areas, and to the greatly increased vacation travel.

The highway network has been greatly enlarged in the postwar years, with 35 per cent of all roads now hard surfaced. Highway freight and passenger traffic has increased, but still accounts for only 3 per cent of the total inland transportation. The newly constructed Zeran automobile plant has under way a greatly enlarged program for the production of passenger cars and trucks. Air traffic has increased during the last 10 years, and the official Polish state airline (LOT—Polskie Linie Litnicze) reports for 1956 a total of 88.6 million passenger-kilometers. Most of the major cities are connected by regular service.

Poland's inland waterways include 2,750 miles of navigable rivers and canals. The importance of the Odra, navigable for more than 400 miles and connecting the Baltic Sea with the important industrial region of Upper Silesia, has greatly increased since the war. Sixty-two per cent of all the Polish waterway traffic moves on this river. Ore shipments and other bulky raw materials are its main freight. The southern Odra is canalized and offers a connection to Katowice. The Vistula is navigable for most of its length, but below Warsaw accommodates only very small vessels (less than 400 tons). Its importance for the movement of freight is negligible. The lowlands have a number of important canals. The most important east-west connection follows the lower Bug River and a stretch of the Vistula to the city of Bydgoszca, continuing on the Noteć Canal to the Noteć River, which in turn flows into the Warta and it in turn into the Odra near Kostrzyn. A good part of this important east-west route is in need of modernization to make it navigable even for vessels up to 250 tons. Poznań also is well located and connected with the major river and canal systems of the Polish lowlands. Plans call for additional canals, especially the canalization of the Bug between Modlin, northwest of Warsaw, and the Soviet city of Brest.

Owing in part to German merchant-marine reparations, the Polish deep-sea fleet has now reached more than 250,000 tons. Additional cargo vessels, tankers, and small passenger vessels are scheduled to be added during the next few years. The freight turnover at the important ports is steadily increasing and has reached over 15 million metric tons annually. Besides Szczecin, Gdańsk, and Gdynia, several other ports have local importance.

Foreign Trade. The structure of Poland's foreign trade has undergone basic changes from the prewar period, when trade was predominantly with the United Kingdom, Germany, and the United States; today, the Soviet Union heads the trade list. More than half of Poland's total foreign trade is carried on with the Soviet Union and the other People's Democracies. This is the lowest intrabloc trade percentage of any of the members of the Council for Mutual Economic Aid (see Chapter 10). Coal, coke, rolled products, machines and machine tools, zinc and zinc sheets, chemicals, foodstuffs, and cotton and wool fabrics head the exports. Among the most important imports are iron ore, petroleum products, crude oil, zinc concentrates, rubber, cotton, wool and other textile raw materials, rawhide, oils and fats, tobacco, coffee, rice, and maize. Since 1956, Poland has again emphasized its trade with non-bloc countries without giving up any of its ties with Communist countries.

CZECHOSLOVAKIA

Population

The prewar Republic of Czechoslovakia had a lifetime of less than twenty years. Between the organization of the country in October, 1918, and its breakup as a result of the Munich Agreement in September, 1938, it constantly had to cope with its multinational population. Between the annexation by Germany of the largely German-speaking Sudetenland and the Treaty of Moscow in July, 1945, when the country's easternmost province of Ruthenia was incorporated in the Soviet Union, Czechoslovakia underwent tremendous population and territorial changes.[24] Between Munich and the end of the war, a large strip of the country's territory in southern Slovakia and Ruthenia, with approximately one million people, was awarded to Hungary. Poland, in October, 1938, occupied and later annexed the small and contro-

---

[24] Approximately 2.4 million Sudeten Germans were transferred to Germany under the Potsdam Agreement, and an additional 800,000 Germans fled either with the retreating German army or after the war. More than 24,000 Hungarians who had moved to territory awarded them in Czechoslovakia in 1939, returned to Hungary. Roughly 140,000 Czechoslovak nationals could not be accounted for at the end of the war. Another 800,000, living in Ruthenia, were transferred to the U.S.S.R. About 55,000 Jews survived the war, but most of these have emigrated to Israel. Altogether, Czechoslovakia lost roughly 3.4 million people between 1939 and 1945. Another 50,000 political refugees left after the Communists came to power in mid-February, 1945.

versial Těšin region. In March, 1939, Czechoslovakia itself was removed from the map as an independent country. With the occupation of the Czech territory by Germany (Bohemia and Moravia
became a German protectorate), Slovakia became independent under
German protection and Ruthenia was occupied by Hungary. After
the war, however, territories annexed by Germany, Hungary, and
Poland were restored to Czechoslovakia.

The estimated population of some 13 million people dwell in an
area of 49,453 square miles, roughly the size of New York State, with
an over-all population density of about 268 per square mile. Administratively, Czechoslovakia is divided into 10 regions, *kraje*, and 108
districts, *okresy*. The prewar provinces of Bohemia and Moravia are
now comprised of 7 *kraje*, the remaining 3 *kraje* comprise the former
province of Slovakia.[25] Prague is the capital, with a population of
close to 1 million, and administratively has the rank of a province. Of
the five cities with over 100,000 inhabitants, Prague, Brno, Ostrava,
Plzen, and Bratislava, only the last is located in Slovakia. In 1957,
2.2 million people lived in cities of over 100,000. The country has
eight cities in the population group 50,000 to 100,000. Greatest population densities are found in the industrial regions of Ostrava, Prague,
and Plzen, where there are over 500 people per square mile. Densities
in the mountainous areas of the western Carpathians, however, are
less than 70 per square mile.

Because of Czechoslovakia's increased industrialization and the
greater mechanization of agriculture, many rural communities have
lost people, and this is clearly reflected in the increase of those living
in urban localities—49 per cent in 1946 as against 58 per cent in 1958.
In addition, the war had a different impact on the Czech and the
Slovak region. In the Czech region, population increased much more
slowly and population changes between 1938 and 1947 were more
profoundly felt. Population dropped in the Czech region by 21 per
cent, while it dropped by only 5 per cent in the Slovak region.

The various migrations and war losses naturally have affected the
average annual growth as well as the whole population structure.
Natural increase has always been slow and between 1950 and 1956
averaged 11 per thousand annually. Birth rates increased to a peak
of 22.9 per thousand of the population in 1950, but death rates were
still relatively high, averaging 11.9 per thousand, not counting still-
births. For detailed population figures, see Appendix III.

Ethnographically the population is now much more homogeneous
than in the prewar years. Minorities have greatly declined with the

---

[25] The present administrative organization went into effect during the spring of
1960. Slovakia continues its autonomous administrative organization.

mass migration of the Germans (ethnic Germans made up 1.2 per cent of the population in 1956, as against 23.6 per cent in 1930). Hungarians occupy a narrow strip to the south, along the Hungarian boundary. No religious census has been taken since 1930, but, at that time, 77 per cent of the Czechoslovakian people declared themselves Roman Catholics, 13.2 per cent belonged to various Protestant denominations, and persons without religious affiliation numbered about 6 per cent. Most of the Germans who have since left were listed as Roman Catholic.

Illiteracy has had only a minor role in Czechoslovakia since 1930. It was 1.3 per cent in the Czech region according to the 1930 census (population 10 years of age and over) and 8.2 per cent in the Slovak region, but a concerted effort has reduced this figure in the last 30 years. Public schools in Czechoslovakia had a high reputation before World War II. The whole system was reorganized in 1948, when a uniform educational system was established. Much emphasis has been placed on additional educational training since that time, and the 1956 figures showed that 4 per cent of those in school were attending universities.

The occupational distribution has undergone important changes during the last 20 years. In 1956, almost half of the total population were economically active and, of those, 33 per cent were engaged in agriculture and forestry, 33 per cent in industry and mining, 7.5 per cent in construction, 6 per cent in commerce and trade, and 5.5 per cent in transportation and communications. This development is typical for all Eastern European countries: a fast growth in industrial and a gradual decline in agricultural employment.

Present Economic Life

With the breakup of the Austro-Hungarian Monarchy, an independent Czechoslovakia retained nearly 60 per cent of all the industries of the Monarchy. Over 80 per cent of the Monarchy's coal production was located in Czech territory. The Ostrava-Karvina region, with important reserves of coking coal and iron ore from the Slovak Ore Mountains, which was developed as an important ferrous-metallurgy center for the Monarchy, now became available to the new state. These raw materials and industries, together with a highly developed agriculture, were a great asset. On the other hand, the old Monarchy's free markets were lost and much of the prewar period was consumed in adjusting Czechoslovakia's large industrial production to the needs of the reduced market area and in increasing the country's foreign trade. After the liberation of Czechoslovakia from

Nazi rule, property of wartime collaborators was confiscated. Nationalization and land reforms set the pattern typical for Communist countries. When the Communists came to power, government control of the economy was made complete. Subject to the guidance of the Soviet Union, the economic development since that time has been closely connected with the changing goals of the various Soviet plans. Industrial expansion received top priority. Investments in agriculture were small and progress lagged far behind. The large industries which had been in existence in pre-Communist times and the relatively little war damages gave Czechoslovakia a unique position among the Soviet satellites. From a purely economic point of view, Czechoslovakia's contributions of technical knowledge, and her export of machinery, tools, instruments, processed food, railroad rolling stock, and engines, are the most important contributions to the whole Soviet bloc.

Agriculture and Forestry. Fifty-eight per cent of the total land area of Czechoslovakia is classified as agricultural; roughly 41 per cent of the agricultural land is arable, 17 per cent is permanent meadows and pastures, 34 per cent is forested, and 8 per cent is classified as waste and unproductive (Fig. 8–10). Agriculture is dominant in Bohemia, but, measured by the number of those engaged in it, plays a greater role in Slovakia. The prevalence of agriculture, however, decreases toward the east; the Bohemian Basin, the Moravian depression, and the Slovakian part of the Little Alföld are the most intensively agricultural regions. The Carpathians are important for pasturage. Wheat, barley, oats, and rye are the most important cereals; corn is cultivated for the most part in the Slovakian portion of the Little Alföld. Yields have generally reached or surpassed those of the 1934–8 average. The size of the harvest has also either reached or exceeded the totals of prewar years. Grapes are grown in southwestern Slovakia, the Morava Basin, and the Labe Valley. A greatly decreased harvest of hops, important for the beer industry, comes from the Ohre Valley and the Moravian Basin. Tobacco-production area has increased, most tobacco being grown along the lower Morava and Danube rivers. Over 4 million cattle, mainly in Bohemia and Moravia, pigs, sheep, goats, and poultry make up an important livestock industry. Higher quality and increased exports have been the aims during the last few years.

Although the forest lands in Ruthenia are lost to the Soviet Union, forests remain an important natural resource in Czechoslovakia. Close to half of the forests are coniferous, 30 per cent are deciduous, and the rest are mixed. The Administration of State Forests controls nearly all forest lands. Because of overcutting during the war and increased demands for industrial production, timber cutting has been curtailed. Coniferous woods supply most of the wood production, with roundwood, pulpwood, and pit props predominant. The importance of forestry is shown in the large number of those employed in it, over 100,000 in 1958.

Collectivization of agriculture was introduced shortly after the war, and the socialized sector [26] included 80 per cent of all agricultural land in 1959. One hundred per cent socialization is the ultimate goal. Peasants have put up stubborn resistance at times, and this follows the general pattern of other Communist Eastern European countries. Most of the remaining private farms average 5 to 10 acres. Many of these farmers received their land in the land reforms following the war, and they resist strongly the introduction of large collectives.

Mining and Manufacturing. Large deposits of coal, various other minerals, and large quantities of lumber and pulpwood enabled Bohemia and Moravia and later Slovakia to build an old and diverse manufacturing industry (Fig. 8–9). Roughly 26 million tons of bituminous coal and 54 million tons of lignite were mined in 1958. The main center for coal mining is the southern part of the Upper Silesian coal basin near the city of Ostrava. Smaller fields are distributed throughout Bohemia. Lignite is mined mainly in the Teplice-Sanov-Chomutov area and the upper Nitra Valley in Slovakia. Iron ore in the Ore Mountains of Bohemia southwest of Prague and in the Slovakian Ore Mountains is insufficient for Czechoslovakia's domestic requirements and the quality has decreased rapidly. Kaolin, of great importance to the world-famous china and glass industry, occurs in the Karlovy Váry and Plzeň regions of Bohemia. Graphite is mined near Brno and Plzeň and is of importance for the pencil production; small quantities of lead and zinc are mined at Pribram; antimony, mercury, magnesite, and tin in the Ore Mountains; copper and pyrite and some gold and silver ores in the Carpathian Mountains. The extraction of uranium from wolframite and pitchblende ores, mined in increasing quantities during the last few years, is of great importance to the expanded atomic-energy projects of the Soviet Union. New mines have been opened and more than 15,000 workers were employed during 1958 in seven major mining regions. Pribram and Březnice (8 miles south of Pribram) are the main centers for administration and transshipment.[27]

[26] The socialized sector includes collectives, state farms, and state tractor farms. The latter are in the process of a basic reorganization following the Soviet Russian example of 1958.

[27] "Der Uranerzbergbau in der Tschechoslovakei," *Berichte und Informationen* 640 (October 24, 1958): 5–6.

Supplies of non-metallic minerals are plentiful. Mention should also be made of a small production of petroleum, 110,000 tons in 1957, and natural gas (mainly from eastern Slovakia), but hardly of importance, considering the huge imports necessary. The well-known mineral springs and spas centering around Karlovy Vary (Karlsbad) serve as important health resorts.

Manufacturing industries are concentrated in three important regions: (1) the coal area of Ostrava-Karvina, (2) the Prague-Plzeň region, and (3) a minor region in the Ore Mountains. Additional in-

Fig. 8–12. Karviná, an industrial city in Czech Silesia, near the Czech-Polish border. (Pictorial Service, Czechoslovakia.)

dustries of importance are widely distributed, especially in Bohemia and in the larger cities. Czechoslovakia's metallurgical industry is concentrated in the Ostrava-Karviná (Fig. 8–12) and Kladno districts. Smaller centers are Chomutov (northwestern Bohemia), Plzeň and Rokycany (western Bohemia), Zdar (Moravia), and Brezno (Slovakia). The industry was hardly touched by the war and contributed much to the postwar industrial expansion in the Soviet-bloc countries. The location of the plants is closely related to coal. A dense railway network, most of which was built before World War I, helps to transport the great variety of products within the country and to various foreign countries. Czechoslovakian industrial capacity has been much enlarged since 1939, e.g., the new metallurgical combine near Ostrava has an annual production capacity of over 1 million tons of steel.

Ground has been broken for a new integrated iron and steel plant near Košice, in eastern Slovakia. Production at Košice is expected to bring the national steel output to over 9 million tons by 1965. The location of this new plant is significant. Iron ore will be shipped from Krivoi Rog in the Ukraine and coal from the Czech fields in Ostrava. This will cut the distance for the iron-ore shipments by close to half (the ore now goes to Ostrava), which is especially important considering the long homeward journey the empty ore cars must make. Products of the metallurgical industries include rolling stock, power equipment, tools, precision instruments, and armaments.

Other major industries are the chemical and drug, textile, and woodworking industries. The chemical industry, especially, received much attention during the first five-year plan. With the use of various by-products of synthetic fuel manufacture, it has greatly increased its production. Production includes synthetic products, e.g., polyamids and polyvinyl chloride (used as substitutes for non-ferrous metals, synthetic fibers, and leather), rubber, pharmaceuticals, artificial fertilizers, dyes, and paints. Plants are well distributed, with the largest in Usti on the Labe River, Prague, and Plzeň. The center of the textile industry is in Bohemia, with Liberec the center for cotton and linen production and Brno for the wool industry. Woodworking industries are mainly in northeastern Bohemia and southern Slovakia.

Some importance should be credited to the long-established home and small-scale industries for the production of leather goods, musical instruments, toys, jewelry, lace, and other consumer products. Industries producing flour and sugar, dairy products, malt, starch, glucose, and tobacco, and the well-known beer industries of Plzeň and Ceské-Budějovice, play their role in the economy of the country. Of all the Eastern European countries, including East Germany, Czechoslovakia has the best industrial base, including a traditionally well-trained labor supply.

Communications. The communications network is extremely dense in the Czech region, but the mountains of Slovakia form a barrier and have few railroads and highways. The roads are of excellent quality and all important main railroad lines are double tracked. Prague is the chief railway center, with lines fanning out in all directions, and Bratislava, in Slovakia, is an important terminus. Freight carried by railroads has shown a small increase during the last few years, with coal and coke comprising close to 40 per cent of the tonnage. Freight carried on highways increased 18 per cent between 1949 and 1956.

Navigable waterways, a total of roughly 300 miles, play a decidedly secondary role, with the Danube, the Labe, and the Vltava as far as

Prague the only navigable rivers. There has been much talk and planning for an Odra-Danube canal, economically of great importance in an integrated Eastern Europe. Plans for such a canal predated World War I and also were considered during the Nazi regime. Domestic air traffic has greatly increased during the last few years.

Foreign Trade. As have those of all Eastern European countries, the trading partners of Czechoslovakia have changed considerably since the prewar period. Germany, the United States, and Great Britain, in that order, were the chief customers for Czechoslovakian exports and the principal sources of her imports. Trade with the Soviet Union was very minor, and trade with the other countries in Eastern Europe also played only a secondary role. Today Soviet trade amounts to roughly one-third of Czechoslovakia's total trade and that with the other Communist countries 36 per cent. Czechoslovakia's basic aim in her foreign-trade policy is to buy and sell within the Soviet bloc. Although trading partners have changed since prewar years, the basic pattern of goods exported or imported has varied only slightly. Czechoslovakia has a favorable trade balance. Forty per cent of all goods exported consist of machinery, equipment, and armaments; 20 per cent consist of consumer goods (other than foodstuffs) such as textiles, glass, china, and furniture. Imports of fuel and raw materials rank first, followed by foodstuffs.

HUNGARY

Population

The only territorial change for Hungary after World War II was the loss of a small area, 24 square miles, opposite the Czech city of Bratislava. Otherwise, the area remained unchanged, because territories gained during World War II were also lost. Today Hungary is one of the People's Democracies of Eastern Europe, with a population of 9.8 million (January, 1958), an area of 34,752 square miles (roughly the size of Indiana), and a population density of 275 per square mile, the greatest density in any Eastern European country. Administratively, Hungary is now divided into 19 counties (*megye*) and these are subdivided into districts (*járás*), cities or towns (*város*), and communes (*község*). Budapest, the capital, with a population of 1.8 million, and the cities of Pécs, Szeged, Debrecen, and Miskolc are called autonomous cities, equivalent to districts. The population of each of these cities is close to 100,000. The greatest population density is found in and around the major cities, and the range of population in the counties varies between 153 and 308 persons per square mile, the lowest density being found in the southern part of Transdanubia (see footnote 7, p. 550) and on the Hortobágy steppe.

With increased industrialization and some forced resettlement of the population along the Austro-Hungarian border (the "Security Zone"), population densities have undergone important changes since 1945. These shifts are also shown in the changing rural-urban ratio of the population, with a decline in the rural population from 64 per cent in 1941 to 59 per cent in 1956. Urban growth has been rapid, but uneven, e.g., the population of Hungary's cities increased by an average of 12 per cent in the period 1949–54, but nine industrial towns increased by almost 50 per cent whereas 12 typical rural towns decreased by 5 per cent.[28]

Hungary too has had considerable population transfer since 1939.[29] The various migrations and war losses naturally have affected the average annual growth as well as the population structure. Great fluctuations are characteristic, and a rise in the birth rate and a decline in the death rate during the last several years have brought the natural increase to approximately 11 per thousand. On the whole, the nation's net population growth has been exceedingly small. Hungary's population has, of course, grown older, with the median age now 31 years.

Ethnographically, the population of Hungary is extremely homogeneous (Fig. 8–5). Ninety-seven per cent of the population speak Hungarian as their mother tongue; the language is Magyar. Germans are the largest minority group, others are Slovaks, Serbs, Croats, and Rumanians. The people of Hungary are predominantly Roman Catholic (70 per cent), and about 27 per cent are members of various Protestant sects.

Illiteracy in Hungary is nearly non-existent; less than 4 per cent of the population 10 years and older can neither read nor write. Technical training and higher education receive much emphasis. Enrollment in technical fields of higher education tripled between

---

[28] United Nations, *Economic Survey of Europe in 1957*, Geneva, 1958, pp. vii and 21.

[29] This includes people transferred because of the various territorial changes during the war, e.g., Czechs and Slovaks expelled during 1939; and the Hungarians moved from truncated Rumania to the pre-1939 Hungary. A number of exchanges were arranged after World War II. By far the largest change involved the German ethnic group, of which about 260,000 were expelled or fled from Hungary. Mention should also be made of war losses and of the reduction in the Jewish population. Few survived the war, and most of those emigrated to Israel or the United States. Another mass movement of people occurred in connection with the 1956 revolt. A net migration loss of 186,000 resulted from the movements between October, 1956, and the end of 1958. More than 86,000 were permanently resettled in various European countries, 84,000 in overseas countries.

1937–9 and 1956–7, and similar developments are noticeable in secondary schools. The shortage of skilled workers, which is typical for all Eastern European countries, has brought increased attention to specialized training, in both secondary and higher education. Hungary has six universities, but some of them consist of individual departments only. Finally, the occupational structure of the population shows that about 46 per cent of the total population are economically active. Of these, about 44 per cent are active in agriculture (the percentage is declining), about 25 per cent are in manufacturing and mining, and 5 per cent are in construction.

Present Economic Life

Hungary's economic structure underwent major changes after World War II. Considerable war damage slowed postwar recovery. Communist influence in Hungary became complete after 1949, and plans to change the largely agricultural character to that of a mixed agrarian-industrial country started with the first five-year plan, 1949–54. Constantly changing goals, forced industrialization, stagnation of agriculture, requisitioned exports, and the aftereffects of the 1956 upheavals (when industrial production remained inactive for more than three months) influenced the whole economic development of the country.[30]

In spite of the fact that Hungary's new iron and steel industries must import the key raw materials, coal, coke, and iron ore, the building of these industries in itself is certainly not to be blindly condemned. With close economic integration among the Eastern European countries and the Soviet Union and with an excellent rail and river transport network available with the neighboring states, these needed raw materials can easily be shipped in. In addition, Hungary has ample labor and excellent technical schools. The problem is one of paying for these raw materials. Export of surplus bauxite and manganese ore, together with agricultural surplus, could easily pay for the needed minerals. This would be even easier if the new industries were better fitted for the needs of the country, e.g., tool making and food processing instead of heavy machinery. Unfortunately, surplus cereals for export are a thing of the past and agriculture on the whole is stagnating. With one branch of the economy in poor health, the other part is unable to carry the total load. This is the real problem of Hungary's unbalanced economy.

[30] The Soviet Union and its allies had to support the Hungarian government's purchase of raw materials with loans in excess of $250 million. See *The New York Times*, November 21, 1958.

Agriculture and Forestry. Seventy-eight per cent of the total land area of Hungary is classified as agricultural, 13.5 per cent as forests and woodlands, and 8.4 per cent as unproductive; 62 per cent of the total area is arable. Cereals (Fig. 8–10) are traditionally the most important crops, and the acreage is about equally divided between the bread grains (wheat and rye) and coarse grains (maize, barley, and oats). Wheat, with yields generally unchanged from the prewar era, is grown mainly in the Transtisia, and rye in the Danube-Tisza-Mesopotamian region and Transdanubia. In 1958, the total acreage was about 12 per cent below the prewar average, and it is the government's hope that production can be increased by a greater use of fertilizers and mechanization. Wheat exports have been completely stopped since 1953; as a matter of fact, drought years resulted in imports being necessary for the first time in Hungary's history. Barley and oats are widely distributed, with special emphasis in the Little Alföld. Potatoes dominate on the sandy areas of eastern Hungary and near the Austrian border. Sugar beets, the cultivation of which has been expanded, are found in both the Little Alföld and Transdanubia. Many new industrial crops have now been planted, foremost among them being cotton, which is planted in the southern part of the Transtisia region, and leguminous plants such as peas, beans, and lentils are common. Irrigated vegetable acreage increased by more than 10 times between 1939 and 1957. Rice acreage has also increased in the last few years, especially in the semiarid alkaline soils of the Hortobágy Plain. Hungary has now changed from a rice importer to a rice exporter and claims to be the leading producer in Europe. The production of paprika (eaten dried, as a spice, or green) is sufficient to permit export of large quantities. The marketing center is at Szeged. Mention also should be made of the important viticulture. Wines were an important export item in the foreign trade of prewar years. Those from the Lake Balaton and Tokaj regions are world-famous and output has again reached prewar levels.

Animal husbandry provided close to 25 per cent of the total agricultural output before World War II. Losses in livestock between 1939 and 1945 were more than 50 per cent. The number of livestock has reached prewar levels, except for horses, but it is hoped that animal draft power will be replaced by increased mechanization. Cattle numbered nearly 2 million in 1956 and are of the special Hungarian breed, white and long horned (Fig. 8–13). These are slowly being replaced by Austrian and Swiss breeds which are better milk producers. Transdanubia is the main cattle-breeding region, and the seminomadic cattle and horse of the *puszta* and the Hortobágy are, for the most part, a thing of the past. Fattened cattle also are exported. Pigs are common in the corn areas of the south and the Little Alföld, the Hungarian breed called "Mangalitsa" is slowly being replaced by the better meat-producing Yorkshires, Berkshires, and Cornwalls. Sheep raising has slowly increased since the low of 1950 and is mainly concentrated in the northern highlands and eastern Hungary. Geese are much valued because of their feathers, down, liver, and fat. Shortage

Fig. 8–13. Animal husbandry in the Great Alföld. Long-horned white Hungarian cattle at a *gémes kút* (crane-shaped well) in the Hortobágy.

of fodder has been the main handicap in increasing the quality of the animals.

Forestry is of minor importance in Hungary, and imports are essential for nearly every type of lumber and wood product. The oak predominates and only six per cent of the forests are coniferous. Considerable effort has been made in forestation, e.g., for windbreaks and shelter belts, and to increase Hungary's slim forest reserves.

Collectivization [31] has had its ups and downs in Hungary since the war. It started in the latter part of 1948 and reached its height during 1952. Its low was reached after the 1956 revolution, and since that

[31] Includes both individual collectives and state farms.

time it has slowly increased, accounting for over 50 per cent of the total arable land in the beginning of 1959. The general effect of the postwar land reforms has been an increase in the small and medium-size peasant holdings, generally at the expense of the prewar large estates. Much of the confiscated land was put into state farms, which constituted 11 per cent of the total agricultural land in 1957. Part of Hungary's difficulty in raising agricultural production is the unwillingness of the peasant farmers to part with their small farms (the majority averaging 10–15 acres—often received during the postwar reforms). And the government is dependent upon these farmers.

Mining and Manufacturing. All important industries depend upon mineral supplies from abroad. Minerals available in quantities sufficient to be mined include the coal near Pecs, on the southern slopes of the Mecsek hills, and a small field in the north. Bituminous coal accounts for approximately 10 per cent of the total coal production (24 million tons in 1958), and some coking coal has been produced from the coal in the Mecsek fields. Lignite is used extensively for power production and transportation and as a household fuel. With few waterpower sites, this low-grade coal plays a key role in the economy. Lignite is located in three major basins: (1) the Vertes hills west of Budapest and the Esztergom-Dorog region northwest of Budapest—this lignite is used in Budapest and in the aluminum plants north of Lake Balaton; (2) the Sajo Valley of Borsod County, whose lignite is used by the iron and steel industries of Miskolc; and (3) north of Miskolc along the Slovak boundary, this lignite used locally in the chemical industry.

Petroleum and natural-gas production was originally started by the Standard Oil Company, in 1937. Petroleum production rose to 1.6 million metric tons by 1955, but declined to a low of 820,000 tons in 1958. Fields are located in southwestern Hungary and southeast of Budapest. Pipelines connect these fields with refineries at Budapest. Natural-gas production has increased during the last few years and is found in several parts of the country. Iron-ore production was 240,000 tons in 1956, at a large surface mine of Rudabanya in the vicinity of Miskolc. Manganese is mined in the Bakony Forest, and a small amount was exported before the war. Small quantities of copper, arsenite, pyrites, gold, lead, and uranium are mined. Bauxite, however, is Hungary's richest mineral resource, and reserves are estimated at close to 16 per cent of the world reserves. Bauxite is found in many places, but the chief mines are southwest of Budapest and in the Bakony Forest, near important lignite mines. Some of the bauxite includes important by-products such as aluminum oxide, iron, and sulphur. Hungary's exports of bauxite are of great importance to the Soviet Union, Poland, and Czechoslovakia.

Three major industrial regions and a number of minor areas can be clearly defined.

1. Budapest, with its suburban region, has Hungary's largest industrial concentration in terms of manpower employed and value of output. There exists a great diversity: metallurgical plants, paper and textile mills, machine and tool factories, airplanes and armaments, tractors, diesel and electric locomotives, coaches, freight cars, trucks, sugar, tobacco, flour mills, food processing and various pharmaceuticals.

2. The second major region includes all of northeast Transdanubia. This region combines mining and the manufacture of such items as rolling stock, textiles, electric equipment, and glass. The factories make use of the coal at Ajka, and the power plants use local lignite. The Tatabanya lignite region includes cement plants and power production. Much of Hungary's bauxite and manganese production also originates in this region.

3. The third important region extends along Hungary's northern border from Salgótárjan to Ózd and Miskolc. This region has numerous minor but important minerals and is one of Hungary's oldest industrial regions. Its machinery, tool, and armament industries make important contributions to the whole economy.

Newly developed industrial concentrations include the integrated iron and steel works at Sztálinváros, south of Budapest, on the Danube (Fig. 8–14). This plant originally was planned for Mohács near the Yugoslav frontier, to process Yugoslav ores, but after the Tito-Stalin break this site was abandoned even though much had been invested in it. Iron ore is shipped on the Danube from Krivoi Rog, coke comes from Poland and East Germany by rail and on the Danube. The supply picture would improve if the often-projected Odra-Danube canal, now again under discussion, is undertaken. Ultimately, Sztálinváros will have three large blast furnaces and several open-hearth furnaces. Another industry greatly expanded since the war is the chemical industry. Numerous small plants existed before the war, and most of them have been modernized. The output of caustic soda, chlorine, oxygen, and other gases has been increased. With increased demands for fertilizers, organic dyes, drugs, rubber goods, etc., the expansion of the coal-chemical and petrochemical industry has become an urgent necessity.

A large new chemical combine at Tiszapalkonya on the middle Tisza River is one of the first integrated industries built in close cooperation with other Soviet-bloc countries. The hydroelectric plant was built with the participation of Czech engineers and capital. Natural gas via pipeline from Rumania has an important role; some coal is available locally. When this plant achieves full production it will manufacture nitrogen and plastics based on polyvinyl and polystyrene, orlon, etc., which will be available to other member countries of the Council for Mutual Economic Aid (see Chapter 10).

Fig. 8–14. Part of the new industrial combine, Sztálinváros, south of Budapest. Its favorable location on the Danube gives it easy access to raw materials and markets. (Photo: MTI, Hungarian News Agency.)

Other manufacturing is scattered over the whole country, most of it in larger cities, e.g., Debrecen, Szeged, Pécs. Plants include sugar refineries, food-processing plants, tobacco-processing plants, textile mills, flour mills, etc.

Communications. Budapest is the transportation hub of the country, with lines radiating in every direction. Highways, many asphalted, parallel the important rail lines. With the whole transport network originally built to serve a much larger region, many of the double-tracked rail lines have lost their original importance. The most important rail lines in terms of freight traffic are: (1) the line linking Vienna, Budapest, and Arad, in Rumania; (2) the two lines between Budapest and the Soviet Union, one via Miskolc and the other via

Debrecen [32]—the border station at Zahony reportedly has 100 wide-gauge tracks and has been greatly extended (15 miles) to change the axle width of 25 fifty-car trains each day; (3) the Budapest-Kecs-kemet-Szeged line to Timisoara in Rumania. The most important additions to or rebuilding of the rail network have been in the direction of the Soviet Union. Mention should be made that several new tracks in northeastern Hungary use the wider Soviet gauge and run parallel to existing tracks. Hungary plays a most important role in the whole rail network of the satellite states. Numerous feeder lines and important railroad bridges over the Danube and Tisza have been rebuilt or built new since the war. Rolling stock has barely been able to keep up with the increased freight loadings. Use of the average freight car in 1955 was one and one-half times that in France or twice the rate of Italy. Much of this resulted from a reduction of turn-around time.

About 1,000 miles of waterways are navigable, which mileage includes all of the Danube and the Tisza as far north as Tokaj. Most of the waterways are obstructed by ice for 60 to 90 days, and barges and boats must remain in winter ports. The Danube is navigable for boats up to 900 tons, the Tisza for craft up to 600 tons. Other navigable waterways include the Körös and Drava rivers and the Sio Canal. Hungary's floating stock has not been materially increased above the prewar level, even though freight loadings had more than doubled by 1955. Traffic on waterways is advantageous for the import and export of bulky goods and much of the iron ore and coal.

Foreign Trade. The pattern of Hungary's foreign trade has undergone many changes from the prewar period, when agricultural goods were the main products exported. Before 1939, trade with the Soviet Union was non-existent and Germany, Austria, Rumania, Czechoslovakia, and the United Kingdom were the main trading partners. Today exports of agricultural products have completely stopped, with the exception of highly specialized products such as rice or wines. Exports to the Soviet Union occupy first place. Foreign trade with the People's Republics, including the U.S.S.R. and China, amounted to 75 per cent of the total in 1958. Important trading partners, besides the bloc countries, are Austria, France, the Netherlands, and the United Kingdom. The more important exports today consist of fuels ✓ (24 per cent); raw materials such as bauxite, manganese ores, and leather (29 per cent); and machinery, miscellaneous equipment, and

[32] Information is summarized from a report discussing the importance of the Danube-Carpathian rail network to Soviet Russia. "Die sowjetische Eisenbahnpolitik im Donau-Karpatenraum," *Wissenschaftlicher Dienst Suedosteuropa* 7 (July, 1958): 89–91.

tools (28 per cent). Imports consist of fuel and raw materials (coal, coke, iron ore, lumber, petroleum, and bauxite), 68 per cent; machinery, equipment, and tools, 11 per cent; and foods, 17.5 per cent.

RUMANIA

Population

Postwar Rumania was reduced by three regions: northern Bucovina and Bessarabia were annexed by the Soviet Union, and the loss of the southern Dobruja to Bulgaria in 1940 was made permanent. At the end of World War II the country was occupied by the Red Army, and Communist leadership was gradually introduced, not unlike the shift in the other Eastern European countries. Rumania is administratively divided into 18 regions (*regiune*) and these are subdivided into *raions* and *comunes*. The total population was 17.5 million, according to the census of February, 1956, occupying an area of 91,675 square miles (somewhat smaller than the state of Oregon). Over-all population density was 192 per square mile. Bucharest, with a population of 1.2 million, is the capital and the largest city. The regional divisions are based mainly on economic-geographical units, similar to the development in the Soviet Union. *Raions* are units closely related to political, economic, and administrative criteria. Sixty-nine per cent of the population is classified as rural and 31 per cent as urban, with an over-all increase of 8 per cent since 1948, again following the pattern of the other Eastern European countries. Six cities have a population of over 100,000: Cluj, Timişoara, Stalin (Braşov), Ploeşti, Iaşi, and Arad. Eight cities have a population of over 50,000. The most densely populated areas, aside from the urban concentrations, are in the Wallachian Plain, the Siret Valley, and the central part of the Transylvanian Basin between Cluj and Târgu Mureş. The population densities in the Carpathian Mountains are very low, averaging five inhabitants per square mile. Population increases in urban areas have been very uneven, e.g., in twenty-one industrial towns between 1948 and 1956 they amounted to 43 per cent, in fifteen others the increase was only 16 per cent, in still others even less.[33]

Rumania, like all other Eastern European countries, has experienced great population changes. Tying its fortunes to a possible German victory, it did not escape considerable territorial losses (1939–44). After the German defeat, Rumania's turn-about at the end of the war did not save her from losses to the Soviet Union and to Bul-

---

[33] United Nations, *Economic Survey of Europe in 1957*, Geneva, 1958, pp. vii and 21.

garia, although Transylvania was recovered from Hungary.[34] The losses clearly show in the latest census, which lists the population by nationalities and mother tongues. Those listed with Rumanian mother tongue comprise 86 per cent of the population, and those with Hungarian over 9 per cent.

The Hungarians are the Szekelies, descendants of early free frontiersmen, who live in very concentrated areas in Transylvania, and the Magyars, who spread throughout Transylvania and the Banat. In 1952 an "Autonomous Hungarian Region," including most of the Szekelies, was organized. The Hungarian population has well-developed cultural centers, including schools up to the university level. Some separate universities and high schools have recently been combined with Rumanian schools.

The German population was reduced from 700,000 in 1930 to 391,000 in 1956 and now is found largely in Transylvania and the Wallachian Plain, having been transferred from the Banat after the war. Ethnic Germans consist of the Saxons, predominantly city dwellers and Lutherans and the ancestors of the earliest foreign settlers, and the Swabians, originally concentrated in the Banat and settled by the Hapsburgs in the seventeenth century. They are largely farmers and Roman Catholics. Their position has greatly improved during the last few years and they too have their own cultural centers. Nearly 80 per cent of the Rumanians are members of the Rumanian Orthodox Church; 9 per cent are Greek Orthodox.

The population structure is similar to that of the other Eastern European countries. The high war losses and population transfers have left their impact. Annual natural growth has averaged 14 per thousand inhabitants since the war, a rate which is not much different from the prewar period. The population is relatively young, with over 30 per cent under the age of 15 and 47 per cent between 15 and 44 years of age. There is a certain structural similarity with Poland and Yugoslavia. War losses and emigration largely affected the 15–30 age group.

Total enrollment in all sorts of educational institutions increased by 32 per cent between 1938–9 and 1956–7, with the largest increase in the 7-year schools on the elementary level, secondary technical

[34] Rumania lost 6.8 million in the population transfers of 1940 and regained 2.6 million in 1945. War losses are estimated as slightly over half a million. So-called Volksdeutsche (in this case the earlier-mentioned Saxons) first joined the German Army and over 200,000 fled at the end of the war; close to 100,000 ethnic Germans were deported to the Soviet Union in 1945. The Jewish population was reduced almost 80 per cent by German and Hungarian deportations, and most of those who were left have emigrated to Israel since the war. Taking all this into consideration, the population had a net loss of close to 2.7 million people.

schools, and higher education. Elementary school is compulsory for 4 years. Illiteracy was high in the prewar purely Rumanian regions and, while this has declined, exact up-to-date figures are not available.

To complete the picture of the population structure, the occupational distribution should be noted. The latest available figures (1955) show a slower impact of industrialization than in most other Eastern European countries. Those employed in industry constitute 13 per cent of the total employed population; those in agriculture, 69 per cent; in construction, 4.4 per cent; in transportation and communications, 1.8 per cent; in internal trade and food production, 2.6 per cent; and in various branches of administration, 7.5 per cent. The change in industrial employment in the preceding five years was approximately 1 per cent; those employed in agriculture showed a 4.5 per cent decline for the same period.

Present Economic Life

Changes in Rumania's economic life have been slower but just as insistent as in the other Eastern European countries. This can clearly be seen in the structural changes in the national income, where the relative share of agriculture fell from 46 per cent in 1949 to 29.6 per cent in 1955, with the share of industry increasing from 40 per cent to 55 per cent in the same period. Low output in agriculture is only partially responsible for this drop. The relative increase in industrialization is the main contributing factor. All means of production have been nationalized during the last ten or more years, and the drive for greater socialization in agriculture also has received increased impetus. On the other hand, the changes in the economy have been less erratic and sudden than in some of the other satellite countries.

Agriculture, Forestry, and Fishing. Sixty per cent of the total land area of Rumania is classified as agricultural. Forest land amounts to 27 per cent and the rest is classified as waste, water, and fallow. Forty-one per cent of the total land area is arable. The highest percentage of arable land is found in the Wallachian Plain and other Danube districts, the lowest percentage is in Transylvania, and arable land is almost completely absent in the Carpathians. On the other hand, most of the pastures and meadows are in the mountains (Fig. 8–10). Corn is the main cereal, grown mainly in the Wallachian Plain, the Banat, and Moldavia. Highest yields come from the Banat and Transylvania. Corn meal is the main food of the people and is called *mamaliga* (*puliszka* in Transylvania). Wheat is the second most important cereal but is more limited in its distribution; most is grown in the Wallachian Plain, the Banat, and the bordering regions of the

Great Alföld. Oats are third among the cereals and are widely grown except in the Wallachian Plain. Rye and barley are of lesser importance, with rye common in the Transylvanian Basin and barley in the steppe plateau of the Dobruja. Potato acreage has increased considerably since prewar years, but the 1956 acreage was still only 2.7 per cent of the total arable land. The sugar-beet acreage has greatly increased, the beets being grown mainly in the western lowlands. The acreage under sunflower, rape, cotton, rice, and tobacco has increased, but these crops still play only a minor role in the total production. Other important products are beans and peas, but average yields are low; linseed and soybean (some of which is exported) are cultivated in the Wallachian Plains and are important for vegetable oil. In addition, the cultivation of grapes is widespread, but the average yields are less than half of the 1934–8 average. The important production of fruit is also below that of prewar years. The apples and pears of Baia Mare and the plums of Bistrija are well known for their quality. In spite of greatly increased use of fertilizer and tractors, Rumania's yields, in cereals as well as in industrial crops and potatoes, are generally unsatisfactory.

Livestock is equally important for food and as the main source of traction power. The total numbers of cattle and pigs have increased by approximately one-third between 1938 and 1956; sheep have increased only slightly. The sheep are similar to the Merino, with which they have been crossed, and are valued for wool, cheese, and milk, an important cash income for the farmer. They are most common in Moldavia, the Dobruja, and the Banat. Cattle are more widely distributed, with roughly 20 per cent in the two districts of Cluj and Craiova.

Important fishing regions were lost to the Soviet Union—nearly all the caviar-producing lakes. Danube fish contribute close to 80 per cent of the catch. Great possibilities exist in the marshy lagoons of the Black Sea coast and the Danube Delta. The many Carpathian streams permit much trout, carp, perch, and pike fishing. The entire fishing industry is nationalized, and exports are strongly pushed.

Forestry is of great importance to the country's economy. Exports of a great variety of timber played a key role in the interwar period and have increased since the war. As was the case in Czechoslovakia, a realization of the danger of overcutting has finally set in and conservation measures, e.g., reforestation, shelter belts in the plains, etc., have received added attention. Coniferous forests, especially in the Carpathian Mountains, with the fir and spruce predominant and deciduous forests, predominant in Transylvania, contain the most useful trees. The famous oak forests have been completely depleted.

Land ownership in agriculture has undergone many changes. In mid-1957, only 40 per cent of the total agricultural lands were privately held and 60 per cent were socialized. Privately held agricultural areas in pasture were lowest (18 per cent) and those in meadows were highest (88 per cent). Socialization of agriculture was nearly completed in the Dobruja, where 100 per cent participation was reported in 1958. Based on the amount of arable land, the Dobruja and the Banat had the highest percentage of socialized land; according to the number of peasants, it was the Dobruja, Moldavia, and the Wallachian Plains. The obvious conclusion to be drawn from these facts was that the best agricultural land also had the lowest number of private land holdings.

Mining and Manufacturing. A wide range of mineral wealth exists in Rumania. Petroleum takes first place. Although bituminous coal is scarce, lignite is plentiful (Fig. 8–9). The production of natural gas has been greatly increased, as has iron-ore output. Phosphates, the rich bauxites of the Bihor Mountains, copper, lead, zinc, pyrites, and uranium all have increased in output, and are important to Rumania's growing industries.

Rumania is the largest oil and natural-gas producer of Europe outside the U.S.S.R. Most of the petroleum comes from the Prahova district (with Ploeşti the center), which accounted for 64 per cent of the total production between 1857 and 1945 (Fig. 8–15). The Dambovita district accounted for 33 per cent. The same relationship holds good today. Crude-oil production has increased rapidly since the low of 3.5 million tons in 1944, to over 11 million in 1957.[35] During the first five-year plan, the government placed close to 28 per cent of its total industrial investment in the oil and natural-gas industry, and 25.5 per cent in the second plan. Exploratory drilling has also been greatly expanded, e.g., in the Moldavian fields, and new fields were opened in Pitesti and Targu Jiu. Closely related to the petroleum expansion has been the greatly increased production of natural gas, found either with crude oil or in independent strata within the general oil-bearing layers. Rumania's greatest success in the expansion of natural-gas production has been achieved in the Transylvanian Basin. The natural methane gas there is perhaps the purest in the world and has only few other hydrocarbons. Natural gas from the oil fields contains 60–80 per cent methane, and was wasted for many years; today it is important in factories, refineries, and private homes. Pipelines connect important industrial centers

[35] Domestic needs are estimated at 5 million tons. Approximately 73 per cent of the exports go to the U.S.S.R.

and cities, and an important line connects the fields with the integrated chemical combine at the middle Tisza River in Hungary (see
pp. 601–02). Rumanian natural gas will make a major contribution
to the Hungarian chemical industry. The shortage of steel pipe is the
major obstacle to a more rapid expansion.

Lignite mining in the upper Jiu Valley has been increased, and the
bituminous coal mines at Reşiţa (Banat Mountains) are the only
important coal source. Iron ore is mined in the Pojana Ruska and the

Fig. 8–15. Derricks in the Ploeşti oil fields, Rumania. (Legation of the Rumanian People's Republic.)

Banat Mountains and the output has tripled during the last 10 years.
Rumanian industries, however, are still dependent upon Soviet iron-
ore exports, and, with further expansion of these industries envisioned,
the small reserves of domestic ores will be even less able to keep up
with the demand. Phosphates are found at Lugoj, and manganese
at Maramureş, both in Transylvania; the latter is also mined at Bros-
teni, in Moldavia, but the total output is small and the manganese
content of the ore is very low (20 per cent). Of great importance are
the bauxite deposits in the Bihor Mountains. Although the ores have
excessive silica content, large quantities are exported to the Soviet
Union. The Carpathian Mountains have small deposits of a great

variety of ores and minerals: gold, silver, copper, lead, zinc, pyrites, some radioactive minerals, and others.

Every Rumanian government during the last 80 years has put major emphasis on industrialization and in this way has hoped to broaden the base of the economy. With complete control of all the means of production, transportation, and labor supply, the Communist government has systematically stressed heavy industry. An excellent base already was available. The emphasis after the war was on capital-goods industries; consumer industries received very little or no investments, and only recently have these increased. Generally speaking, the major emphasis is still on the oil, steel, chemical, and timber industries, with less attention given to machinery, construction, and textiles. To press for industrialization, joint Soviet-Rumanian enterprises were organized, but owing to large-scale dissatisfaction among the people were again abolished in 1954–5.

Iron and steel works in operation before the Communist take-over were in Reșița in the Banat, where they have been in operation since 1771. They were modernized in the interwar period and again in 1950. In addition, new blast furnaces were added. Another important iron and steel plant was the prewar Hunedoara (Transylvania) state-owned industry. These works, too, have now been much expanded. The third-largest steel enterprise is the Titan-Nadrag-Calan works in Transylvania; smaller plants are located in Bucharest, Cluj, Brașov, and Brăila. The total steel output has increased more than two and one-half times since 1938. The steel industry has provided an excellent basis for the engineering, armament, and electrotechnical industries, all expanded since the war. All the presently producing plants existed before World War II but have been expanded and modernized. Many have technical schools located nearby for the training of their increased labor forces. Among the goods produced are farm machinery, drilling equipment, trucks, diesel engines, machine tools, precision apparatus, turbines, generators, armaments, and seamless pipes. Many of the plants were completely dismantled by the Soviet Army after the war.

The chemical industry is based on a large number of natural resources such as petroleum, natural gas, salt, pyrites, etc. Before 1938 it was second only to the metallurgical industries in value of production. Its centers are in Bucharest, Baia Mare, and Cluj, not counting the petroleum refineries. Methane gas is used to produce carbon black, and four factories are now engaged in its production, permitting some export. Other products of the chemical industry are mineral fertilizer, caustic soda, sulphuric acid, synthetic rubber, and paper. Of special importance is the greatly increased production of pharmaceutical products, mainly of salicylic acid and its derivatives, saccharine, and antibiotics. Superphosphates, ammonium sulphates, and calcium cyanamide are produced in growing quantities. Sodium carbonate is produced in three factories, of which the Ocna Muresului plant in Transylvania is the largest.

Rumania has a variety of smaller widely distributed agricultural industries such as: distilling plants; flour mills; various textile plants in Bucharest, Arad, and Timişoara; and the many small woolen industries in Székelyland. Jassy is the center for linen manufacturing, Cluj for leather and drugs. Industries producing construction materials, including cement, are scattered all over the country, especially in the Transylvanian Basin and the valleys of the Carpathians. Among the new industries is a big fiberboard and paper mill in the Danube Delta. The 150,000 acres of marsh reeds will be used as raw materials for this new industry. A key industry in much need of expansion is the production of power, both thermal and hydroelectric. Rumania's use of electric power per unit of population is among the lowest in Europe.

Communications. Rumania's transportation network is underdeveloped, in part because it was originally oriented toward centers away from the present borders. Attention has largely been focused on connecting existing lines or adding short lines important to the economic growth of a particular industry (Fig. 8–2). The most important new line connects the coal fields of the Jiu Valley with southern Rumania. There has been a shortage of rolling stock and engines, but the latter have slowly been modernized and increased in number. The main west-east lines connect Bucharest with the western part of the country. Two lines cross Transylvania and cut across the Carpathians at Turnu Roşu Pass, and at Stalin there is an important crossing of two western lines and an eastern line. One line traverses the Wallachian Plain and continues to Constanţa on the Black Sea. The Carpathians are skirted by a line running northeast from Ploeşti. Another line runs south from Bucharest to the Danube, crossing it over a 2-kilometer-long bridge to connect with an important Bulgarian line to the Maritsa Basin.

The Danube is the only navigable waterway and can be used from the Black Sea to Braila by vessels with a draft of up to 21 feet, 7 feet for the rest of its course. The much-talked-about Danube–Black Sea Canal has never been completed and presumably has been abandoned. Constanţa is the most important port on the Black Sea and Braila and Galati are Danube ports.

Foreign Trade. The structure of Rumania's foreign trade has undergone changes similar to those of other Eastern European countries, with regard not only to its geographic distribution but also to the types of goods involved. Germany as the major trading partner was replaced by the U.S.S.R., which, together with the other People's Republics, now absorbs some 72 per cent of Rumania's foreign trade. Chief exports before the war were wheat, flour, petroleum, timber, and livestock. These have been replaced by petroleum and petroleum goods, machinery, certain chemicals, and timber. Imports of raw materials, especially coking coal and iron ore, have become essential for the greatly expanded iron and steel industry. Other imported items include cotton and cotton goods, leather, and chemicals. Rumania's foreign trade with the rest of the world is indeed very small.

BULGARIA

Population

World War II had relatively little effect on the people and the economic life of Bulgaria. The southern Dobruja was regained from Rumania in 1940, and was permanently assigned to Bulgaria after the war. Bulgarian troops, as allies of Germany, occupied portions of Greece and Yugoslavia (Macedonia), but had to retire to their pre-war boundaries at the end of the war. The Soviet Union then declared war on Bulgaria and occupied the country, and thus was able to establish the Communist party in power. In Bulgaria, the country traditionally closest to Russia, with a strong Communist party, nationalization of industries and property, including collectivization, was accomplished much faster than in any of the other People's Republics.

The population of Bulgaria is estimated at nearly 8 million, occupying an area of 42,741 square miles, roughly the size of Tennessee, with a population density of about 176 per square mile. Administratively, Bulgaria is divided into 27 districts (okrŭzi), and three cities with the rank of district—Sofiya, the capital, with a population of 591,000; Plovdiv, 140,000; and Stalin (Varna), 50,000. Districts are subdivided into counties (obstini). The cities of Dimitrovgrad and Ruse also have a population of 50,000 each. The over-all population-density figure is somewhat misleading because 26 per cent of the country's area is unproductive with a population density of less than 100 inhabitants per square mile in the mountainous regions, while in the arable lands (43 per cent of the total area) population densities of over 400 per square mile are the norm. Bulgaria is still a land of predominantly rural population (two-thirds rural in 1956), but the urban population is rapidly increasing. Sofiya, which has more than doubled its population since 1934, and Plovdiv are the traditionally industrial cities. Several newly developed or reoriented towns, with new industries or newly started or enlarged mining activities, have undergone rapid growth, e.g., Dimitrovgrad, a Soviet-style industrial boom town, is now one of Bulgaria's most important industrial centers, with a population of 45,000 in 1957, as compared with 3,600 in 1946. Dimitrovo (Pernik), an old coal and iron-ore center, now has an important ferrous metallurgical industry (population 40,000 in 1953, in comparison to 16,000 in 1934).

Today 93 per cent of the people are Bulgars. Ethnic minorities are numerically very small.[36] Ninety per cent of the population belongs to the Eastern (Bulgarian) Orthodox Church. Moslems comprise about nine per cent of the population, and there is a very small minority of Roman Catholics and Protestants. Most of the 50,000 Jews shown in the 1934 census emigrated to Israel. A majority of the 147,000 Gypsies,[37] who are Moslems, now have been integrated into the economy. The Pomaks, who live in the Rhodope Mountains, are Bulgarian-speaking people of Moslem faith (similar to the Serbs and Croats of Moslem faith in Bosnia and Herzegovina); 134,000 were officially listed in 1934.

Because of relatively few war losses, Bulgaria is one of the few Eastern European countries which do not have a male deficit in their population. Sixty-six per cent of the population is of working age (15 to 64 years of age), 27 per cent are under 15 years of age. This indicates a relatively high percentage of labor potential now and in the future. The Bulgarian birth rate was originally the highest in Europe (39.6 births per thousand of population in 1920–24) but has dropped to an estimated natural increase of 11 per thousand (in 1955). Among its neighbors, Bulgaria ranks high in literacy, 77 per cent in 1946. Since 1950, education has been compulsory from age 7 to 15 years, in either 4- or 7-year primary or 11-year general-education schools. Technical training on the secondary level, such as vocational and professional education, has been greatly accelerated. Sofiya has the only university, but various higher institutes, e.g., for agricultural economy, veterinary medicine, economics, mining and geology, etc., have been established in a number of cities. The working population amounts to more than half of the total population, and is predomi-

[36] Population movements, such as the departure of 190,000 Turks after World War II, have been customary in the history of Bulgaria. Over 200,000 Turks and 40,000 Greeks left after World War I; 250,000 Bulgars came from the Thracian and Macedonian parts of Greece. With the incorporation of the southern Dobruja in 1940, about 62,000 Bulgarians were exchanged for 110,000 Rumanians.

[37] Gypsies, presumably coming from India, entered Bulgaria with the Turks in the fourteenth century. They have preserved their ancient language and customs. The nomadic way of life is traditional with them, and it is extremely difficult to persuade them to live in permanent settlements.

nantly occupied in agriculture. One-eighth of the workers are in industry and mining, and the rest in commerce, trade, and administration.

Present Economic Life

Khrushchev has said, and not without reason, that the "Bulgarian Communist Party is setting an example for all the Eastern European countries by its consistent policy of socialization and collectivization." Nationalization of all sectors of the economy proceeded rapidly and the various long-term plans have completely changed the economic structure. A better economic balance has been established and the problem of the surplus agricultural population and unemployment, for the first time, has been successfully attacked. The relationship between agriculture and industrial production has been completely reversed, as the following figures clearly indicate: in 1939, production was 75.5 per cent agricultural and 24.5 per cent industrial; in 1957, the proportions were 32.5 per cent and 67.5 per cent, respectively.

Ninety-six per cent of the arable land now has been collectivized. It accounts for 87 per cent of the total agricultural output. The socialist sector of the national economy now accounts for 98 per cent of the total industrial output and more than 99 per cent of the retail trade. This is the highest percentage of any of the People's Republics, and certainly is in line with their ultimate goal. In addition, existing collectives have been amalgamated since 1958 and plans are under way to organize farms of several thousand acres.

Agriculture, Forestry, and Fishing. In spite of the drive for industrialization, Bulgaria remains basically an agricultural country. Forty-one per cent of the total area is classified as agricultural, 26 per cent as unproductive, and 33 per cent as forest. Of the total agricultural area, 38 per cent is arable. The best arable land is in the Danubian part, southern Dobruja, and the central areas of the Maritsa Basin (Fig. 8–10). Meadows are common in some of the western districts, pastures in the coastal lands south of Burgas, in the central part of the Balkan Ranges, and in some western mountain areas. The chief areas for cereal production are the Danubian Plateau, southern Dobruja, and the Maritsa Basin. Wheat and corn are the main agricultural crops, although rye, barley, and oats are well distributed. The area under corn has increased slightly; that sown to wheat, rye, and oats has decreased; and barley acreage has remained stable. Yields are smaller than immediate prewar averages or have only slightly increased. Industrial crops now cover 13 per cent of the total arable land. Other important agricultural products include sunflower seeds, sugar beets, potatoes, fodder, beets, and alfalfa. Production of all these has increased in varying degrees since the interwar years. Bulgaria is well known for its vegetables, e.g., tomatoes, eggplants, pumpkins, beans, and peas. Olive trees are found in the southern coastal regions. Cotton has received greatly increased attention and is grown in the central part of the Maritsa Basin. An excellent-quality tobacco (Virginian) is grown, mostly in the Arda Basin and on the southern slopes of the Rhodope Massif. Yields are high. The so-called mountain variety (*jebel*), which is well suited for mixing, is exported.

Bulgaria also has a wide range of fruits and wine grapes. Apple orchards are concentrated in the Sofiya district, lemons on the Black Sea coast south of Burgas, plus widespread peach, apricot, pomegranate, almond, fig, and plum orchards. Of great importance—Bulgaria being the leading world producer—is rose oil (attar), derived from roses grown on the Tundzha depression. Much effort is made to grow those agricultural, fruit, and wine crops which are unique for Bulgaria, and the area under cereals has been decreased to make room for an expansion of those exportable crops. Large-scale irrigation projects have been undertaken to raise the yields and to add new agricultural lands. Over 1.5 million acres will ultimately be under irrigation. Agriculture is highly mechanized, with thousands of small tractors.

Animal husbandry, too, characterizes Bulgarian farming. Sheep, a large number of cattle, pigs, and poultry indicate the rural wealth. The main grazing areas are in the central part of the Balkan Ranges, in the area between Sofiya and Plovdiv, and southeast of Burgas. The water buffalo is still common in the northern part of the country. With the exception of pigs and poultry, however, livestock numbers have not increased greatly since 1939.

Dense and largely virgin stands of coniferous forest are found in the Rila Planina of the Rhodope Massif. Deciduous and mixed forests are widely distributed. Scrub growth is found in the hill lands, and oak woods are common in the eastern part of the Balkan Ranges and south of Burgas. Overcutting during and following the war has been replaced by conservation and reforestation. Commercial fishing is poorly developed. Meager supplies of mackerel account for approximately two-thirds of the Black Sea fishing.

Mining and Manufacturing. Forced industrialization under the various long-term plans has generally been achieved, and consumer-goods production has, until recently, been neglected. The main objectives of these plans were: increases in the production of the electrical-equipment, mining, non-ferrous and ferrous metallurgical, chemical, building, and food-processing industries. The production increases brought about were largely exported to the Soviet Union and to the other satellite countries.

The newly built heavy industries are based on Bulgarian lignite and on the small reserves of bituminous coal (Fig. 8–9). Metal ores are available in limited quantities: some iron ore, manganese, chromium, copper, lead-zinc, pyrites, magnesite, and molybdenum. Most of the production totals show a remarkable increase over the interwar years. Bulgaria's mineral resources have only recently been explored, and future possibilities of increased ferrous and non-ferrous metal mining are considered good. Large prospecting parties are constantly combing the country and have been successful in many different regions. Discoveries of petroleum and natural gas have also been made in the last few years, and the production of crude oil has jumped from 4,700 tons in 1954 to 280,000 tons in 1957. Most of the wells have been drilled in the Dobruja. Bulgaria has no modern refineries at the moment and therefore must export her crude petroleum.

Much attention has been given to increased power production. Although the per-capita production is still behind the other Eastern European countries, progress has been made. Conditions favor the building of smaller plants, and the larger ones are linked by a grid which has been connected with the Rumanian grid.

The majority of Bulgaria's industrial workers are occupied in manufacturing on a small scale, e.g., home industries and handicrafts. A medium-size integrated iron and steel works has been constructed at Dimitrovgrad (Lenin Works), and five open-hearth furnaces and a rolling mill have been completed. The plant uses local coal, and pig iron is shipped by boat from the Soviet Union via Stalin and Burgas. Domestic coke is now used. An electrolytic smelter has been completed east of Sofiya, and a lead-zinc smelter at Kurdzhali in the Rhodope Mountains. The Stalin Chemical Combine, at Dimitrovgrad, produced over 100,000 tons of nitrogenous fertilizer in 1958, on the basis of low-grade lignite. Inorganic acids and salts, organic compounds, explosives, dyes, soap, drugs, and cellulose are now being produced in small quantities. Soda ash and caustic soda are produced at Devnia, west of Stalin, from local salts and brine. Carbide and sulphuric acid (a by-product of copper and lead-zinc smelters and from local pyrites) is produced at Dimitrovgrad. With the financial and technical aid of the Soviet Union, additional expansion of the chemical industry is under way. Various textile plants in a number of old manufacturing towns have been modernized and enlarged, and sugar refineries, flour mills, food-processing plants, and tobacco factories are widely scattered. The food and tobacco industries depend exclusively on domestic raw materials. Among the important food-processing industries are food canning, vegetable-oil production, milk

processing, etc. Generally speaking, Bulgaria's important larger indus- ᵛ
tries are located in the Maritsa Basin, between Burgas and Sofiya,
while craft and manufacturing towns are widely distributed in the
Danubian Plateau, the Stara Planina, and the Thracian Plain.

Communications. The Maritsa Basin has the densest transportation network in Bulgaria. Highways follow the major railroads, but
few are all-weather roads. A large improvement program is under
way. The major rail pattern is west-east and north-south, with some
branch lines (Fig. 8–2). The program of the last few years has been
to complete and connect individual lines. While construction of rail
lines has been rapid, improvements in the rolling stock have been
slow. Most of the needed freight cars and locomotives must be imported. Both freight shipments and the number of passengers carried
have greatly increased since the war. Sofiya, Plovdiv, and Stara Zagora
are the most important railroad loading stations. The Danube is the
only navigable waterway but is of negligible importance as far as
Bulgaria is concerned.

Foreign Trade. The Soviet Union has replaced Germany as Bulgaria's most important trading partner. Of trade in 1956, 46 per cent
went to or from the Soviet Union, 38 per cent to or from other
People's Republics, and 16 per cent to or from the rest of the world.
Before the war 88 per cent of Bulgaria's trade was with the rest of the
world and 12 per cent with the countries of Eastern Europe; trade
with the Soviet Union was non-existent. The structure of the foreign
trade has also basically changed. Major exports today are fresh and
canned fruits and vegetables, tobacco, and non-ferrous metals. A
special effort has been made to increase the export of fruits and vegetables, textile goods, and wood materials. Before the war, tobacco,
vegetables, and fruits were nearly the only export items of importance.
Imports include tractors and agricultural machinery, power and electrical equipment, petroleum and petroleum products, ferrous metals,
and raw and semiprocessed textiles. The total value of exports and
imports is relatively small.

ALBANIA

Population

Albania is the smallest country in Eastern Europe. It is strategically located along the Adriatic shore, facing Italy at the entrance
to this sea. Its population was 1.4 million at the census of 1955,
living in an area of 11,096 square miles, roughly the size of Maryland,

with a density of 127 per square mile. Administratively Albania is divided into 27 districts (*rethi*), and these are subdivided into localities (*lokaliteti*) and numerous villages (*fshati*). The capital is Tiranë, with a population of over 108,000. Other large towns are Shkodër (30,000) and Korçë (28,000). More than 72 per cent of the population is classified as rural, but densities are very uneven. Most of the people are concentrated in Tiranë, Shkodër, and Korçë and around Durrës on the coast, with densities in the mountainous part of the country as low as six persons per square mile.

The mountainous topography of most of Albania has often restricted the influence of invaders to coastal regions, giving the people a natural refuge from outside domination. The many small natural regions, at the same time, have isolated the people from each other and have retarded the growth of their national unity. The country's independence was proclaimed only in 1912 and it was among the Balkans' longest foreign-controlled areas. Because of World War I, which was fought in part on its territory, independence was not implemented until 1920. However, the freedom of Albania was short-lived, wedged as the country was between rival powers. Italy occupied Albania in April, 1939, and used it as a base for her attack on Greece. Under pressure from a new and stronger Yugoslavia at the end of World War II, Albania's leaders welcomed Stalin's break with Tito, and ever since have supported Russia's strong stand against the independent-minded Yugoslavs. This offered Albania an ally, albeit some distance away, and at the same time provided security against a new occupation.

The people of Albania are divided by the Shkumbi River into two major groups, the Gegs in the north and the Tosks in the south. These two groups comprise close to 98 per cent of the total population.[38] In addition, scattered Vlach settlements occupy the highland pastures and Greeks (30,000) are found along the southern boundary. Some Gypsies, Bulgars, and Turks live in the rural areas. About 70 per cent of the people are Moslems, as a result of the long Turkish rule; 20 per cent are members of the Albanian Orthodox Church; and 10 per cent are Roman Catholics. Over 1.3 million Albanians live outside their country. The largest number live in Yugoslavia, where they are organized in an autonomous region within the Serbian republic. Emigration continues over the mountainous border, which is hard to control. About 50,000 Albanians live in the United States,

---

[38] There are cultural differences between these two peoples, e.g., the traditional family system is still strongly developed among the Gegs. They are also considered the better fighters, while the Tosks are more industrious. Two-thirds of the Albanians are Gegs and most of the Albanians living in Yugoslavia are also Gegs.

and between 150,000 and 250,000 live in southern Sicily and Italy, to which their ancestors fled from the Turks in the fifteenth and sixteenth centuries. Smaller numbers live in Greece and Turkey. The Albanian language is classified as one of the Thraco-Illyrian subfamilies of the Indo-European languages, and has many similarities to Rumanian (Vlach).

Constant wars against foreign invaders and tribal feuds have had their effect on the population structure. Albania has the highest birth and death rates of any Eastern European country. The natural increase is estimated as 27 people per thousand inhabitants. The working population (ages 15 to 65) comprises two-thirds of the people.

The illiteracy rate is among the highest in Europe, but a concerted effort has been made to reduce it. A law promulgated in 1946 made learning to write obligatory for all persons from 12 to 40 years of age. At the same time it created a preschool system for the whole country.

Teachers' training schools, adult-education centers, and professional schools for medicine, finance, commerce, and agriculture have been organized since 1950. A university was organized just a few years ago. The Albanian educational system in many ways has been patterned after that of the Soviet Union, with the Russian language compulsory in all secondary schools.

Present Economic Life

Following World War II, Albania patterned its economic organization after those of the Communist countries, especially (in the first few years) after that of Yugoslavia. Planning received first priority and the foundation for an industrial base and an improvement in transportation was laid. Between 1951 and 1955 (first five-year plan) 43 per cent of the total state budget was spent for industrialization. During this period the ratio between industrial and agricultural production was changed from 27.5 and 72.5 per cent to 43.5 and 56.5. The same trend continued during the second five-year plan, with the aim of changing Albania from a backward agrarian country to an agrarian-industrial country.

In view of the absence of reliable figures it is estimated that about 70 per cent of the working population is engaged in agriculture and cattle raising, 15 per cent in mining and industry, and the rest in various administrative services.

Agriculture and Forestry. In spite of all these efforts, Albania remains the most backward of the Eastern European countries. Agricultural yields have increased as a result of the introduction of mechanization and the use of fertilizers, etc., but in the mountainous country its use is limited. Of the total area, 42 per cent is agricultural, 39 per cent is forest, and 19 per cent is unproductive marsh, rocks, scrub woodland, or eroded mountain slopes. Only 12 per cent of the total agricultural land is arable—tilled or in orchards and vineyards (Fig. 8–11). It is generally agreed that, with proper soil conservation and reclamation measures, the arable area could be increased by another 15 per cent. Large-scale investments are necessary, and, with the present direction of investments into industrialization, these worthwhile long-term projects are being neglected.

Corn, as a staple food for the farmer and fodder for cattle, is the main crop and is grown on 60 per cent of the arable land. Wheat is second in acreage and is concentrated in the Korçë Basin. The wheat acreage is to some extent restricted by the excessive moisture of the soil in winter at low elevations. Rye and potatoes are cultivated in various mountain valleys. Sugar beets, cane sugar, and various vegetables are grown for local use. Rice is cultivated around Tiranë, Vlonë, Berta, and Elbasan; and cotton acreage has increased, but yields are still extremely low. Fruit growing at Vlona and Elbasan now receives greater attention. Walnuts, olives, and tobacco are exported in small quantities.

Animal husbandry is important and is the traditional occupation of the population. Cattle, generally underweight and having low milk production, are valued as both food and draft animals. The most important animals are the sheep and goats, raised for their wool, cheese, and milk. Pigs, because of the religious belief of the high percentage of Moslems, are limited to the Christian communities. Horses have been replaced by mules and donkeys. Poultry raising, especially of turkeys, is widely distributed.

Forests for many years have been "mined," not only by the different occupying powers but by the people themselves. Only recently have conservation measures been undertaken. Woodlands, richest in the northern part of the country, consist of different varieties of oak, with beech and coniferous species also represented. Walnut and chestnut trees are of special value. Maqui is widespread in the drier lowlands and hill lands. On the whole, second-growth forests of immature trees are widespread, especially in the southern part of the country. The effects of drought, erosion, and forest mining as well as of tree browsing by sheep and goats have almost completely destroyed the vegetation cover in the neighborhood of settlements.

The drive to collectivize was started as early as 1947 and peasants put up strong resistance. Confiscation of farm tools, land, and herds of over 50 sheep or goats, together with high delivery quotas and low prices, did not succeed in forcing the peasants into collectives. The drive was slowed down between 1951 and 1957, but the pace has again increased. By the beginning of 1959, 80 per cent of the arable land was in collectives (nearly 100 per cent in the southern regions).

Mining and Manufacturing. Until 1930, industries were practically non-existent in Albania. In 1938 the only industries were small sawmills, two modern olive-oil-extracting plants, four medium-size cigarette plants, one large brewery, one modern cement plant, and several smaller plants producing soap, furniture, cardboard, hand-made tools, and carts. Since 1947, economic planning has stressed industrialization, in part based on little-developed local metallic and non-metallic minerals (Fig. 8–9), some of which were exploited by the ancient Greeks and the Roman Empire. In the Albanian economy, mining employs the largest share of the industrial labor force and mining industries form a vital part of the country's industries. Most of the output is exported. Petroleum, one of Albania's greatest economic assets, has been exploited since 1918. The petroleum-bearing region is in the southwest, the most important fields being located at Stalin (Kucovë) and Patos. Production in 1957 amounted to 490,000 tons, an increase of 150 per cent over 1950. Albanian crude oils have a great density and are valued for their great average weight. A number of refineries have been built and pipelines, some built by the Italians, bring the petroleum to Krionere, on the Vlonë Bay, or to Cerrik, near Elbasan. The Cerrik refinery, completed in 1955, can process 150,000 metric tons of crude oil annually. Most of the raw oil is shipped to Poland and the Soviet Union. Natural gas from the oil fields is now being exploited by the different industries and power stations of the country. Much exploration is going on.

Another important mineral is high-quality lignite, some of which resembles asphaltite. The main mines are between Tiranë, Elbasan, and Lushnje in the Krrabe Mountains, in the Vijose River Valley, and in the Pogradec-Korçë area. Also important are the bitumen and asphalt deposits between the Kudhesi Mountain and the Vijosë River. Asphalt occurs in a semiliquid state in the limestones. The output of both asphalt and bitumen has been increased considerably since 1945, and the bitumen-processing plant at Vlonë provides a number of important by-products for paving, waterproofing, and the manufacture of insulators and roofing shingles. Of the principal metallic minerals, chromium, mined at Klos, takes first place. The production, which constitutes about 2 per cent of the world total, is largely exported to the other Eastern European countries. Copper is mined in northern Albania, but the ore content is reported to be very low. Iron ore averaging 25 per cent iron is found in widely scattered areas, but, because of both the lack of processing plants and the high costs of transportation, mining never has been more than exploratory. Magnetite ores are found in northern Albania. Minor deposits of pyrites, arsenic ore, mercury, lead, zinc, nickel, and bauxite are reported. Large deposits of clay in the Shkodër district and other scattered areas have always been important to the Albanian pottery industry.

Few of Albania's industries compare in size and output with those developed in other Communist countries, and handicraft cooperatives produce articles such as cotton, wool fabrics, housewares, mats, furniture, agricultural implements, timber, bricks, electrical equipment, and foodstuffs. New, mostly small, industrial plants include a cement plant in Vlonë, the mechanical establishments at Tiranë and Durrës, where trucks and other machinery are assembled and repaired, and small shipyards at Durrës. Food processing is an important industry and has been enlarged considerably; textile plants have been enlarged and some added; tobacco-curing factories have been built in Tiranë and Shkodër; and several small soap factories, paper mills, and a small glass factory have been added during the last 10 years.

Communications. Little effort has been made to build Albania's transportation network, owing to the large investment needed in such a topographically difficult country. The standard-gauge lines built since the war brought the total railroad network to 155 miles in 1955. All connect newly developed mines with the larger cities or ports. Roads have received more attention than rails during the last few years. However, only those roads used for heavy traffic are asphalted. The Drin and Bojane rivers are navigable, but only for a very short distance. Albania has three principal seaports, Durrës, Vlonë, and Sarande, possessing warehouses and petroleum-storage tanks. Vlonë has a good natural harbor with a bay 9 miles long, protected by the strategically important island of Sazan (Saseno), controlling the Straits of Otranto at the narrowest part of the Adriatic between Italy and Albania.

Foreign Trade. Prewar trade was largely with Italy, Greece, and Yugoslavia; today, the Soviet Union and members of the Soviet bloc contribute roughly 80 per cent of Albania's trade turnover. Albania is a member of the Soviet-sponsored Council for Mutual Economic Assistance (see Chapter 10). Major exports to the Soviet bloc consist of minerals, including petroleum products, and agricultural products. Imports are nearly all made up of industrial-plant equipment, rolling stock, tools, and electrical equipment. Mention also should be made of considerable free economic aid from other members of the Soviet bloc.

YUGOSLAVIA

Population

The Federal People's Republic of Yugoslavia, with a 1960 population of over 18 million, an area of 98,740 square miles (roughly equal in size to Wyoming), and a population density of 184 per square mile, is eighth in population in Europe and second among the countries of Eastern Europe. It occupies a transitional position between the Alps of Austria and the mountains of the Southeast European Highlands, between the Adriatic Sea and the Carpathian Basin. This location played a most important role throughout history and left distinct marks on the political, social, and economic development of the various regions of the country.[39] Yugoslavia has undergone many political and economic changes since its organization in 1918–19. None had more far-reaching results than those brought about by World War II. After being occupied and divided among its neighbors during the war, a new Yugoslavia was organized as a multinational Communist state. Territorial gains were small, but important: the former Italian cities of Zara (Zadar), on the Dalmatian littoral, and Fiume (Rijeka), together with Istria. But the city of Trieste remained within Italy by the agreement of 1954.

Administratively, Yugoslavia is a federation of six People's Republics: Serbia, Croatia, Slovenia, Bosnia and Herzegovina, Macedonia, and Montenegro. The People's Republic of Serbia includes Serbia proper, the Autonomous Region of Vojvodina, and the Autonomous Region of Kosovo-Metohija, often referred to as Kosmet. Serbia is the largest republic, both in area and population (40.8 per cent of the total population), followed by Croatia (22.7) and Bosnia and Herzegovina (17.3). Each republic and autonomous region is divided into districts (*srez* or *kotar*) and communes (*opstine*). These communes are peculiar to Yugoslavia, each consisting of a town and its surrounding area; a district consists of several communes. The capital of Yugoslavia is Belgrade, with approximately 570,000 inhabitants in 1960; it is also the capital of the Republic of Serbia. Zagreb is the capital of Croatia and is the second-largest city, with a population estimated

[39] Some material contained in this section has been taken, by permission, from George W. Hoffman, "Yugoslavia: Changing Character of Rural Life and Rural Economy," *The American Slavic and East European Review* 17 (December, 1959): 555–78. See also George W. Hoffman, "Yugoslavia in Transition: Industrial Expansion and Resource Bases," *Economic Geography* 32 (October, 1956): 295–315.

at 500,000 in 1960. Sarajevo, Ljubljana, and Skoplje are cities of over 100,000. As is the case in all underdeveloped countries, the urban increase has been rapid. The Autonomous Region of Vojvodina and the Morava Valley in Serbia proper have the most densely populated areas, and Montenegro and sections in Herzegovina and Macedonia the least, but within each political area there are big differences in density.

The present population structure shows the effects not only of three wars within one generation but also of the large population migrations during and following World War II. Altogether, Yugoslavia lost between 2 million and 2.6 million people between 1939 and 1959.[40] The war losses during the Balkan wars and World War I are reflected in the 55 to 74 age groups. The impact of World War II is clearly visible in the smaller number of people, especially males between the ages of 25 and 39. The present structure indicates a rather young population, with more than three-fifths (63.5 per cent) in the economically important ages between 15 and 64 years. The annual increase during the years 1953–8 has varied between 13 and 18 per thousand. Again, differences in age structure among the republics and autonomous regions are important to note. They generally follow historical and cultural developments.

About 88 per cent of the people of Yugoslavia belong to the various groups of the South Slavs (Fig. 8–5). These include Serbs, Croats, Slovenes, Macedonians, and Montenegrins. National minorities include Albanians (called Shiptars), Magyars, Turks, Slovaks, Gypsies, Germans (0.4 per cent as against 3.6 per cent in 1931), Rumanians, Bulgars, Vlachs, Czechs, and Italians. The Vojvodina has the largest number of non-Slavic people, more than a third of its total population. Generally speaking, the individual Slavic peoples form a large majority of their respective political units, e.g., in the People's Republic of Serbia Serbians account for three-fourths of the total population, but in the two autonomous regions of the Vojvodina and Kosmet their percentage of the total population amounts to only 51 and 24 per cent, respectively. Bosnia and Herzegovina is a special case inasmuch as most of the original Slavic Serbs and Croats became

[40] These losses are explained as follows: 1.7 million people died as a consequence of warlike actions; 100,000 of a total of 700,000 Yugoslav prisoners or workers in German war industries chose to remain abroad; and at least another 100,000 Yugoslavs fled abroad after hostilities ended (many of these emigrated to the United States). The ethnic German population was reduced by 90 per cent, roughly 445,000 (many of whom fled with the retreating German Army). Most of the Italians (150,000) living in Istria, which was transferred to Yugoslavia after the war, emigrated to Italy; most of the surviving Jews, roughly 8,000, emigrated to Israel; and 104,000 Turkish inhabitants, mostly from Macedonia, returned to Turkey between 1950 and 1959, a movement still continuing.

Moslem and list themselves by religion and not by nationality. In the 1953 census, 86.7 per cent of Yugoslavia's population indicated adherence to one of the religions, approximately: 41 per cent Orthodox, 32 per cent Roman Catholic, 12 per cent Moslem, and 1 per cent Protestant. The rest are listed as "others" and "undeclared."

One of Yugoslavia's most pressing tasks is its drive for reduction of its large illiteracy rate, which in 1953 was 25.5 per cent among those over 10 years of age. The proportion of illiterates was highest among the Shiptars (64 per cent), Gypsies, and Turks. It was between 35 per cent and 55 per cent in Macedonia, Kosmet, and Bosnia and Herzegovina, and was almost non-existent in Slovenia. Most of Yugoslavia's illiterate people live in the mountainous parts of the country, and even mobile schools have difficulty in reaching some of these settlements. Another factor in the divergent cultural development was the long Turkish occupation of the southern and central parts of the country and the closer association of the Slovenian and Croatian areas with Western European cultural developments. Much effort has been made to increase educational opportunities and to raise the quality of instruction. From 4 years, compulsory education was extended to 7 years. New universities have been opened, so there is at least one in every republic except Montenegro. National minorities have their own schools.

Present Economic Life

The economic geography of Yugoslavia reflects the different historical-political developments and influences in the individual provinces. From earlier discussions it can be seen that basically the country can be divided into two large divisions: (1) the mountain core, with interspersed fertile valleys and forested hill lands, with isolated settlements, a great variety of mineral resources, and some localized industries, many of which were built after 1945; and (2) the peripheral lands, consisting of fertile plains, hill lands, and basins connected with isolated mountain blocks and interior valleys—a rich mixed-agricultural region with a large variety of industries which have greatly increased since the war. The critical overpopulation in the agricultural areas, indicated by the fact that there were 100 people to every 247 acres of agricultural area in 1953, one of the highest ratios in all of Europe, and the backwardness of agricultural production have been at the bottom of most difficulties during the last 40 years.

Broadening the basis of the economy by a greatly expanded program of industrialization was the cure prescribed by every government since 1919. Internal opposition and the huge task of building unifying economic and social conditions among the different peoples slowed down progress before World War II. But, starting in 1946, industrialization became one of the basic principles of the new state. Increasing the amount of consumer goods and improvements in agriculture were at first given low priorities, and only in the last few years, with a proper industrial base established, has added attention been given to these two neglected branches of the economy. The industries are supplied by an increased domestic raw-material output. Production increased in the new heavy industries and in the consumer industries. Agricultural output and the quality of yields responded well to increased investments and to more liberal governmental policies. Large-scale United States foreign aid ($1.2 billion between 1950 and 1959), in addition to aid from France and the United Kingdom, contributed greatly to the success of these policies. Today the economic base of prewar Yugoslavia has completely changed. Industry now contributes 42 per cent of the national income, agriculture 29 per cent, and commerce 11 per cent, as against 25, 50, and 3 per cent, respectively, in 1938.

Fifty-one per cent of the economically active population depend upon agriculture for their principal income, and 49 per cent are in non-agricultural occupations. The population depending on agriculture shows a reduction from 76.5 per cent in twenty years, which indicates the tremendous changes in the rural life and economy brought about in a relatively short time.

Agriculture, Forestry, and Fishing. Of the total land area, roughly 58 per cent is classified as agricultural land, 35 per cent as forests, and 7 per cent as unproductive. Of the agricultural land, 51 per cent is arable land and gardens (Fig. 8–10). The area of agricultural production is widely scattered with the main grain regions in the northern and northeastern sections, the watersheds of the Sava, Danube, and Morava rivers. There are great differences in the distribution of arable land in the country, e.g., 11 per cent in Montenegro, 86 per cent in the Vojvodina. The reverse is true of permanent pasture land, where percentages vary from 12 in the Vojvodina to 88 in Montenegro. Slovenia has the greatest percentage of meadows. The Vojvodina also shows the greatest percentage of and the most intensive use of arable land. The heavy concentration of arable land (21 per cent) in the relatively small area of the Vojvodina, which comprises 8.4 per cent of the total land area of the country, is one of the problems of agriculture. Climatic influences in this region also create great fluctuations in the production of maize (corn) and wheat, the most important grains for the country.

Market and consumer customs, as well as climatic conditions, influence the production of a large number of products. Besides maize and winter wheat, barley, rye, and rice production have some local importance. These, together, are cropped on 73 per cent of all arable land. Industrial crops likewise provide a variety of products, e.g., hemp, flax, cotton, sugar beets, tobacco, and hops. The Vojvodina and the Vardar Valley are the main regions for sugar beets and tobacco. Hemp production is among the highest in Europe. The area under cotton and flax has been greatly increased in the postwar years, but both products must also still be imported. The area and yield of tobacco have also greatly increased, and over two-thirds of the production is now exported. Among the oil-bearing fruits and seeds grown in Yugoslavia are sunflower seeds, olives, linseed, etc. The production of a greater variety of vegetables is encouraged, and, thanks to favorable climatic conditions, especially along the Adriatic coast and in sections of Macedonia, many vegetables can be produced throughout the year. A small but important contribution is made by the fruit and vineyard production. A large variety of fruits is grown. Yugoslavia is best known for its plum orchards, which comprise 70 per cent of the total number of fruit trees. A portion of the plums is exported either fresh, dried, or processed; fresh prunes are used in making brandy, called *Sljivovica*. Other fruits include apples, olives, pears, cherries, apricots, and a large variety of grapes. Slovenia produces the most apples. On the whole, fruit growing is largely considered a secondary occupation for the peasant.

Following grains in importance is livestock breeding. The extensive pasture lands and meadows in Yugoslavia naturally encourage this branch of agriculture. But the low milk production of the small cattle, the insufficient weight and inferior quality of wool clip of the sheep, and the extremely fat hogs all point to the need for increased attention to the improvement of livestock quality. With constantly recurrent droughts during the 1945–60 period, livestock production fluctuated greatly.

Agricultural yields have increased only since 1956. The low priority given to agriculture for such a long time, serious droughts, various attempts to collectivize agriculture, and expropriation of all cultivable land of over 25 acres per person in 1953 resulted in stagnation of agricultural output. During the period 1952–6, net imports of agricultural products accounted for an average of 17 per cent of the caloric value of food supplies. An all-time high in agricultural production was reached in 1959, and, on the whole, production seemed to have reached a turning point for the better. The introduction of special wheat varieties, hybrid corn, greater mechanization, and more modern agrotechnical methods is slowly raising the rate of production.

Forests are of great importance for the national wealth. Large quantities of timber and firewood are supplied for domestic needs, and raw materials for the domestic production of cellulose, artificial fiber and paper, dry distillery products, etc. are of great importance. Most of the woods are coniferous forests (pine and juniper); the broadleaved trees are mainly beech and oak. Forest conservation and reforestation (51 per cent of the forests require constant artificial reforestation) are given much attention.

Fishing has some importance, especially among the rural population along the Dalmatian coast with its many deep channels and islands. Over 3,000 fishermen are engaged in this branch of the economy as a permanent occupation, while over 15,000 fish seasonally. Mackerel and sardines are the main catches. Most of the fishing is done by individuals, but cooperatives assist the fisherman in buying equipment and selling his catch. Several processing plants are located along the Adriatic coast.

Land ownership, too, has undergone important changes during the last 40 years. As a result of three land reforms, Yugoslavia has become a land of small family holdings (legal limit: 24–36 acres of agricultural land). Of the agricultural population, 96 per cent own their land and 94 per cent live in their own homes. Collectivization was discontinued in 1953 and the Peasant Work Cooperatives, the main organs for collective farming, were permitted to disband. In 1958 only about 9 per cent of the cultivated area was part of the socialized sector. The socialized sector, especially the remaining Peasant Work Cooperatives and the General Agricultural Cooperatives, is largest in the most fertile lands of the Vojvodina, the area which not only had the largest land holdings before the war but also lost many of its people with the departing German population. General Agricultural Cooperatives now play an increasingly important role; they own tractors, supply the peasants with technical assistance, fertilizers, seeds, etc., and generally act as credit and market organizations. They are the main source of help for the peasant who wishes to raise his income by increased production on small landholdings.

Mining. Industrialization in Yugoslavia has always had available an important base: raw materials and a large labor supply; the real problem has always been their exploitation. The prewar development was characterized by large foreign capital investments in Yugoslavia's mineral resources and by the building of certain selected industries which concentrated on primary production of domestic products.

The creation of employment opportunities by locating new industries or by expanding existing ones was not of primary interest to foreign investors. Yugoslavia's economy was brought to a standstill by the war.

With the exception of bituminous coal, Yugoslavia ranks high in reserves of a great variety of minerals (Fig. 8–9). Close to 82 per cent of the coal reserves are lignite and 17.8 per cent brown coal (both of which are widely distributed throughout the country), while only 0.2 per cent is bituminous coal. The mines in Bosnia and Herzegovina today account for more than one-third of the total production of the country, and production has tripled since 1939. The shortage of carboniferous coal is a considerable handicap in the development of a steel industry, and imports are essential. The brown-coal and lignite mines in northern Bosnia are the largest in the country. Over 11 per cent of the coal output comes from strip mines. Yugoslavia in 1958 had 94 coal mines, of which 40 employed more than 500 miners each. Coking plants, producing over 1 million tons of coke, have been erected in Bosnia.

Since 1939, the production of petroleum and natural gas has considerably increased and estimates of reserves are constantly being revised upward. While the production covers roughly half of the needs, successful drillings will, in the near future, probably satisfy all domestic needs. Production is concentrated in the middle Sava Valley of Croatia (five-sixths of the total Yugoslav production) and in smaller fields in the Vojvodina and in northeastern Slovenia. Production of natural gas has also been greatly expanded and pipelines have started to send gas to industries and urban consumers.

Mining has always played an important role in Yugoslavia. Ores are well distributed in the Dinaric mountain region, and increased discoveries have added to the reserves. Iron-ore deposits are numerous, and have an average iron content of 50 per cent. The center of iron-ore mining is near Ljubija and Vares in Bosnia, whose ores are shipped directly to the main steel-producing industries. New mines have been opened west of Prilep, in Macedonia. Together with nearby coal fields, they form the basis for the new iron and steel works in Skoplje, Macedonia. Iron-ore production has more than tripled since 1939, and production now is sufficiently large to permit a small export surplus. The copper ores of northeastern Serbia, in Bor and Majdanpek, are being mined in increasing quantities, making Yugoslavia Europe's most important producer; the most important lead mines are in Trepča and Kopaonik (Serbia). Between 1954 and 1957 the export of these ores contributed, on the average, 6 per cent of the value of exports. Most of these exports went to the United

States. Production now covers all domestic needs and places Yugoslavia in first place in the production for all of Europe (27 per cent of Europe's production, 4.4 per cent of world production). Proven ore reserves are equal to 2.6 per cent of the world's and 20 per cent of Europe's reserves. The lead-zinc ores contain valuable by-products, e.g., silver, bismuth, antimony, manganese, and sulphur. Zinc production, too, is important. It accounted for 13 per cent of the European and 2.2 per cent of the world's production in 1958. About 85 per cent of the mercury production, from the Idrija mine in Slovenia (the only producing mine) is exported. Yugoslavia's bauxite is of excellent quality, and reserves are estimated at 5.5 per cent of total world reserves. The largest deposits occur along the Adriatic coast. Because of its excellent location close to a large hydroelectric potential and to lignite, plans call for a great expansion of aluminum production.

Other important ores include chromium (second in Europe), manganese, the rare ore molybdenum, and antimony. Magnesite mining increased greatly (75 per cent in Serbia). Yugoslavia and Austria are the two largest producers in Europe. Graphite is mined principally in Slavonia (Croatia), gypsum in western Macedonia, and important deposits of rock salt are found near Tuzla, in Bosnia. There are also sizable deposits of fine chalky marl near Split and Istria, very important for the manufacture of cement. Raw materials necessary for construction are widely distributed in the country with clay for brickmaking, in the Pannonian Plain, and marble quarried in Istria, on the island of Brač, and in Venoac, Serbia.

Production of sufficient power plays a key role in Yugoslavia's plans for industrialization. Sufficient waterpower resources are available to place Yugoslavia among those countries with the largest unused reserves;[41] only 6.5 per cent of the hydroelectric potential, however, has been tapped. Precipitation is advantageously distributed. In the Alps and the Dinaric Mountains the maximum rainfall occurs in the spring and fall, as well as the beginning of winter. Southern Serbia and Macedonia have dry summers, but snow in the higher mountains supplies the rivers with abundant water during the early part of the dry season. Karst mountains dropping sharply toward the Adriatic Sea provide a great potential and several hydroelectric plants utilize this drop. The United States is assisting in the financing of some projects. A hydroelectric project with great possibilities is the often-talked-of joint Rumanian-Yugoslav development for harnessing the waters of the Danube at the Iron Gate. If developed, this project would be Europe's largest hydroelectric undertaking.

[41] Milos Brelith, *Yugoslav Water Resources as a Power Reserve* (Belgrade: Jugoslavija, 1958).

Manufacturing. Before 1938, most industrial production was concentrated in and around the Ljubljana Basin, Maribor, Zagreb, and Belgrade, with a few smelters near important mines. Twenty years later, the base of industrial production had been greatly broadened. The largest concentration of industries is to be found in the Sava River Valley, between Zagreb and Belgrade, including northern Bosnia. Industrial production located in this region has several advantages. A large number of key raw materials, e.g., coal, iron ore, timber,

Fig. 8–16. The Zenica iron and steel works. (Yugoslav Information Center.)

and oil, are nearby. The Sava is navigable from its confluence with the Danube to Sisak, and the railway network and road system could easily be expanded.

A new industrial region has been developed in many of the valleys between Banja Luka-Zenica-Tuzla and Doboj. Zenica is the largest iron and steel center in Yugoslavia, producing over 50 per cent of the total Yugoslav raw-steel output and 60 per cent of the pig iron and coke (Fig. 8–16). Production is constantly being expanded. Sisak also has a large iron and steel mill and a large modern refinery, and, in addition, is the center of newly expanding petroleum fields. A great variety of manufactured goods is being produced in this newly developed region. Other industrial centers are more dispersed.

The oldest industries are in Slovenia and in Zagreb. Ljubljana-Jesenice produces machinery and various other high-quality metal products. The iron and steel mills at Jesenice are the oldest in Yugoslavia. The Drava River Valley, with industrial concentrations at Maribor, Varazdin, and Osijek, manufactures agricultural machinery, weaves textiles, and processes foods; Rijeka, and to a smaller extent Pula, are important for shipbuilding and miscellaneous industries. A great expansion of food processing and fertilizer production has gone on in the Vojvodina.

There is hardly any branch of industry which is not now producing or for which plans have not been made to start production in Yugoslavia. Both increased diversification and the purchase of licenses from foreign firms are part of this intensive drive to make Yugoslavia an industrial country. Self-sufficiency is not expected; rather, the intention is to integrate Yugoslavia's productive efforts with those of other advanced industrial countries, hoping in this way to raise the standard of production and increase the standard of living.

In 1958 over 200 enterprises employed 1,000 or more people, 300 employed 500 to 1,000. The largest number of employed were in the metal, lumber, and textile industries and in coal mining. Ljubljana had the largest number of enterprises; Macedonia, Montenegro, and the Autonomous Region of Kosmet are generally considered underdeveloped areas, but even in these regions new industries have started production. The abundance and variety of their resources, together with large manpower reserves, make the location of new industries highly desirable in these areas. Bosnia and Herzegovina, an underdeveloped region until recently, has greatly increased industrial production, and this is in no small way due to large reserves of hydroelectric power (28 per cent of all of Yugoslavia's reserves), iron ore (90 per cent), lignite (50 per cent), timber (33 per cent).

Communications. The basic problem of transportation in Yugoslavia reflects both economic and historical influences. Slovenia, large parts of Croatia, and the Vojvodina formed part of the Austro-Hungarian Monarchy and had excellent rail connections with each other as well as with the core, the Vienna and Budapest area. The rail network in these regions has largely remained unchanged, but on the whole is sufficient to meet demands, even though the many single-track lines are a handicap.

Connections between the peripheral regions, the mountainous core, and the Adriatic littoral are inadequate and were little improved during the interwar years. In addition, the low transportation density, brought about in part by different rail gauges, is in itself a great handicap to the economic development of the country. Single-track lines made up 84 per cent of all railroads in 1957. Fundamentally, then, the problem in rail and road transportation is one of interconnecting three physiographically and economically diverse regions: the northern lowlands, the mountainous core, and the Adriatic littoral. This is especially important since the main contributions of these regions—food production, heavy industry, mining, and foreign trade—are essential to the country's economy.

From 1939 to 1957 total rail mileage increased from 6,520 miles to 7,266 miles. Freight carried increased in the same period by two and one-half times and passengers carried by three and one-half times. Railroad rolling stock has increased more slowly than have the amount of freight and the number of passengers carried, but a few new crack trains, especially those for the international through traffic, are now in operation. Railroads account for about 85 per cent of the total transportation in the country. A program of modernization, especially in the Vojvodina, has begun, and, when sufficient electric power becomes available, a number of key lines will be electrified. Of greatest need is the expansion of important narrow-gauge lines.

The highway transportation network has been poorly developed and great effort, including the use of voluntary youth brigades, is being made to provide up-to-date modern roads for at least the main thoroughfares of the country. The superhighway from Belgrade to Zagreb was completed shortly after the war. A new superhighway between Ljubljana and Zagreb was completed in 1958, and the connection between Belgrade and the border of Greece, as well as the so-called Adriatic Road from Rijeka to Kotor Bay, is being built. The Adriatic Road will eventually be extended to Skoplje.

Yugoslavia has spent much effort on increasing its merchant marine since the war. The indented 460-mile-long Adriatic coast line has a number of good ports, but the mountainous hinterland has limited their effectiveness. Rijeka is the main port. The merchant marine has been greatly modernized and expanded, but most of the building has been for foreign orders. With the exception of traffic on the Danube, and to a much lesser degree on the Tisza and the Sava, traffic on the waterways is of minor economic importance. The new Danube-Tisza-Danube Canal in the Vojvodina not only serves for the movement of freight but is also useful for irrigation purposes. Lastly, Yugoslavia's air network has been greatly expanded.

Foreign Trade. It is obvious from the foregoing discussions that Yugoslavia's whole foreign-trade structure has undergone basic changes from prewar times. Changes have been made not only with regard to the type of goods but also geographically. The break with the Soviet Union in 1948 caused Yugoslavia's trade to be reoriented.

In prewar years Yugoslavia traded mainly with Austria, Italy, Czecho-slovakia, and Germany. In the first postwar years trade was directed mainly toward the Soviet Union and other countries in Eastern Europe. In 1958 imports were divided, with 28 per cent coming from the Soviet bloc, 42 per cent from other European countries, 19.6 per cent from the United States, and the rest from other overseas countries. Thirty-two per cent of the exports went to the countries of the Soviet bloc, 47 per cent to other European countries, 8 per cent to the United States, and 13 per cent to other overseas countries. According to value, the United States has been the largest trader since 1950, but this was brought about largely by economic aid.[42] Other important trading partners are the Soviet Union, Italy, the United Kingdom, and Austria. Yugoslavia's greatly increased exports went to a large number of countries, e.g., Italy, the Soviet Union, West Germany, the United States, the United Kingdom, and many newly opened markets, especially in the Asian and African areas. Before the war, Yugoslavia's main exports consisted of food products, min-erals, and forest products; today, this list has been expanded, greatly broadened, and changed. Food exports amount to about 26 per cent, raw materials to 24 per cent, semimanufactured and manufactured goods 28 per cent, machinery 5 per cent, beverages and tobacco 8 per cent, and chemical products 4.5 per cent. Imports are divided be-tween food (32 per cent), raw materials (15 per cent), consumer goods (12 per cent), machinery and transport equipment (20 per cent), fuel and lubricants (10 per cent), chemical products (7 per cent), and miscellaneous items. The over-all volume of goods ex-changed with foreign countries has risen constantly in the last eight years. Yugoslavia has made a special effort to reduce its large depend-ence on food imports, e.g., wheat (two-thirds of the imports of wheat came from the United States), rice, cotton, and lard, and on chemical products, especially fertilizer. Special mention should also be made of the increasing benefit to Yugoslavia's trade balance of the expenditures by foreign tourists.

*   *   *

The developments in Eastern Europe permit a number of impor-tant conclusions:

1. The instability of the area has been due to its location with re-gard to its powerful neighbors, first the empires of Austria, Prussia,

---

[42] Besides foreign aid, the United States exported to Yugoslavia powdered milk, wheat, raw cotton, soya oil, pit coal, etc. Yugoslavia exported to the United States fermented tobacco (22 per cent of the total exports go to the United States), refined lead, hops, ferromanganese, etc.

Russia, and Turkey (Ottoman), and later Germany and the Soviet Union. When the four pre-World War I empires disappeared in 1917–19, the newly created national states were too weak to uphold their independence against increased pressure, first from Germany and later from the Soviet Union. Yugoslavia alone has been able to reassert her independence since 1948 and cannot be counted as part of the Soviet bloc. Another important factor of Eastern Europe's instability is the many diverse cultural characteristics of its many peoples.

2. The basic economic geography of the region has been changed in the last 10 years so much that a return to the pattern of prewar Europe is inconceivable. Economic developments in the region differ from those of the West. Economics are of planned and nationalized character. Trade and investment policies, raw-material distribution, and production quotas are being more and more integrated.

3. Six of the seven Eastern European countries: Poland, Czechoslovakia, Hungary, Rumania, Bulgaria, and Albania—and East Germany as well—are being closely integrated with the Soviet Union's economic and political aims. Economic integration (and for that matter integration of all aspects of life) between these countries and the Soviet Union is being accelerated; the Soviet Union is in complete economic, political, and military control and, as the developments in Hungary in the fall of 1956 have amply proven, will use force if necessary to keep these countries under its absolute domination. Poland has a certain independence of action, but it must be remembered that Poland is dependent on Russia for key raw materials for her heavy industries (and thus for maintaining full employment), and that Poland depends on the Soviet Union's wholehearted support to retain the important areas acquired from Germany. Poland's future can therefore only be one of close alliance to the Soviet Union.

BIBLIOGRAPHY

(Major references are asterisked.)

Books in English

BOYD, LOUISE A. *Polish Countrysides.* New York: American Geographical Society, 1937.
*BYRNES, ROBERT F. (ed.). *East-Central Europe Under the Communists.* Separate volumes on Poland, Czechoslovakia, Hungary, Rumania, Bulgaria, Albania, and Yugoslavia. New York: Frederick A. Praeger, Inc., 1957–8, published for Mid-European Studies Center.
KERNER, ROBERT J. (ed.). *Czechoslovakia.* Berkeley, Calif.: University of California Press, 1940.
———. *Yugoslavia.* Berkeley, Calif.: University of California Press, 1949.

MILOJEVIĆ, B. Ž. *Yugoslavia: Geographical Survey*. Belgrade: Committee for Cultural Relations with Foreign Countries, 1958.

*POUNDS, NORMAN J. G. (ed.). *Geographical Essays on East-Central Europe*. Russian and East European Series, Vol. XXIV. Bloomington, Ind.: Indiana University Press, 1961.

POUNDS, NORMAN J. G. *The Upper Silesian Industrial Regions*. Slavic and East European Series, Vol. XI. Bloomington, Ind.: Indiana University Press, 1958.

*POUNDS, NORMAN J. G., and SPULBER, NICOLAS (eds.). *Resources and Planning in Eastern Europe*. Slavic and East European Series, Vol. IV. Bloomington, Ind.: Indiana University Press, 1957.

*SANDERS, IRWIN T. (ed.). *Collectivization of Agriculture in Eastern Europe*. Lexington, Ky.: University of Kentucky Press, 1958.

SCHMITT, BERNADOTTE (ed.). *Poland*. Berkeley, Calif.: University of California Press, 1945.

*SETON-WATSON, HUGH. *Eastern Europe Between the Wars 1918–1941*. London: Cambridge University Press, 1945.

*SPULBER, NICOLAS. *The Economics of Communist Eastern Europe*. New York: John Wiley & Sons, Inc., 1957.

TELEKI, COUNT PAUL. *The Evolution of Hungary and Its Place in European History*. New York: The Macmillan Co., 1923.

*TOMASEVICH, JOZO. *Peasants, Politics, and Economic Change in Yugoslavia*. Stanford, Calif.: Stanford University Press, 1955.

TROUTON, RUTH. *Peasant Renaissance in Yugoslavia 1900–1950*. London: Routledge & Kegan Paul, Ltd., 1952.

*WANKLYN, HARRIET G. *The Eastern Marchlands of Europe*. London: George Philip & Son, Ltd., 1941.

———. *Czechoslovakia: A Geographical and Historical Study*. London: George Philip & Son, Ltd., 1954.

WILKINSON, H. R. *Maps and Politics: A Review of the Ethnographic Cartography of Macedonia*. Liverpool: University of Liverpool Press, 1951.

WSZELAKI, JAN. *Fuel and Power in Captive Middle Europe*. New York: The National Committee for a Free Europe, 1952.

Books in Foreign Languages

BLANC, ANDRÉ. *La Croatie Occidentale* (Western Croatia). Paris: Étude de Géographie Humaine, 1957.

BULLA, B., and MENDE, T. *A Kárpátmedence földrajza* (The Geography of the Carpathian Basin). Budapest: Egyetemi Nyomda, 1947.

*CVIJIĆ, JOVAN. *La Péninsule Balkanique* (The Balkan Peninsula). Paris: Librairie A. Colin, 1918.

KÜNDIG-STEINER, WERNER. *Nord-Dobrudscha* (Northern Dobruja). Zürich: Aschmann & Schiller, 1946.

MAČURA, MILOS. *Stanovništvo i radna snaga kao činicci privrednog razvoja Jugoslavije* (Population and Labor Force as Factors of Economic Development of Yugoslavia). Belgrade: Ekonomska Biblioteka, 1958.

*MARKERT, WERNER (ed.). *Jugoslawien*. Osteuropa-Handbuch. Cologne-Graz: Böhlau Verlag, 1954.

MARKERT, WERNER (ed.). *Poland*. Osteuropa Handbuch. Cologne-Graz: Böhlau Verlag, 1959.

UNITED NATIONS, FAO. *Yougoslavie*. Projet FAO de Développement Méditerranéen. Rome, 1959.

Articles

BEYNON, E. G. "Budapest: An Ecological Study," *Geographical Review* 33 (1943): 256–75.

"East Central Europe: A Re-examination," *Journal of International Affairs* 101 (1957).

FREITAG, ULRICH. "Der Verkehr Bulgariens" (Bulgaria's Transport), *Zeitschrift für Wirtschaftsgeographie* 3 (1959): 134–40.

GAVAZZI MILOVAN. "Die Kulturgeographische Gliederung Südosteuropas" (Cultural Geographic Divisions of Southeast Europe), *Südost Forschungen* 15 (1956): 5–21.

*HOFFMAN, GEORGE W. "Eastern Europe: A Study in Political Geography," *Texas Quarterly* 2 (1959): 57–88.

———. "The Shatter-Belt in Relation to the East-West Conflict," *The Journal of Geography* 51 (1952): 267–75.

———. "Yugoslavia: Changing Character of Rural Life and Rural Economy," *The American Slavic and East European Review* 17 (1959): 555–78.

———. "Yugoslavia in Transition: Industrial Expansion and Resource Bases," *Economic Geography* 32 (1956): 294–315.

HOROWITZ, MARIA. "The Rise of the Western Territories," *Polish Perspectives* 6 (1958): 50–55.

JOHNSTON, W. B., and CRKVENCIC, I. "Examples of Changing Peasant Agriculture in Croatia, Yugoslavia," *Economic Geography* 33 (1957): 51–71.

LESCZYNSKI, STANISLAW. "The Geographical Bases of Poland," *Journal of Central European Affairs* 7 (1948): 379–73.

LESZCZYCKI, STANISLAW, *et al.* "Miscellaneous Articles," *Przeglad Geograficzny* 32, Supplement. Special issue for the 19th International Geographical Congress, 1960 (Warsaw, 1960).

MAČURA, MILOS. "Changes in the Socio-economic Structure of FPRY," *Review of International Affairs* 10 (March 1, 1959): 13–14.

MONTIAS, JOHN M. "The Polish Iron and Steel Industry," *The American Slavic and East European Review* 16 (1957): 300–22.

MOODIE, ARTHUR E. "The Eastern Marchlands of Europe," *The Changing World*, W. Gordon East and Arthur E. Moodie, eds. Yonkers, N. Y.: World Book Co., 1956: 110–37.

NORTH, GEOFFREY. "Poland's Population and Changing Economy," *The Geographical Journal* 124 (1958): 517–27.

PUCIC, EUGEN. "The Family in the Process of Social Change in Yugoslavia," *The Sociological Review* 5 (1957): 207–24.

ROBERTS, HENRY L. (ed.). "The Satellites in Eastern Europe," *The Annals of the American Academy of Political and Social Science* 317 (1958): 163.

SZCZEPANSKI, JAN. "Poland," *The Institutions of Advanced Societies*, Arnold M. Rose, ed. Minneapolis: University of Minnesota Press, 1958: 235–73.

TABORSKY, EDUARD. "The Old and the New Course in Satellite Economy," *The Journal of Central European Affairs* 17 (1958): 378–403.

TELEKI, GEZA. "Industrial and Social Policies Between the Wars," *Challenge in Eastern Europe*, C. E. Black, ed. New Brunswick, N. J.: Rutgers University Press, 1954: 81–97.

WILKINSON, H. R. "Jugoslav Macedonia in Transition," *The Geographical Journal* 118 (1952): 389–405.

9

The Soviet Union

In contrast to the maritime and peninsular nature of Europe in the west, a broad continuity, massiveness, and continentality characterize it in the east. No longer is the continent dissected by long arms of the sea into great tongues of land. Instead one finds Europe, at its widest extent, forming a bridge to Asia. This entire transition area falls within the confines of the Union of Soviet Socialist Republics (U.S.S.R.), commonly known as the Soviet Union.

Although the U.S.S.R. covers large parts of both Europe and Asia, it is clearly one of the most strongly unified political units in the world and cannot rationally be divided for discussion. Since the general scope of the present volume is limited to Europe, the European part of the U.S.S.R., which also happens to be the core area of the entire Soviet Union, will receive most of our attention in this chapter. However, major facts of the geography of the Asiatic section will be discussed, especially where they are of exceptional magnitude in relation to the entire country or where they bear more or less directly on a particular aspect of the European U.S.S.R.

THE PHYSICAL LANDSCAPE

Size, Location, and Boundaries

With a total area of 8,500,000 square miles, the Soviet Union is the largest continuous political unit in the world (Fig. 9–1). It is about two and a half times as large as the United States (including Alaska and Hawaii).

The European U.S.S.R. (including Transcaucasia) occupies roughly the eastern half, or 2,000,000 square miles, of Europe. Vast as this area is—corresponding to two-thirds of the continental United States—it represents only one-fourth of the total area of the Soviet Union. The remainder of the country—Siberia, Kazakhstan, and central Asia—covers the northern third of Asia.

To realize just how vast the Soviet Union is, let us recall that from the westernmost point of the country, at 20° E., near Kaliningrad in former East Prussia, it ranges over 170 degrees of longitude to Cape Dezhnev (170° W.) on the Bering Strait opposite Alaska, or almost halfway around the world. In terms of time zones, this means that when it is noon on the Soviet-Polish frontier it is 11 P.M. on the shores of the Bering Strait; by way of comparison, when it is noon in San Francisco it is only 3 P.M. in New York City.

This vast east-west span is matched by a spectacular north-south extent. From the northernmost continental point, at Cape Chelyuskin (77° 44′ N.) on the Arctic Ocean, a latitude corresponding to Spitsbergen (Svalbard), the Soviet Union extends nearly 3,000 miles south to Kushka (35° N.) on the Afghanistan frontier, at the latitude of Crete. It should be noted that, in addition to the arctic island groups of Franz Josef Land and Severnaya Zemlya (North Land), the U.S.S.R. lays claim to the entire polar sector between the meridians of Murmansk (32° E.) and of the Bering Strait (168° 45′ W.) and as far as the North Pole itself.

The size of the Soviet Union is also evident from the length of its land and sea boundaries, which total about 37,000 miles. In contrast, France, the largest country of western Europe, has frontiers with a total length of 3,300 miles. More than two-thirds (27,000 miles) of the Soviet boundaries are coast line.

Although the length of its coast line far exceeds the length of its land borders, the Soviet Union is far more a continental than a maritime nation. Most of its littoral is bordered by frozen seas and low, marshy shores. The greater part of the coasts lies in sparsely settled or totally uninhabited regions along the seas of the Arctic Ocean. Where the coastal density of population is somewhat higher, closed or nearly closed seas make access difficult. Only a few rocky shores provide the country with natural harbors, and year-round access to the open sea is offered only by one short stretch of shore line.

In terms of their significance for transportation, the seas bordering on the Soviet Union may be divided into four groups:

1. Seas that permit direct access to the oceans of the world—the Barents Sea, the White Sea, and the Sea of Japan. Of these, only the Barents Sea, warmed by the North Atlantic Drift, permits year-round navigation at its port of Murmansk. The White Sea, an appendage of the Barents Sea, with which it is connected by a 30-mile neck

Fig. 9–1. Loc

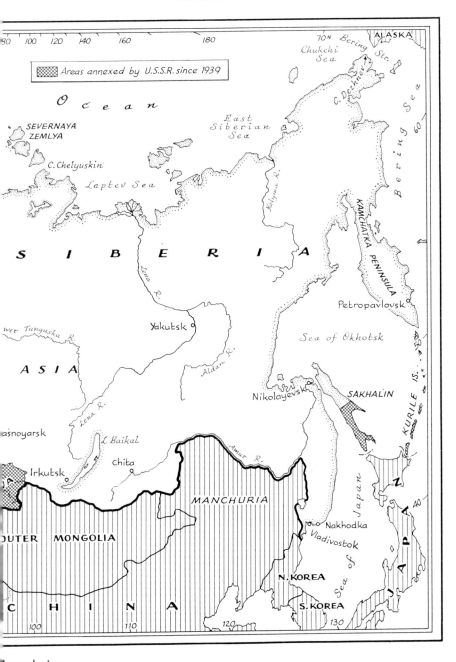

boundaries.

(*gorlo* in Russian), is frozen from November until May, bottling up
its lumber port of Archangel. The Sea of Japan, in the Soviet Far
East, provides access to the Pacific Ocean from the Soviet ports of
Vladivostok and Nakhodka. However, a cold ice-carrying current
along the Soviet Siberian coast also rules out year-round utilization
except with the use of icebreakers.

2. Seas that permit access to the world oceans through straits
controlled by other nations—the Baltic Sea and the Black Sea. These
seas, which are the ones nearest to the main Soviet population and
production centers, provide the most important maritime routes for
Soviet foreign trade. The Baltic Sea, for example, offers the shortest
route between the U.S.S.R. and the countries of western Europe and
the Atlantic Ocean. Although its most important port, Leningrad,
is icebound from November until April, the more westerly ports of
Liepaja (in Latvia) and Kaliningrad are ice-free almost the year-
round. Similarly, the Black Sea offers the shortest route to the Mediterranean and southern Europe from the Soviet ports of Odessa,
Nikolayev, and Kherson in the Ukraine, and Novorossisk, Poti, and
Batumi in the Caucasus. Winter ice conditions are negligible in the
Black Sea and its usefulness, from the Soviet point of view, is im-
paired only by the fact that Turkey controls the straits at the exit
from the sea. However, the Black Sea–Danube route is now heavily
used for bulk-goods traffic between the Soviet Union and its allies in
eastern Europe.

3. The Caspian Sea, which is actually a lake and is used almost
entirely for Soviet domestic shipping, such as petroleum cargoes between Baku, Astrakhan, and Krasnovodsk. Shipping links with Iran,
the other Caspian nation, are negligible.

4. The arctic and subarctic seas, where ice conditions through the
greater part of the year and the absence of economically developed
coast lines reduce navigation to negligible proportions. The much-
discussed Arctic Sea Route serves the scattered coastal settlements of
northern Siberia during the brief navigation season, but does not play
a major role in carrying goods between European Russia and the
Pacific.

Arctic seas, which account for most of the Soviet shore line, are
the Kara, Laptev, East Siberian, and Chukchi seas of the Arctic
Ocean, and the Bering and Okhotsk seas of the Pacific.

On land, the Soviet Union borders on 12 countries. In the extreme northwest, in the Pechenga area, the U.S.S.R. has a short
common frontier with Norway. Before World War II, the Pechenga
area (then known as Petsamo) was part of Finland and provided
access to the Barents Sea. Since the war, the Pechenga area, with

important nickel mines, has been part of the Soviet Union. Farther south, other Soviet-Finnish border changes resulted in the cession of the Karelian Isthmus and nearby areas to the Soviet Union.

The Baltic states of Estonia, Latvia, and Lithuania, which had been part of Russia before World War I and had been independent between the two world wars, were incorporated into the U.S.S.R. in 1940.

The Soviet frontier with Poland starts on the Baltic Sea and traverses former East Prussia, which has been divided between the two countries since the end of World War II. The rest of the Soviet-Polish border was also agreed to in 1945 along an ethnic partition line that shifted Belorussian and Ukrainian settlement areas formerly under Polish rule to the Soviet Union. A similar ethnic adjustment took place in 1945 between the Soviet Union and Czechoslovakia, when the latter ceded the Transcarpathian Ukraine (Ruthenia), an area inhabited by Ukrainians. The cession of this area also gave the Soviet Union a common border with Hungary. At the southern end of the Soviet Union's European frontier, Rumania ceded northern Bucovina, with a predominantly Ukrainian population, and Bessarabia, with Ukrainians and Moldavians, to the U.S.S.R. in 1940.

South of the Caucasus, in Asia Minor, the Soviet Union borders on Turkey and Iran, the Iranian frontier being continued east of the Caspian Sea. Afghanistan, which follows as the next neighbor of the Soviet Union, forms a peculiar panhandle in the northeast, separating the Soviet Pamirs from Pakistan across an area only 10 miles wide. The Soviet frontier with China is interrupted by Outer Mongolia, which intervenes between China's Sinkiang and Manchuria. Finally, the Soviet Union has a brief common border with North Korea, on the Sea of Japan. Territorial transfers along the Soviet Union's Asian frontier include Tuva (the former Tannu-Tuva), which passed to Soviet control in 1944, and southern Sakhalin (the former Karafuto) and the Kurile Islands, seized from Japan in 1945. It should also be noted that Soviet territory is close to American across the Bering Strait.

Landforms

The U.S.S.R. (Figs. 9–2 and 1–3) consists, essentially, of a vast lowland lying north of the high mountain and plateau belt that extends east and west across the heart of the Eurasian land mass. The major divisions of this lowland are the Great Russian Lowland (plains and tablelands) west of the Ural Mountains; the West Siberian Plain, east of the Urals; the Turan Lowland, east of the

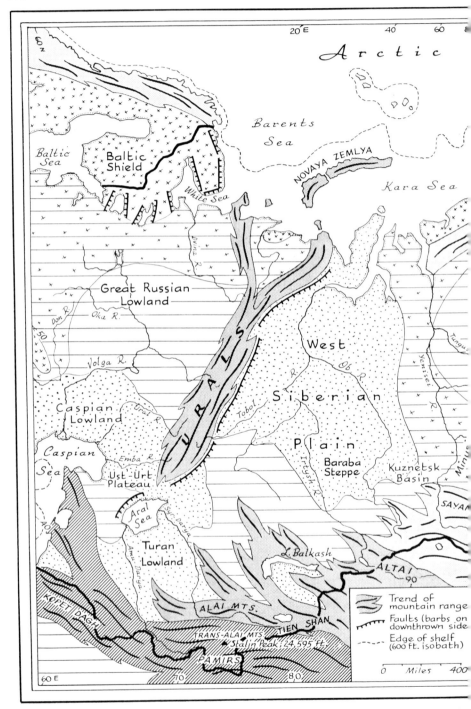

Fig. 9–2. Structural

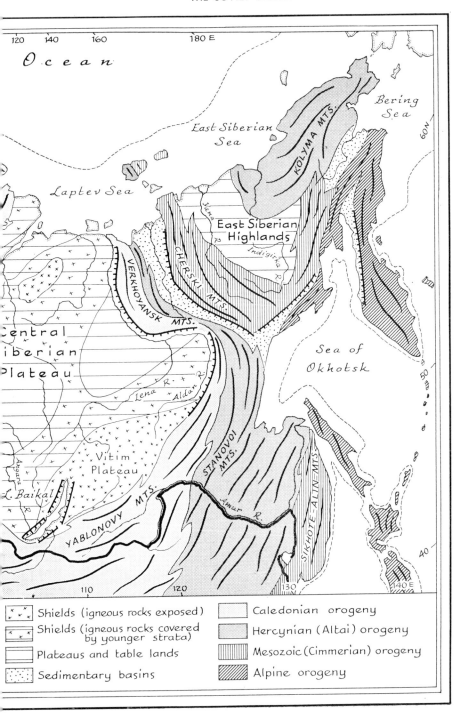

Caspian Sea; and the Central Siberian Plateau. These major low-lands are bounded in the south and east, roughly along the Soviet frontier, by the Carpathians, the Caucasus, the Kopet Dagh, the Tien Shan and Pamirs, the Altai and Sayans, and the east-Siberian high-lands.

By far the dominant feature of the U.S.S.R. in Europe is the Great Russian Lowland. Representing an eastward broadening of the North European Plain, this lowland, interrupted occasionally by low hill lands, rises almost imperceptibly toward the Urals in the east. Geo-logically [1] it consists of a basement of Pre-Cambrian crystalline rocks, overlain by sedimentary deposits of marine and continental origin. At the northwestern and southwestern rims of the plain, the Pre-Cambrian formations appear as surface outcrops in the form of crystalline shields or blocks. In the northwest the Baltic Shield in-cludes Karelia and the Kola Peninsula; in the southwest, the Azov-Podolian Massif extends through the Ukraine, forming an eroded upland.

In addition to these crystalline outcrops, further relief has been added to the plain by occasional downfaulting, as in the Donets Basin, where major coal deposits of the Carboniferous period have been preserved, and by upthrusting, as in the Voronezh Block. Other eroded remains of uplifts are the Volga uplands (with the Zhiguli Mountains) along the right bank of the middle Volga, the horst of the Ufa Plateau, west of the Urals, and the Stavropol Plateau north of the Caucasus. However, the rolling lowland topography of the Great Russian Lowland never rises above 1,300 feet.

While the main relief features of the Great Russian Lowland reflect past tectonic action, the detailed topography has resulted from the Pleistocene ice sheet that covered the northern part of the low-land and from recent marine transgressions in the extreme north and the southeast.

As in the rest of northern Europe, ice radiating from the Scandi-navian highlands covered the northwestern and middle portions of the Great Russian Lowland. A subsidiary center of ice expansion was located on Novaya Zemlya. The ice sheet reached its maximum pene-tration during the Riss (Illinoian) period, when the southern bound-ary of glaciation extended to the edge of the Azov-Podolian hills and the central-Russian hill lands, forming two tongues in the Dnieper and Oka-Don valleys. The Riss glacial boundary then followed the western edge of the Volga uplands and continued to the middle Urals at about 60° N. Although the ice sheet thus covered the greatest

[1] For geological terms, see Appendix I. For a more detailed discussion, see Chap-ter 1.

area in the Riss stage, it is the latest glacial period, the Würm (Wisconsin) stage, that left behind most of the effects of the Ice Age, having partly obliterated the marks of the Riss period.

The advancing and retreating ice scoured and denuded the ancient rocks of the Kola-Karelian Shield, leaving a topography of bare crystalline outcrops and glacial lake basins and virtually no soil mantle. Most of the deposition of morainic materials (boulders, pebbles, sand, clay) took place in the northern part of the Great Russian Lowland. Here terminal moraines, arrayed in festoons, are a conspicuous feature of the landscape. The most important morainic ridge remains as a continental watershed, separating the Baltic-Arctic drainage system in the north from the Black Sea and Caspian basins in the south. This major divide consists of the Lithuanian-Belorussian hill lands, the Valdai Hills, and a series of low ridges extending to the Urals.

Beyond the moraines, in southern European Russia, the plain is dominated by outwash valleys of sheets of sand and clay deposited by the great streams that formed along the ice margin during the melting phase. Finely ground silt from these outwash plains was later spread by the wind and deposited over the Ukraine in the form of loess. Erosion of this fine-grained dustlike material has produced the characteristic ravine and gully relief of the Ukraine. In the southeastern part of the Great Russian Lowland, any traces of glacial deposits have been obliterated by the action of the repeated transgressions of the Caspian Sea, which reached far up the Volga Valley during the Ice Age. In the north of European Russia, detailed surface relief dates from postglacial transgressions of the Baltic, Barents, and White seas.

Among the mineral resources of the Great Russian Lowland, metals are associated with the ancient magmatic and metamorphic rocks of the Kola Shield (apatite and nephelite) and of the Azov-Podolian hills (iron ore of Krivoi Rog). The sedimentary mantle of the plain contains rich fuel and other non-metallic resources such as coal of the Donets Basin, the Moscow Basin, and Vorkuta; petroleum and natural gas of the Volga-Urals area and the north-Caucasus foreland; potash, rock salt, oil shale, and phosphates.

The Urals extend almost 1,500 miles south and north, separating the Great Russian Lowland from the West Siberian Plain. This narrow mountain range was formed in the Hercynian orogeny, and was repeatedly eroded and reuplifted in subsequent periods. The contemporary Urals reach an elevation of 6,000 feet in the undeveloped northern part and in the south, where they consist of several parallel ranges. However, in the heavily industrialized middle section, where the Trans-Siberian Railroad makes use of low passes, the Urals resemble a heavily eroded plateau rather than a mountain range. Prolonged denudation of surface rocks has given access to the older rock formations rich in minerals that have provided the basis for the highly developed mineral-extracting and -processing industry of the Urals. Among the main metals found there are iron ore, copper, bauxite, platinum, nickel, and chromium.

The Urals drop abruptly in the east to the West Siberian Plain, a low, level region that displays far less local relief than the Great Russian Lowland. The Siberian Plain is underlain at great depths by a crystalline basement, and even the younger Tertiary and Jurassic rocks outcrop only in a few isolated places through the thick mantle of unconsolidated sedimentary rocks. Like the Great Russian Lowland, the Siberian lowland has been shaped largely by glacial topography. The low-lying Arctic coast was subjected to postglacial marine transgressions. The plain displays moraine topography as far south as 60° N. Beyond the moraines the landscape is dominated by mighty outwash plains with broad, swampy interfluves. Still farther south we find perfectly level tableland studded with lakes, as in the Baraba Steppe, the Siberian dairy land.

East of the West Siberian Plain, beyond the broad Yenisei Valley, the terrain rises to the Central Siberian Plateau, a dissected upland. As late as the middle Tertiary period this region was a rolling lowland, and it was once again uplifted in the Quaternary period and deeply dissected by rejuvenated river systems. Most of the Central Siberian Plateau is below 3,000 feet.

South of the West Siberian Plain, the Turgai tableland leads to the large Turan Lowland of central Asia. This lowland consists of rolling plains and low plateaus rising to not more than 1,300 feet. Surface forms, especially in the plains, are made up largely of sand, believed to have been deposited by Ice Age streams whose old river channels still traverse the Turan Lowland.

The mountain ranges that skirt the great inland plains of the Soviet Union extend in an almost unbroken belt from the southwest, along the southern and eastern borders, to the northeast. The Great Russian Lowland and the western part of the Turan Lowland are bounded on the south by the Soviet examples of alpine mountain building. They are the Carpathians, the Crimean Mountains, the Caucasus, and the Kopet Dagh.

The Carpathians enter the Soviet Union over a short distance, separating the Transcarpathian Ukraine from the rest of the Ukraine. Made up of rocks such as sandstone and shale that are easily eroded in a humid climate, the Carpathians display rounded contours further accentuated by their forest cover. The highest point in the Soviet Carpathians is Mount Goverla (6,800 feet).

The Crimean Mountains, in the southern part of the Crimea, consist of three parallel ranges, of which the highest and southernmost drops abruptly to the Black Sea coast around Yalta, the Soviet subtropical "Riviera." The highest point of the mountains, which are made up largely of Jurassic limestones, is the Roman-Kosh (5,000 feet).

By far the most impressive example of alpine structure in the Soviet Union is the Greater Caucasus system, extending 800 miles across the isthmus between the Black Sea and the Caspian. Several peaks exceed 15,000 feet, the highest being Elborus (18,500 feet). The Caucasus rises far above the snow line, and valley glaciers are found on the slopes of the main peaks. Glacially eroded mountain features, such as U-shaped valleys, cirques, knife-edge divides, and comb ridges, are typical of the high middle reaches of the Caucasus.

The southern slopes of the Greater Caucasus drop sharply to the Transcaucasian lowland, made up of the valleys of the Kura and Rion rivers. These sediment-filled tectonic troughs separate the great range to the north from the so-called Lesser Caucasus, a system of folded and blockfaulted mountains adjoining the Armenian highlands. The Lesser Caucasus and the Armenian highlands consist both of sedimentary rocks and of volcanic formations such as tuffs, lavas, and volcanic breccia.

East of the Caspian Sea lies the 400-mile-long Kopet Dagh on the Soviet-Iranian frontier. Of considerably less deviation and complexity than the Caucasus, the Kopet Dagh rises to almost 10,000 feet.

Except for copper and other non-ferrous metals found in the Caucasus, these alpine mountain systems are poor in ores. However, foreland troughs filled with great thicknesses of recent sediments contain some of the main oil fields of the Soviet Union.

The highest mountain systems along the southern border of the U.S.S.R. are found in the southeastern part of Soviet central Asia, in the Pamir-Alai and Tien Shan complexes. The Pamir-Alai system consists of the Alai and Trans-Alai ranges, rising to 24,595 feet at Stalin Peak, and the adjoining Pamir high plateaus, with an average elevation of more than 15,000 feet. The Tien Shan rises to 24,400 feet at the Pobeda (Victory) Peak, which was discovered by Soviet mountain climbers during World War II. The Tien Shan and the Pamir-Alai are separated by the Fergana Valley, a deep tectonic depression which is one of the main economic and population centers of Soviet central Asia.

Southern Siberia is bounded by the mountains of the Altai and Sayan systems, both of which were originally formed during the Caledonian orogeny of the early Paleozoic era. After a period of peneplanation, the rigid basement rocks were once again plicated in the Tertiary period into broad gentle folds that were also disrupted by faulting. The combination of downthrusting and uplifting gave rise to the present complex folded and blockfaulted character of the Altai and Sayan systems. The tectonic depressions between these mountains include the Minusinsk Basin, an agricultural and mining area, and the Kuznetsk Basin, an industrial district based on local coal deposits.

Eastern Siberia contains a complex array of mountain ranges with a predominant southwest-northeast trend. The most important systems are the Yablonovy, Stanovoi, and Sikhote-Alin ranges, in the south, and the Cherski, Verkhoyansk, and Kolyma mountains in the north.

Climates

Except for a small modified Mediterranean region in the southern Crimea and nearby parts of the Caucasus coast, the humid subtropical section of Transcaucasia, and the monsoon region of the Soviet Far East, the U.S.S.R. has a continental climate par excellence, with continentality increasing from west to east. This quality of the Soviet climate results from the weakness of moderating maritime influences; low precipitation, most of which occurs in summer; a great annual temperature range; long winters; and brief spring and autumn seasons.[2]

The Soviet Union is situated in latitudes where the Eurasian land mass reaches its greatest east-west extent, so most of the country is far from the moderating effects of the Atlantic and Pacific oceans. The efficiency of the humidity-laden westerly winds of Atlantic origin, which play such an important role in the climate of Europe north of the Alps, decreases noticeably eastward. Nevertheless, maritime air is responsible for most of the precipitation within European Russia. Being situated on the shores of the Arctic Ocean and lacking any major east-west mountain ranges except on its southern borders, the U.S.S.R. is exposed widely to invasions of arctic and polar air masses.

A key factor in determining the average climate conditions of the U.S.S.R. is the great continental high-pressure ridge, especially well

---

[2] See climatic graphs, Appendix II. See also the discussions in Chapter 1 on climatic types and regions, pp. 57, 59–60, 62–63.

defined in winter, which extends, as a continuation of the Azores High, along the line Kishinev-Kharkov-Saratov-Uralsk in southern European Russia. This high-pressure ridge can be traced eastward through Kazakhstan until it joins the Siberian High. This anticyclonic ridge governs the wind circulation of European Russia, particularly during the cold season. To the north, winds are predominantly westerlies and southwesterlies, relatively humid and warm, while to the south they are primarily dry, cold easterlies and northeasterlies. The effect is generally milder winters in the northwestern half of European Russia and drier and colder winters in the southeast.

During the summer, the Siberian High disappears and is replaced by a low-pressure system located over the heated interior of southwest Asia. At the same time, the permanent Azores High, shifting northward, has an even more pronounced effect on the climate of the Soviet Union by governing predominantly westerly and northwesterly winds over most of the country. Although the anticyclonic ridge extending through European Russia loses its eastern support in the Siberian High, it does not disappear in summer. It is maintained, though to a much weaker degree, by the intensified summer activity of the Azores High, from which high-pressure cells occasionally travel eastward into the continent. Being considerably weakened, the anticyclonic ridge loses its wind-dividing role in summer.

The year-round predominance of westerlies holds true for almost all of the Soviet Union except along the Arctic coast and on the Pacific. There we find a monsoonic circulation, with winds blowing outward from the frigid continent in winter, and inward from the cooler oceans in summer.

In terms of air masses, the Soviet Union is dominated by three types: arctic, polar continental, and tropical continental. Arctic air, formed over the Arctic Ocean and distinguished by low temperature, low humidity, and high visibility, affects the northern half of the Soviet Union. Arctic air plays an especially important role in eastern Siberia, where the westerly drift from the Atlantic is greatly weakened or entirely absent. From time to time arctic air breaks through to the south, even reaching the mountain systems along the southern frontiers of the country. These invasions of arctic air into the middle and lower latitudes are especially significant in spring and autumn, when they cause either late May frosts or early fall frosts. As the arctic air moves south it is transformed into polar air, with higher temperatures and lower relative humidity. Frequent invasions of this desiccated arctic air are one of the basic causes of droughts in the newly cultivated virgin lands of southern Siberia and northern Kazakhstan. In southern European Russia, anticyclones traveling eastward from the Azores High are a contributing factor in droughts.

Maritime polar air from the Atlantic Ocean hardly ever reaches the territory of the Soviet Union in its pure form, having lost much of its moisture en route over Europe and having acquired the characteristics of continental polar air. Invasions of this modified maritime polar air in winter produce prolonged thaws in the Great Russian Lowland. Most of the polar air of the Soviet Union is of continental origin, being generally dry, as well as hot in summer and cool in winter.

Continental tropical air affects the climate of the southern U.S.S.R. mainly during the warm season. This air is formed over central Asia, Kazakhstan, the north-Caucasus foreland, and the southern plain of European Russia through transformation of continental polar air and is distinguished by high temperatures, low humidity, and low visibility. Tropical air penetrates northward as far as the forest steppe zone and, in the peak of summer, even into the forest zone. In winter, however, even central Asia is dominated by polar air, though of a warmer type than is found elsewhere in the country.

Average January temperatures are below freezing in almost the entire Soviet Union (Fig. 9–3). The only exceptions are the south coast of the Crimea, Transcaucasia, and the extreme south of central Asia. The combined effect of the moderating Atlantic westerlies and the cooling of the Eurasian interior produces a roughly northwest-southeast alignment of January isotherms. The coldest area is northeastern Siberia with $-50°$ F. or less. In July, on the other hand, only some Soviet arctic islands have temperatures close to freezing (Fig. 9–4). The hottest summers occur in southern central Asia, where average July temperatures exceed $90°$ F. In contrast to the January isotherms, the July temperature lines run close to the parallels of latitude, with downturned ends in the east and west being caused by the relatively cooler air near the Atlantic and Pacific oceans.

Precipitation ranges from 20 inches or more in the western-Russian plain to about 5 inches in eastern Siberia (Fig. 9–5). Except for the Pacific summer monsoon in the Soviet Far East, virtually all the precipitation in the Soviet Union is of Atlantic origin. In addition to decreasing from west to east, precipitation also drops noticeably toward the north and the south from a relatively moist middle zone centered at $60°$ N. This precipitation pattern is particularly well expressed in the eastern part of the Great Russian Lowland and in western Siberia, where the tracks of cyclonic storms generally move

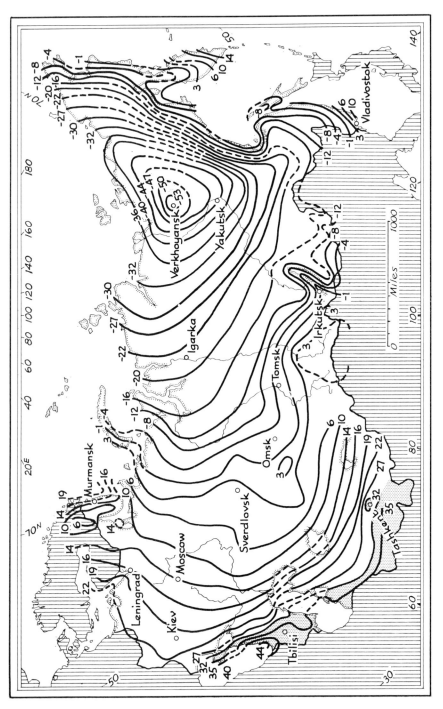

Fig. 9–3. Average January temperatures.

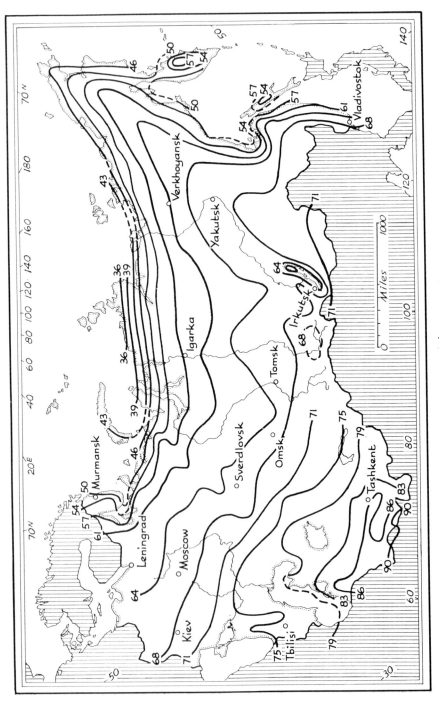

Fig. 9-4. Average July temperatures.

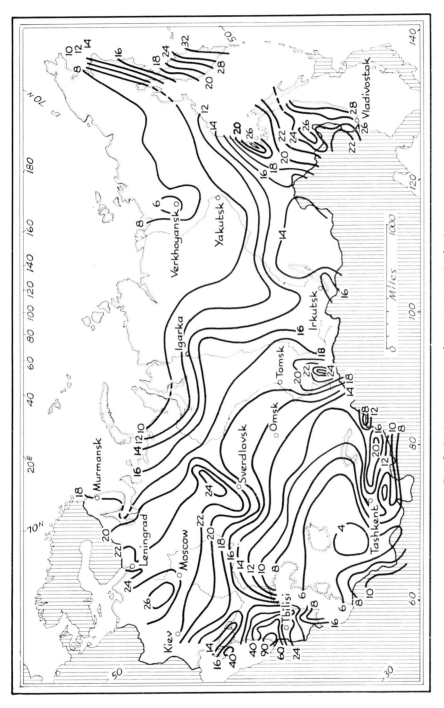

Fig. 9–5. Average annual precipitation (inches).

along the middle belt astride the 60th parallel. The lowest precipitation is recorded in the Turan Lowland of central Asia and southern Kazakhstan, where the annual total is less than 5 inches. Over almost the entire area of the U.S.S.R. there is a well-defined warm-season maximum of precipitation associated with more-active cyclonic activity during that part of the year. The maximum occurs in the second half of summer in the northern tundra and forest zone, in early summer in the steppe, and in spring in the arid regions. Winter precipitation maxima are typical of the Mediterranean-type climates on the shores of the Black Sea.

The duration of the snow cover ranges from 260 days in the northern tundra of Siberia to 40 days in the Ukrainian steppe and 20 days in central Asia. The thickness of the cover also varies widely, reaching a maximum of more than 30 inches northeast of the Great Russian Lowland, on the western slopes of the Urals, and northeast of the Siberian plain, where long frosts combine with relatively ample winter precipitation. In the northwestern part of the Great Russian Lowland, abundant snowfall is neutralized by frequent thaws, and in the colder southeast snowfall is relatively limited.

The special climatic province of the southern Crimea, sheltered against northern air masses by the Crimean Mountains, has its counterpart on the southern slopes of the Caucasus between Novorossisk and Tuapse. Yalta, a typical station in this Mediterranean-type climate, is the center of the Soviet "Riviera." It has hot, dry summers, with a July average of 76° F., and relatively mild, moist winters with a January temperature of 38° F. Of the annual precipitation of 24 inches, 11 inches fall in winter (November–February) and 6 inches in summer (May–August).

Another separate climatic province is the humid subtropics of western Transcaucasia, which combine a hot summer and mild winter with high precipitation and high relative humidity. Batumi, a typical station in this Soviet tea- and citrus-growing area, has an annual precipitation of 100 inches. The annual range of temperatures is one of the smallest in the Soviet Union, with averages of 75° F. in July and 40° F. in January. Occasional invasions of cold air from the northern steppes across the Caucasus can be disastrous for the local citrus crop, as in the winter 1949–50 when the temperature dropped to 8° F. The humid subtropical climate of the Lenkoran area on the Caspian, on the opposite side of the Transcaucasian isthmus, is a more continental variant of the coast climate, with hotter summers, cooler winters, and only half as much precipitation.

An important physical aspect of the Soviet Union is the widespread occurrence of permafrost. Permanently frozen subsoil characterizes 47 per cent of the entire territory, being found mainly in eastern Siberia. Its geographical distribution coincides with areas that have average annual temperatures below zero and cold, relatively snowless winters. Because of the great thickness of the permafrost layer, which exceeds 1,000 feet in many areas, and occurrences of well-preserved remains of the mammoth, a Pleistocene elephant, and beds of fossil ice, some geographers suggest that permafrost is a residual phenomenon of the Ice Age. Others maintain that permafrost is a currently active phenomenon, disturbing the soils and producing the waterlogged conditions in large parts of Siberia in summer. Because the top layers of soil thaw and become waterlogged under permafrost conditions, allowance must be made for the settling of buildings, roads, and railroad track in construction projects of the far north and eastern Siberia.

Drainage Patterns

In spite of the long and cold winter, which freezes rivers up to 8 or 9 months a year, and the accident of relief, which orients over half the drainage area of the Soviet Union toward the Arctic Ocean, the river systems of the country have long played a vital role in its history and economy. From earliest times, they have served as routes across the steppes as well as the forests. Low, short portages, later partly replaced by canals, have welded the systems together, particularly in European Russia. Russia's early territorial expansion, especially the drive through Siberia in the sixteenth and seventeenth centuries, was effected by means of these interconnecting water routes. The railroad era of the late nineteenth century brought the waterways into partial decline. Recent developments, such as the use of hydroelectric power, the construction of new canals, and the renovation of old ones, have given the waterways of the U.S.S.R. a renewed role in the economy.

The rivers of the Great Russian Lowland are characterized by an insignificant gradient and a consequently slow, meandering course (Fig. 9–6a). This is a direct result of the low elevation of the main morainic divide, which forms the Lithuanian-Belorussian and Valdai hills and reaches its highest point in the Valdai section at 1,053 feet. The streams rising on the northern slope of the divide, which trend generally west-southwest–east-northeast, flow to the Baltic Sea and the Barents Sea. Drainage south of the main divide is into the Black and Caspian seas. Most of the rivers of the Great Russian Lowland have a well-defined spring maximum as a result of melting snows; a low-water level in the summer, when high temperatures cause increased evaporation, canceling out the summer maximum of precipitation; and a secondary maximum in the fall, when reduced evaporation results in greater river flow. The duration of the ice cover in European

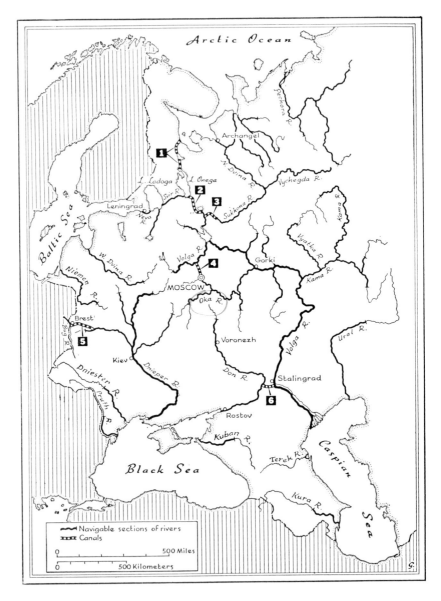

1. Baltic–White Sea Canal
2. Mariinsk Waterway
3. North Dvina Canal
4. Moscow Canal
5. Dnieper–Bug Canal
6. Volga–Don Canal

Fig. 9–6a. Chief waterways of the European U.S.S.R.

Russia ranges from 2 months in the extreme southwest (Dniester River) to 7 months in the northeast (Pechora River). In winter, the water level is maintained only by ground-water supply and is once again at a low stage. The principal rivers of European Russia are the Pechora and the Northern Dvina, which flow, respectively, to the Barents Sea and the White Sea; the short but important Neva River and the Western Dvina and Niemen, which drain into the Baltic Sea; the Dniester, Dnieper, Don, and Kuban rivers, which enter

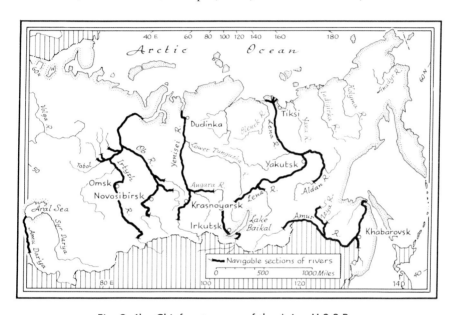

Fig. 9–6b. Chief waterways of the Asian U.S.S.R.

the Black Sea and the Sea of Azov; and the Volga, Ural, and Terek rivers, which flow to the Caspian Sea.

Unlike the rivers of the Great Russian Lowland with their strong spring maximum, the streams associated with the mountains on the southern margins of European Russia (Carpathians, Crimea, Caucasus) are fed by fairly regular rainfall all through the year and lack a well-defined seasonal high-water stage. The uniform precipitation and the higher gradient of these mountain streams have made them suitable sites for harnessing waterpower. Most of the hydroelectric stations of the Great Russian Lowland rely on rapids, where rivers cross resistant crystalline outcrops (as in the Kola Peninsula, Karelia, and the Ukraine), or simply on the large volume of a great stream with low gradient (as the Volga River).

The rivers of the West Siberian Plain, which are all part of the Ob-Irtysh drainage system, have a longer spring maximum than the streams of European Russia. The longer duration of the Siberian high-water stage is caused by three major factors: the delayed melting of snow under the vast forest cover of the Ob-Irtysh basin, the slow runoff from the virtually flat watersheds typical of the Siberian plain, and the abundance of lakes and marshes, which tend to store water for a period of time. On the Central Siberian Plateau, on the other hand, the spring maximum is high and brief, the summer and fall levels are subject to sudden rises after rains, and the winter stage is quite low. In this category are rivers of the Yenisei and Lena systems. In this case, the sharp break between winter and summer, which is characteristic of the climate of this region, the deeply dissected relief and steepness of slopes, and the presence of permafrost greatly reduce penetration of water into the ground, speed the runoff, and thus neutralize the effect of the dense forest cover in slowing the melting of snows. The rivers of the Turan Lowland are characterized by an extremely short, high spring stage fed almost exclusively by the rapid melting of snow on the bare steppes and semideserts, followed by a long, low stage during which many rivers dry up under arid, hot summer conditions.

Rivers that descend from high-mountain systems, especially in Soviet central Asia, have a high water stage through the entire warm season, when they are fed by the increased melting of mountain glaciers. Under these conditions, the maximum level often corresponds with the highest summer temperatures in July and August. These glacier-fed streams are extremely useful as the need for irrigation water in the arid piedmont plains is greatest during the height of the warm season. Examples of these rivers are the Ili, Chu, Syr Darya, and Amu Darya.

In the Soviet Far East, in the basin of the Amur River, the rainy summer monsoon produces a high summer stage in the rivers. The spring maximum is short-lived or entirely absent, in view of the thin snow cover left by the dry, cold winters of the monsoon region.

The Soviet Union is rich in lakes ranging in size from the huge Caspian Sea to small glacial lakes dammed by morainic hills. Most of the large lakes are of tectonic origin, including the Caspian Sea, the Aral Sea, and lakes Issyk Kul, Baikal, and Balkhash.

The Caspian Sea is a salt lake whose water level lies 94 feet below sea level, having dropped 8 feet between 1929 and 1956. The currently increasing deficit in the water balance of the Caspian Sea is attributed to reduced precipitation and increased evaporation due to greater solar activity, and to the growing economic utilization of the water of tributary rivers for irrigation, industry, and hydroelectric power generation. Several plans for replenishing the water level of the Caspian have been proposed, including some that called for the diversion of the rivers of Siberia and northern European Russia or for a direct link with the Black Sea. However, none of these plans has reached the stage of implementation. The salinity of the Caspian Sea (13 per thousand) is lower than that of the world oceans (35 per thousand) and reaches its lowest value in the northern shallow portion of the sea near the inflow of the fresh water of the Volga and Ural rivers. The deep middle and southern sections of the Caspian Sea are connected through a narrow inlet with the shallow gulf Kara-Bogaz-Gol on the east coast, which acts as a natural evaporating basin for the Caspian. This basin, of very high salinity, deposits salt beds that can be used as sources of chemical raw materials.

Other tectonic lakes, if located in lowlands, tend to be relatively shallow, e.g., the Aral Sea and Lake Balkhash. Those situated in mountain country are deep, with steep shore lines and uneven bottom relief. Lake Baikal, which fills a graben with a maximum depth of nearly 6,000 feet, is the deepest inland body of water in the world. Despite its distance from the oceans, Lake Baikal contains animals of oceanic habitat, such as true seals.

Soils and Vegetation

Largely as a result of the predominantly lowland topography and climate, particularly the east-west trend of summer isotherms, the territory of the Soviet Union falls into a pattern of latitudinal soil and vegetation zones. The zones are the tundra, the forest, the steppe, and the desert.

These biotic zones (Fig. 9–7) developed after the retreat of the last Pleistocene ice sheet. While the tundra remained along the margins of the retreating ice, the rest of the freed territory was invaded by deciduous trees from western Europe and by conifers from Mongolia, as well as by steppe and desert associations from the foothills of the Altai and the Caucasus.

Tundra Belt. The tundra belt lies along the coasts and on the islands of the Arctic Ocean; it is widest in northern Siberia on the Kara Sea and reaches as far south as 60° N., at the neck of the Kamchatka Peninsula. The tundra covers more than 10 per cent of the total area of the U.S.S.R. Its chief characteristic is the absence of forest vegetation. Low temperatures hinder the development of physical and chemical decay of the scanty plant cover, producing only a thin top layer of humus above the permanently frozen subsoil. The short growing season (2 to 2½ months, with no monthly mean above 50° F.), the low annual mean temperature (below 32° F.), the

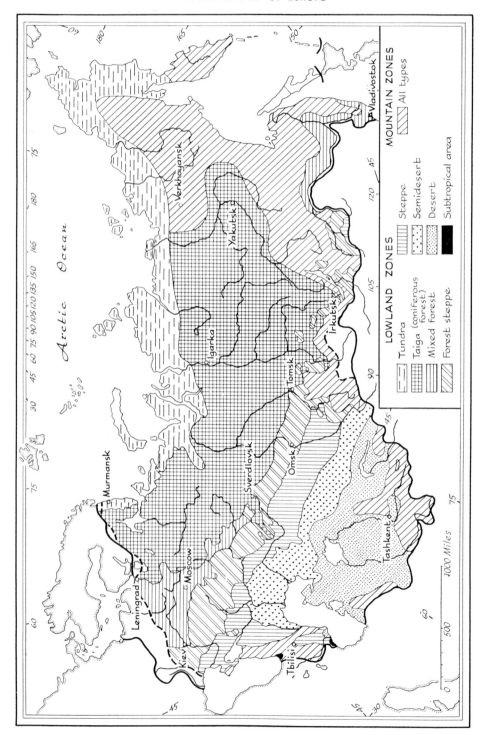

LOWLAND ZONES

Tundra

Taiga (coniferous forest)

Mixed Forest

Forest steppe

Steppe

Semidesert

Desert

Subtropical area

MOUNTAIN ZONES

All types

low precipitation (8 to 12 inches), and the thin, though widespread, snow cover make it difficult for plants to exist. Dwarf birches and willows hug the ground where warmer temperatures prevail. Lichens are found in dry sandy areas, while moss and sedge occur in damper low-lying locations. On south-facing slopes, small flowers come to life during the short summer. Along the southern margin of the tundra, the wooded tundra forms a transition to the forest zone. Typical animals are the reindeer, the lemming, the hare, and the arctic fox and the ermine, which are of special value for their furs. The white partridge and the arctic owl are the most characteristic birds. During the summer, masses of waterfowl nest on the cliffs along the coast.

Forest Zone. South of the tundra lies the vast forest zone which occupies more than one-half the U.S.S.R. The light-grey podsolized soils, typical for this zone, consist of a topsoil layer, 3 to 6 inches thick, of a white-to-grey color and contain about 2 per cent of humus. Below them is an ash-colored horizon, up to 12 inches thick, which contains a considerable amount of silica and has been leached of most of the plant food. The lowest layer, a brownish zone, colored by iron hydroxide, contains the material washed out from the upper horizon and lies on the unaltered parent material, which is usually clay or sand. The podzol-forming process is speeded by the abundance of moisture and the consequent leaching of the soil. These conditions are best met by a clay base and a correspondingly high water table, while on sandy parent material, where ground water lies deeper below the surface, the process is developed to a lesser extent.

The vast taiga or coniferous forest (see Chapter 1, p. 71), comprising about one-third of the forest lands of the world, extends through the northern part of the European U.S.S.R., across the Ural Mountains, and over most of Siberia. In the European U.S.S.R. pine and spruce are the most common species. Toward the Urals they merge with the Siberian larch, fir, and stone pine. The most widespread species in eastern Siberia is the larch, which penetrates farther north into the tundra than any other tree and provides an unbroken cover over the mountains. A subzone of mixed coniferous and deciduous forests extends in a wedge from the western frontier of the U.S.S.R. to the Ural Mountains. In Siberia its extent is negligible. In addition to coniferous types, the mixed forests include elm, oak, maple, and ash. The linden extends farthest north of all the deciduous types. A separate mixed-forest zone in the Amur-Ussuri region is characterized by a mixture of northern conifers (spruce, pine, larch, and fir) with Manchurian walnut, oak, and elm, as well as wild apricot and peach. Large sections of the forest zone are covered by marshes and peat bogs. This is especially true of western Siberia, where considerable precipitation and nearly level watersheds produce marshes extending over tens of thousands of square miles. Large mammals such as elk, reindeer, and other deer are common in the forest zone. The brown bear and the lynx are the principal carnivores, while rodents such as squirrels, rabbits, and beavers are also widespread. Typical birds are the woodpecker and the grouse.

Steppe Zone. The steppe zone extends in an uninterrupted belt from the western border of the U.S.S.R. to the Altai Mountains. It is characterized by a natural grass cover and limited tree growth and covers about 12 per cent of the total area of the U.S.S.R. The transition between forest and steppe is gradual and gives rise to the so-called wooded steppe. The characteristic soil is black earth (Russian *chernozem*), which is one of the most productive of the world and accounts for two-thirds of the arable land of the U.S.S.R. It is generally developed on loess or loess-like loam; its color varies from black to chocolate brown, and its thickness from 3 to 5 feet. The highly developed root system of the steppe grasses is favorable to the formation of humus, which, in the prevailing dry climate, is not leached from the topsoil and accumulates on the loess base. The high humus content of the black earth, generally ranging from 5 to 10 per cent and reaching even 20 per cent in some areas, renders this soil remarkably fertile. Along the edges of the black-earth belt, the humus content decreases gradually and the black earth changes into grey forest soil in the north and into chestnut and brown soils in the south. The principal causes for the limited tree growth are low precipitation, occasional droughts, and the deposition of mineral salts below the humus layer. In the wooded steppe the scattered tree clusters consist of oak in the European areas and birch in Siberia. Few large expanses of virgin steppe have been preserved. Most of the black earth has been put under cultivation. In the remnants, meadow grass occurs in the northern wooded portion of the steppe, while elsewhere fescue and feather grass are typical.

Desert Zone. To the south and the southeast the steppe is succeeded by the desert zone, where vegetation is scattered or wholly absent. The scanty growth results from low rainfall and excessive summer temperatures. This zone, which includes the northern and the eastern shores of the Caspian Sea and the Turan Lowland, extends to about 51° N., where it meets the mountains of central Asia. Covering about 18 per cent of the U.S.S.R., the desert belt is divided into the northern subzone of the semidesert and the southern subzone of the desert proper. The semidesert is a transition area, similar to the wooded tundra and the wooded steppe. The climate becomes progressively drier, rainfall averages 8 inches yearly, and bare areas appear amidst the patches of grass. The humus content of the brown soils decreases, while the salinity shows a definite increase. In many areas where the salt is washed to the surface, salt marshes (Russian, *solonets* and *solonchak*) are formed. Characteristic plant forms are wormwood and, in the saline soils, saltwort. In the desert proper, rainfall is sometimes less than 4 inches annually. Winters are short, though relatively cold, and summers become unbearably hot, the temperature reaching 120° F. in the shade. Stony and clayey desert flats are nearly devoid of vegetation. Sandy deserts have some wormwood and sage growth, and thickets of *saksaul* bushes are common. The grey desert soil contains considerable quantities of carbonate of lime and yields rich crops when properly irrigated.

Subtropical and Mountain Vegetation. Subtropical forest vegetation is confined to the western and eastern sections of Transcaucasia and to the slopes of the Crimea, the Caucasus, and some mountains of central Asia. In these areas forests have continued to exist since the Tertiary period. They are usually a mixture of deciduous and coniferous types, accompanied by a luxuriant undergrowth. Except in Transcaucasia, where conditions of warmth and moisture continue to approach the climate of the Tertiary period, plants have undergone a selective process resulting in the dominance of a few types adapted to the changed climatic conditions. These are generally trees such as oak, hornbeam, and beech, in the Crimea and the Caucasus, and maple, pistachio, almond, walnut, and apple, in the mountains of central Asia. The lateritic yellow and red soils in these regions have also remained from the Tertiary period. They contain no calcium, only a little silica, and a large proportion of clay and may be the remains of weathered volcanic rocks.

High mountain or alpine vegetation occurs below the snow line throughout the mountain regions of the U.S.S.R. The lower limits of the alpine-meadow belt vary from 1,000 feet in the northern Urals, where they tend to be replaced by tundra, to 8,000–9,000 feet in the Pamir-Alai mountain system in the south. The elevation of the snow line, which represents the upper limit of the alpine zone, varies with the precipitation and the location of the slopes. In the mountains of the Far East and eastern Siberia, alpine meadows are entirely absent. The forest cover extends virtually to the summits and leaves only the highest elevations covered with mountain tundra. Less than 0.5 per cent of the total area of the U.S.S.R. falls within the alpine-vegetation zone.

CULTURAL AND HISTORICAL BACKGROUND

Historical Geography

Early Russian history has been shaped to a very large extent by the nation's forests and rivers. It was in the forests that early Slav settlement took place, in relative seclusion from the nomadic or semi-nomadic Asiatic tribes that roamed the southern steppes. And it was the extensive river system of the Great Russian Lowland that was instrumental in the rise of the Muscovite state and ultimately brought about the unity of the Russian lands.

At the beginning of the Christian era, Slav tribes inhabited the west-central reaches of the vast Russian lowland, on both sides of the north-south river axis formed by the Volkhov, Lovat, and Dnieper rivers. This was the zone of the mixed forests, in which the primitive population engaged in rudimentary agriculture, beekeeping, and trapping.

Along the Black Sea coast, Greek colonies had been established at the river mouths and in the Crimea as early as the seventh and sixth centuries B.C. These settlements, some of which had probably been based on earlier Phoenician sites, were Tyras at the mouth of the Dniester, Olbia near the Dnieper estuary, and Tanais on the Don Delta. On the Crimean coast were the colonies of the Heraclean Chersonese (the modern Sevastopol), Theodosia (the modern Feodosiya), and Panticapaeum (the modern Kerch).

Between these two settled belts, the forests and the littoral, extended the steppe, dominated since earliest times by warlike horsemen from Asia. The earliest reference is to the Cimmerians, who are believed to have occupied the area between the Dniester and the Don from the tenth to the eighth century B.C. and are mentioned by Homer. They were followed by the Scythians who, according to Herodotus, occupied these open spaces until displaced in the third century B.C. by the Sarmatians. During the first millennium of the Christian era many peoples passed here in the great migration: the Goths, who split (about 200 A.D.) into west and east wings—the Visigoths and the Ostrogoths; the Huns under Attila, who swept through in the late fourth century; the Avars, on their way to the Balkans; the Bulgars, who also divided here (about 500 A.D.), one branch continuing to modern Bulgaria and the other moving into the middle reaches of the Volga River. Finally, following the passage of the Magyars (about 800 A.D.) a certain stability returned to the steppe with the formation of the Khazar domain in the Don-Volga area, with its headquarters at Itil, which was located on the site of modern Astrakhan.

In the meantime, intruders from Scandinavia had also appeared in the secluded forest, beginning in the early ninth century. These were the Varangians or Northmen who, in search of a trade route to Constantinople, had made their way south along the Volkhov-Dnieper river axis. They settled at trading sites that already had been occupied by the Slavs: Novgorod, Pskov, Smolensk, Chernigov, and Kiev. Moved by their common interest in trade and by their need for defense against the steppe peoples, the Slav tribes gradually consolidated under Varangian leadership into what became known as Rus (or Russia), a name of uncertain origin. Originally centered on Novgorod, this early Russian state moved its capital to Kiev in 882 and is therefore known today as Kievan Russia.

Kievan Russia, one of the leading states of early medieval Europe, was essentially a loose confederation of principalities, each centered on a trading town, united under the rule of a senior prince. The Varangian trade route along the Volkhov and Dnieper rivers was its life line, and as long as the perilous Dnieper rapids and the threat of the steppe peoples could be overcome Kiev prospered. Commerce was primarily with Constantinople. The Slavs sent furs, honey, and slaves, and imported silks, wine, fruit, and gold. It was also from Constantinople that Eastern Orthodox Christianity penetrated into Kievan Russia. The conversion of the eastern Slavs to the Orthodox religion was an important factor in their subsequent isolation from the mainstream of Roman Catholic European culture. Trade also moved along the Volga, in whose upper reaches stood the remote Slav towns of Rostov, Suzdal, and Murom. The Volga was the direct link with central Asia, serving en route the domains of the Volga Bulgars and of the Khazars.

The Kievan state was to be short-lived. In the tenth century, new warlike nomad tribes appeared in the steppe, ending the relatively stable rule of the Khazars and making the Dnieper route more and more difficult to use. Raids by these nomads began to threaten Kiev and led to its gradual decline in the twelfth century. A shift in the political center of gravity of the Slav domain followed. One new power nucleus formed in the southwestern principalities of Galicia and Volhynia, which were shortly to be absorbed by the expanding Polish and Lithuanian states.

The major movement from the Kievan area was, however, to the northeast, into the remote forests in the upper reaches of the Volga. A period of intensive colonization began in the watershed area between the upper Volga and Oka rivers. This mesopotamia, or *mezhdurechye* as the Russians know it, had already been sparsely settled by Slavic and Finnic tribes. The influx of refugees from the southern forest margins resulted in a great increase in population and the consequent political rise of the principality of Suzdal-Rostov, later known as Vladimir-Suzdal, or simply Vladimir, as the ruling power shifted from city to city.

The central watershed in the midst of the Great Russian Lowland was the nucleus of the future Russian state. It was relatively less exposed to attack from the nomad horsemen of the southern steppe, and was also protected by the river lines of the Volga and Oka and by the surrounding forest clearings. Many of the population turned to handicraft industries as a livelihood. Linen, leather, woolen cloth, wood, and metal goods were produced. Trade was with Kiev by the Dnieper route, with the Caspian area via the Volga, and with western Europe through the trade centers of Pskov, Novgorod, and the Baltic Sea coast. Goods were also traded with the Genoese ports in the Crimea, notably Kaffa, the modern Feodosiya.

Novgorod had built an empire of its own, following the decline of Kiev. Situated on the direct route between the Volga Valley and the Baltic Sea, Novgorod became one of the chief trading depots of the Hanseatic League. Merchants extended Novgorod's power throughout northern European Russia to the arctic shores and across the northern Urals, levying fur tribute and founding colonies.

During the thirteenth century, the nascent Russian domain was threatened by foreign incursion. Tatars under Mongol leadership established the Golden Horde on the southeastern margins, following devastating raids through Russian towns in 1237–40. In the northeast, the Novgorod empire, under the leadership of Alexander Nevski, defeated the Swedes (1240) and the Teutonic and Livonian Knights (1242), but the rising Lithuanian state annexed the southwestern-Russian principalities in the fourteenth century.

Ringed by the Tatars in the east and the Lithuanians in the west, the Russian state proceeded to consolidate its holdings (Fig. 9–8). Political leadership had passed to the small principality of Moscow, or Muscovy. Spurred by the victory (1380) of Dmitri Donskoi over the Tatars, the Muscovite state expanded through the fifteenth century, absorbing the other Russian principalities and, in 1478, absorbed Novgorod with its vast northern holdings. Under Ivan III, who reigned from 1462 to 1505, Muscovy ceased to pay tribute to the Golden Horde (which had disintegrated into the Tatar khanates of Kazan, Astrakhan, Sibir, and the Crimea) and began to call itself the "Russian" state. Ivan IV (the Terrible), who reigned from 1533 to 1584, was the first to assume the title of tsar (in 1547).

With the consolidation of the Russian state completed, Ivan embarked upon the initial conquests of non-Russian territory. The weak-

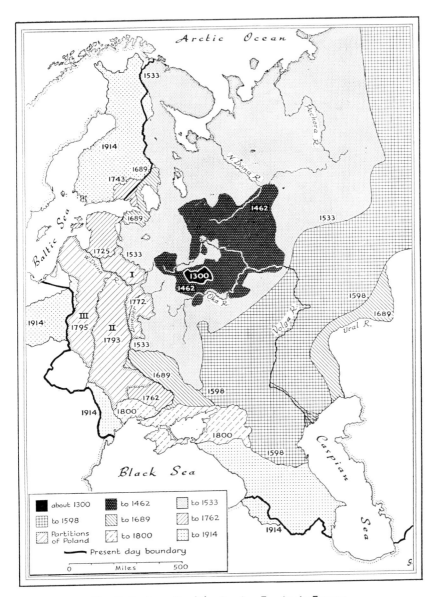

Fig. 9–8. Growth of the Russian Empire in Europe.

ened Tatar khanates of Kazan (1552) and Astrakhan (1556) fell and the Volga became for the first time an all-Russian river. Samara (the present Kuibyshev) in 1586, Tsaritsyn (the present Stalingrad) in 1589, and Saratov in 1590 were founded in rapid succession as the first Russian outposts on the lower Volga.

On the western slopes of the Urals, the Stroganovs, a landed family of salt and fur merchants, eyed with envy the reputed riches beyond the Urals. On their initiative, the Cossack Yermak and his band crossed the Urals in 1581 and subdued the Tatar khanate of Sibir, on the lower Irtysh River. Other Cossacks followed and penetrated rapidly eastward by land and river, building a string of small fortified posts (ostrogs) and levying fur tribute from the sparse indigenous population. In less than 60 years, the vast reaches of what came to be known as Siberia were traversed and the Pacific shores reached by 1640.

Following a period of chaos, the "Time of Troubles," marked by the appearance of pretenders (the false Dmitris) and by Swedish and Polish-Lithuanian intervention, Russia rallied again in 1613 under Michael, the first of the Romanovs. In a series of wars against Poland during the seventeenth century, the Russians even succeeded in annexing the left-bank Ukraine and Kiev.

However, the country was still a semioriental state. Medieval in culture and outlook, it was not regarded as a member of the European community of nations. In its economic development Russia was far behind the European West, and its distrust of foreign ways and innovations kept it ignorant and isolated. Whatever industry had been developed was concentrated in the Moscow region. There were a number of ironworks based on Tula ore, linen, leather, and other handicrafts. Salt, obtained at Solikamsk on the Kama River and Solvychegodsk on the Vychegda River (sol is the Russian word for "salt"), was an important article of trade. Grain and flax were the leading agricultural products; fur-bearing animals were hunted in the northeast and in Siberia, while grazing was the main activity in the southeastern steppe adjoining the lower Volga. Except for Astrakhan, on the closed-in Caspian Sea, the only maritime outlet was Archangel, through which English merchants had established trade links in the late sixteenth century.

It remained for Peter I (the Great), who reigned from 1689 to 1725, to revolutionize Russia politically, economically, and culturally. Peter, who was the first to assume the title of emperor, westernized Russia by a series of reforms that were imposed on the people by the most stringent measures. He created a Russian navy, modernized the army, founded the first major industries, and recast the administrative organization of the country. Moved by the desire to make

Russia a maritime European power, Peter directed his efforts at territorial expansion toward the Baltic Sea. In the Northern War, he
wrested Estonia and Livonia from Sweden and shifted the Russian
capital from Moscow to his newly founded St. Petersburg, a "window
on Europe." He also began the push toward the Black Sea and succeeded in briefly winning (1696–1711) the fortress of Azov from the
Crimean Tatars, but it remained for his successors to reach the Black
Sea on a broad front. Peter the Great also temporarily gained hold
(1723–32) of Baku from Persia.

It was particularly in the economic sphere that Peter's achievements were remarkable from the geographic point of view. He began
the industrialization of the Urals, establishing a number of copper and
iron smelters and arms factories to supply his troops. Yekaterinburg
(the present Sverdlovsk) in 1723, Yegoshikha (the present Perm) in
1722, and Nizhni Tagil in 1725 were founded at this time. A Russian
shipbuilding industry was developed, with yards at St. Petersburg
and Archangel, as well as at Voronezh (on the Don) and Kazan (on
the Volga), while the Vyshnevolotsk Canal, the first to link the upper
Volga with the Baltic Sea, was built from 1709 to 1722. The reorientation of Western European trade, which began to flow predominantly
through St. Petersburg, led to the gradual decline of Archangel in the
north.

Following Peter's death, a number of inferior rulers kept Russian
achievements static, but the country soon became a leading European
power under Catherine II (the Great). Under her "enlightened
despotism," Russia secured the lion's share in the successive parti-
tions of Poland (1772, 1793, 1795), reaching approximately the present Soviet boundary, with the exception of Galicia, Bessarabia, and
East Prussia. Catherine's wars against Turkey were equally successful,
and, by the treaties of Kutchuk-Kainardji (1774), the surrender of
the Crimean khanate (1783), and the treaty of Jassy (1791), Russia
conquered the southern steppe and reached the Black Sea between
the lower Kuban River and the Dniester. The Russian colonization
of Alaska also dates from Catherine's reign.

Under Catherine's successors, Russia became involved in the
French Revolutionary, later Napoleonic, wars which culminated in
Napoleon's disastrous march on Moscow. Among the territorial
acquisitions in the early nineteenth century were the greater part of
the Caucasus (1801–13), Finland (1809), Bessarabia (1812), and,
following the Congress of Vienna (1815), the Grand Duchy of Warsaw (Russian Poland). Except for minor changes, Russia's European
frontiers were to remain unaltered until World War I.

Economically, Russia underwent a great transformation in the
nineteenth century. The agricultural frontier was expanded with the

settlement of the rich chernozem zone of the southern steppe, which began to yield hard-grained export wheat and sugar beets. With the construction of ports on the nearby Black Sea (Odessa, Nikolayev, Mariupol, Novorossisk), an active export trade in grains began to develop during the nineteenth century. This flow was speeded after the building of railroads. The first long line linked St. Petersburg and Moscow in the 1850's, and a rail net developed in radial fashion around centrally located Moscow. In addition to those in the old industrial region of the Urals, manufacturing complexes developed at St. Petersburg (mainly metal fabricating, based on imported raw materials) and in the Moscow-Ivanovo belt, where textile mills were supplied first by foreign, later by central-Asian, cotton. The development of the use of metallurgical coke led to the decline of the once-flourishing charcoal-based metallurgy in the Urals and to the rapid rise of the coking coal of the Donets Basin and the nearby iron-mining district at Krivoi Rog in the Ukraine. In addition to the Black Sea grain ports, Russian foreign trade was handled through the Baltic ports of Libau (Libava), Riga, and Reval (Tallinn), as well as St. Petersburg. The development of the northern lumber industry for export also gave new impetus to the port of Archangel.

These were, in very broad terms, the conditions that existed on the eve of World War I, which Russia entered on the side of the Allies. The territorial adjustments that followed the war and the Russian Revolution of 1917 were outlined at the beginning of this chapter. The considerable economic transformation that followed the establishment of the Soviet regime is described below in the section on Russia's present economic life.

Evolution of the Political-administrative Structure

We have noted that Peter the Great was the first Russian ruler to introduce (in 1708) a modern administrative structure into the expanding Russian Empire, creating large internal divisions known as governments (*guberniya*). The first such divisions were the governments of Moscow, Ingermanland (renamed St. Petersburg in 1710), Archangel, Kiev, Smolensk, Kazan, Azov, and Siberia. The number of units increased steadily through the eighteenth and nineteenth centuries, in part through the incorporation of new territories, but essentially as the result of the subdivision of originally larger units. The governments were divided into *uyezds*, and these in turn into volosts. In 1917, on the eve of the Revolution, the Russian Empire consisted of 101 governments, 812 *uyezds*, and 16,760 volosts.

Although the tsarist system of local government cannot be described as static, the changes in the structure seldom reflected reorganization for economic-geographic purposes. The creation of new units or the abolition of existing divisions was usually predicated on purely administrative or military criteria. This is especially obvious in view of the later Soviet reorientation of the administrative system on strictly economic grounds. To cite a typical example of the lack of economic dynamism in the tsarist system, let us consider the case of Ivanovo-Voznesensk (now called simply Ivanovo). This city, a major cotton-milling center northeast of Moscow, had a population of 54,208 according to the census of 1897. Although it was the largest city within the government of Vladimir, it remained relegated administratively to the rank of a minor provincial town within Shuya *uyezd* of the Vladimir government. One of the first administrative measures of the Soviet regime was to create a new government with Ivanovo-Voznesensk as its center.

The profound changes that occurred in Russia following the Bolshevik Revolution of 1917 were closely reflected in the political-administrative structure. The process of territorial change took place along two parallel lines: (1) creation of national autonomous units for non-Russian ethnic groups, and (2) reform of the administrative-territorial units along economic lines.

In the late nineteenth century about 100 distinct ethnic groups inhabited the territory of the Russian Empire. According to the 1897 census, out of a total population of 130 million, only 43 per cent were reported as Great Russians. As a result of this circumstance, the young Soviet regime proclaimed in the very first days of the Revolution the "Declaration of Rights of the Peoples of Russia." This act guaranteed (1) the equality and sovereignty of the peoples of Russia; (2) their right to self-determination, even to the extent of secession and the formation of an independent state; (3) the abolition of all national and national-religious privileges and restrictions; and (4) the free development of national minorities and ethnic groups inhabiting Russian territory. Following this declaration and subsequent legislation, the formation of national autonomous units proceeded rapidly, though it now appears clear how far short of realization all these ideals have been, put into practice.

The Russian Soviet Federated Socialist Republic and the Ukrainian Soviet Socialist Republic were proclaimed in 1917. After an interval of civil war, the Belorussian S.S.R. and the German Volga and Bashkir autonomous republics were organized. In 1922, the Georgian, Armenian, and Azerbaidzhan republics were joined to form the Transcaucasian S.F.S.R. Finally, in December, 1922, the Russian, Transcaucasian, Ukrainian, and Belorussian republics were joined in the Union of Soviet Socialist Republics. By that time about twenty lesser autonomous units had also been created.

While the formation of autonomous national units was proceeding during the early years of the Soviet regime, plans were laid for the reform of administrative units within ethnically homogeneous areas. This reform was essentially a reorganization of the then-existing structure into integrated economic units. In 1922, at the start of the New Economic Policy of relaxed state control, there began the gradual transition from the former structure of government-*uyezd*-volost to a new territorial system of *oblast*-okrug-*raion*. By 1930, the last government had been abolished. Originally only a few large economic regions of the *oblast* (or *krai*) type were to be constituted in the U.S.S.R. Large size was soon found to be an obstacle to efficient administration, however, and during the late 1920's smaller first-order divisions were formed, and the intermediate unit—the administrative okrug—was dropped in 1930. The *raions* were subordinated directly to the first-order unit, whether *oblast, krai,* or republic.

The present administrative-territorial structure of the U.S.S.R. has thus evolved along two parallel, though closely integrated, patterns: the creation of national autonomous units and the reform of the administrative divisions for purposes of economic management.

It is the principle of national autonomy that governs the division of the U.S.S.R. into the so-called union republics, which are the country's primary units (Fig. 9–9). These republics are said to form a voluntary union of nations and to reserve the right of free secession, according to the Soviet constitutions of 1924 (Article 4) and 1936 (Article 17). Of course, in view of the purely nominal autonomy, no union republic has ever raised or is likely to raise the question of secession. From the original 6 union republics at the time of the formation of the U.S.S.R., their number increased to 11 at the time of the promulgation of the 1936 Constitution, and to 16 in 1940, with the formation of the Karelo-Finnish and Moldavian republics and the accession of the 3 Baltic states. The Karelo-Finnish republic was reincorporated into the Russian S.F.S.R. in 1956, and the present number of union republics is 15. All except the Russian S.F.S.R. are known as Soviet Socialist Republics, the form "Socialist Soviet Republic" being no longer in use. The Russian S.F.S.R., which is the leading and most important republic in every respect, is a federation of a number of major nationalities associated with the Russian nation and therefore continues to be known as a Soviet Federated Socialist Republic, or simply as the Russian Federation.

The principle of national autonomy determines also the formation of lesser units, below the rank of union republic. These are the autonomous republic, the autonomous *oblast*, the national okrug, and, of minor importance, the national *raion* and the national village council.

The autonomous republic is subordinated directly to the union republic in which it is located and is formed by relatively important ethnic groups. The Russian S.F.S.R., as would be expected, contains the greatest number of autonomous republics—15 out of a total of 19. The autonomous *oblast*, formed by less important minorities than those in the preceding category, is subordinated to a *krai* within the Russian S.F.S.R. and directly to the union republic in the case of the lesser constituent units of the U.S.S.R. Out of a total of 9 autonomous *oblasts* 6 are contained within the Russian S.F.S.R. The national okrug is the lowest category of the major types of the autonomous units. It occurs only in the Russian S.F.S.R. and forms the basis of organization primarily of small Siberian ethnic groups. Finally, the national *raions* and village councils are of only local importance and are generally formed on the basis of small isolated minorities.

The various categories of autonomous administrative units form what has been called the "nationalities ladder." Theoretically, in accordance with the Soviet nationalities policy, an ethnic group is assigned an autonomous category in accordance with its population and its degree of political and cultural advance. Then, depending on future growth and development, the group may ascend the rungs of the ladder to higher categories of autonomous units. Four autonomous republics—the Kazakh, Kirghiz, Karelian, and Moldavian units —have been raised to the status of full constituent republic during the three decades of Soviet rule. Of these, the Karelian unit was again demoted in 1956 because of its small size and population. In practice union republics have been created only on the periphery of the Russian S.F.S.R.—in order to enable them to secede if they so desired, according to the Soviet view—and only for groups having more than 1 million people (the Karelo-Finnish S.S.R., with about 600,000 inhabitants, was a notable exception, probably the result of temporary political expediency). As a result of this policy, important ethnic groups within the Russian Federation—such as the Tatar and Bashkir autonomous republics—have little chance of ever achieving the status of union republic, although they may number more than 3 million people.

The greatest number of promotions in autonomous categories has been from autonomous *oblast* to autonomous republic. About ten such transfers took place in the Russian S.F.S.R. during the 1930's. Only in one isolated case—the Kirghiz group—was an advance through two successive categories achieved: the Kirghiz Autonomous *Oblast*, formed in 1924, became an autonomous republic in 1926 and a full union republic in 1936. However, with the exception of the Karelian and Moldavian groups, no group has been promoted since the promul-

Fig. 9–9. Soviet union repub

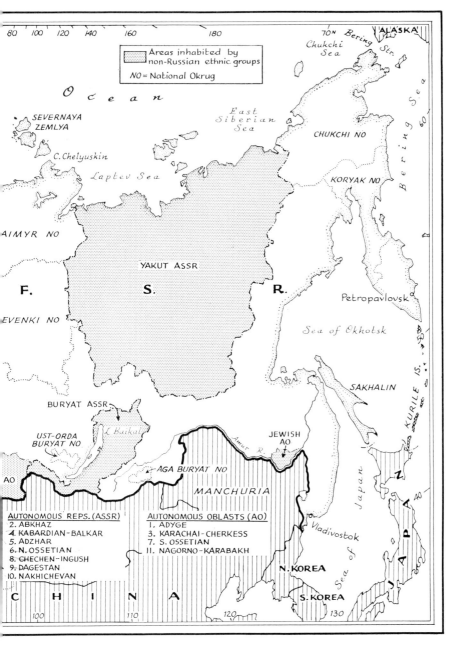

80   100   120   140   160   180   70N Bering Str.   ALASKA
                                                              Chukchi Sea

Areas inhabited by
non-Russian ethnic groups
NO = National Okrug

O   c   e   a   n

SEVERNAYA
ZEMLYA   East Siberian Sea   CHUKCHI NO

C. Chelyuskin

Laptev Sea   KORYAK NO

AIMYR NO

YAKUT ASSR

F.   S.   R.   Petropavlovsk

EVENKI NO   Sea of Okhotsk

                                                                              SAKHALIN

BURYAT ASSR

UST-ORDA   L. Baikal   JEWISH
BURYAT NO   AO

AO   AGA BURYAT NO
                                    MANCHURIA   Vladivostok

AUTONOMOUS REPS.(ASSR)   AUTONOMOUS OBLASTS (AO)
2. ABKHAZ   1. ADYGE
4. KABARDIAN-BALKAR   3. KARACHAI-CHERKESS
5. ADZHAR   7. S. OSSETIAN
6. N.OSSETIAN   11. NAGORNO-KARABAKH
8. CHECHEN-INGUSH   N. KOREA
9. DAGESTAN
10. NAKHICHEVAN   S. KOREA

C   H   I   N   A
  100   110   120   130

other autonomous areas.

gation of the 1936 Constitution, and it would appear that at least
the autonomous aspect of the Soviet administrative structure has
assumed a certain stability after the early dynamic period.

National autonomy in Soviet administration is reflected in the
organization of the highest legislative body of the U.S.S.R.—the
Supreme Soviet of the U.S.S.R. This body consists of two chambers,
the Soviet of Nationalities and the Soviet of the Union. According
to the Constitution, members of the Soviet of Nationalities are elected
on the basis of the major autonomous divisions—25 for a union republic, 11 for an autonomous republic, 5 for an autonomous *oblast*, and
one for each national okrug. In the Soviet of the Union, on the other
hand, the representation is based on the population at large, with one
deputy for every 300,000 inhabitants. In the union republics and the
autonomous republics, the Supreme Soviets are unicameral. There
election proceeds on a population basis only, with the size of an elec-
toral constituency varying from 150,000 (Russian S.F.S.R.) to 2,000
(Nakhichevan A.S.S.R.).

Parallel to the autonomous aspect of the Soviet administrative
system is the economic-administrative unit. Ethnically homogeneous
territories are divided into units delimited so as to represent a well-
integrated economic region. Ideally, such regions produce one or
more commodities for export to other parts of the U.S.S.R., while
remaining as self-sufficient as possible in basic consumer goods, construction materials, and similar items. The *oblast* is the largest type
of economic unit and is found in most of the union republics. The
Russian S.F.S.R. also contains the *krai*, which has essentially the same
status as an *oblast*. The existence of a *krai* is determined by the fact
that it contains an autonomous *oblast*.

Rural local government resides in the *raions*, villages, and other
local bodies, such as nomad headquarters. The *raion*, first formed in
1924, is intended to be a miniature *oblast*. The same economic principles guide its creation, though on a much reduced scale. All major
administrative units, such as *oblasts, krais*, autonomous divisions, and
the lesser union republics, are divided directly into *raions*. These vary
tremendously in area, from nearly 150,000 square miles in the sparsely
inhabited Siberian north to less than 100 square miles in the Ukrainian chernozem zone. The village Soviet, and other types of local council, are the smallest rural administrative units of the U.S.S.R. and
comprise one or more villages, hamlets, or other populated places.

Urban local government resides in the cities and towns, the latter
being called city-type settlements and workers' settlements in Soviet
terminology. Just as in the case of the territorial units, economic
considerations guide the creation of the urban centers. The establishment of an industry or the opening of a mine in a previously rural

agricultural community generally leads to the establishment of a workers' settlement or a city-type settlement. In the Russian S.F.S.R., the criterion for the creation of such a town is a minimum population of 400 adults, 65 per cent of which are industrial workers or employees. As the locality grows and its population and production increase, it may be converted into a city, which in turn may be subordinated successively to the *raion*, the *oblast*, or *krai*, or even to the republic. The progressive rise of urban centers is thus an excellent clue to industrial development.

POPULATION

In discussing the national-autonomous aspect of the Soviet administrative structure we have already indicated one of the key features of the population of the U.S.S.R., that is, its multinational aspect. Other characteristics that distinguish the demographic development of the U.S.S.R. from that of other European countries are: (1) the high rate of natural increase—17.4 per thousand in 1959; (2) the spectacular urbanization, which went hand in hand with the forced-draft industrialization starting in the early 1930's; and (3) the state-sponsored internal migration of large segments of the population.

With a population of 208.8 million, according to the complete results of the census of January, 1959, the Soviet Union ranks third in population among the world's nations, after China and India. Of the total, 162.2 million live in the European part of the U.S.S.R. (including the Urals) and 46.6 million in the Asian part.

From the long-range point of view, the most important characteristic of the population has been its rapid natural increase. From 1913 to the first Soviet census of 1926, the population of the country (within its 1926 limits) increased from 139.3 million to 147 million. This increase was achieved through the difficult periods of World War I, the Russian Revolution, and the subsequent civil war. During the following 13 peacetime years until the census of 1939, about 23 million were added to the Soviet population, which thus reached 170.6 million.

During 1939 and 1940, the U.S.S.R. annexed large sections of Eastern Europe, including the Baltic states of Estonia, Latvia, and Lithuania, eastern Poland, northern Bucovina, and Bessarabia, with an estimated population of about 21.5 million as of 1939. This brought the total population of the U.S.S.R. to 192.1 million as of 1939 (including 1.4 million in areas which were returned to Poland in 1945). On the basis of natural rate of increase (13.2 per thousand in 1940), it can be estimated that the population of the Soviet Union was about 197 million in early 1941 and, if there had been no war, would have risen to about 212 million by early 1946. Actually the population of the Soviet Union at the end of World War II is now estimated to have been 170–175 million. In other words, the wartime effects, including military losses, excess civilian deaths, a deficit in births, and forced or voluntary emigration, set back the Soviet population by about 40 million. The Soviet Union again reached its 1941 population level by about 1955. In recent years, the population has been growing at the rate of 3.5 million a year.

The Soviet Union's high rate of natural increase has been to some extent the result of the positive population policy inaugurated by the Soviet government in the middle 1930's. In those years a series of regulations prohibited abortion, except on medical grounds; provided for state aid to mothers and children; and discouraged the theretofore easy divorce. The effect of these regulations became evident in a rise of the birth rate during the late 1930's. This pro-natalist trend was further emphasized in 1944, when state aid to mothers and children was greatly increased, providing particularly allowances and awards to mothers of large families. Mothers of ten or more children began to receive the Order of Mother Heroine, and their names were published with those of other recipients of decorations and awards. In 1957 there were 3.4 million mothers with four children or more, entitling them to monthly state benefits. In recent years, the Soviet birth rate has been about 25 per thousand annually, while the death rate has been about 7.5 per thousand.

The effect of wartime losses and emigration has been especially pronounced in the western areas of the Soviet Union which were occupied by the Germans in World War II (see Table 27).[3] In 1959 two of the western republics that were completely overrun by the Germans—the Belorussian S.S.R. and the Lithuanian S.S.R.—still had not recovered their prewar population level. Others, such as Estonia, Latvia, and the Ukraine, just barely exceeded the 1939 level. The republics that escaped German occupation, by contrast, show larger population increases. This is especially true in the cases of Armenia, whose population was swelled by the return of about 200,000 Armenians from abroad during the postwar period; Uzbekistan, which received many evacuated industries and their labor force during the war; and Kazakhstan, the site of large-scale industrialization and agricultural development in the postwar period.

A noteworthy characteristic of the Soviet population is the predominance of females over males. The percentage of females was 52 in the censuses of 1926 and 1939, and rose to 55 in the census of 1959. This male-female ratio reflects the huge male-population losses in wars, especially in World War II, and applies particularly to the

[3] For statistical data, see Appendix III, Tables 20–31.

older-age groups. According to the preliminary report of the 1959 census, the percentages of males and females are more or less identical in age groups below 32 years, which have not been affected by wartime losses.

Rural and Urban Settlement. The share of the urban population has steadily increased under the Soviet Union's industrialization program. Before the start of this program in 1928, the urban percentage had been relatively stable at 18 per cent. Subsequently it rose to 33 per cent in the 1939 census, and to 48 per cent in the 1959 census. The geographical distribution of both the urban and rural population is extremely irregular, as one would expect from the diversity of climatic and other physical-geographic factors. These disparities in density, while particularly marked in the Asian part of the U.S.S.R., are evident also in Europe. A dense-population wedge with its base on the Leningrad-Odessa line penetrates eastward on the population map, coming to a point in the middle Urals and continuing in a narrow ribbon along the Trans-Siberian Railroad. The densely inhabited heartland of the European U.S.S.R. coincides roughly with the mixed deciduous-coniferous forest zone and the chernozem steppe. The density is generally more than 50 per square mile. Lower densities are found in the coniferous taiga of the European north and Siberia and in the semidesert and desert of southeast-European Russia and central Asia.

In these sparsely populated areas, rural settlements lie along communication lines, notably rivers and, more recently, railroads. The gravitation of population to newly built railroads was dramatized during World War II by the construction of the North Pechora Railroad leading to the coal-mining center of Vorkuta in the European north. This rail line, which cut diagonally across the relatively dense population bands along river routes, in turn became an artery attracting settlement. In these northern forests, rural population centers tend to be small agglomerations. By contrast, in the southern steppe, villages are traditionally large, frequently reaching a population of 15,000 or more in the so-called *stanitsas* of the Kuban Cossacks.

Collectivization of agriculture in the 1930's produced a revolution in the rural settlement pattern. In general, the trend was toward concentration of the population of scattered villages and hamlets in centrally located collective farm settlements characterized by a rectilinear main street, orchards and gardens, and administration and recreation buildings of the collective. Hamlets and isolated farmsteads were gradually abolished. The collective-farm mergers in 1950, which were designed to combine the already substantial farms into even larger units, also presaged the creation of even more centralized farm settlements or "rural cities" (*agrogorod*). The creation of such urbanized farm centers met opposition and was not pressed, although collective farms were merged as planned. The *agrogorod* plan remains the ultimate goal of Soviet rural-settlement planners and may yet be realized as part of their agricultural reforms.

While the future of Soviet rural-settlement patterns is still in doubt, the trend in urban settlement can be assessed more precisely. The rapid rise of urban population under the Soviet regime can be ascribed to several factors. Foremost has been the rural-urban migration needed to fill the growing manpower need of Soviet industry. A large part of the urban increase was of course contributed by the natural increase of the urban population itself. Moreover, changes in the definition of urban centers led to the reclassification of hundreds of villages as urban communities, in accordance with the Soviet concept of the urban center. Moreover, new urban centers developed from virtually nothing, as a result of the construction of new industrial plants or mines. One of the most spectacular examples of such Soviet urban growth is Karaganda, an insignificant village as late as 1930 that became a city of 166,000 in 1939 and expanded further to 398,000 in 1959. Equally impressive is the rise of the steel center of Magnitogorsk in the Urals, which was founded in 1931 and rose to a population of 146,000 in 1939 and 311,000 in 1959.

Industrial areas of the Soviet Union where the urban population accounts for 75 per cent or more of the total include the Moscow and Leningrad areas, the Urals, the Donets Basin, the Kuznetsk Basin, and the Karaganda area. Other urban centers are scattered throughout the country wherever mining or industrial activity has caused the formation of such agglomeration. In 1959, the Soviet Union had 148 cities with a population of 100,000 or more each, compared with 79 such cities in 1939. The 25 largest cities and their 1939 and 1959 populations are shown in Table 28.

One of the factors in the rapid urbanization of the U.S.S.R. is the facility with which the Soviet regime has regulated internal migration in accordance with state policies. The transfer of large numbers of people has been in part compulsory, but has also been effected through higher incentives such as increased pay and better housing, in areas that had a shortage of industrial labor. Such regions include the European north and vast sections of Siberia and the Far East, where climatic and other physical conditions are inhospitable and do not attract settlement.

Another type of compulsory migration occurred during World War II, when a number of ethnic groups accused of collaboration with the Germans and of fifth-column activity were forcibly removed from their historic homelands and exiled to Siberia and central Asia.

These groups were the Volga Germans, the Crimean Tatars, the Kalmyks, and, in the northern Caucasus, the Karachai, Balkar, Chechen, and Ingush peoples. Under the current liberalized regime, these peoples regained their civil rights in 1956–7, and most of them returned to their homelands.

Another mass migration was the settling by Russians from densely inhabited regions of central European Russia in the annexed areas of northern East Prussia and southern Sakhalin, from which the German and Japanese populations, respectively, had been expelled after the war.

Ethnic Groups. Although the number of ethnic groups in the Soviet Union is generally put at 100 to 150, the so-called multinational character of the population has to be considered in proper perspective. In this connection two facts are of the greatest importance. These are the dominant position of the Russian people and the relatively small number of national groups with, say, more than 20,000 persons.

No exact figure on the number of nationalities is meaningful. The 1926 census recognized 188 individual groups, but in a few cases numbers were either not reported or only a few individuals were reported for a specific ethnic group. In the incomplete returns of the 1939 census, in which a number of important Siberian peoples were not reported, the total number of nationalities with more than 20,000 persons was 49. When the major missing Siberian groups (Yakuts, Buryats, Khanty or Ostyaks, and Evenki or Tungus) and the Tuvinians, who were incorporated into the U.S.S.R. in 1944, are taken into account, the number of ethnic groups with more than 20,000 persons was 54. The 1959 census listed 108 ethnic groups including 68 with more than 20,000 persons each.

The most meaningful classification of the Soviet Union's ethnic groups is based on their languages. The major language families in the Soviet Union are tabulated on page 684 with the number of persons in each group according to the 1959 census.

The Russians constitute more than half the total population of the U.S.S.R., with the ratio somewhat higher (about 60 per cent) in Asia and somewhat lower in Europe. As would be expected, the percentage of Russians is greatest (83 per cent in 1959) within the territory of the Russian S.F.S.R., while in the other union republics and in some of the lesser autonomous units they constitute generally less than 25 per cent of the population. With the Ukrainians and the Belorussians, who form 18 per cent and 4.5 per cent, respectively, of the Soviet population, the Slavic element stands out clearly as the dominant group with nearly 75 per cent of the total number of people

Languages of the U.S.S.R.

Language Family	Language Subgroup	Major Languages	Number of Persons in Thousands
Indo-European	Slavic	Russian	114,114
		Ukrainian	37,253
		Belorussian	7,913
	Baltic	Latvian	1,400
		Lithuanian	2,326
	Iranian	Tadzhik	1,397
		Ossetian	410
		Tat	11
		Kurdish	59
	Armenian	Armenian	2,787
	Romance	Moldavian (Rumanian)	2,214
Turkic		Tatar	4,968
		Bashkir	989
		Azerbaidzhani	2,940
		Uzbek	6,015
		Kazakh	3,622
		Kirghiz	969
		Turkmen	1,002
		Yakut	237
Finnic	Eastern branch	Komi	431
		Mordvinian	1,285
		Chuvash	1,470
		Mari	504
		Udmurt	625
		Nentsy (Samoyedes)	23
	Western branch	Estonian	989
		Karelian (Finnish)	260
		Lappish	2
Caucasian	Southern	Georgian	2,692
	Northern	Abkhaz	65
		Cherkess (Circassian)	30
		Kabardian	204
		Chechen-Ingush	525
		Dagestan languages	947
Mongolian		Buryat	253
		Kalmyk	106
Manchurian Paleoasiatic		Evenki (Tungus)	25
		Minor Siberian languages	

within the Soviet Union. Lesser Slavic peoples are the Poles, who are scattered among the Belorussians and the Ukrainians, and the Bulgarians, who live largely in southern Bessarabia.

Next in importance are the Turkic and Finnic language families. The more numerous Turkic peoples (about 8 per cent of the total) live largely in Asia, and the Finnic peoples (less than 3 per cent) primarily in Europe. The Finnic peoples occupy the tundra and forest, while the Turkic groups extend across steppe and desert.

The Tatars, the most important European branch of the Turkic family, are concentrated in the Volga region, where they have an autonomous republic, but are also widely dispersed through the rest of the country. The related Crimean Tatars, estimated at 200,000 on the eve of World War II, were ousted from the Crimea in 1944 because of collaboration with the Germans in World War II and were resettled in Soviet central Asia. There they regained their civil rights in 1956. Adjoining the Volga Tatars are the Bashkirs, a Turkic steppe people that settled on the western slopes of the Urals in the tenth century. Like the Volga Tatars, who are descended from the fifteenth-century Kazan khanate, the Bashkirs are organized politically in an autonomous republic. The third major Turkic people in the European U.S.S.R. are the Azerbaidzhani Turks in Transcaucasia on the Caspian Sea. Although their language is closely related to that of the Osmanli Turks, the Azerbaidzhanis have acquired their culture and the Shiite Moslem religion from the Persians who dominated the present Soviet Azerbaidzhan until the early nineteenth century. The leading Turkic groups in the Asian U.S.S.R. are the Uzbeks, Kazakhs, Kirghiz, and Turkmen in central Asia, and the Yakuts in Siberia.

Of the Finnic ethnic family, the Volga-Ural division (or the Eastern Finnic branch) is the most numerous. These peoples live on the western slopes of the Urals and along the middle Volga River, in close contact with the Tatars and the Bashkirs. The leading representatives in numbers are concentrated along the Volga. They are the Mordvinians (or Mordvians) and the Chuvash (the latter with considerable Turkic linguistic influence) on the right bank, and the Mari (formerly called Cheremiss) and the Udmurt (formerly called Votyak) on the left bank. Finnic primarily from the linguistic point of view, these peoples have acquired a predominantly Russian culture through centuries of contact with the Slavs, with some survivals from their Finnic ancestors and the ancient Khazars and Volga Bulgars. To the north of this Finnic concentration, along the northern Urals, are the more primitive Komi (formerly Zyryan) and the closely related Komi-Permyaks (or Permian Komi). Along the shore of the Arctic Ocean, in the far north of the European U.S.S.R., are the

Nentsy (formerly known as Samoyedes), who are distantly related to the Finnic family. With the exception of the Nentsy and the Komi-Permyaks, who are organized into national okrugs (the only such autonomous units in the European U.S.S.R.), the Eastern Finns form autonomous republics within the Soviet administrative scheme.

The Western Finns along the Baltic region are considerably fewer within the confines of the U.S.S.R. The main group are the Estonians, who came entirely under Soviet control in 1940 and constitute the northernmost of the three Baltic republics. They are traditionally Lutheran Protestants and have long been under the influence of Germanic culture. The next Finnic group, the Karelians, number only about one-fourth of the 1 million Estonians. They are very closely related to the true Finns, whose language they speak, but are of Russian culture and traditionally Russian Orthodox. In conjunction with the true Finns, who are few in number (93,000 in 1959) in the U.S.S.R., the Karelians constituted from 1940 to 1956 the Karelo-Finnish S.S.R. Since then they have returned to their original status of autonomous republic. In the Kola Peninsula live the Soviet Lapps (known as *Saamy* in the Soviet terminology), constituted in a national *raion* of Murmansk *oblast* of the Russian S.F.S.R. Finally, the Western Finns include a number of small splinter groups in the vicinity of Lake Ladoga and Lake Onega. These are the Veps, the Vote, and the Izhora (Inger), numbering no more than 50,000 in 1959.

The two southern Baltic states, Latvia and Lithuania, are inhabited by peoples of the Baltic language subgroup. The Lutheran Latvians (or Letts) were influenced by a Germanic cultural veneer and are associated in their republic with the closely related Roman Catholic Latgalians of Polish culture. Polish cultural influence, typical also for the Lithuanians, dates from the long period of Polish rule in these regions after the sixteenth century.

Farther south along the relatively narrow European isthmus between the Baltic Sea and the Black Sea we find at its southern end another important non-Slavic minority, the Moldavians (Romance subgroup). Russia's century-long control over the Moldavians in Bessarabia after 1812 added some Russian strains to their essentially Latin and Rumanian background. As a result the Moldavians use the Rumanian language written in the Cyrillic script. After World War I only about 250,000 Moldavians remained within the U.S.S.R. and constituted the Moldavian Autonomous S.S.R. within the Ukraine, on the left bank of the Dniester River, then the Soviet-Rumanian frontier. Following the acquisition of Bessarabia in 1940, the number of Moldavians under Soviet control rose to more than 2 million and their political organization was raised to that of a union republic.

By far the greatest ethnic diversity, exceeding even that of the middle-Volga region, exists in the Caucasus. Russians having settled predominantly in the steppes of the northern Caucasus, the largest minority groups are found on the southern slopes, in Transcaucasia. Here, in addition to the Azerbaidzhani Turks, are the Armenian and southern-Caucasian (Georgian) subgroups, each constituted as a union republic. The Armenians form a distinct linguistic group of the Indo-European family. Settled traditionally around Mount Ararat, within the territories of Russia, Turkey, and Persia (Iran), the Armenians were greatly decimated between 1894 and 1915 by systematic Turkish policies of extermination. As a result of these trials, the bulk of the population remained in Russian Armenia, a considerable minority in northwestern Iran, and the rest scattered through the lands of the Middle East and other parts of the world. Of the present estimated Armenian world population of 3.5 million, two-thirds live in the U.S.S.R. However, only 40 per cent of the Soviet Armenians live in the Armenian S.S.R. proper, with the remainder scattered through the rest of the Soviet Union. After World War II, the Soviet government invited Armenian *emigrés* to return to Soviet Armenia. About 200,000 *emigré* Armenians returned, chiefly from the Middle East. In addition to their own union republic, the Armenians also constitute the majority population (89 per cent in 1926) of an exclave—the Nagorno-Karabakh Autonomous *Oblast*—within the Azerbaidzhan S.S.R.

The Georgians in the U.S.S.R. numbered 2,692,000 persons in 1959. They are concentrated in their relatively homogeneous republic and constitute the leading member of the Caucasian language family. Within the Georgian S.S.R., the Mingrelian, Svanetian, and Adzhar groups are associated with Georgian in the south-Caucasian languages. The Adzhars, who are Georgians of Moslem religion and influenced by Turkish culture, form a separate autonomous republic within Georgia. Another Georgian dependent unit— the Abkhaz Autonomous S.S.R.—is the chief representative of the north-Caucasian languages on the southern slopes of the mountains. The other members, considerably dissected by areas of Russian settlement, are the Cherkess (Circassian) people, also known by their own native appellation of Adighe; the related Kabardians (or Kabardinians); and the diverse mountain groups of Dagestan, including the Lesghians, Avars, Darghins, Laks, and Andi. The Chechen and Ingush peoples, who temporarily lost their ethnic identity after World War II, also are members of the north-Caucasian subgroup.

Several peoples of the Caucasus are members of the Iranian sub-group of the Indo-European language family. These are primarily the Ossetians, settled in the central part of the Caucasus, where they constitute the North Ossetian Autonomous S.S.R. of the Russian S.F.S.R. and the South Ossetian Autonomous *Oblast* of the Georgian S.S.R. The Ossetians are believed to be descendants of the ancient Alans, a steppe people of the northern Caucasus, last reported at the time of the Mongol-Tatar raids of the thirteenth century. Smaller Iranian splinter groups are the Talysh, in the Talysh (or Lenkoran) lowland adjoining the Caspian Sea; the Tats, at the eastern foot of the Caucasus, in Azerbaidzhan; and the Kurds, on the slopes of Mount Ararat, in Armenia.

Alone among the leading ethnic groups of the Soviet Union, the Jews have no political autonomous division commensurate with their numbers. Reported at 3,020,141 in 1939 (then the seventh-largest group), the Jews are estimated to have reached a total of 5,000,000 on the eve of World War II, as a result of the annexation by the U.S.S.R. of eastern-Polish areas with large Jewish elements. However, following the systematic massacre of the Jews by the Germans during the war, their postwar number dropped to 2,268,000 by 1959. This physical extermination of a great section of Soviet Jews was followed in the years after the war by a cultural "extermination" within the Soviet Union. Though still recognized by the Soviet government as an ethnic group, the Jews were deprived in 1948 of their schools, newspapers, books, and other institutions ordinarily associated with cultural autonomy within the U.S.S.R.

Such cultural autonomy has been retained to some extent in the Jewish Autonomous *Oblast* (commonly known as Birobidzhan), on the Amur River, in the Soviet Far East. This administrative unit was set up in 1930 to encourage Jewish settlement in the area. However no mass migration developed from the traditionally Jewish settlement areas of Belorussia and the western Ukraine, or from the large urban Jewish population scattered through the cities of the U.S.S.R. Today no more than 50,000 to 75,000 Jews are believed settled in the autonomous region. They are the only Soviet Jews who are permitted the official use of the Yiddish language in newspapers, radio, and other cultural institutions.

Religions. Before the Bolshevik Revolution of 1917, the Russian Orthodox Church was the state Church of the Russian Empire, with the tsar as its head. Other religious denominations were tolerated. An abrupt change took place after the revolution, with the separation of state and Church and the expropriation of all Church property.

Atheism, formerly a crime against the state, was welcomed by the new Soviet regime and supported by active antireligious propaganda.

Public places of worship had been a characteristic feature of the urban and rural settlements of Russia. This applied not only to the typical bulbous church towers of the Russian Orthodox Church but also both to the mosques and minarets of central Asia and to the Lamaist monasteries of Buryat-Mongolia. After the revolution, this feature of the landscape remained in part, though many churches were demolished, and a great number of these places of worship became public buildings, clubs, theaters, libraries, or museums. Moreover, the house of worship has not been considered a necessary element in the planning of collective farm settlements or new industrial and mining towns and has remained in older centers only as a reminder of the past.

The intense antireligious propaganda that swept the Soviet scene during the 1930's was temporarily abandoned during World War II in order to remove any obstacle to the marshaling of all forces against the German invader. The Russian Orthodox Church resumed some of its former authority, but merely as a voice of the Soviet government, and is credited with a considerable share in the mobilization of the Soviet people during the war.

After the war antireligious propaganda was resumed, but the major religious denominations of the U.S.S.R. have been maintained in the postwar period.

Thus, while religion has definitely been relegated to a very minor position, the Church has not been abolished, and it may prove useful to survey briefly the religious affiliations of the major ethnic groups of the U.S.S.R.

By far the dominant Church is the Russian Orthodox Church, which embraces not only all the Slavs but also the Finnic peoples of the European U.S.S.R. that have been long exposed to Russian culture. Among the Belorussians and Ukrainians there is a considerable Roman Catholic minority, particularly among the people of western Belorussia and the western Ukraine, both annexed from Poland in 1939. Also among the Ukrainians, notably in Transcarpathia, there are adherents to the Uniate rite of the Roman Catholic Church. Roman Catholicism is the predominant denomination of the Lithuanians and the Latgalians, both peoples of Polish cultural background. Lutheran Protestantism is prevalent among the Latvians and Estonians, as well as among the few Finns in the U.S.S.R., whose religion is their chief distinction from their Russian Orthodox Karelian colinguists.

The Armenians and the Georgians each have their own independent Church. The Armenian, also known as Gregorian, is an independent Christian Church with Western and Eastern elements in its rites, while the Georgian is one of the oldest Orthodox Churches of Byzantine heritage. Islam is important in European U.S.S.R. among the Azerbaidzhani Turks, the Tatars, and the Bashkirs, while additional adherents may be found among the Turkic peoples of central Asia. Mention should be made, finally, of the Buryats of southern Siberia, who are the only representatives of Lamaist Buddhism in the U.S.S.R.

PRESENT ECONOMIC LIFE

Before the Bolshevik Revolution, the Russian Empire had a primarily agrarian economy. Today the U.S.S.R. is an industrial power second only to the United States. While it would be profitless to discuss the question—one that is sometimes raised—of whether Russia would not have made the same progress under the old regime, it is pertinent to recall some of the major developments of Soviet economic history since the revolution.

Soviet Economic History

In the wake of the overthrow of tsarist power came a period (1917–21) of extremist and ruthless measures used by the young Soviet regime in the chaos of civil war and foreign intervention. State control spread rapidly over all phases of the economy; all land and mineral resources were nationalized; industries, means of transportation, and all buildings were declared state property; private banks were merged into the state bank; and a government monopoly over foreign trade was instituted. At the same time, arbitrary food requisitions, mounting inflation, and a confused economic administration created dissatisfaction among the peasants, which, coupled with a decline in industrial discipline among the workers, endangered the very existence of the struggling new state.

In order to appease the peasantry and revive the economy, Lenin initiated the New Economic Policy (NEP), which was in effect a temporary concession to capitalism. Domestic commerce and small- and medium-scale industry were partly returned to private hands, with the government retaining control over all key industries and means of transportation. Under this mixed economy the U.S.S.R. gradually raised its production and by 1928 had regained or exceeded the output of 1913. At the same time the state had expanded its share in the economy and gradually reduced the role of private enterprise through a variety of restrictive measures such as high profit taxes and discrimination in the supply of raw materials and in the use of transportation facilities.

In 1928 the Soviet regime initiated the first of its five-year plans aimed at a sharp increase in industrial output under strict government control and planning. Shortly thereafter began the process of agricultural collectivization. This forcible consolidation of individual farms into cooperatives reached its climax in the early 1930's, in one of the most tempestuous periods of Soviet history, marked by the deportation of rich peasants (kulaks), the slaughter of cattle, and a drop in agricultural production, with a resulting famine in 1931–2.

Nevertheless, under planned conditions, industrial output soared during the first (1928–32) and second (1933–7) five-year plans. Emphasis was placed on heavy industries at the cost of consumer goods. A gradual eastward shift of the industrial center of gravity of the U.S.S.R. resulted in a new geographical distribution of industry. At the same time, agricultural production began to increase, after the upheaval of collectivization, through the application of modern farming methods, mechanization, and similar measures facilitated by the creation of large collective farms.

The third five-year plan (1938–42) was interrupted by the German invasion in June, 1941. Although the principal economic regions of the U.S.S.R. fell to the invader in 1941 and 1942, the results of the industrial expansion of the 1930's bore fruit. Industrial production of the eastern part of the U.S.S.R., dating chiefly from the first two five-year plans, and the removal of some 1,300 plants from the path of the German forces played a key role in enabling the Russians to stem the German advance. This and the subsequent expulsion of the enemy from the U.S.S.R. were aided in no small measure by vital shipments of supplies by the Allies.

The early postwar period was dominated by the fourth five-year plan (1946–50), designed to rebuild the war-damaged economy and to foster the further development of eastern industries untouched by the war. The fifth five-year plan (1951–5) was marked by further increases of production. A sixth five-year plan (1956–60), adopted by the Twentieth Communist Party Congress, in February, 1956, was scrapped in September, 1957, in favor of longer-range planning. A fifteen-year program announced in November, 1957, sets as its aim the surpassing of the United States by 1972 not only in over-all production but in per-capita output as well. A new seven-year plan (1959–65) was adopted in January, 1959, by the Twenty-first Communist Party Congress, as the first part of the fifteen-year program.

Agriculture

The present organization of Soviet agriculture is the result of revolution following a long process of evolution. Having been dominated by conditions of serfdom and feudalism until the partial emancipation of 1861, later modified by the reforms of 1906, agriculture in Russia before the revolution was mainly in the hands of more than 13 million peasant households owning 500 million acres and of 30,000 large-estate owners who aggregated 380 million acres. The estates were either in pasture land or tilled by tenant farmers. According to Soviet data, the peasant holdings included 1 million so-called rich farms that averaged 126 acres compared with the average poor farm of 19 acres.

After expropriation of estates in the 1917 revolution and redistribution of land among the peasants, there emerged 25 million small peasant holdings. About 35 per cent of these were classified as poor, 60 per cent as medium wealthy, and 4 to 5 percent as rich. The so-called rich peasants (kulaks) employed outside labor. On the eve of collectivization in 1928, only 1.7 per cent of the farms were of the collective type. As a result of the mergers in the early 1930's, the 25 million small farms of the 1920's were welded into fewer than 250,000 collectives.

The Soviet agricultural revolution was repeated on a smaller scale in 1939–40 in areas annexed by the U.S.S.R. The redistribution of largely expropriated estates was begun soon after the assumption of Soviet control, was partly canceled under German occupation in World War II, and was resumed by the Russians after the war. Peasant farms in the annexed areas, which included the Baltic states, remained in private ownership until 1949 before being collectivized.

The completion of the collectivization process throughout the Soviet Union was followed in 1950 by a consolidation of collective farms into larger units. These mergers took place primarily in areas where the average acreage per collective farm was relatively small: in the central, western, and northern sections of the European U.S.S.R.; in the Caucasus; and in the irrigated areas of central Asia. As a result of the consolidation, the number of collective farms declined from more than 200,000 before 1950 to about 54,600 in 1959. While the collective farm (kolkhoz) dominates the agricultural picture of the Soviet Union and produces the great bulk of agricultural output, the actual work of raising crops and livestock is also done on two other types of farms, the state farm (sovkhoz) and the individual farm or garden.

State farms occupy a special position in the agricultural organization of the country. Unlike collective farmers, who share the net proceeds of their farm in proportion to their labor input, peasants on state farms are simply employees of the state. Payment is on a straight piecework basis, with the farmers obtaining the highest crop yield per acre or the most production from their livestock at the top of the income scale. From their beginnings in the early 1920's, Soviet state farms have served as model farms. They are usually located in areas presenting difficult agricultural conditions because of either climate or soils. One of the principal tasks of state farms is experimentation with new crops and livestock breeds. The average cultivated area of a state farm is 15,000 acres, which is about three times that of the average collective farm. The number of state farms has been increasing in recent years as new land has been brought under cultivation, and was about 6,500 in 1959. State farms tend to specialize in wheat, cotton, sugar beets, or other crops, as well as in the raising of livestock for milk, meat, or wool.

Individually owned peasant farms are a negligible factor in the Soviet agricultural economy. Their number had been reduced to 1.3 million by 1938, as a result of collectivization, and by 1940 only 300,000 were left. But the Soviet annexations in Eastern Europe added more than 3 million privately owned farms to the Soviet economy, and these remained until final collectivization in 1949–50. At the present time there are only 100,000 individually owned farms in the Soviet Union, nearly all of them in the annexed areas. In addition to these farms, private farming of a sort persists on the collective farms, where each household is permitted to keep its own private plot, and in the suburbs of cities and towns, where some workers and office employees keep vegetable gardens. These various private farm plots and gardens account for nearly one-half the total Soviet output of vegetables and potatoes.

In addition to collective and state farms, the system of organization of farming in the U.S.S.R. formerly also made provision for the existence of an additional unit—the machine-tractor station (MTS). These stations, which were in effect state agencies, owned most of the agricultural machinery used by the collective farms and supplied technical aid through agronomists attached to the stations. The services rendered to the collective farms were paid for in kind, usually a share of the crop. In 1957 there were 8,000 machine-tractor stations, serving, on the average, ten collective farms each. Under a reform carried out in the spring of 1958, the machine-tractor stations sold their agricultural equipment to the collective farms for the farms' permanent use and the stations were converted into repair and technical stations (RTS), charged with repair and maintenance of the now farm-owned machinery.

Although emphasis is usually placed on the industrial aspect of the Soviet economy, it may be well to remember that agriculture is still a key sector of enterprise. About 40 per cent of the Soviet population derives its livelihood from agricultural pursuits.

Of the Soviet Union's total area of 8.6 million square miles, 30 per cent is classified as land suitable for agricultural use. This sector includes 19 per cent pastures and hay meadows and 11 per cent arable land. The rest of the Soviet Union's area consists either of forest and brushland (38 per cent) or of other agriculturally unsuitable land such as swampy, saline, sandy, or mountainous land (32 per cent).

Although some agricultural land may be found in each of the natural vegetation zones of the U.S.S.R., ranging from the tundra in the north to the humid subtropics in the south, most of the sown acreage is concentrated in the wooded-steppe and steppe zones of the country. The fertile chernozems of that belt account for more than 60 per cent of the nation's sown acreage. To the north and south of the chernozem zone, there is a sharp drop in agricultural use. Only slightly more than 4 per cent of the forest zone is considered arable, and in the drier chestnut-soil steppe to the south the share of arable land is 25 per cent. The degree of agricultural use of Soviet territory decreases also from west to east. This may be explained not only by worse climatic and soil conditions in the Asian parts of the Soviet Union but also by the later settlement and development of these eastern areas compared with the European U.S.S.R.

New Agricultural Lands. In an effort to assure a more reliable supply of food from year to year, the Soviet government sponsored a major expansion of the sown acreage between 1954 and 1956. In these three years, 90 million acres of previously fallow or virgin land were plowed and sown almost entirely in wheat. About 45 per cent of the new land was in the eastern parts of the Russian republic, mainly in western Siberia; 55 per cent was in the northern *oblasts* of Kazakhstan, where chernozems and darker chestnut soils are found (Fig. 9–10). Most of the new land was organized as huge state farms or new collective farms employing much machinery and relatively little manpower. Migrants from European Russia who responded to the government's appeal for new settlers flocked eastward to the virgin lands. During harvest time these permanent residents must be supplemented by thousands of seasonal volunteers who travel from the western industrial cities to bring in the crop.

The new lands are situated in an area which is excellently adapted to mechanized farming but noted for certain serious natural handicaps. Precipitation is insufficient and unreliable, with an annual average of 10 to 15 inches. A relatively high degree of alkalinity in the soils also adds to the risks for dry farming. In view of these conditions, wheat growers in the area may expect at best an alternation of medium and low yields with an occasional good crop year. However, even with low yields, the total output on the millions of acres involved in the new-lands program represents a substantial addition to the Soviet wheat crop. In fact, droughts do not appear to occur simultaneously both in the European part of the U.S.S.R. and in the

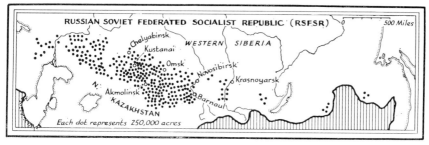

Fig. 9–10. Development of virgin lands, 1954–6.

new lands of Siberia and Kazakhstan, so each area represents a kind of safety cushion for crop failure in the other.

Besides greatly expanding the arable acreage in the middle 1950's, the Soviet Union has continued to carry on a number of moisture- and soil-conservation measures designed to combat the ever-present danger of drought in the wooded-steppe and steppe zones of the country. Among these measures has been the planting of windbreaks and shelter belts. Trees have been planted along field boundaries, across hill slopes (to reduce soil erosion), and along gullies and ravines. The windbreaks result in more equal accumulation of snow in areas between tree belts, reduce snow drifting into gullies and ravines, and produce more even thawing and absorption of moisture into the soil. At the same time, windbreaks tend to slow wind velocity near the ground, thus reducing wind erosion and evaporation.

According to Soviet experience, grain yields in unusually severe drought years have been three to four times higher in windbreak-protected fields than in fields that lacked such protection. Since World War II, 6 million acres of windbreaks and tree belts of various types have been planted in the grass steppes of the southern European U.S.S.R., transforming many parts of this area into a checkerboard pattern of tree lines.

Besides the systematic local planting of windbreaks by state and collective farms, a more ambitious state-sponsored program of planting great shelter belts has been under way since 1949. The program, which was one of Stalin's widely publicized projects, called for the planting of huge tree zones for a total length of 3,500 miles, extending generally northeast-southwest between the southern Urals and the northern Caucasus. The program was temporarily abandoned after Stalin's death, and many freshly planted saplings died for lack of care. However, since 1956 the plan has been revived, gaps have been replanted, and several shelter belts have been officially inaugurated in the steppes between the Don and Volga rivers.

In the deserts, semideserts, and dry steppes of central Asia and other arid parts of the country, irrigation is required for the raising of crops and, when successfully applied, provides high yields. The Soviet Union has the world's third-largest irrigated acreage, after China and India. It rose from 10 million acres before the Bolshevik Revolution to 15 million in 1940. The present Soviet irrigated area is 27 million acres out of a total sown area of nearly 500 million acres. Work is also proceeding on swamp drainage and the reclamation of marshy soils adjacent to major crop regions. Among areas where drainage work is being carried on are the Pripet Marshes of the western Ukraine and western Belorussia, parts of the Baltic republics, northwestern and central parts of the European U.S.S.R., and the Baraba Steppe of western Siberia. A major reclamation project is under way in the Colchis lowland of Georgia, along the Black Sea, where a formerly malarial swamp is gradually being transformed into tangerine groves and plantations for tea and other subtropical crops.

While these soil-conservation and land-reclamation measures may ultimately result in minor changes in the geographical distribution of Soviet agriculture, the wooded-steppe and true-steppe zones will undoubtedly remain the chief agricultural belt of the U.S.S.R. for a long time to come.

Production and Yields. The expansion of acreage that has already taken place is reflected in Soviet statistics. The total sown area increased from nearly 300 million acres in 1913, the last year of peace before World War I, used by Soviet statisticians as a base year, to almost 500 million acres at the present time. The relatively short growing season permits only one crop a year to be grown on this acreage. Less than one-third is sown in winter crops, which are found in areas that do not have excessively cold winters or where a thick snow cover provides protection for the germinating seeds. Most of the Soviet acreage is planted in the spring. The increase in sown area under the Soviet regime was accompanied by changed proportions of the various crops: the share of grain crops has gradually been reduced with expansion of acreages devoted to industrial crops (cotton, flax, hemp, sunflowers, sugar beets), potatoes, vegetables, and especially fodder crops.

In spite of these changes of emphasis, grain still dominates Soviet agriculture, accounting for 66 per cent of the total sown acreage, having decreased from 88 per cent in 1913. The Soviet grain area remained fairly constant after the Bolshevik Revolution, fluctuating between 250 and 275 million acres. Since 1953, however, it has rapidly expanded as a result of the virgin-lands program, reaching 325 million acres in 1957. Grain yields in the Soviet Union are generally low because of poor soil and climatic conditions and inadequate fertilizer application. The Soviet Union long made a practice of estimating crops before the harvest and publishing these estimates as production figures. These inflated figures, which amounted to 120 to 130 million metric tons of grain in the early 1950's, concealed losses incurred during the harvest. As it turned out, the actual barn crop was only 65 to 70 per cent of the published figures. Recently the Soviet government decided to publish barn-crop data for the years starting in 1950 (Table 22, Appendix III). The production increase since 1954 reflects the sharp increase in acreage resulting from the virgin-lands program in western Siberia and Kazakhstan. In fact, the 1958 grain harvest was the highest in the country's history. The Soviet Union has long aimed at obtaining a grain harvest of 180 million metric tons, a goal originally set for 1960. The seven-year plan, approaching the problem more realistically, now looks to a harvest of 165 to 180 million metric tons by 1965. It hopes to achieve increased yields through greater use of fertilizers, pesticides, and herbicides to be supplied by an expanded chemical industry. The supply of fertilizers for agriculture is planned to rise from 10.3 million metric tons in 1958 to 31 million in 1965.

Grain-growing Areas. The principal grain-growing areas in prerevolutionary Russia were in the chernozem zone of the southern and southwestern European U.S.S.R. Since the eighteenth century, grain production in the northern non-chernozem areas had continued to decline under the impact of the cheaper grain of the newly settled chernozem zone. The country thus combined a grain-deficit region, consisting of the non-chernozem belt extending from Belorussia in the west to the upper Volga around Gorky in the east, and a grain-surplus region, coinciding essentially with the chernozem zone. Although efforts were made under the Soviet regime to achieve a more uniform distribution of grain production, the non-chernozem areas continued to require grain shipments from other parts of the country.

At the same time, the grain-surplus regions shifted eastward. The seven-year plan looks to western Siberia, the Urals, the middle Volga lands, and Kazakhstan—areas of recent expansion of grain acreage—as the principal producers of surplus grain in the Soviet Union. Lesser surpluses are expected from the more densely settled Ukraine, the northern Caucasus, and the chernozem *oblasts* of central European Russia, where industrial crops and animal husbandry increasingly compete for acreage with grain. The seven-year plan also calls on the non-chernozem areas of the north-central parts of European Russia, Belorussia, and the Baltic republics to raise yields to the level that will enable them to meet their own grain needs. The fact that the plan asks for a grain-output rise of 70 to 100 per cent in the non-chernozem zone, compared with a 40 to 50 per cent increase in the nation as a whole, suggests the current low level of grain yields in that zone.

A significant characteristic of Soviet grain farming, reflecting the nature of the country's diet and level of nutrition, is the heavy dominance of food or bread grains. Wheat, rye, buckwheat, millet, and rice account for 70 per cent of the total grain acreage. Such heavy reliance on cereal grains is generally typical of relatively backward agricultural economies. More advanced farming countries show a crop pattern tending more toward feed grains as a basis for a meat-dairy diet. In the United States, for example, feed grains (corn, oats, barley, and sorghum) in 1958 accounted for 80 per cent of the total grain harvest. The United States corn crop alone reached 120 million tons, nearly equivalent to the total grain crop in the Soviet Union.

Wheat is by far the most important grain in the Soviet Union, accounting for 50 to 55 per cent of the grain acreage. The Soviet Union is the world's leading wheat producer, ahead of China and the United States. Most of the wheat acreage is concentrated in the chernozem belt, extending from the Ukraine in a generally north-easterly direction through the middle Volga Valley and the southern Urals to western Siberia and northern Kazakhstan. Winter wheat is grown at the southwestern end of the chernozem zone, while reduced snow cover and more extreme winter temperatures toward the east necessitate the sowing of lower-yielding spring wheat (Fig. 9–11). The recent eastward shift in grain growing has in fact resulted in a reduction of the winter-wheat share. Before the virgin-lands expansion, in 1953, the winter sowings accounted for 37 per cent of all wheat acreage. By 1959, the winter-wheat share had dropped to 28 per cent.

Rye, the only grain except wheat commonly used to make bread, is the second-most-important Soviet grain, and, as of wheat, the

Soviet Union is also the world's leading producer of rye (the only other important rye producers are Poland, West and East Germany, and Czechoslovakia). Rye has less exacting soil and moisture requirements than wheat and is grown in the poor, acid podzolic soils of the central regions of the European U.S.S.R. Under the Soviet regime rye sowings have been steadily losing ground, declining from 70 million acres (28 per cent of the grain acreage) in 1913 to 45 million (14 per cent) in 1956. Much of the rye has been replaced

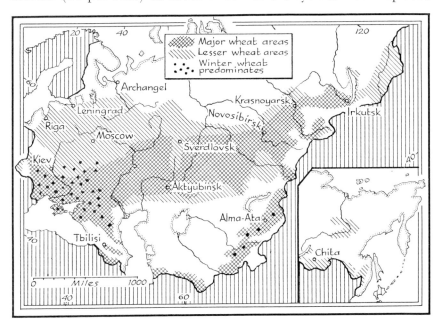

Fig. 9–11. Wheat areas.

by winter wheat. Lesser food grains include millet and buckwheat, which are used to make kasha, a mush or porridge that is a traditional Russian dish. Rice, an unimportant crop in the Soviet Union, is grown on 350,000 acres, mainly in irrigated lands of the Uzbek and Kazakh republics of central Asia, in the Kuban Delta of southern European Russia, and in the Soviet Far East.

Oats and barley are the traditional Soviet feed grains. Oats thrive in a moist, cool climate and have less demanding soil requirements than any other small grain except rye. Most of the Soviet oats acreage (12 per cent of the grain acreage in 1956) is in poor, acid soil unfit for either wheat or barley. Barley is a short-season crop and can be grown farther north and at higher elevations than any other grain.

Before 1955, corn production in the U.S.S.R. was largely limited to the southernmost parts of European Russia (southern Ukraine, northern Caucasus, Moldavia, Georgia), the only areas that combine sufficient heat and moisture for corn growing. The Soviet Union has no counterpart of the Corn Belt of the United States, which is unique in its ideal conditions for corn growing. In spite of the natural handicaps, the Soviet government launched a major corn-growing campaign in 1955, inspired by the example of the United States, to bolster the lagging forage supply. The Soviet authorities conceded that not much of the corn in the Soviet Union would mature as well as corn does in the United States, because of the short Russian growing season. A large part of the Soviet corn was therefore to be used for silage or green fodder rather than for grain. Under the new program corn acreage rose from 10 million acres in 1954 to 60 million in 1956. Of the 1956 acreage, 35 per cent was harvested for grain and the rest for silage and green fodder. In an old corn district, such as Moldavia, where climatic conditions encourage corn growing, 85 per cent of the total corn area is harvested for grain. In a northern zone, such as Latvia, on the other hand, corn does not mature and is used entirely for silage or green forage. The seven-year plan calls for a feed-grain supply of 85 to 90 million tons to be made available to livestock by 1965, a two-and-a-half-fold increase over 1958. Great reliance in this plan is placed on increased corn yields. It remains to be seen whether such a sharp rise in production can be achieved in spite of the adverse natural conditions.

Industrial Crops. Under the Soviet regime, increases in the sown acreage have been accompanied by a growth in the percentage of industrial-crop acreages. The area sown in industrial crops rose from 12 million acres in 1913 to 32 million in 1956. The principal crops are sugar beets, cotton, flax, hemp, and sunflowers.

Sugar beets, the Soviet Union's only source of sugar, require moisture and warmth and find these conditions in the wooded-steppe zone of the European U.S.S.R. About 70 per cent of beet sowings are concentrated in the western Ukraine, with an additional 20 per cent coming from the adjoining chernozem areas of the Russian S.F.S.R. (Belgorod, Kursk, Voronezh). Under the Soviet regime, the sugar beet has been introduced into many other areas, including irrigated fields in central Asia. The new areas account for 10 per cent of the national beet production. The Soviet Union is by far the world's leading sugar-beet producer, but its yields per unit area are relatively low.

The sunflower is the Soviet Union's principal source of edible oils. Its major production areas coincide with the wheat-surplus areas of the southern steppes. The largest sunflower sowings are found in the southeastern Ukraine, the Kuban plains of the northern Caucasus, the middle Volga Valley, western Siberia, and northern Kazakhstan. Nowhere else in the world are sunflowers planted on such a huge scale. In addition to sunflowers, which supply two-thirds of the Soviet Union's edible oils, oil-bearing crops include castor beans, soybeans, and sesame seeds.

Cotton, the Soviet Union's principal fiber crop, is now grown entirely on irrigated lands of central Asia, southern Kazakhstan, and Transcaucasia. Attempts to expand cotton growing to the non-irrigated lands of the northern Caucasus and the southern Ukraine have been abandoned in recent years. At one time, these areas accounted for 25 per cent of the entire cotton plantings, but yields were so low that the non-irrigated lands contributed only 4 to 5 per cent of the cotton crop. Two-thirds of the Soviet cotton comes from the Uzbek S.S.R. of central Asia, and 10 per cent from the Tadzhik S.S.R., which regularly achieves the highest yields per hectare.

The northwestern part of the European U.S.S.R., in the forested podzolic belt, has conditions favorable to the growing of fiber flax, a plant that flourishes under cloudy, humid climate with a July mean below 70° F. Because of the plant's high demands on the soil, it is generally cultivated in rotation with alfalfa, which provides a basis for dairy farming. Almost half of all the flax area is in the Kalinin and Smolensk *oblasts* and in the Belorussian S.S.R. Soviet flax growing underwent a serious crisis in the early 1950's, when the planted acreage was sharply reduced because of a shortage of seed. The seed shortage, in turn, resulted from low yields and excessive losses during the harvest and threshing in previous years. Greater government concern for the flax crop resulted in a recovery in recent years. The Soviet Union is the world's only major fiber-flax producer.

Hemp, another important Soviet fiber, requires more warmth than flax and is grown farther south, between the flax and sugar-beet zones. Hemp grows best in low-lying floodplains and reclaimed marshlands, such as are found on the margins of the Pripet Marshes in southern Belorussia and the northwestern Ukraine.

While no tropical products such as coffee, cacao, and bananas are grown in the Soviet Union, its subtropical areas do produce tea, citrus fruit, wine, and tobacco. Most of these products are grown in Transcaucasia and on the southern coast of the Crimea. The cultivation of tea and citrus fruit, mainly tangerines and lemons, is concentrated along the Black Sea coast of the Georgian S.S.R., where humid subtropical conditions prevail. Wine is produced in the Moldavian S.S.R., the Crimea, the northern Caucasus, and elsewhere. As to tobacco, the Russian inferior *makhorka* type stems mainly from the chernozem belt. The better-grade Turkish tobacco is produced in the southern Crimea and the Caucasus.

Livestock. Just as the European U.S.S.R. contains the greater part of the sown acreage, it harbors the greater proportion of the Soviet Union's livestock, with emphasis on hogs in the west, dairy cattle in the north, and sheep in the southeast.

Dairy farming is promoted both in areas that furnish adequate pastures and in the suburbs of large cities, which constitute an important market for fresh milk. In the more remote areas, the emphasis is on butter and cheese making, as well as the production of condensed and powdered milk. The latter areas include the flax-growing zone, where alfalfa and other grasses are grown in rotation with flax, and the vast natural meadowlands of the northern European U.S.S.R., especially Vologda *Oblast*, and of southwestern Siberia.

Although most populated parts of the Soviet Union now combine the raising of dairy and beef cattle, the latter type is characteristic of the seminomadic grazing areas in the arid lands of the southeast, where the stock is grazed in the mountains during the summer and in the lowlands during the winter. In contrast to the former nomadic way of life, the stock is now accompanied only by its herders while the rest of the population, settled in permanent villages, raises crops.

Sheep raising is the principal type of animal husbandry in arid regions and mountainous areas. Before World War II, the Soviet regime sought to promote the production of finer grades of wool, the so-called merino and crossbred types, and their share in the wool clip rose from 9 per cent in 1913 to 64 per cent in 1940. The war seriously set back the Soviet sheep economy, and by 1956 the share of the finer wool grades was only 40 per cent of the total clip. The northern Caucasus, especially the Stavropol area, specializes in merino-type sheep. A special type of sheep is the karakul, which is raised chiefly in the Uzbek and Turkmen republics of central Asia.

Hogs are raised mainly in the Ukraine, Belorussia, the Baltic republics, the Kuban, and the central chernozem areas, where potatoes, corn, and by-products of the food industry are used as feed.

The livestock sector was long a problem area of the Soviet economy, largely because of feed shortages. Since 1953, government policy has encouraged expansion of the feed base, especially corn, with a view to achieving an increase in livestock numbers and animal products (see Tables 23 and 24, Appendix III).

If we discount India, whose cattle population is the world's largest but has low productivity, the Soviet Union is second only to the United States in its cattle holdings. In hog numbers, both the Soviet Union and the United States fluctuate around 50 million head, sharing second place behind Communist China. In its sheep population, the Soviet Union is second to Australia.

Among other non-industrial activities in the U.S.S.R., hunting and fishing play an important role in the economy. The hunting of fur-bearing animals has been a traditional source of riches in the history of Russian expansion. The Soviet Union continues to be the leading world supplier of furs, exporting about 150 million rubles ($37.5 million) worth each year, more than half of it to Britain. The principal Soviet fur-hunting regions are eastern Siberia, the Soviet Far East, and northern European Russia. Fox farming is also being fostered.

Fisheries. Most Soviet fisheries are located in the Barents Sea, the Baltic, the Caspian, and the Far East. The Caspian Sea, accessible by the Volga to the consumption centers of European Russia and to salt supplies (at Lake Baskunchak), accounted for 65 per cent of the total Russian catch before Soviet times. With the huge amounts of organic matter carried into the Caspian Sea by the Volga, the Ural, and other rivers and the shallowness of its coastal reaches, the Caspian has been regarded traditionally as a natural fish nursery. However, with the gradual development of modern deep-sea fisheries under the Soviet regime, the share of the Caspian dropped to 15 per cent by 1956. The Far Eastern waters of the Sea of Okhotsk and, more recently, the Barents Sea have moved to the foreground in fish production. The share of deep-sea fisheries in the total catch rose from 0.2 per cent in 1913 to 67 per cent in 1956, while inland and coastal fisheries declined proportionately. The most recent development has been the sending of Soviet trawlers to the fishing banks of the North Sea, Newfoundland, and other parts of the North Atlantic, which now accounts for about 10 per cent of the total Soviet catch. Since World War II, Soviet whaling ships have also made their appearance in the Antarctic. The principal fishing ports are Murmansk on the Barents Sea and Astrakhan on the Caspian. Soviet whalers have their base at Odessa.

In terms of its total catch, the Soviet Union is one of the world's leading fishery nations, rivaling the United States and surpassed only by China and Japan.

Mining and Industry

Since the start of the first five-year plan, in 1928, the Soviet Union has experienced a remarkable growth in industrial production, set back temporarily by World War II. New factories, power stations, and mines have been put into operation and modern machinery and techniques have been introduced. In accordance with the aim of achieving a self-sufficient industrialized economy in the briefest possible time, emphasis was laid on the rapid growth of heavy industry, such as the production of machinery, industrial chemicals, and power-generating and transportation equipment, as well as the mining of fuels, metals, and other minerals. The production of consumer goods, though increasing, lagged proportionately behind the development of heavy industry.

Typical of this tendency is the emphasis on the production of trucks in the automotive industry. In the peak production year before World War II, 1938, the Soviet Union turned out 182,400 trucks and only 27,000 automobiles. In the postwar period, auto production has increased more rapidly than that of trucks, but trucks still outnumber cars. In 1958, for example, Soviet plants produced 122,000 cars out of a total motor-vehicle output of 511,000.

The rapid development of industry under the Soviet regime has been accompanied by a considerable shift in the geographical distribution of production from a few old industrialized areas to vast new underdeveloped regions. Before the Bolshevik Revolution and through the 1920's, there was a heavy concentration of industry and mining in five areas of the European U.S.S.R.: the Donets Basin, the Urals, Moscow, Leningrad, and Baku. Outlying European regions such as the Kola Peninsula, the northeastern Pechora area, and the arid southeast were entirely undeveloped. Beyond the Urals, exploitation of natural resources was restricted to the narrow forest-steppe and steppe zone along the Trans-Siberian Railroad, and, in Kazakhstan and central Asia, only the long-settled oases could be considered as playing any substantial role in the economy.

The gradual shift of the industrial center of gravity toward the east first became apparent during the prewar five-year plans, particularly in the case of the Urals-Kuznetsk combine. This much-publicized Soviet industrial experiment involved the exchange of Kuznetsk coking coal and Urals iron ore over a distance of 1,200 miles and resulted in the creation of two of the Soviet Union's leading new steel centers—Magnitogorsk in the Urals and Stalinsk in the Kuznetsk Basin. In more recent years, the Kuznetsk Basin has relied increasingly on local iron-ore resources, and the Magnitogorsk plant on coking coal from a less remote source at Karaganda.

The gradual eastward shift of industry received a sudden impetus during the emergency period of World War II, which led to both the removal of about 1,300 industrial plants from war-threatened areas west of the Leningrad-Moscow-Stalingrad line and the accelerated building of industries and mines in the east. During the war, industrial output in the Urals and Siberia, as well as the Volga Valley, rose by three to four times. A further indication of the industrial growth of the east is the increase of cities in the war period. Of the total number of 67 new cities created in the U.S.S.R. during the years 1942–5, 53 were situated east of the Volga River. After the end of the war the eastern industries remained in their new location, while the destroyed areas of the west were rehabilitated, in part with the aid of machinery removed by the U.S.S.R. as war booty from East Germany and Manchuria.

Although the European U.S.S.R. continues to harbor by far the greater share of Soviet industries, as it does of Soviet population and agriculture in general, an increasing share of industry is located in the Urals and beyond. The seven-year plan (1959–65) continues to emphasize the development of the eastern territories, to which it assigns more than 40 per cent of the total capital-construction fund of the plan period. By 1965, the Urals and all territories to the east are expected to contribute the following shares of major industrial commodities: 43 per cent of Soviet pig iron, 47 per cent of steel, 50 per cent of coal, 46 per cent of electric-power output, 88 per cent of copper, 71 per cent of aluminum, and more than 45 per cent of sawn wood.

In pursuing this policy of geographical decentralization, the Soviet regime has been motivated by several considerations. There was first the urge to move some industries nearer to the sources of raw materials and to some of the outlying markets. By such means long rail hauls would be reduced. Typical of these long hauls was the shipment of central-Asian cotton to the mills of the Moscow-Ivanovo region in central European Russia and the return of finished textiles to the consumers of the cotton-growing area. This the Soviet regime attempted to avoid by building cotton mills in the heart of the cotton belt. Another consideration was the desire to develop industries in previously non-industrial areas, which were often inhabited by non-Russian ethnic minorities. It was felt that industrialization of these areas would give the indigenous population a sense of accomplishment and strengthen their loyalty to the Soviet regime. Above all, a more equalized distribution of industries would tend to reduce the heavy strain on the railroads of shipping raw materials and finished goods.

Although decentralization of industry was the keynote of economic development in the Soviet Union, the management of industry was for a long time highly centralized in industrial ministries in Moscow. Each major industry, such as coal, petroleum, and steel, was placed in the charge of a specific ministry, which administered the plants and mines of that industry wherever they might be in the Soviet Union. This centralized management resulted in the creation of huge industrial empires in which the lines of command all led to Moscow. If a given plant wished to deal with a neighboring enterprise of another industry, the chain of administration leading to and from Moscow made direct dealings virtually impossible. In the summer of 1957, the government reorganized the existing structure fundamentally, abolishing all industrial ministries in Moscow and placing industry under the management of regional bodies. The reform led to the creation of about a hundred industrial-management councils, each placed in charge of industries within a given administrative region. These regional bodies were responsible to the governments of the various union republics that make up the U.S.S.R. Nationwide coordination of industrial planning and production remained in the hands of the State Planning Committee (Gosplan) in Moscow. Since 1957, production increases and more efficient operation of industry have been credited by the Russians in part to the establishment of the regional management councils.

Power and Fuel Resources. The areal distribution of Soviet power and fuel resources is in general unfavorable. Most of the population and the economy are still concentrated in the European part of the country, but 90 per cent of both coal and waterpower resources lie in the Asian part. This maldistribution may be one further reason why the government is engaged in the rapid industrialization of the outlying eastern parts of the Soviet Union.

The distribution of coal reserves is especially adverse because coal accounts for more than 90 per cent of the Soviet Union's total fuel reserves. In the period after World War II, coal made up 60 to 70 per cent of all fuel consumed in the Soviet Union. Long-haul coal shipments from Siberia to European Russia have grown in volume in recent years, because of a fuel shortage in the highly industrialized sections of the European part of the Soviet Union.

The seven-year plan calls for a more rational utilization of fuel resources, as a result of the growing development of petroleum and natural gas in European Russia. The share of coal in fuel utilization in European Russia is expected to drop from 68 to 49 per cent while the oil and gas share will rise from 20 to 42 per cent. This shift will be even more dramatic in the Urals, which have been increasingly dependent on long rail hauls of steam-raising coal from Karaganda and the Kuznetsk Basin. In the Urals the share of coal will drop from 81 to 47 per cent and that of natural gas (brought by proposed pipelines from other parts of the country) will rise from 1 to 28 per cent. Siberia, where vast coal resources can be mined cheaply in open-cut operations, will continue to rely predominantly on coal. The effect of the planned changes in fuel consumption will be to reduce the share of coal in the Soviet economy from 60 per cent in 1958 to 43 per cent in 1965 while the oil and gas share is expected to rise from 31 to 51 per cent.

COAL. Soviet coal reserves are sufficient to meet the foreseeable needs of the country for many centuries to come. Of the major producing fields (Fig. 9–12), the Donets Basin, the Kuznetsk Basin, and the Karaganda Basin contain high-grade coals, in part suitable for conversion into metallurgical coke. The Donets Basin, in the Ukraine, and adjoining Rostov *Oblast* of European Russia have by far the best locations with respect to the Soviet Union's industrial centers. The Donets Basin (commonly abbreviated Donbas) has been the country's largest producer. Before World War II it mined considerably more coal than all the other fields together. Although the share of the Donbas has now dropped to about 36 per cent of the total, its actual production has steadily increased and reached 180 million metric tons in 1958. It is the Soviet Union's principal supplier of coking coal, accounting for about 60 per cent of the national output. The Donets Basin, whose reserves are estimated at 190 billion tons, serves industry and transportation in most of European Russia as far east as the Volga Valley.

Next in importance among Soviet coal fields is the Kuznetsk Basin (Kuzbas), of southern Siberia. This field, with reserves of more than 800 billion tons, provides easier mining conditions than the Donets Basin. The Kuznetsk Basin has thick seams of good bituminous coal which is mined at an average depth of 500 feet compared with almost 1,000 feet in the Donets Basin. An increasing share of Kuzbas coal is being obtained from open-cut mines. The cheap Kuzbas coal supplies mainly the industries of western Siberia and the Urals. However, because of the fuel deficit in European Russia, 15 per cent of the output of the Kuznetsk Basin had to be shipped beyond the Urals in recent years.

The third major coal field of national importance is the Karaganda Basin of central Kazakhstan, whose development began in 1930. A large part of Karaganda's coal reserves of 60 billion tons is suitable

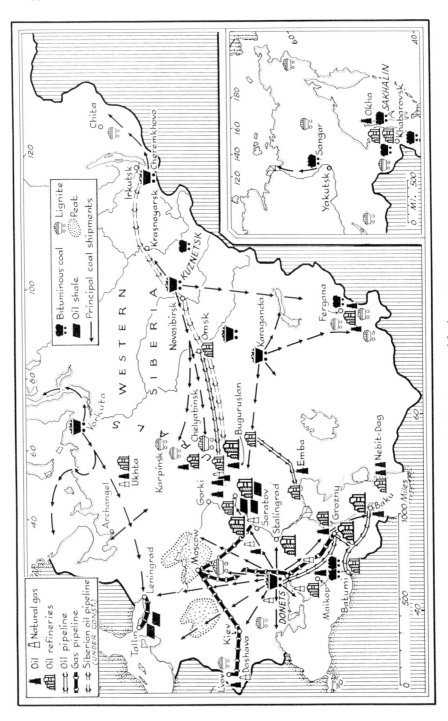

Fig. 9–12. Power and fuel resources.

for coking. Its output supplies chiefly the Urals, Kazakhstan, and central Asia, but, as in the case of Kuzbas coal, about 15 per cent has gone to European Russia in recent years.

Among the remaining coal basins in European Russia are those of Vorkuta, Moscow, and the Urals. The Vorkuta basin, whose development began during World War II, supplies steam coals and some coking coals to the northern part of European Russia, including Leningrad. The low-grade-lignite basin south of Moscow is important only because of its proximity to the Soviet capital. Its coal, high in ash and moisture content, has been used primarily in local power stations serving Moscow. During the seven-year plan, when Moscow will rely increasingly on natural gas, coal production of the Moscow basin is scheduled to drop by about 30 per cent from its 1958 output of about 40 million tons. Of the various coal fields of the Urals, the leading producers are the Kizel field of subbituminous coal, some of it suitable for coking, and the Chelyabinsk and Karpinsk lignite basins.

In view of the growing role of petroleum and natural gas, the seven-year plan schedules only a modest 20 per cent increase in coal production from the 1958 level of 496 million tons to about 600 million tons by 1965. Emphasis will be placed on the expansion of coking-coal mines and on the mining of cheap steam coals from open cuts in the Nazarovo and Irsha-Borodino areas of southern Siberia.

Although Soviet coals range widely in rank, all types are lumped together in production statistics. In recent years, Soviet coal output has consisted of 15 per cent anthracite, 20 per cent coking coal, 35 per cent other bituminous coals, and 30 per cent lignite. Anthracite is mined almost entirely in the Donets Basin, coking coal mainly in the Donets, Kuznetsk, and Karaganda fields, and the other ranks in scattered deposits throughout the Soviet Union. Changes in the regional distribution of Soviet coal production are shown in Table 34.

PETROLEUM. The geographical shift of industrial production in the Soviet Union is perhaps most dramatically illustrated by the petroleum industry (Fig. 9–12). Before World War II, the old oil fields of Baku, Grozny, and Maikop, in the Caucasus, accounted for about 86 per cent of the Soviet Union's total crude-oil output. By 1958, Soviet production had increased more than three and a half times the 1940 level and about 70 per cent of the total output came from a vast new petroliferous province between the Volga and the Urals. The rapid emergence of the Volga-Urals region since 1950, notably the fields in the Tatar, Bashkir, and Kuibyshev areas, is comparable to the dramatic discovery and exploitation of the world's other great oil fields in America and along the Persian Gulf. Intensive exploration has led to the discovery of rich oil-bearing horizons of Devonian age in the Volga-Urals area, which is situated more favorably with respect to industrial markets than the old Baku district. The seven-year plan calls for a major program of oil-pipeline construction in order to carry crude oil from the Volga-Urals region to new refineries to be built at consumption centers in European Russia and in Siberia.

Outside of the Volga-Urals region, the Soviet Union still obtains crude oil from Baku and the other old fields of the northern Caucasus (Grozny, Maikop), from the Emba district of Kazakhstan, the Nebit-Dag and Fergana areas of central Asia, Okha in Sakhalin, Ukhta in the Komi A.S.S.R., and the Ukraine. However, none of these fields shows any promise similar to the Volga-Urals. As a result of the growing output of this rich oil-bearing region, the Soviet Union is expected to pass Venezuela in the early 1960's and assume a place second to the United States. Changes in the geographical distribution of Soviet crude-oil production are shown in Table 26, Appendix III.

NATURAL GAS. The sudden upsurge of the Soviet petroleum industry has been paralleled by a similar development of the natural-gas industry. Before World War II, the Soviet Union recovered only 375 million cubic meters of dry natural gas, which, in the absence of long-distance pipelines, was used locally. Most of the country's gas output in 1940 was so-called casing-head gas, or wet gas, obtained in conjunction with petroleum and separated from the crude oil at the well head. The first major Soviet gas pipeline was built during the war, in 1943, in the Volga Valley, carrying natural gas from Buguruslan to Kuibyshev. This was followed after the war by the completion of the Saratov-Moscow pipeline, in 1946, and of the Dashava-Kiev line, in 1948, which was extended in 1951 to Moscow. Natural-gas output rose tenfold by 1950, compared with 1940.

Exploration of prospective natural-gas deposits was greatly intensified after 1950 and resulted in the discovery of several important commercial sites. They include Shebelinka, south of Kharkov, in the Ukraine; Stavropol and several sites near Krasnodar, in the northern Caucasus; Karadag, near Baku; Dzhebol, on the upper Pechora River, in northern European Russia; Berezovo, on the lower Ob River, in Siberia; and Gazli, near Bukhara, in central Asia (Fig. 9–12).

In order to carry the newly discovered natural gas to consumption centers, the Soviet Union proposes during the seven-year plan to lay 15,000 miles of pipelines. The beneficiaries of the new fuel source will be the traditional fuel-deficit areas of Moscow, Leningrad, and the Urals. Pipelines to Leningrad are scheduled to originate in the old Dashava field, of the western Ukraine, and in the new fields of the northern Caucasus. Lines from the northern Caucasus to Moscow will furnish the third gas source for the Soviet capital, in addition to the previous lines from Saratov and Dashava. Finally, the Urals are to receive gas from Dzhebol, the Volga Valley, and, most spectacularly, from the Bukhara area, 1,400 miles distant.

These natural-gas lines are expected to replace millions of tons of long-haul coal that have had to be shipped to the Leningrad, Moscow, and Urals areas at high cost. In the Urals, for example, gas consumption is expected to rise from less than 1 billion cubic meters in 1958 to 25 billion by 1965, reducing the need for long-haul steam coals by more than half and producing savings of about 1.4 billion rubles in 1965. Moscow's fuel expenses will be reduced by 5 billion rubles over the seven-year period. During this time, Moscow's incoming fuels are expected to change from the present 4 billion cubic meters of gas and 6 million tons of coal to more than 13 billion cubic meters of gas and only 700,000 tons of coal.

In addition to natural gas and casing-head gas, which is also being recovered to an increasing extent, the Soviet Union obtains gas from the distillation of oil shale and the underground burning of coal. Oil shale is mined and processed mainly in Estonia, which accounts for 70 per cent of the total production, and in Slantsy (Leningrad Oblast) (Fig. 9–12). The crude shale is converted into gasoline and fuel oil, as well as gas, which are piped from the Estonian field and from Slantsy to Leningrad and to Tallinn, the Estonian capital. Underground-coal gasification plants exist in the Moscow coal basin and in the Kuznetsk Basin, with others under construction.

PEAT. The Soviet Union has vast peat resources. Although peat has little heat value, the location of peat bogs near the great industrial centers of the central European U.S.S.R. (Fig. 9–12) has enhanced the importance of peat as a power-station fuel. Confronted with this abundant, though largely uneconomic fuel, the U.S.S.R. had developed processes to mechanize and speed the laborious extraction, dehydration, and transportation of peat to power plants, which must be located in the immediate vicinity of the bogs. In 1955, out of a total Soviet peat production of 50 million tons, central European Russia accounted for 54 per cent, Belorussia for 14 per cent, and the Leningrad area for 9 per cent. With the impending arrival of natural-gas pipelines in these major peat-consuming areas, the importance of peat may be expected to decline.

WATERPOWER. Although most of the potential waterpower resources of the U.S.S.R. lie in Siberia, hydroelectrical development thus far has been taking place chiefly in European Russia in the vicinity of the large consumption centers. Until recently, waterpower development was restricted almost entirely to the Caucasus mountain torrents, the rapid-strewn rivers of the Leningrad area and the Kola Peninsula, and the slow-moving but large streams of the middle reaches of the European U.S.S.R.—the Volga and the Dnieper. It was only after 1950 that dam construction began in earnest on the great rivers of Siberia—the Ob and its major tributary, the Irtysh; the Yenisei and its tributary, the Angara. Among the giant hydroelectric stations under construction in Siberia are the Bratsk plant, with a generating capacity of 4.5 million kw, on the Angara River, to be completed by 1965, and the 5-million-kw Krasnoyarsk station on the Yenisei River. Two other hydroelectric stations, each exceeding 2 million kw in generating capacity, have already been completed on the Volga River at Kuibyshev and Stalingrad. Surplus electric power from the Volga Valley is being transmitted by high-voltage lines to Moscow, the Donets Basin, and the Urals.

In an effort to hasten the construction of electric-power plants at lower cost, the Soviet Union will continue to emphasize thermal-power stations during the seven-year plan. The principal considerations dictating priority for thermal power are its considerably lower cost (1,300 rubles per kw of installed capacity compared with 4,000 rubles for hydroelectric power) and speedier construction. By increasing the capacity of new thermal stations and converting them to cheap open-cut coal, natural gas, and fuel oil, the Soviet Union expects to be able to lower the cost of producing electric power from steam. The expected change in the structure of thermal-power-station fuels during the seven-year plan is shown in Table 27, Appendix III (the table excludes atomic-power stations, of which several types are under construction). Out of a total generating capacity of 58 to 60 million kw to be installed during the seven-year plan, 47 to 50 million kw will be from thermal power and 10 million from hydroelectric plants. The total installed capacity as of the end of 1958 was 52 million kw, of which about 12 million kw were supplied by hydroelectric stations. The capacity and output of Soviet thermal and hydroelectric stations are shown in Table 28, Appendix III.

Iron and Steel. The first ironworks appeared in Russia in the early seventeenth century in the region between Tula and Moscow, using local iron ore and charcoal. During the reign of Peter the Great, Russian ferrous metallurgy shifted to the Urals, where higher-quality iron ore and timber were abundant. During the late nineteenth century, when Russia began smelting iron with coke instead of charcoal, the center of production shifted again—to southern European Russia, where the proximity of Krivoi Rog iron ore and Donbas coal furnished the basis of a new, expanded industry (Fig. 9–13).

This southern region, which lies essentially in the Ukraine, is the leading Soviet producer of iron and steel and has maintained dominance longer than the old coal and petroleum areas. In 1913, the south accounted for 75 per cent of the country's iron ore, 69 per cent of its pig iron, and 57 per cent of its steel. By 1958, the Ukraine's share in Soviet production was still 62 per cent for iron ore, 51 per cent for pig iron, and 40 per cent for steel. The old iron-ore mines of Krivoi Rog are expected to play the chief role in supplying the Soviet steel industry with raw material. Although reserves of high-grade ore have been seriously depleted at Krivoi Rog—the average metal content of the ore dropped from 58.8 per cent in 1940 to 55.5 in 1956—the potential of Krivoi Rog remains undiminished, because of the presence of vast untapped low-grade-ore reserves suitable for concentration. The first concentrator of low-grade ore, which is mined cheaply in open cuts and contains 36 per cent iron, was opened in 1955 and soon contributed 10 per cent to Krivoi Rog's total output of blast-furnace-grade ore. The seven-year plan calls for the building of five additional concentrators, which by 1965 are expected to supply 36 per cent of Krivoi Rog's output.

The southern metallurgical plants are grouped in three clusters—two near sources of iron ore and one near the source of coking coal, the Donets Basin, which also has large limestone deposits and contains the integrated iron and steel centers of Makeyevka, Stalino, Yenakiyevo, and others. The second cluster, situated along the Dnieper River in the vicinity of Krivoi Rog iron ore, consists of the plants at Zaporozhe, Dnepropetrovsk, and Dneprodzerzhinsk, as well as an expanding plant at Krivoi Rog itself. The third cluster, which is based in part on Kerch iron ore, consists of Zhdanov and Kerch, which are linked by water across the Sea of Azov. Kerch iron ore, highly phosphoric, watery, and powdery, requires extensive treatment before use. It has been relatively unimportant as a Soviet iron-ore supply in the postwar period and must be mixed with Krivoi Rog ore in the Zhdanov blast furnaces. The Kerch iron and steel plant, destroyed during World War II, has not been rebuilt.

The second-most-important iron and steel district is the Urals, the plants of which are based on Urals iron ore and coking coal from the Kuznetsk Basin and Karaganda. The limited iron-ore reserves of the Urals are gradually being exhausted and the district is expected to depend increasingly on outside supplies. Of the three large integrated iron and steel plants there, those of Magnitogorsk and Chelyabinsk

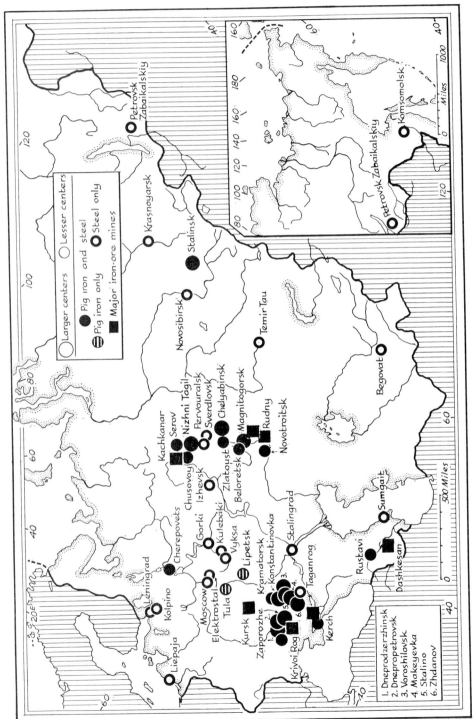

Fig. 9.13. The iron and steel industry

are expected to be supplied by newly developed Rudny iron mines in the near-by Kustanai area of northwest Kazakhstan, while Nizhni Tagil will rely on the new Kachkanar mine in the Urals. The Urals' share in the country's pig-iron output rose from 18 per cent in 1940 to 36 per cent in 1956, and its steel share from 21 per cent in 1940 to 36 per cent in 1956.

Outside the Ukraine and the Urals, the only large integrated iron and steel plant has been operating since 1932 at Stalinsk in the Kuznetsk Basin of western Siberia. As one of the links of the Urals-Kuznetsk combine, the Stalinsk plant was at first supplied by iron ore from the Urals, but after the discovery and exploitation of local ore deposits it converted largely to Kuzbas ore.

During the seven-year plan, three large integrated plants are to be built in the Asian part of the Soviet Union. They are a second plant at Stalinsk in the Kuznetsk Basin, the so-called west-Siberian plant; a plant planned for Taishet in eastern Siberia; and the Karaganda plant in Kazakhstan. In connection with the construction of these three large steel enterprises, the Soviet authorities are developing new iron-ore resources in central and northwestern Kazakhstan, in the Altai Mountains, and in the Angara-Ilim area of central Siberia. Further development is also under way in the so-called Kursk Magnetic Anomaly of European Russia, where an experimental mine has been operating. Low-grade ferruginous quartzite and newly discovered high-grade ores appear to be promising despite difficult mining conditions. The first large industrial mine opened in 1959, and by 1965 about 11 million tons are to be produced annually.

Development of the Kursk Magnetic Anomaly would be especially important for the expansion of the iron and steel industry of European Russia, which has lacked a major local iron-ore supply. Limited local iron-ore reserves near Tula and Lipetsk have supplied blast furnaces in those two cities with a combined annual output of less than 2 million tons of pig iron. Scrap and long-haul pig iron have also been used in the steel furnaces of plants located at Moscow, Gorky, and elsewhere, which have a combined steel output of 3 million tons.

To the leading iron and steel districts of the Ukraine, the Urals, Siberia, and central European Russia, the Soviet regime has added a number of smaller plants using local coal and scrap or iron ore. An integrated plant at Rustavi in Soviet Georgia uses local coking coal and nearby iron ore from Dashkesan in Azerbaidzhan. It produced 803,000 metric tons of steel in 1957. Another integrated plant, at Cherepovets, in northern European Russia, uses coking coal from Vorkuta and iron ore from the Kola Peninsula. Other outlying plants are limited to steel production. They include steel plants at Begovat

(Uzbek S.S.R.), Temir-Tau (Kazakh S.S.R.), Stalingrad (Volga Valley), Petrovsk (eastern Siberia), and Komsomolsk (Soviet Far East). Changes in the distribution of the Soviet iron-ore and steel industry are shown in Tables 29 and 30, Appendix III.

Closely associated with the iron and steel industry is the production of ferroalloys. Manganese, the most important of these alloys because it is indispensable in the production of steel, is mined at Chiatura in Soviet Georgia and at Nikopol in the Ukraine. These two deposits alone account for about two-thirds of the world's manganese production. In 1955, out of the U.S.S.R.'s manganese production of 4.7 million metric tons, Chiatura produced 2.8 million metric tons and Nikopol 1.7 million metric tons, with lesser amounts mined in the Urals, Siberia, and Kazakhstan. During the seven-year plan, the Ukraine is expected to catch up with Georgia's production and become the world's leading manganese producer, with an output of about 4 million metric tons in 1965.

Non-ferrous Metals. Intensive geological exploration throughout the vast territory of the U.S.S.R. has uncovered adequate reserves of virtually all non-ferrous metals needed by a modern industrial economy. Until World War II the chief centers of the copper industry were in the Urals, where production began in the early eighteenth century. As late as 1937, the Urals smelted 84.2 per cent of the Soviet Union's copper. Since then the development of the copper deposits of Kazakhstan, notably at Balkhash and Dzhezkazgan, has placed this Soviet Asian republic in the lead with about 45 per cent of the country's copper-smelter output, and more than 60 per cent of the nation's copper-ore production. Copper is also produced in Armenia (at Alaverdi) and in the Uzbek S.S.R. (at Almalyk).

Lead and zinc are commonly found together in so-called polymetallic ores, with which silver, gold, copper, and other metals may also be associated. The chief Soviet mining region of lead-zinc ores is the Altai region of eastern Kazakhstan. Lead is usually smelted near the mines because it requires a large degree of concentration and relatively little coal. The principal Soviet lead smelters are therefore located near the nation's zinc- and lead-mining areas: Chimkent and Leninogorsk, in Kazakhstan; Ordzhonikidze, in the northern Caucasus; and Tetyukhe, in the Soviet Far East. Zinc, on the other hand, must be shipped to cheap power sources for electrolytic processing. The Soviet Union's zinc is refined in the Donets Basin (at Konstantinovka), in the Urals (at Chelyabinsk), in the Kuznetsk Basin (at Belovo), in the northern Caucasus (at Ordzhonikidze), and at the large Ust-Kamenogorsk plant, completed in 1955.

The first Soviet aluminum was produced in 1932 at Volkhov, near Leningrad, on the basis of bauxite mined nearby at Boksitogorsk. A second aluminum plant was opened later in Zaporozhe, on the Dnieper. During World War II, when these two plants were partly dismantled and moved eastward, the Soviet aluminum industry developed in the Urals at Kamensk and Krasnoturinsk, on the basis of bauxite mined at Severouralsk. Although new aluminum plants were built during and after the war, in Siberia (at Stalinsk), in Transcaucasia (at Yerevan and Sumgait), and in northern European Russia (at Kandalaksha and Nadvoitsy), the Urals retained their dominant position, producing about 80 per cent of the country's alumina (an intermediate product) and 40 per cent of the aluminum. The seven-year plan calls for the construction of a large aluminum plant at Krasnoyarsk, in Siberia, utilizing nephelite (a low-grade aluminum silicate). Another non-bauxitic raw material, alunite, is to be processed and used in Transcaucasia.

Nickel production is centered in the Urals at Verkhni Ufalei, Rezh, and Orsk. Other plants are located at Monchegorsk and Nikel in the Kola Peninsula and at Norilsk in north-central Siberia. Most of the mining and processing of other non-ferrous and rare metals—tin, mercury, tungsten, molybdenum, and gold—takes place in the Asian U.S.S.R., particularly in the Kolyma Basin, Transbaikalia, central Asia, and the Altai.

During the seven-year plan, stress will be laid on the development of metals with growing applications in electronics, jet propulsion, and other modern technologies, including titanium, germanium, and silicon. The Soviet authorities also plan to place into full production large diamond deposits recently discovered in Yakutia (Siberia).

Manufacturing. In the past, manufacturing (particularly metal fabricating) was concentrated in Leningrad, Moscow, Gorky, Kharkov, Riga, and other cities of central and western Russia. Although the old manufacturing centers still retain a dominant position in national production, metal fabricating is now distributed throughout the entire country. In 1955, the European part of the Soviet Union accounted for three-fourths of the machinery output while the share of the Urals and the rest of the U.S.S.R. was one-eighth each. During the seven-year plan, further emphasis is to be given to the development of manufacturing in Siberia and Kazakhstan.

The production of heavy machinery, such as mining and metallurgical equipment, is oriented toward sources of raw steel. The largest centers in this category are Sverdlovsk, in the Urals; Kramatorsk, in the Donets Basin; and Novosibirsk, near the Kuznetsk Basin.

Since the building of railroad rolling stock requires large amounts of steel, the production of locomotives also gravitates toward steel-producing areas, with diesel engines being produced at Kharkov and Lugansk, and electric locomotives at Novocherkassk, all near the Donets Basin. Farm machinery, on the other hand, is manufactured near consumer areas, because of the great bulk of the finished product and the need for adapting it to local conditions. The largest producers of agricultural implements are at Rostov, in southern European Russia; at Saratov, in the Volga Valley; at Kurgan and Omsk, in western Siberia; and at Tashkent, in central Asia. Other manufacturing plants working for specific industries also tend to be located near such industries. For example, most of the Soviet Union's petroleum equipment still originates in the old oil centers of Baku and Grozny, and textile machinery is manufactured predominantly in the Moscow-Ivanovo textile belt of central European Russia.

Automobile and tractor plants have been sited, in the Soviet Union, with respect to proximity to suppliers of steel products and to consumer areas and with respect to the availability of skilled labor. The first Soviet automobile plants were located in Moscow, Gorky, and Yaroslavl, all in central European Russia. Under the impetus of World War II and postwar expansion, further auto plants were built in the Urals (at Miass), in the Volga Valley (at Ulyanovsk), in Transcaucasia (at Kutaisi), and at Minsk. The earliest Soviet tractor plants were at Stalingrad, Kharkov, and Chelyabinsk. New plants are located at Vladimir and Lipetsk, in central European Russia; at Rubtsovsk, in western Siberia; and at Minsk.

The Soviet chemical industry stresses the manufacture of fertilizers to insure higher agricultural yields. The apatite ore of the Kola Peninsula supplies about 80 per cent of all the raw material for the phosphate-fertilizer industry. The principal superphosphate plants are located at Leningrad, Odessa, Konstantinovka, Dzerzhinsk, Perm, and Alga (near Aktyubinsk). Other phosphate sources are the phosphorite deposits of Chulak-Tau, in southern Kazakhstan, supplying superphosphate plants at Dzhambul, Samarkand, Kokand, and Chardzhou in central Asia, and high-phosphorus blast-furnace slag, produced at Zhdanov as a by-product of the smelting of Kerch iron ore. Low-grade phosphate rock found in several parts of European Russia is used to make simple ground fertilizer for application in the non-chernozem belt.

Nitrogen fertilizers have been obtained in the U.S.S.R. either as a by-product of coke-oven installations or by synthesis from the air. Most of the Soviet nitrogen-fertilizer plants are located near coal sources: Gorlovka, in the Donets Basin; Kemerovo, in the Kuznetsk

Basin; Stalinogorsk, in the Moscow basin; and Berezniki, in the Kizel Basin of the Urals. The Chirchik fertilizer plant in the Uzbek S.S.R. uses cheap hydroelectric power for nitrogen fixation from the air and water. Under the seven-year plan, increasing amounts of Soviet nitrogen are to be derived from natural gas, and by 1965 this new Soviet fuel source is to account for more than half the nitrogen-fertilizer production.

Potash fertilizer has been produced in the Urals, at Berezniki and Solikamsk, and at Kalush, in the Ukraine. A third potash center is under construction during the seven-year plan at Starobin in Belorussia, on the base of newly discovered deposits.

Other chemical raw materials found in the U.S.S.R. include rock salt (at Artemovsk, in the Donbas; in Lake Baskunchak, on the lower Volga; and elsewhere), mirabilite or Glauber salt (in the Kara-Bogaz-Gol inlet, of the Caspian), and native sulphur (in the Kara-Kum desert, of Turkmenia; at Alekseyevka, near Kuibyshev; and at the new Rozdol mine, of the western Ukraine). Most of the Soviet Union's sulphuric acid is derived from pyrites and from non-ferrous smelter gases, rather than from native sulphur.

In the absence of natural rubber sources, the U.S.S.R. placed early emphasis on the development of a synthetic-rubber industry. Starting in the early 1930's, it built synthetic-rubber plants in central European Russia (at Yaroslavl, Voronezh, Tambov, Yefremov, and Kazan), utilizing potato and grain alcohol to make general-purpose synthetic rubber by the butadiene process. Another method, based on limestone, was used by a plant at Yerevan (Armenia) to make a special-purpose synthetic rubber known as chloroprene or neoprene. In recent years, in an effort to save feed crops for greater livestock production, Soviet authorities have pressed for the substitution of petroleum gases as a raw material for synthetic-rubber production. The first Soviet synthetic-rubber plant utilizing oil-refinery gases went into operation in 1953 at Sumgait, near Baku. Since then, additional rubber plants based on petrochemicals have been built in the petroleum-bearing province of the Volga-Urals, at Sterlitamak (Bashkir A.S.S.R.) and Stavropol (Kuibyshev *Oblast*). Another synthetic-rubber plant using limestone as an initial material has been built at Temir-Tau, in Kazakhstan.

With an upsurge of the petrochemical and natural-gas industries during the seven-year plan, the Soviet Union proposes to enter industrial chemical fields that it neglected until now. These include synthetic resins, plastics, synthetic fibers, and detergents. The proposed shift is particularly dramatic in the textile field. Out of 500 million meters of "woolen" goods planned for 1965, 450 million meters, or

90 per cent, are to be made of man-made fibers. Similarly in the silk industry, out of 1.5 billion meters of cloth about 85 per cent is scheduled to be synthetic.

In view of the immense amount of new industrial construction in the U.S.S.R., emphasis is still being given to expansion of the building-materials industry. The policy has been to provide each major economic area with its local production, and, therefore, no concentration of the industry is evident. However, the production of cement has been traditionally associated with two major centers—Volsk, on the middle Volga, and Novorossisk, on the Black Sea. The recent conversion of kilns at these two centers from coal burning to cheaper natural gas illustrates the impact the new fuel is having on the Soviet economy. In the future, a new cement source is expected to be added to traditional raw materials (cement rock or limestone). This will be the cement obtained as a by-product from the processing of nephelite to alumina in the new Siberian aluminum industry.

Timber is one of the Soviet Union's leading resources. About 30 per cent of the country is in forest, which accounts for more than one-fifth of the world's total wooded area. The Soviet Union's forests are especially valuable because 80 per cent of the stands consist of coniferous woods used for construction lumber and pulpwood. As with so many of the Soviet Union's resources, most of the timber is found east of the Urals, in Siberia, far from the main population centers. Because of the inaccessibility of most of the Siberian timber stands, the center of gravity of the industry remains in the European U.S.S.R. Sawmills are typically located at the mouths of northern rivers used for logging or at river-rail crossings. Some of the leading sawmilling centers in European Russia are Archangel, the Soviet Union's chief timber-export port, and Leningrad and Stalingrad, where logging routes terminate. In Siberia, most of the timber is processed along the Trans-Siberian Railroad, except for the northern Siberian port of Igarka, which ships out sawn wood during the brief Arctic ice-free navigation season.

The plywood industry, which uses the deciduous birch and alder as raw material, is concentrated in the mixed-forest belt in the middle and western reaches of the European U.S.S.R. Paper mills, in contrast, use coniferous softwoods and are located predominantly as large integrated plants in the European north. Most of the Soviet pulp and paper mills lie north of the line Kiev-Moscow-Gorky-Perm, with older centers toward the west and newer plants toward the east.

Cotton milling is the most important branch of the Soviet textile industry. It continues to be concentrated in the old production centers of the Moscow-Ivanovo region and Leningrad, which still supply more than 80 per cent of the cotton cloth. However, new mills have been established in the cotton-growing areas of central Asia and Transcaucasia, as well as in other textile-consuming areas, such as the Ukraine, the Volga Valley, the Urals, and Siberia.

The Soviet Union is one of the few remaining producers of linen. This industry was traditionally located in the Central Industrial Region of European Russia, with Vyazniki and Kostroma as the principal centers. Under Soviet rule, new mills have been established in flax-growing areas of western European Russia, notably at Smolensk and Pskov and in Belorussia. Under the seven-year plan, linen mills are planned for Zhitomir and Rovno, in the flax-growing areas of the western Ukraine.

The Soviet woolen industry has had its traditional textile centers in the Moscow and Leningrad areas, for fine cloths, and in the Central Chernozem Region and the middle Volga, for coarse cloths. In recent years, the industry has been further decentralized with the establishment of new woolen mills in sheep-raising areas (the Caucasus and central Asia) and in other consumption centers, such as the Ukraine.

In the food-processing sphere, the U.S.S.R. occupies a leading place in the world in the production of wheat flour and beet sugar. The food industry is widely distributed with a view to local self-sufficiency. The largest food-processing centers are located both in consumption areas and in agricultural regions. Meat-packing plants, for example, are found in such large urban centers as Moscow, Leningrad, Gorky, and Sverdlovsk as well as in the stock-raising areas of the Volga Valley, Kazakhstan, and Siberia. Dairying has two favored locations for butter production—the Vologda region in the northern European U.S.S.R. and the Omsk-Novosibirsk belt of western Siberia. The canning of fruit and vegetables is markedly found in the northern Caucasus, the Ukraine, and Moldavia.

Transportation

In a country the size of the Soviet Union, where production and consumption centers are often thousands of miles apart, modern means of transportation are of vital importance. The U.S.S.R.'s transportation net has been shaped by a number of geographic factors. The predominance of lowland country has offered few obstacles to the building of railroads. Most of the rivers, in contrast, are frozen 3 to 9 months a year, the navigation season being longest in the southwest and shortest in the northeast. Moreover, the largest rivers flow through the virtually undeveloped forests of Siberia to an Arctic

Ocean that is frozen most of the year, thus restricting economic utilization of the greatest natural waterways. Highways have played a negligible role because of the Soviet lag in the construction of roads and in the production of motor vehicles. Coastwise shipping, while of some importance, is beneficial only where raw materials and consumers are located near the seaboard. As a result of these factors, it easily becomes apparent that railroad transportation greatly outweighs all other means of transport in the Soviet Union. In 1955, railroads accounted for 83.4 per cent of all freight traffic, followed by waterways (inland and coastal) with 11.7 per cent, trucking with 3.7 per cent, and pipelines with 1.2 per cent.

A glance at the railroad map of the U.S.S.R. (Fig. 9–14) shows a relatively dense net (approaching the density found in Western Europe) west of the line Kharkov-Moscow-Leningrad, a gradual thinning out toward the Urals, and east of the Urals only isolated strands, seemingly lost in the vast regions they traverse. In the European U.S.S.R., where Moscow is the natural center of the rail net, the greatest density of lines is found in the Central Industrial Region and in the Ukraine, notably the Donets Basin.

Since the Bolshevik Revolution in 1917, when the new Soviet state inherited 44,000 miles of lines, the length of the Soviet railroads has risen by nearly 80 per cent. With a total system of 75,000 miles in 1956, the Soviet Union was second only to the United States in the length of railroad lines. Tsarist railroad construction, which proceeded rapidly after the 1870's, was restricted almost entirely to European Russia, with only the Trans-Siberian and the Trans-Caspian railroads extending into the outlying regions of Siberia and central Asia. About 85 per cent of the tsarist-Russian railroad net was located in European Russia. Soviet rail construction, in contrast, was motivated largely by a desire to obtain access to raw materials and potential industrial sites in the outlying regions. As a consequence, the overwhelming majority of new lines were laid to reach these sites. Among the most important railroad projects of Soviet times are the Turkestan-Siberia Railroad, paralleling the Trans-Siberian between Magnitogorsk and Taishet; the north-south Trans-Kazakhstan Railroad, through Karaganda; and the Pechora line to the Vorkuta coal basin in the remote Arctic section of northern European Russia. The Trans-Siberian Railroad and other important lines have been double-tracked to increase their capacity.

Although the length of lines in operation is only about one-third of that in the United States, railroad freight volume has risen rapidly in recent years with increased production of major commodities. Since 1955, Soviet railroads have carried more freight every year than

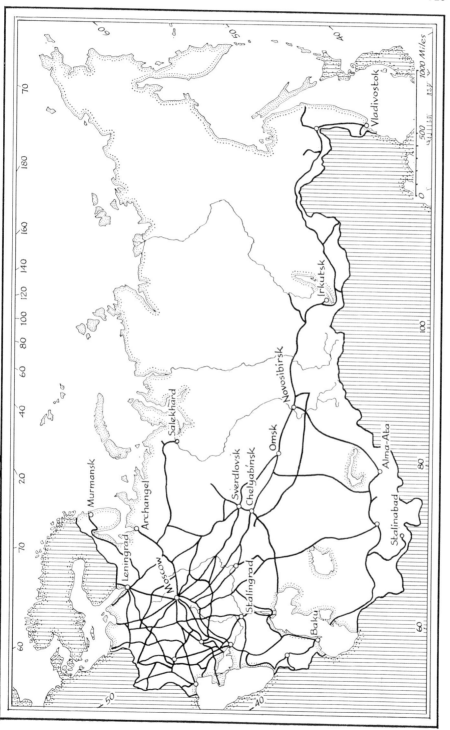

Fig. 9-14. Main railways.

United States railroads, which means that Soviet freight-traffic density (ton-miles of freight per mile of road) is more than three times as high as it is in the United States. However, modernization of equipment has lagged behind the heavy use that is being made of the Soviet railroad system. In 1958, steam locomotives still accounted for 74 per cent of all railroad traffic. Under the seven-year plan, however, the production of steam locomotives is to be sharply curtailed in favor of diesel and electric engines, and by 1965 the Soviet Union expects to cut the traffic share of steam locomotives to 15 per cent. Major railroads that are to be electrified under the seven-year plan include the Trans-Siberian, Moscow-Gorky-Sverdlovsk, Moscow-Kazan-Sverdlovsk, and Moscow-Rostov-Caucasus.

In spite of the natural handicap imposed by the long winter season, the waterways of the Soviet Union, particularly of the European part, play a major role in carrying freight during the open season. The total length of navigable waterways is about 80,000 miles. Although much of this mileage is accounted for by the great Siberian rivers, these play a relatively minor role in transportation. About half the waterway traffic is handled by the Volga River and its tributaries. If the northwestern rivers (including the Neva, at Leningrad) are included in the Volga system, we find that less than one-quarter of the navigable waterways of the U.S.S.R. carry 70 per cent of the river traffic.

The dominant position of the Volga system is explained by the fact that it serves the most populated and economically the most developed part of the country. The Volga system extends from the Baltic to the Caspian and from Moscow to the Urals, thus covering most of European Russia. The Volga's position has been further enhanced by the construction of canals linking it to other river systems of European Russia. The eighteenth-century Mariinsk canal system, to be enlarged and modernized during the seven-year plan, links the upper Volga with Leningrad. This major Baltic port, in turn, is connected with the White Sea by the Baltic-White Sea Canal, completed in the early 1930's. The upper Volga is linked with Moscow by a canal completed in 1937. The Volga River is also connected with the Don River, and thus with the Sea of Azov and the Black Sea, by the Volga-Don Canal, at Stalingrad, completed in 1952. The Volga-Don Canal is navigable only for shallow river boats, thus limiting its usefulness as a transport route.

In view of the continental character of the Soviet Union, maritime shipping plays a distinctly subsidiary role. However, a large part of Soviet foreign trade is sea-borne, and from this point of view shipping is of some importance. The Black Sea handles more than half of

Soviet overseas trade, particularly oil, grains, and coal. The leading Black Sea ports are Odessa, Nikolayev, Zhdanov (on the Sea of Azov), Novorossisk, and Batumi. On the Caspian Sea, the coastwise shipping of petroleum and petroleum products between the ports of Baku, Astrakhan, Makhachkala, and Krasnovodsk accounts for a substantial share of Soviet water freight. The Baltic Sea is the shortest route from the Soviet Union to the Atlantic Ocean. Some of the Baltic ports such as Leningrad, Tallinn, and Riga are frozen in during part of the winter, but others farther west (Liepaja, Kaliningrad) can be kept open. The Arctic seacoast of European Russia is accessible all year in the area of Murmansk, thanks to the North Atlantic Drift. Archangel, the White Sea port, is frozen in during the winter. Although the remainder of the Arctic coast in Siberia is frozen 9 months a year, some ships, aided by icebreakers, use the so-called Northern Sea Route during the brief navigation season, to carry goods from the European Arctic to the Soviet Pacific area. There the principal ports are Petropavlovsk, on the Kamchatka Peninsula, and Vladivostok, the eastern terminus of the Trans-Siberian Railroad. Because of the lack of other means of transport, shipping routes are the lifelines in the Soviet Far East, maintaining links between the mainland and the outlying Soviet settlements on Sakhalin, Kamchatka, and northeastern Siberia. A new port, Nakhodka, which has been developed in recent years, east of Vladivostok, because of its ice-free harbor handles most of the Soviet Union's foreign trade in the Pacific. Vladivostok, the former main Pacific port, is plagued by ice during the winter.

Trucking plays a minor role in the Soviet freight-forwarding scheme. Long-distance trucking such as the coast-to-coast services in the United States is virtually unknown. Trucks handle primarily short-distance hauls to and from railroads and river landings, as well as between nearby urban centers. The total length of hard-topped roads in the Soviet Union is 135,000 miles, of which only 30,000 miles are asphalt-covered or concrete highways. The highway net of European Russia has been improved somewhat in recent years with the construction of first-class highways between Moscow and Brest (on the Polish border), Simferopol (in the Crimea), Yaroslavl, Kazan, Kuibyshev, Leningrad, and other cities.

The Soviet Union has an active air transport system, with a total length of 125,000 miles of scheduled air lines. These are especially important in northern Siberia, where, except for sleds and ships in summer, they provide the only means of transport, although at infrequent intervals. Elsewhere, the most heavily traveled routes parallel the Trans-Siberian Railroad and other major rail lines.

Foreign Trade

The foreign trade of the U.S.S.R. has been increasing rapidly in recent years, as a result of a government policy change designed to strengthen trade relations with other countries. The volume of Soviet foreign trade rose from $1.8 billion in 1946 to $8.3 billion in 1957 when it accounted for 3.6 per cent of all world trade. About three-fourths of the Soviet Union's trade is with other Communist countries. The Soviet Union is the leading trade partner of nearly all the Communist countries, and its share in the foreign trade of these countries as of 1957 ranged from 97 per cent for Albania and 82 per cent for Outer Mongolia down to 45 per cent for East Germany and 44 per cent for China. Only in the case of remote North Viet-Nam does the Soviet Union play a lesser role, accounting for only 9 per cent of the total foreign trade of that country. The leading trade partners of the Soviet Union are East Germany, China, Czechoslovakia, Poland, Hungary, Rumania, and Bulgaria. Among the other European countries, the U.S.S.R. does most of its trading with Britain and Finland. Among the underdeveloped countries of the world, the principal Soviet trade partners are the United Arab Republic and India.

Almost half the exports of the Soviet Union consist of the products of heavy industry. The U.S.S.R. has become a major exporter of machinery and industrial equipment, having risen from eleventh place in 1950 in the export of these categories to fifth place in 1957, after the United States, Britain, and West and East Germany. The Soviet Union is also an important exporter of ores and metals. Its exports of iron ore, which amounted to 11 million metric tons in 1957, were exceeded only by those of Canada, Sweden, and France. In shipments of manganese ore, pig iron, and aluminum, the Soviet Union was in second place in 1957 among world traders. Coal, crude oil, and refined oil products are also significant export items. In 1957 the Soviet Union exported 3.5 million cubic meters of sawn wood, placing third after Canada and Sweden. A number of chemical products figure importantly in Soviet foreign trade. They include synthetic rubber, of which the Soviet Union is the fourth-largest exporter, and apatite concentrate, a fertilizer raw material. The Soviet Union accounts for one-third of world exports of naphthalene and one-fifth of world exports of turpentine. In the realm of agricultural products, the Soviet Union is second among world exporters of flax fiber (after Belgium) and third for cotton and grain. Other traditional Soviet exports are furs and asbestos.

As for imports, the Soviet Union has been a traditional buyer of machinery and industrial equipment. In 1932, when the Soviet Union was in its early stages of industrialization, it imported almost half of all the machinery and equipment that entered world trade channels. With increasing development of domestic machinery-fabricating industries, the Soviet Union's needs for such imports have decreased somewhat, but it is still an important buyer of such goods, second only to Canada. Typical Soviet imports are tropical products such as coffee, cocoa beans, and natural rubber. With 146,000 metric tons in 1957, the Soviet Union was the third-largest buyer of natural rubber. Other imports are rice, salt herring, and rawhide, as well as chemical fibers.

The increasingly important role played by the Soviet Union in world trade is due to a large extent to its industrialization program. This program continues to receive high priority in the current seven-year plan (1959–65). However, stress should be laid on the fact that, in contrast to its earlier period, the Soviet Union is giving increasing attention to the production of consumer goods and to raising the standard of living. While the early five-year plans were concerned mainly with basic industries such as coal, iron and steel, industrial machinery, and heavy chemicals, the current effort stresses the development of cheap petroleum and natural-gas resources and the growth of a chemical industry able to produce cheap plastics and other synthetics for the Soviet consumer. At the same time, Soviet economic planners are promoting greater mechanization and increased efficiency in agriculture, which has been a long-neglected sector of the Soviet economy. The trend toward economic modernization is evident even in transportation, where diesel and electric traction is gradually replacing steam. Thus, having reached a stage of industrial development second only to that of the United States, the Soviet Union can be expected during the next few years to modernize its economy and to seek greater efficiency of production in order to attain its ultimate goal of surpassing the United States.

BIBLIOGRAPHY

(Major references are asterisked.)

Books in English

*Balzak, S. S., Vasyutin, V. F., and Feigin, Ya. G. *Economic Geography of the U.S.S.R.* American edition edited by Chauncy D. Harris. New York: The Macmillan Co., 1949.

*Berg, Lev S. *The Natural Regions of the U.S.S.R.* New York: The Macmillan Co., 1950.

CLARK, M. GARDNER. The Economics of Soviet Steel. Cambridge, Mass.: Harvard University Press, 1956.

HARDT, JOHN P. Economics of the Soviet Electric Power Industry. Montgomery, Ala.: Air University Press, 1955.

HUNTER, HOLLAND. Soviet Transportation Policy. Cambridge, Mass.: Harvard University Press, 1957.

*SCHWARTZ, HARRY. Russia's Soviet Economy, 2d ed. Englewood Cliffs, N. J.: Prentice-Hall, Inc., 1954.

*SHABAD, THEODORE. Geography of the U.S.S.R.: A Regional Survey. New York: Columbia University Press, 1951.

SHABAD, THEODORE. The Soviet Aluminum Industry. New York: American Metal Market Co., 1958.

SHIMKIN, DEMITRI B. Minerals: A Key to Soviet Power. Cambridge, Mass.: Harvard University Press, 1953.

Books in Foreign Languages

BARANSKIY, N. N. Ekonomicheskaya Geografiya S.S.S.R. (Economic Geography of the U.S.S.R.), 16th ed. Moscow: Uchpedgiz, 1955.

CHEFRANOV, S. V. Fizicheskaya Geografiya S.S.S.R. (Physical Geography of the U.S.S.R.), 12th ed. Moscow: Uchpedgiz, 1953.

DOBRYNIN, B. F. Fizicheskaya Geografiya S.S.S.R. (Physical Geography of the U.S.S.R.). Moscow: Uchpedgiz, 1948.

LEIMBACH, WERNER. Die Sowjetunion: Natur, Volk, Wirtschaft (The Soviet Union: The Land, Its People, and the Economy). Stuttgart: Franck'sche Verlag, 1950.

LYALIKOV, N. I. Ekonomicheskaya Geografiya S.S.S.R. (Economic Geography of the U.S.S.R.). 2d ed. Moscow: Uchpedgiz, 1958.

MILKOV, F. N., and N. A. GVOZDETSKY. Fizicheskaya Geografiya S.S.S.R. (Physical Geography of the U.S.S.R.). Moscow: Geografizdat, 1958.

STROYEV, K. F. Fizicheskaya Geografiya S.S.S.R. (Physical Geography of the U.S.S.R.). 2d ed. Moscow: Uchpedgiz, 1958.

Articles

HOOSON, DAVID J. M. "The Middle Volga: An Emerging Focal Region in the Soviet Union," The Geographical Journal 76 (June, 1960): 181–90.

HUNTER, HOLLAND. "Soviet Transportation: How It Functions Today," Automotive Industries 118 (January, 1958): 96–7.

JACKSON, W. A. DOUGLAS. "The Virgin and Idle Lands of Western Siberia and North Kazakhstan: A Geographical Appraisal," Geographical Review 46 (January, 1956): 1–19.

MILLER, J. "The Decentralization of Industry," Soviet Studies 9 (July, 1957): 65–84.

NEWTH, J. A. "Some Trends in the Soviet Population," Soviet Studies 10 (January, 1959): 252–79.

ROOF, MICHAEL K., and LEEDY, FREDERICK A. "Population Redistribution in the Soviet Union," Geographical Review 49 (April, 1959): 208–21.

WILLIAMS, ERNEST W. "Freight Transportation in the Soviet Union," Proceedings of the American Economic Association 48 (May, 1958): 412–22.

10

Europe's Place in the World

The Introduction and first two chapters of this book reviewed Europe and its borderlands as a whole and discussed, in particular, the principal features of their physical, historical, and economic geography. Succeeding chapters described and explained the main regional divisions of Europe and also those of countries which merge with its eastern marchlands, namely, the U.S.S.R. and Turkey. The reader will have become well aware that Europe, as conventionally delimited by the Ural Mountains, is indeed only a geographical expression which has merely continuity but no unity of a political, economic, or cultural kind. Indeed, on the simplest basis, Europe consists of two contrasting and divergent units, as unequal in area as they are unlike in ideology and in forms of government and, in addition, some other countries, including Yugoslavia, Sweden, Switzerland, and Austria, which are unattached to either group. Moreover, these two parts are in no sense socially homogeneous units; rather they consist of assemblages of nations culturally distinguished by their long and distinctive histories.

It is clearly fitting, as a conclusion to this collaborative study, to look again at Europe and its borderlands, taking note of their degree of cultural differentiation, to try to underline their distinguishing characteristics, and to assess the part which they play in the world. Clearly, we shall be mainly concerned, on the one hand, with Europe west of the Iron Curtain and, on the other, with the U.S.S.R. and its satellites. We shall look at these from within and from without and consider their economic status, their political patterns, and their immediate prospects.

EUROPE'S INDUSTRIAL ADVANCE

The extent, degree, and speed with which the many sharp social and economic changes associated with the Industrial Revolution took place in the different countries of Europe varied considerably. This revolution was already in progress in the United Kingdom in the late eighteenth century, whereas it had little affected tsarist Russia before the early twentieth century, while many countries of southern and eastern Europe still remain largely agricultural in their economies.

The expansion of markets and of maritime trade, made possible by the overseas imperialism of Portugal, Spain, the Netherlands, France, and Britain, stimulated industrial expansion in western Europe during the last 150 years. Britain was first to be able to expand her markets in every continent, for trade followed the flag. Being internally united, Britain could focus its energy fully on economic expansion. Germany, in contrast, was divided until 1871 into a large number of petty states, thus its market was split into fragments. It was not until the latter half of the nineteenth century, with the creation of a large customs union (the *Zollverein*) and Bismarck's unification policy, that internal trade in Germany became easy and industrial development and expansion could take place rapidly.

The United Kingdom. In Britain the steam engine not only served to drive machines in factories and mines but also offered superior means of transport by railways and steamships. The transport revolution opened up the grasslands of the New World to immigrant farmers and thus enabled the United Kingdom to import increasing quantities of food at low prices, to feed the ever-expanding industrial population. By the mid-nineteenth century Britain had changed from a predominantly agricultural country to the leading industrial country, with a large overseas trade, which exchanged manufactures to pay for necessary food and raw materials. Much of the surplus income from this trade was used for overseas investment; railways, mines, ports, and other installations in many parts of the New World owed their existence to British capital. These investments brought their returns and Britain was soon able to buy more than she sold, by using the interest from her overseas investments to make up the difference. This situation persisted until World War I, when Britain was forced to sell some of her overseas investments; during World War II most of the rest had to be sold to help finance the war effort.

France. This was the second major power to move toward industrialization. Shortage of good-quality, easily mined coal proved one of the chief drawbacks, especially as the coal fields were divorced from the chief ore fields. It was not until after the Thomas-Gilchrist invention of 1878, which made it possible to use the phosphoric iron ore of these fields, that they were fully exploited and the French iron and steel industry became well established. By then France was not far ahead of Germany in the industrial race, and the latter soon overtook her. Industrialization in France, compared with that in the United Kingdom, was slower and less complete, partly because of more modest natural endowment and partly because the policy of protecting agriculture reduced the flow of industrial workers from agriculture. Further, France had smaller overseas markets and a different social attitude toward large-scale industry, which starved it of adequate capital.

Germany. The political fragmentation of Germany—the so-called German Confederation—long remained a formidable obstacle to industrial progress. The cost of sending goods across so many frontiers was prohibitive, so trade and industry stagnated. The establishment by the Great Powers in 1815 of free navigation on the Rhine, following Napoleon's overthrow of a medley of feudal principalities there, marked one advance, while a yet greater advance was made by the *Zollverein*, which, from its beginning in the 1830's, gradually grew to include most of the major states. However, the real era of large-scale industrial development began under the leadership of Prince Bismarck, after the successful conclusion of the Franco-Prussian War of 1870–71, which won eastern Lorraine and Alsace for the newly established German Empire. Germany, like Britain, possessed much good-quality coking coal (in the Ruhr and Upper Silesian fields) and some iron ore, while more of the latter could be obtained from Sweden and Lorraine. In the center of peninsular Europe, therefore, a large European trade area developed, especially east of and along the Rhine; canals were dug and railways were built to provide necessary transport facilities. As a late starter, Germany benefited by the mistakes, experience, and inventions of others. Thus, by 1900 she had become a powerful industrial country. Also entering late the competition for colonial territories, she joined in the final scramble for Africa and, not being satisfied there, looked for further politico-economic conquests in Europe—with disastrous results in two wars world-wide in extent.

Austria-Hungary. Until its collapse in 1918 at the close of World War I, this multinational empire, ruled by the Hapsburg dynasty from its capitals at Vienna and Budapest, comprised a considerable area mainly within the Danube Basin and enjoyed outlets to the sea at the head of the Adriatic. Toward the end of the nineteenth century modern industries were established in its chief towns and in Bohemia, the Empire's "workshop." Bohemia provided the bulk of the Empire's coal and iron ore, while important consumer industries were developed in and around Prague and Pilsen. The Danube River, internationalized in 1856, together with railways, provided means of transport within the Empire, which, except for Dalmatia, became a single customs unit in 1866.

Russia. Industrial progress came late to Russia. Even so, before 1900 her production of petroleum was the highest in the world and by 1913 that of coal, pig iron, and steel was roughly at the level reached in France. The emancipation of the serfs in 1861, the adoption of the gold standard in 1897, and the resort to foreign capital (especially from France) marked stages toward modern industrialization. Railway building, late to start, was rapid after 1891, and before the outbreak of World War I Russia had a railway system in her European territory and links with her Pacific, central-Asian, and south-Caucasian provinces. Such industries as she had developed were then technologically advanced and were restricted to European Russia. The latter had become the major center of the iron and steel industry based on the Donets coal field and the rich iron-ore deposits of Krivoi Rog, while in and around the capital (St. Petersburg) and Moscow were the two largest single industrial concentrations. The textile industry, established in factories at Moscow, Ivanovo, St. Petersburg, and Lódź (Polish part of Russia), was relatively large, was using Russian-grown flax, and was already drawing one-third of its supplies of raw cotton from Russian central Asia. The sugar-beet industry in the Ukraine had also been built up. But Russia was still a land of peasant farming and of surpluses of primary products (grain, flax, hemp, timber), and her very considerable industrial resources, especially those which lay beyond the Volga, remained largely untapped before the planned development of the U.S.S.R. began a generation ago.

THE EFFECTS OF TWO WORLD WARS ON EUROPE

World War I had considerable economic effects upon both victors and losers. Large amounts of property, private and industrial, were destroyed, the economic life of the continent was disrupted, and several million people were killed or died as a result of war. It was followed by a period of inflation and economic unheaval and, although some degree of economic stability was achieved in the late 1920's, this was soon disrupted in the 1930's. The economic depression was first evidenced by the Wall Street crash of 1929, which was followed by the failure of some European banks and a period of depression which lasted well into the 1930's. Although recovery began during the later 1930's, it was cut short by the outbreak of World War II.

An unforeseen result of World War I was the Bolshevik Revolution of 1917 and the creation, in place of the Russian Empire, of a territorially reduced and federated Soviet Union or U.S.S.R. The Soviet Union soon vigorously set about the planned development of its economy and its defense forces.

Tsarist Russia was not alone in being brought to ruin by the unbearable strains of World War I. This period also witnessed the collapse of the German, Austro-Hungarian, and Ottoman empires and, out of their ruins, the emergence of many new national states: Poland, Austria, Hungary, Czechoslovakia, Yugoslavia, Turkey, and the four Baltic republics. But the interwar period (1919–39) was marked also by the rise of dictators in several countries, notably, Hitler in Germany, Mussolini in Italy, and Franco in Spain. And dictatorships, as history abundantly shows, commonly lead to wars; in this case, World War II, which established beyond doubt the primacy of the United States in the Western world.

The second world war, like the first, resulted in great loss of life and in destruction which, however, was even greater and more widespread. Once again trade and economic life generally were seriously disrupted, although recovery was remarkably rapid. To the economic rehabilitation of Europe the United States contributed generously and wisely, where its financial and/or technical aid were welcomed.

In the political field the results of World War II were decisive. To effect the defeat of Germany and Japan the industrial and military might of the United States, the manpower of the U.S.S.R., and the resources of the British Commonwealth were all committed. From the conflict the United States and the U.S.S.R. emerged as the only Great Powers. Much had changed geopolitically since 1914, when five of the seven acknowledged Great Powers were in Europe. Moreover, in Europe, as in the world, the legacy of World War II has been division along ideological lines. In Europe, the so-called "Iron Curtain" divides the Western states from the U.S.S.R. and its bordering satellites. It divides Germany into the German Federal Republic and the German Democratic Republic, leaves Yugoslavia under the Communist rule of Marshal Tito, and leaves a few neutral states situated uneasily between Western and Communist Europe. Thus the political pattern or dichotomy of Europe merely reflects the broad geopolitical situation, since in Asia the Communist Chinese People's Republic lowers another curtain, the "Bamboo Curtain."

THE RESOURCES OF EUROPE AND THE U.S.S.R.

With a population estimated for 1960 at nearly 600 million,[1] one of Europe's chief economic resources is clearly labor. Adequate labor, skilled and unskilled, has been available for the industrialization of many countries. Workers have quickly acquired skills, and new technological inventions make possible the continuance of industrial progress. Not only is the population large, but it is also unequally distributed so that the population density in the more industrialized countries is very high and provides a stimulus to local markets, as it also enables them to pay for imported food. The increase of population in Europe over the last hundred years has been remarkable, indeed unprecedented: better living conditions, greater medical knowledge, a steady birth rate, and, above all else, a decreasing death rate lie behind this demographic change which has exerted increasing pressure on the economy. One result of this expansion (and a remedy for its effects) has been large-scale emigration—particularly from Ireland in the last century and, more recently, from Italy and other south-European countries. Since the 1920's, many of the doors formerly open to immigrants have been closed. The United States, for example, has operated a strict quota scheme for a number of years. But emigration, although it relieves temporary pressure, has drawbacks, for it is selective to the disadvantage of the country of origin. The young, strong, and skilled wage earners and professional workers tend to leave, so the country losing emigrants retains a population with an increasing proportion of the less-productive age groups, has therefore a larger burden of social services, and thus may face a declining birth rate and an increasing death rate.

Although its population is still increasing, Europe now has only about a fifth of the world's population (a fourth in 1800). This change is due in part to emigration from Europe but mainly to the more rapid increase of population in other parts of the world, especially in the Americas. Even though Europe's rate of increase has quickened since 1939, its most advanced countries have shown the slowest increases. The aging of population, which characterizes the United Kingdom and other countries of Western Europe,[2] is of considerable economic importance because it means that a greater proportion of people will have to be supported by a declining proportion of workers.

[1] Of this total, 261 million fall to the U.S.S.R. and its seven satellites.

[2] In this chapter we use the term "Western Europe" to denote all of the countries west of the Iron Curtain, rather than the group of countries properly considered under this title in Chapter 5.

Agricultural Resources. The land is Europe's chief inanimate resource. Although Europe is a highly industrialized continent, agriculture, directly or indirectly, provides a livelihood for the greater proportion of its inhabitants. The land yields a wide range of plants useful for foodstuffs and for industry. If the U.S.S.R. is included, this range includes not only food and fodder grains, temperate fruits, sugar beets, and various oil-bearing plants, but also the principal fibers—wool, flax, hemp, cotton, and raw silk—and forest products. Political obstacles limit the freedom of trade exchanges between Western Europe and the U.S.S.R., so, although the Soviet satellites are usefully supplied with cotton and grain by the U.S.S.R., the Western countries look overseas for raw materials, especially wool and cotton, and also for much of their food. Much food has to be imported, in addition to that which Europe is climatically unable to grow. Some countries, especially the United Kingdom, West Germany, Norway, Switzerland, and Greece, have to import a large part of their needs. However, Europe (outside the U.S.S.R.) produces foodstuffs in very considerable quantities; indeed, it accounts for the following percentages of the world's production: wheat 33, barley 43, oats 44, rye 88, maize 14, potatoes 70, and meat 29. And note that Western Europe achieves the highest yields of many temperate crops. For example, wheat yields (in tons per acre) in 1958 were as follows: United Kingdom 1.24, United States 0.73, and Argentina 0.41. Such high yields in Western Europe are the result of more intensive cultivation, and those of the Americas reflect a low man/land ratio. In Western Europe, too, farming is highly capitalized and mechanized. The same is true of the U.S.S.R., where, however, yields per acre are low. On the other hand, there is little mechanization in parts of the continent where labor is abundant and the holdings are very small. Often areas of the highest densities of agricultural population have the lowest agricultural yields, because capital for improvements is lacking. Labor, being plentiful, is often inefficiently employed; as a result there is underemployment or concealed unemployment. Land reforms to create larger holdings are being carried out here and there, while in Eastern Europe cooperative farming marks a new development of the postwar years. In some areas, too, drainage and irrigation schemes should extend the cultivated area and promote agricultural productivity.

Industrial Resources. Europe's industrial equipment is considerable. A series of rich coal fields stretch from Britain, through Belgium and France, across the Rhine to Silesia, and on to the U.S.S.R. The iron ores contained in the Coal Measures, which supplied the coke-fueled blast furnaces of earlier days, have now been worked out, but several rich iron-ore fields occur, lying apart from the coal fields, notably, the low-grade minette ores of Lorraine and Luxembourg, and the high-grade hematites of both Arctic Sweden and Krivoi Rog in the Ukrainian S.S.R. These major resources are supplemented by large deposits of low-grade Jurassic ores (e.g., in Britain) and of hematite (e.g., in Spain and Norway). The current demand for iron ore by the European steel makers has far outgrown home supplies, and much is imported from Canada, North Africa, Venezuela, Brazil (a new source of supply), and elsewhere. Before charcoal was replaced by coke as a smelting agent, the forests of Europe provided ample fuel for the industry, and the streams of this temperate area provided waterpower to maintain the blast. In this century the waterpower resources of Europe are being harnessed for another form of energy—hydroelectricity. These derive principally from Tertiary mountain systems and from the older glaciated highlands of Great Britain and northern Europe, while on some of the large rivers, particularly in the U.S.S.R., Austria, and France, ambitious power projects have been, and still are being carried out. Even more ambitious are the tidal schemes still in the planning stage.

Although well supplied, as a whole, with coal and electric power, Europe, apart from the U.S.S.R., Austria, and Rumania, largely lacks petroleum. There are many small fields in West Germany, France, Hungary, Yugoslavia, the Netherlands, and Great Britain, but these are quite insufficient for domestic needs. The United Kingdom and the Scandinavian countries import 99 per cent and West Germany 70 per cent of their requirements. Recently, atomic energy has been commercially harnessed for electricity generation and atomic-power stations have been and are being constructed in the United Kingdom, France, U.S.S.R., and elsewhere in Europe.

The main manufacturing belt of Europe broadly coincides with the coal fields. From Britain the belt continues through northern France and Lorraine and the Sambre-Meuse valley of Belgium, into the Saar and the Rhine-Westphalian industrial complex, then along the edge of the Harz Mountains and into Silesia, to reappear in the great industrial areas of the European U.S.S.R. Most of these industrial areas contain the chief centers of the iron and steel industry, alongside which have grown heavy engineering and heavy chemical industries. However, with modern developments in transportation, communications, and power transmission, industry has become much more scattered, so some considerable industrial regions are found outside the main belt, particularly around capital cities such as London, Berlin, and Moscow, and around major ports such as Hamburg, Marseille, Göteborg, and Leningrad, while notable industrial areas, depending mainly on "white coal," lie in central Sweden and the Swiss Plateau.

The major industries of the countries of Europe, and in particular the iron and steel industry, have become largely interdependent. Thus, petroleum and textile fibers for certain Eastern European countries come from the U.S.S.R., West Germany imports much of its iron ore from Sweden, and France receives coking coal from the mines of Rhine-Westphalia. A similar interdependence characterizes the heavy engineering industry: steel sheets and billets, for example, are exported from one country to another where they are used for constructional engineering and the manufacture of automobiles. A new industrial development of recent years is oil refining. Whereas formerly much of this was done in the country of origin, the greater part is now done in the country of consumption. And in association with the refineries has grown a large, complex petrochemical industry in such centers as Fawley (England), Hamburg, Rotterdam, and Marseille. Indeed, the chemical industry, using the by-products of the coal, iron and steel, non-ferrous metals, oil, and other industries, has become of very great importance, yielding products which range from explosives to tooth paste, from plastics to dyes, and from fertilizers to drugs.

The light industries make up another group of industries, of considerable scale measured by the numbers employed and by the value of their output. These industries, being market-oriented, are widely scattered, with concentrations in and around capital cities and other large towns. Among their products are radio and television equipment, electric appliances (telephones, washing machines, etc.), clothing, furniture, and food products. These light industries are more developed in countries where the standard of living is high enough to sustain a demand for varied consumer goods and semiluxuries. In such countries, too, the number of service industries multiplies and transport facilities increase. These service industries, notably, finance, banking, and insurance, like the light industries, are found in the more highly developed countries and particularly in London and to a lesser extent in Zurich, Amsterdam, and Copenhagen.

THE PLACE OF EUROPE AND THE U.S.S.R. IN WORLD COMMERCE

The economies of the countries of western Europe recovered much more rapidly after the second than after the first world war, and the expansion of their output and trade has continued steadily since the initial period of rehabilitation. This favorable course of events owed much to the stimulus of Marshall Plan aid and of other such help from the United States.

An acute trade difficulty since the end of World War II has centered on the balance of payments. Before 1914, when sterling was accepted by most of the world as the principal means of payment, this problem did not arise. The position of sterling, however, weakened after World War I, when many countries, including the United Kingdom, abandoned the gold standard, while other currencies acquired greater strength. Thus, in the world after 1945, a sharp division arose between the dollar trade areas of North America and part of Latin America and the sterling area, which is smaller but more populous and more widely spread. The dollar area occupies about 12.6 million square miles and accounts for a population of 300 million, while corresponding figures for the sterling area are 8.4 million square miles and 705 million. The sterling area includes the United Kingdom, other members of the Commonwealth (except Canada), and the British colonies and trust territories, as well as the Republic of Ireland, Burma, Jordan, Libya, Iceland, and the sheikdoms of the Persian Gulf. During postwar years, Western Europe had a shortage of dollars with which to pay for goods from the United States and other dollar suppliers. Although this shortage was partly overcome by various forms of aid and by loans, it led to a severe curtailment and control of imports from these areas. This situation, however, has radically changed; in 1961, sterling, together with other Western European currencies, became again full convertible. Another difficulty greatly hindering the natural flow of trade arose from political obstacles to trade between Western and Eastern Europe.

Despite all difficulties, Western Europe is still responsible for a remarkably high proportion of world trade. Western Europe, i.e., Europe excluding the U.S.S.R. and its satellites, accounts for 41 per cent of the world's exports, compared with 23 per cent for North America. Similarly, Western Europe (so defined) absorbs the greatest share of the world's imports—45 per cent, compared with North America's 19 per cent. In contrast, the share of the U.S.S.R. and its satellites in world trade is small. Since the last 30 years have witnessed the growth of the foreign trade of the United States at a rate faster than that of Western Europe, it may appear surprising that the latter still maintains the paramount position as buyer and supplier in many markets of the world. This does not apply, however, to Latin America, where for various reasons, and in particular because of its investments there, the United States holds the larger share of the trade.

About four-fifths of the imports of Western Europe consist of agricultural products and raw materials, but the importance of agricultural products, which include not only food and fodder but also fibers such as cotton and wool, has declined considerably during the last 20 years, as the following figures suggest:

Agricultural Imports as Percentages of Total Imports

	1938	1959
U.K.	58	37
West Germany	47	27
Netherlands	26	16

Source: United Nations, *Economic Survey of Europe in 1957* (Geneva, 1958); and United Nations, *Economic Survey of Europe in 1959* (Geneva, 1960).

This decline reflects the results both of domestic drives for increased food production and the growing use of home-produced artificial fibers, which has reduced the demand for fibers other than wool, for which demand has actually increased. Among imported fuels petroleum bulks largest, while iron ore and non-ferrous metals make up a substantial share. Petroleum requirements have increased enormously and are reflected in the large volume of shipments from the Middle East, where several oil-producing countries are members of the sterling area. On the other hand, shipments from Venezuela, a dollar country, which was the chief prewar source, have greatly declined in the postwar years. Changes in its ability to buy dollar goods, as well as changes in demand, have altered the sources of Western Europe's imports as the following figures indicate:

Principal Sources of Western Europe's Imports
(per cent)

	1928	1937/8	1952	1958
United States	31	22	22	20
Canada	9	8	9	7
Latin America	21	19	11	12
Overseas sterling areas	25	31	37	32
Affiliated sterling areas	5	10	12	8
Other primary * exporting countries	8	8	8	14

* The term "primary countries" covers the greater number of the countries which depend on the export of primary products. It refers to all such countries outside Europe, North America, Japan, the U.S.S.R., and mainland China.

Source: United Nations, *Economic Survey of Europe in 1957* (Geneva, 1958); and United Nations, *Economic Survey of Europe in 1959* (Geneva, 1960).

About half of Western Europe's imports come from countries within Western Europe and half from overseas. One-third of its exports go to primary overseas markets; these markets, indeed, take 54 per cent of the United Kingdom's exports and 45 per cent of France's, in contrast to 24 per cent of West Germany's exports, since the first two countries have large overseas dependencies and partners. While there has been a marked decline in Europe's exports of textiles to these markets, because the textile industry is one of the first to be developed in countries undergoing industrialization, the export of capital goods has markedly increased. The effect on trade patterns of the Common Market and of proposed free-trade areas, both of which are discussed below, are not yet clear and will not be measurable for some time. While they may result in more trade within Western Europe, they can hardly affect adversely Europe's trade with countries which supply its required agricultural and industrial materials.

Eastern Europe has always played a much less striking part in world trade than has Western Europe, and this was emphasized after World War II by political obstacles to East-West trade, one of which is the embargo placed by the Western powers on the export of strategic goods. Even so, the share of world trade of the U.S.S.R. and its satellite neighbors increased between 1950 and 1957 from 7 per cent to 8.5 per cent. The U.S.S.R. more than doubled the volume of its trade during these years, while its neighbors nearly doubled theirs. It is noteworthy that the trade of this bloc is, for the most part, politically oriented, i.e., directed to Communist countries within the European Soviet bloc, the Chinese People's Republic, the Mongolian People's Republic, North Korea, and North Viet-Nam. Thus in 1957 the U.S.S.R.'s exports to, and imports from, the other countries of the Communist world amounted to three-quarters of her total trade, while the figures for her European satellite neighbors broadly correspond, as the figures below show.

Eastern Europe's Pattern of Trade, by Areas
(per cent)

	1937			1948			1958		
	U.S.S.R.	Peoples' Democracies	Rest of World	U.S.S.R.	Peoples' Democracies	Rest of World	U.S.S.R.	Peoples' Democracies	Rest of World
East Germany	—	—	—		75	25	73		27
Czechoslovakia	1	10	89	16	15	69	70		30
Poland	1	6	93	23	17	60	62		38
Hungary	—	13	87	17	17	66	30	37	33
Rumania*	1	17	82	34	36	30		75	25
Bulgaria	—	12	88	56	27	17	52	25	23

* Figures for Rumania are for 1957.

Sources: For 1937 and 1948, compiled by Nicolas Spulber and published in "Factors in Eastern Europe's Intratrade and Cooperation," *Journal of International Affairs* XI, 1 (1957), p. 23. Figures for 1958, in *Statesman's Yearbook: 1960* (London, 1960).

The European Soviet bloc, and above all the U.S.S.R., is increasingly concerned in supplying not only China, Mongolia, and India but also the United Arab Republic and Iraq, and is at pains to expand its trade with South America, which can offer coffee, hides, and leather.

Within the European Soviet bloc, the trade pattern has changed as these countries, for currency and other reasons, became cut off from Western markets and as the U.S.S.R. set about coordinating their economies. The policy announced in 1957 of unified seven-year plans within the bloc, which aimed to coordinate their production and to overtake that of the "capitalist world," revealed in its outcome local shortages of fuel and, indeed, of grain, whereas both coal and grain had been staple exports of Eastern Europe. It revealed also that, if such plans were to have any measure of success, the U.S.S.R. would have to supply not only petroleum, iron ore, steel, and textile fibers but capital and equipment as well, especially mining equipment for the further exploitation of the Polish coal resources in Upper Silesia. These needed supplies, a tax on the Russian economy, itself geared to rapid expansion and to the supply of its Chinese ally, are clearly on a scale which involves difficulties and problems for the U.S.S.R. Yet it would seem right to envisage the European satellites as, above all, developing industrial and trading units tied to and dependent on their mighty neighbor.

Faced by basic shortages, the U.S.S.R. and Eastern Europe have clearly welcomed some increase of trade with Western Europe. Of the U.S.S.R.'s imports only 10 per cent came from Western Europe in 1950, but these increased to 13 per cent in 1958, while of her exports only 10 per cent went to Western Europe in 1950, but 16 per cent in 1958. Finally, it is important not to underestimate the role which the U.S.S.R. can, and doubtless will, increasingly play in world commerce. In its avowed purpose of showing the world the alleged superiority of the "Socialist camp," it can trade virtually where, when, and how it pleases, as political expediency suggests. A notable example of its methods was its sudden launching on the world market in 1958 of supplies of tin at prices attractively low for consumers and embarrassingly low for Western tin suppliers. Similarly, it supplied Denmark and others with petroleum at prices well below world-market rates.

The effect on Eastern European countries of the proposed Western European moves toward economic integration is likely to be very limited. It will be most felt by Czechoslovakia, which relies on West European markets for her surplus manufactured goods, and in some degree countries which propose starting manufactures will also be affected. Trade between East and West Germany, too, which up to now has been free of tariffs but not of quotas, may also suffer reduction.

In sum, just as there are at least two Europes in world politics, so there are at least two Europes in world trade. Of the two, Western Europe holds the paramount trade position not only on its own continent but also in the world. The trade of the European Soviet bloc, led by the U.S.S.R., is dominant within the Communist world, which accounts for one-third of mankind; its share of other markets, although small, is growing, and any major reduction of its high expenditure on armaments could release a large portion of its industrial capacity for the manufacture of capital goods for export and of domestic consumer goods. In Western Europe, interest currently focuses on the development of the Common Market as a step toward economic (and political) integration, and on the possibility of creating, in addition, so-called free-trade areas. The broad purpose of these experiments is to substitute the strength of unity for the weakness of fragmentation in a world where economic viability imperatively calls for cooperative thought and action.

THE POLITICAL PATTERNS OF EUROPE
AND ITS BORDERLANDS

Reference was made in the Introduction to the remarkable political fragmentation of Europe and in Chapter 2 an attempt was made briefly to explain it. To this special feature of the continent we now return because the state pattern of Europe is a background fact fundamental to the discussion of its current problems, whether these relate to economic affairs, military defense, or movements for political integration. "We are dealing, in the case of Europe," wrote Count Keyserling a generation ago, "with an astoundingly manifold, astoundingly riven structure: the Balkans constitute its truest prototype." [3] The political map of Europe, a map which has been changing throughout history, and markedly since World War I, epitomizes the disunity of Europe, the *genius loci* of which, until recently, has been political parochialism. In sharp contrast to many lands of more recent settlement and development, for example, North America and Australia, Europe presents an assemblage of independent states of every size and shape, ranging from the immensity of the U.S.S.R., which, with its Asian territories, controls 8.6 million square miles of territory, to the minuteness of the Vatican City which controls only 108.7 *acres*. If a count is made of the European states which are sovereign and

[3] Count Hermann Alexander von Keyserling, *Europe* (New York: Harcourt, Brace & Co., Inc., 1928), p. 343.

independent a total of 32 [4] is reached, equivalent to nearly one-third of the world total. This figure includes 2 states which are legally described as "international enclaves," namely, San Marino and the Vatican City, and 2 other microstates, Liechtenstein and Monaco. Ironically enough, the number of independent states in Europe has increased in this century which has witnessed such rapid progress in transportation and communication. Thus if the European states in 1914 are numbered, the total is only 26.

How can we explain this preference for many hedged states rather than for the broader territorial frameworks which exist in the Americas, Austrialia, and the U.S.S.R.? As was suggested in Chapter 2, the answer is to be sought in the long-operative processes by which Europe was settled by peoples who staked their claim to the land. In both geography and history Europe has been lavishly endowed. Notably west of the Vistula, as also in its southeastern peninsula, Europe's countryside expresses physical and human variety and diversity in contracted space. But everywhere throughout the continent separate languages and nationalities developed, as well as national consciousness and nationalism—a powerful force. Nations, proud of their cultural heritages, struck their roots in particular areas, although political boundaries at any particular time paid scant respect to their limits. At the Conference of Versailles after World War I nationalism was so strong and articulate a force that several new European nations arose out of the ruins of stricken empires, with boundaries which only in rough measure respected their claims. As a result, the length of boundaries in Europe increased from 14,000 miles in 1914 to 17,000 miles in 1938,[5] but this change only increased the number of disputed areas of international friction, no less than 56 of which were reliably noted in the interwar period 1919–39.[6] Europe was then made up of nations each pulling its own way with ever-growing determination, to the detriment of its own interests and those of the world.

World War II brought further territorial adjustments. Germany was truncated and partitioned; it remains divided into two very unequal parts, one of which, the German Federal Republic, has benefited economically from the mass movement of refugees from Eastern

[4] Such a simple arithmetical exercise gives justifiably different results. The total of thirty-two includes the German Democratic Republic, but not the Ukraine S.S.R. and the Belorussian S.S.R., although these two are members of the United Nations. Nor does it include Andorra, which is not fully independent.

[5] S. Whittemore Boggs, *International Boundaries* (New York: Columbia University Press, 1940), p. 13.

[6] Richard Hartshorne, "A Survey of Boundary Problems in Europe," *Geographic Aspects of International Relations,* C. C. Colby, ed. (Chicago: University of Chicago Press, 1938).

Europe,[7] notably from East Germany, which has been organized by the U.S.S.R. as the German Democratic Republic. The German capital, too, was divided into occupation zones and a Russian and three "Western" sectors remain, the three last forming unenviably an international exclave in the German Democratic Republic. Austria suffered military occupation and division into four zones, but its unity and independence were restored in 1955, with its neutrality solemnly affirmed by treaty. The three independent republics of Latvia, Lithuania, and Estonia, born after World War I, were incorporated into the Soviet Union, although this change has never received formal international sanction. Poland was drastically reshaped and its access to the Baltic improved by the gain of land from Germany and by losses to the U.S.S.R. The most notable territorial changes brought by World War II, which cast their shadow over the whole continent, are those which enlarged the Soviet Union on its western side. This expansion, which involved the annexation of territories from Finland, Poland, Germany, Czechoslovakia, and Rumania, projected the U.S.S.R. westward into Eastern Europe. Moreover, the shortened, more westerly boundaries of the U.S.S.R. do not mark the effective limit of its penetration, for with some success it has created a tier of politically dependent and, where possible, Communist states. These consist of former cobelligerents such as Poland, ex-enemy states such as Finland, and former enemies *and* cobelligerents such as Rumania. While Finland, rendered militarily defenseless under postwar treaties, has preserved a Western democratic system of government, and while Yugoslavia under Marshal Tito remains a Communist but nationalistic state independent of Moscow and friendly to the West, the other neighbors or near-neighbors of the U.S.S.R. are under Communist, one-party rule: Poland, Czechoslovakia, Hungary, Rumania, and Bulgaria. Albania, no less tied to Moscow than the others, is geographically detached from the bloc and provides its only frontage to the Mediterranean Sea. Further, under treaty, the U.S.S.R. retains communication rights across Poland to Berlin and to East Germany.

The wheel of history turns. Nazi Germany, from its vantage place in Central Europe, made its bid for the mastery of Europe and failed: Mittel-europa, as the German power center of Europe, has gone. Into Mittel-europa has intruded the Soviet Union, the greatest military power in Eurasia. It holds an advanced position in East Germany and, through its satellites, control of Bohemia and a strong position on the Baltic Sea, and, at the Danube Delta, a foothold on the Adriatic Sea, as well as near access to the Turkish straits. World War II thus

[7] Malcolm J. Proudfoot, *European Refugees: 1939–52* (London: Faber & Faber, Ltd., 1957).

eliminated one major danger only to create another. Postwar Europe has divided along ideological lines into a Western and an Eastern Europe, separated by the so-called "Iron Curtain," a phrase of Nazi origin which Winston Churchill used and thus publicized. The major problem for both Europes has become economic and political survival and the preservation of the civilization for which each stands. The United States has intervened in Western Europe with military, financial, and political force in an effort to preserve the uneasy balance. On both sides of the Iron Curtain, policies have been pursued toward closer association for economic purposes and for security, and it is becoming increasingly recognized that the age of the small independent state is passing and that only larger and stronger political units can face the hazards of the future. In oversimplified terms, Europe is now composed of two rival blocs, over one of which flies the Stars and Stripes and over the other the Hammer and Sickle. Yet a number of countries are unaligned or less clearly aligned. There are neutral states—Switzerland, Austria, Sweden, and the Republic of Ireland; democratic Finland and Communist Yugoslavia, both nicely poised between East and West; and Spain, ruled by a dictatorship, its outlook clearly oriented toward the West.

THE TREND TOWARD ECONOMIC AND POLITICAL INTEGRATION

The "astoundingly riven structure" of Europe has deep roots in history, and it is only by stages that larger functional units and eventual federal union may be expected. Certainly, attempts to create unity by force have always failed: witness the attempts of Napoleon, Kaiser Wilhelm II, and Hitler to dominate the continent. Even powerful persuasion from outside may arouse reactions: although in 1947 the U.S. government offered substantial financial aid to "the entire continent west of Asia, including the United Kingdom and the U.S.S.R.," this offer was accepted by only 17 of the European states (Fig. 10–1), and the emergence of the two Europes became at once apparent. Nevertheless, since the end of World War II, Europe is, at long last, beginning to shed some of its political and economic parochialism. And even though the trend is toward the separate integration of two Europes, opposed and divergent, this may be considered a hopeful trend toward currently attainable ends. Indeed, but for the external danger from Soviet military power, coupled with encouragement from the United States, Western Europe would have hardly advanced toward economic and political partnership to the extent that it has. A considerable difficulty intrudes in that several of the leading countries of Western Europe, notably the United Kingdom and France, have extensive political commitments to overseas territories and peoples. Further, the social, economic, and financial systems of the Western European countries are by no means uniform. We attempt in the table on page 747 to explain briefly the new organizations which have been created or proposed to reduce, if not to eliminate, the weaknesses and dangers of independent statehood in Western Europe.

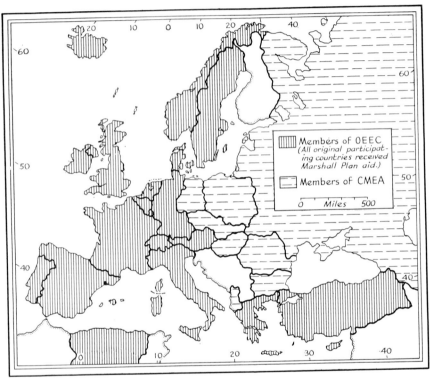

Fig. 10–1. Member states of the OEEC and those of the CMEA.

The initiative of the United States, personified in General Marshall, took the form of imaginative and realistic help for the peoples of Europe, who were exhausted by their war effort. Marshall Plan aid made possible the rebuilding of war-oriented and war-stricken economies and the rapid recovery of production. It gave birth to new cooperative institutions—the Organization for European Economic Cooperation (OEEC) and later the European Payments Union (EPU). OEEC was a notable achievement which has worked fruitfully. Its membership includes no less than 18 countries of Western Europe: even neutral Switzerland, Austria, Sweden, and Ireland are

The States of Europe and the Alliances and Organizations to Which They Belonged in 1960

	Received Marshall Plan Aid	NATO	OEEC	ECSC	EEC (CM)	Euratom	EFTA The "Outer Seven"	Warsaw Pact and CMEA
Albania								X
Austria	X		X				X	
Belgium........	X	X	X	X	X	X		
Bulgaria								X
Czechoslovakia .								X
Denmark	X	X	X				X	
Finland							X?	
France.........	X	X	X	X	X	X		
East Germany ...								X
West Germany ...	X	X	X	X	X	X		
Greece.........	X	X	X		X?			
Hungary								X
Iceland	X	X	X				X ?	
Ireland.........	X		X				X ?	
Italy...........	X	X	X	X	X	X		
Luxembourg	X	X	X	X	X	X		
Netherlands	X	X	X	X	X	X		
Norway	X	X	X				X	
Poland.........								X
Portugal	X	X	X				X	
Rumania								X
Spain			X					
Sweden	X		X				X	
Switzerland.....	X		X				X	
Turkey.........	X	X	X		X?			
United Kingdom .	X	X	X				X	
U.S.S.R.								
Yugoslavia								

NOTE: X? indicates that the country concerned is very likely to join the particular organization.
NATO stands for North Atlantic Treaty Organization.
OEEC stands for Organization for European Economic Cooperation.
ECSC stands for European Coal and Steel Community.
EEC stands for The European Economic Community, alternatively known as The Common Market.
EFTA stands for The European Free Trade Association, alternatively known as The Outer Seven.
CMEA stands for Council for Mutual Economic Aid.

members, but none of the Communist countries, Yugoslavia included, nor Finland.

On the economic front, too, the General Agreement on Tariffs and Trade (GATT), concluded in 1948 by many nations inside and outside Europe, did much to ease the flow of trade but at the same time called attention to the obstacles to the economic integration, in a full sense, even of Western Europe. GATT was instrumental in lowering tariff walls and in preventing tariff wars, but it was in no sense concerned with setting up a supranational authority which would entail a real divestment of the sovereignty of independent states. Herein lies the heart of the problem of economic and political union as distinct from economic and political association. Clarence K. Streit's *Union Now*, which made its vigorous appeal to Europe in 1939 to abandon its time-dusty habits of independent nationalistic and thus parochial organization in favor of an Atlantic Federal Union better suited to an age of mechanized communication and transport, could and can have no effect unless the wide powers of national sovereignties are in some measure curtailed. And the idea of such curtailment has seemed hardest to accept by the greater Western European countries, notably the United Kingdom, which with its role in the Commonwealth feels that it is outside, as well as part of, Europe. Not surprisingly, although disappointingly to advocates of federalism seeking dramatic results, the first steps toward the abandonment of sovereignty with a view to the formation of larger, more viable economic units have been taken by the smaller countries, and their difficulties on this road, by no means trivial, are a warning of the more serious difficulties that confront the greater European powers.

Benelux. In 1921 the small landlocked state of Luxembourg formed a customs union with its neighbor Belgium, and the Netherlands, which borders Belgium, became a partner in 1947 (Fig. 10–2). Benelux has developed by stages, facing and overcoming difficulties and national fears. It has reduced tariffs between the three countries, thus increasing the flow of their trade, and has established a common tariff to the outside world. It has achieved success by hard effort, by give and take, and by willing the success of its venture. It is significant, however, that the attempt to expand Benelux by the inclusion of France and Italy had to be abandoned because of the reluctance of France.

The North Atlantic Treaty Organization. The initiative of the United Kingdom in concluding the defensive Treaty of Brussels in 1948 with France and the Benelux countries, together with stimulus from the United States and Canada, made possible the achievement of the North Atlantic Treaty Organization (NATO) in 1949. While this is fundamentally a grand alliance for defense, it also seeks to strengthen free institutions and contains the seeds of a broadly based multinational community. In the interest of common defense, NATO pools the resources of no less than 15 countries: the United States, Canada, the United Kingdom, France, Italy, West Germany,

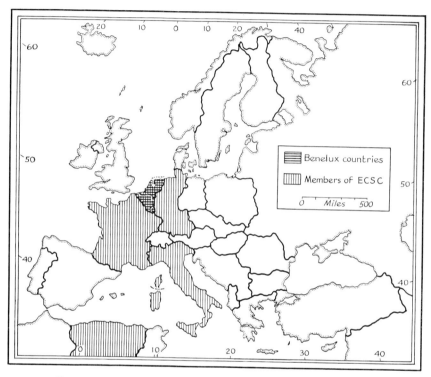

Fig. 10–2. Member states of Benelux and those of the ECSC.

Portugal, Belgium, the Netherlands, Luxembourg, Denmark, Norway, Iceland, Greece, and Turkey; the last two joined the organization in 1952, and West Germany joined in 1955. NATO geared all these countries into cooperative activity for the maintenance of the peace in Europe necessary for economic progress. It recognizes the belief, shared by almost all of its members, in democratic institutions and thus an aversion from totalitarian forms of government. Geographically, NATO gives expression to the concept of the North Atlantic as the "Midland Ocean" and of the Mediterranean Sea as but an arm or tributary of this ocean. Yet, with all its international machinery for action, NATO remains little more than a grand defensive alliance, conceived in military terms. Its façade of unity has conspicuously failed to conceal the divergent foreign policies of its principal partners in extra-European theaters such as North Africa and the Middle East.[8]

The European Coal and Steel Community. Under the leadership and inspiration of M. Spaak, then prime minister of Belgium, "Little Europe" emerged and achieved a striking success when the Schuman Plan for the European Coal and Steel Community (ECSC) was launched on January 1, 1952. Little Europe consists of the German Federal Republic, France, Italy, and the three Benelux countries (Fig. 10–2). Economic interdependence cannot be better illustrated than by the coal, iron, and steel industries of Western Europe, where, on economic grounds, the flow of these commodities across international frontiers should be free, and where, too, industrial locations should be chosen with due regard to the availability of labor, fuel, ore, and existing plants. ECSC commands considerable resources, which include Ruhr coal and Lorraine iron, and is provided with sufficient authority and organization to supervise and coordinate these heavy industries and to strive for economic efficiency. It organizes the pooling of the fuel and ore resources of Little Europe, has established a common market there in coal, iron ore, and steel, and by capital loans and expert advice also facilitates the re-equipment and/or development of these industries in member countries. Already the trade channels have been effectively realigned and discriminatory railroad rates eliminated. The initial success of ECSC owed something to its timely inception when markets were expanding. In 1958–9 it successfully weathered the difficulties arising from a temporary recession in demand. The following table shows the progress achieved between 1950 and 1958:

Comparative Production of ECSC, U.K., and U.S.A.
(million tons)

	1950			1958		
	Coal	Iron Ore	Steel	Coal	Iron Ore	Steel
ECSC	217	44	31.6	247	82	57.9
U.K.	220	13	16.5	219	15	20.0
U.S.A.	505	99	87.8	389	68	77.3

Source: United Nations Statistical Yearbook, 1959 (New York, 1959).

[8] Cf. the views of F. Parkinson, "European Integration: Obstacles and Prospects," *The Yearbook of World Affairs 1959* (London: Stevens & Sons, Ltd., 1959), pp. 140–60.

From the political standpoint, ECSC has achieved much, above all by closely associating France and West Germany, to their mutual benefit, in this fundamental industrial enterprise. It has survived the 5-year "transitional" period of its agreed 50 years of life, and, to the extent that it succeeds in its specified purposes, it lays the foundation for possible political union at a later stage. It is, however, an inter-governmental rather than a supragovernmental organization and must tread warily when it confronts strong national interests at variance with its aims.

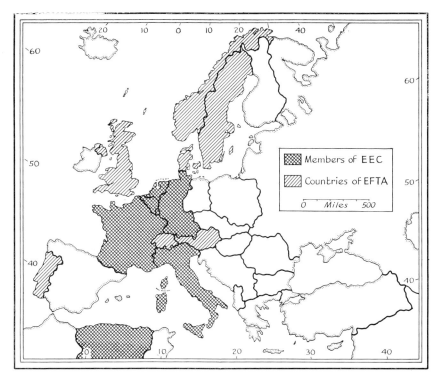

Fig. 10–3. Member states of the EEC and those of the EFTA.

The European Economic Community (EEC): The Common Market. The success in launching the European Coal and Steel Community encouraged the six members of OEEC to explore the possibility of creating a customs union (Fig. 10–3). After meetings at Messina in 1955 and at Venice in 1956 they agreed on the idea of a common market and declared their aim in the Treaty of Rome of March, 1957, as follows:

The Community's mission shall be, by establishing a common market and gradually removing difficulties between the economic policies of member states, to promote throughout the Community by the harmonious development of economic activities, continuous and balanced expansion, increased stability, a more rapid improvement in the standard of living and closer relations between its member states.

The treaty came into force on January 1, 1958, and the common market envisaged was to be achieved in stages spread over 12 to 15 years. The first steps to free trade within the Community were taken 1 year after this date.

The measures envisaged by the EEC, in pursuit of its declared objectives, are comprehensive, radical, and enlightened. Restrictions on trade and on the movement of capital and labor between the six states are being removed; a common policy on agriculture, transportation, and fisheries is being formulated; and a common trade policy is being established toward states outside the Community. A European Investment Bank and a European Social Fund will be set up, and measures to coordinate national economic policies and even to align national laws are contemplated. And the Community will seek to associate overseas countries, e.g., the colonial (or formerly colonial) dependencies of France, Belgium, Italy, and the Netherlands, so as to increase trade and promote economic and social progress.

To carry out this ambitious program the Community has created administrative, legislative, judicial, and financial machinery. This consists of a Council of Ministers, drawn from member countries, which acts either unanimously or by majority decision (the voting powers of members are realistically weighted: France, West Germany, and Italy each have four votes, Belgium and the Netherlands have two each, and Luxembourg has one). The Council of Ministers is advised by a European Commission of nine members who have been chosen by the Council on the recommendation of the governments of member states. The Consultative Assembly will be composed of a number of parliamentarians chosen by the national parliaments. A Court of Justice is to be set up, as will also two committees with consultative powers, an Economic and Social Committee and a Monetary Committee. Further provisions cover national contributions to the European Investment Bank and to the Overseas Investment Fund.

What economic resources do the six states command and how far are these adequate to their set task? They command a total population of 168 million (providing thus a labor force only a little smaller than that of the United States) and a substantial industrial potential, as the comparative figures in the table below clearly show.

It should not be inferred that this promising blueprint will necessarily be translated into the envisaged fine edifice within the pre-

Populations and Production (in Million Tons) of the European Economic Community in 1958 as Compared with Those of OEEC, U.K., U.S.A., U.S.S.R., and Eastern Europe

	EEC	OEEC[1]	U.K.	U.S.A.	U.S.S.R.	Eastern Europe[2]
Population (million)	168.2	267.9	51.9	174.8	208.8[3]	96.7
Coal (hard)	247.3	467.9	219.3	389.3	352.9	130.6
Lignite	97.1	106.3	–	2.2	142.8	317.0
Petroleum	8.1	11.1	0.15	330.9	113.2	13.1
Steel	58.0	83.5	19.9	77.3	54.8	17.0
Aluminum	0.4	0.78	0.13	1.7	?	0.08
Sulphuric acid	8.5	12.0	2.3	14.5	4.8	2.0
Cement	51.6	75.1	11.8	54.8	33.3	18.5
Motor vehicles (all types in million units)	3.0	4.46	1.36	5.13	0.6	0.16

[1] Excluding Turkey and Spain.
[2] Excluding Yugoslavia and Finland.
[3] January, 1959.

Source: United Nations Statistical Yearbook, 1959 (New York, 1959).

scribed period of 12 to 15 years. Its first specific advance was made on January 1, 1959, when 10 per cent reductions of existing tariffs were made, bringing repercussions both within and without. The Community is faced by bristling difficulties at every turn, for each member has its own hopes and expectations and these will be hard to reconcile in the general interest. Will strategic industries, which range from artillery and tanks to watches and optical instruments, be brought under the heading of trade commodities or will they be specially excepted? Will France be able to continue to subsidize her exports indefinitely? Will Italy, with its relatively low living standard and its strong interest therefore in labor mobility, be able to realize this? Are the currencies of the member states sufficiently stable to permit capital mobility, or will an answer to this difficulty ultimately be achieved by a unified currency? Different levels of social services among the six raise difficulties which may prove costly to solve. The practice of subsidizing domestic agriculture for a variety of reasons, including national security, is widely adopted and is clearly unecó-nomic, but for this reason alone is no easier to change. Clearly, too, if tariffs are to be lowered, industrial dislocation, even if only in the short run, will be painful in the several countries. Indeed, when all the present and future difficulties are soberly reviewed, the wonder is that the Common Market has been launched at all, and the greater wonder will be the successful accomplishment of its objectives. Fortunately, the conditions of trade were initially favorable; the advent of a trade depression would surely impose severe strains on this infant organization.

European Atomic Energy Union (Euratom). This organization, established by the Treaty of Rome in 1957 and concerned with the peaceful and profitable use of nuclear energy, owes its origin to the initiative of the six member countries of the European Coal and Steel and the European Economic communities. Euratom takes note of the ever-increasing industrial demands for fuel and power, and of the eventual needs for supplies of nuclear energy at a reasonable cost. It is clearly alive to dangers of this new source of power. The Union will provide funds for research and for the dissemination of knowledge about atomic energy and will try to insure that its uses will be peaceful only. Similar institutions to those set up by the ECSC are contemplated.

European Free Trade Association. The Common Market is an organization of only six of the eighteen countries of Western Europe which are already cooperating within the OEEC (Fig. 10–3). The remaining countries were unwilling, after consideration, to align themselves with the policy agreed to by the six. In particular, the United Kingdom, the chief industrial country outside the Common Market, refused to join, for various reasons.[9] Full membership for the United Kingdom would mean the relaxation of imperial preference, especially for foodstuffs other than wheat and for industrial raw materials. The bulk of its trade is with the Commonwealth and trade with the six accounts for only one-twelfth of its imports and only one-eighth of its exports. The United Kingdom's position as banker for the whole sterling area presents another difficulty, and, more generally, the ultimate aims of the Common Market, involving a surrender of sovereignty, were too radical for its immediate acceptance. But the United Kingdom and, indeed, most of the other members of OEEC are necessarily concerned with their trade prospects now that the Common Market is launched. They are desirous, too, of continuing and strengthening their association, and are apprehensive lest the activities of the six should rend the economic unity of Western Europe toward which they have been arduously striving. Indeed, "the European idea," the eventual need of joint institutions of a political character, is the important issue involved in the EFTA idea.

The idea of the Free Trade area, of which the Common Market might provide the nucleus around which other countries of Western

---

[9] André Siegfried has remarked that "England is as a ship moored off the coast of Europe, always prepared to weigh anchor." Cited by J. Goormaghtigh, "European Integration," *International Conciliation* 488 (February, 1953): 58.

Europe could be grouped, was a United Kingdom proposal which appeared to find general approval. Certainly the United Kingdom estimated that its trade position in Western Europe would suffer under the Common Market and could improve under the FTA if it more attentively studied the market needs of this important trade area. But the broader and more fundamental consideration was that Western Europe as a whole could consolidate and strengthen its economic position in the world only by some such positive and rational policy, which might well effect a general rise in living standards and help toward the development of a community spirit.

The central idea of the Free Trade–area proposal was the removal of tariffs, quotas, and similar restrictions within the area, but the external tariffs of each member would remain. Further, FTA recognized that member countries would be unwilling to renounce agricultural subsidies and that its policies involved no opening of the doors to free movement of labor and no infringement of state sovereignty. While many critics have rated the FTA a weak scheme, it seemed likely to prove acceptable to the six, as well as to the United Kingdom, Austria, and the Scandinavian countries, but not to France, which has the weakest and most protected economy of the Common Market states.

The breakdown of the FTA talks, and the rejection of the British plan for an interim arrangement which would have extended the quota enlargements inside the EEC to all 18 OEEC nations on a reciprocal basis, forced the governments outside the EEC to consider the problem afresh. The way for a possible free-trade area on a limited scale was paved in the summer of 1958, when the employers' organizations and industrial federations of the United Kingdom, Sweden, Norway, Denmark, Austria, and Switzerland agreed on the outlines of a free-trade area which they wished to see in operation for Europe. Discussions on this subject at government level took place in the summer of 1959 at Stockholm, between the representatives of these six countries and also of Portugal. The agreement reached by the Treaty of Stockholm in November was ratified in the spring of 1960. Thus was formed the European Free Trade Association (EFTA), popularly known as "The Outer Seven." It was so called because the seven countries lie around the EEC (Common Market) bloc (Fig. 10–3).

The EFTA is a loose organization of independent states with two distinct purposes. First, it seeks to create by 1970 a free-trade area by the removal of all the trade barriers between the Seven. Second, it hopes to create a good position from which to bargain with EEC. Unlike the six Common Market countries, the Seven have no interest in ultimate federal union: three of them are neutral states—Switzerland, Sweden, and Austria—while the United Kingdom has bonds with the Commonwealth, and Portugal with its overseas dependencies. Also unlike the Common Market, the Outer Seven is not establishing a common tariff against the outside world. Fortunately, the interests of the countries of both trade groups are closely interlocked. West Germany exports more to the Outer Seven than to her Common Market partners, and the Outer Seven as a group exports more to the Common Market than to one another. Thus some bridge between the two trading groups was being sought in 1961 to prevent the division of Western Europe into two economic camps.

Council for Mutual Economic Aid. Under the pressure of Moscow, the Communist countries of Europe refused Marshall Plan aid, and also refused to join the Organization for European Economic Cooperation, which was set up to implement it. In reaction, they set up in 1949 the Council for Mutual Economic Aid (CMEA or COMECON), which, however, confined its activities largely to providing a market place where the Communist countries could coordinate their bilateral trade agreements. Stalin's idea was that the Soviet satellites should industrialize at all costs, whereas Khrushchev's is to link them to each other and to the Soviet Union by economic planning which would achieve regional specialization and division of labor in the interests of the whole bloc. After studies were made of the economic capacity of the member countries, Moscow announced in 1955 a unified five-year plan. It was hoped thus to start in 1956 on a plan which set as its eventual goal "overtaking the capitalist world." The proposed plans were grandiose, however, because they did not take full account of acute shortages of capital, fuel and power, and industrial raw materials which the U.S.S.R. was either unwilling or unable to supply. The assertion by the Poles of some degree of independence of Moscow and the rise to power of Gomulka, coupled with the revolt of the Hungarians, reflected politically the difficulty of carrying out joint economic plans in the satellite countries. These plans had to be scaled down, while the U.S.S.R. was forced to provide emergency economic aid.

Actually, the original targets set for the 1956–60 plan period were replaced in June, 1957, by lower, more realistic ones to be reached during the 7-year period 1959–65. East Germany will concentrate on the chemical industry related to its huge brown-coal deposits, and is to receive petroleum by pipeline from the U.S.S.R. On the other hand, the steel industries of East Germany may receive no further investment funds, which will be turned to the more economic steel-producing centers of Czechoslovakia and of Poland. New Polish mines will be opened, with Czech and East German equipment, but the Zwickaw mines of Czechoslovakia will be eventually abandoned.

Increased aluminum production, using Hungarian bauxite, and cellulose production using reeds from the Danube Delta in Rumania are also envisaged, with technical help and equipment from East Germany. Machine building of various types will be rationalized, so that the most efficiently located sites will be developed and the uneconomic ones shut down. In short, the policy of economic integration in Eastern Europe is now rationally conceived, and as it is applied the Soviet satellites will be tied more firmly to each other and to the U.S.S.R. The pace of development will depend largely on the extent to which the U.S.S.R. is willing and able to supply necessary capital, fuel, and raw materials.[10]

The Warsaw Pact. In reply to NATO, the U.S.S.R. reorganized its defense system by the Warsaw Pact of 1955. It thus associates itself militarily with Poland, East Germany, Czechoslovakia, Hungary, Rumania, Bulgaria, and Albania. Note that the deviation of Yugoslavia from Moscow's line causes a territorial break in the pattern of the Warsaw Pact states.

EUROPE'S ROLE IN THE WORLD

Europe's influence on the world has been unsurpassed. European discoverers ventured across the oceans to chart newly found lands in the Americas and in Oceania, and to penetrate Africa south of the Sahara. They forged, too, maritime routes to the lands of ancient civilization in the Asian Orient. These efforts established two kinds of political dependencies, those which served primarily as trading stations and those which served also as homes for European immigrants. Settlement overseas, particularly in North and South America, Australia and New Zealand, and parts of southern Africa, introduced European languages, techniques, economy, and ideas and initiated the development of the nations of the New World. In time, these nations successively shook off the political control exercised by the mother countries in Europe. Even so, many of these nations are still, if somewhat loosely, associated with their European "parent." The most extensive and powerful group, with territories in every continent, is the Commonwealth, of which the United Kingdom is senior partner. Extensive too, and strategically important, are the territories, mainly in Africa, associated with France. Certain European nations, therefore, contributed much to the unrolling of the world map, and then to the evaluation of the resources of this expanded world. This is not the place to discuss Europe's no less striking contributions in

[10] George W. Hoffman, "Eastern Europe: A Study in Political Geography," *The Texas Quarterly* II, 3 (Autumn, 1959): 57–88.

the fields of science and technology, and of literature and the other arts.

The role of Europe in the world has, however, sharply changed. The works which it initiated in so many parts of the world in establishing railroads, ports and towns, agriculture, industry, and trade have borne fruit, so much so that former economic and political dependencies have acquired enhanced stature both politically and economically. Economic nationalism and economic progress in oversea countries now give them a higher degree of self-sufficiency in manufactures formerly derived from European factories. The impact of two world wars, with all the sheer waste of manpower and wealth and all the dislocation which they entailed, brought to an end Europe's dominant position in the world's economy and politics, as it consolidated the primacy of the United States in the Western world. Europe's changing status is indeed relative, not absolute. It has rehabilitated and even expanded its economy since the end of World War II. Moreover, in Europe's eastern part, the Soviet Union and its European satellites, starting late, and with forceful deliberation, to exploit their very considerable natural resources, are expanding industrially faster than any other country or group of countries and are now becoming increasingly capable of challenging the Western powers in the markets of the world. Also, further afield and making up, together with the U.S.S.R. and its satellites, that third of humanity which is subject to Communist rule, the Chinese Peoples Republic, with its great reservoir of population, moves slowly forward toward a position which, before the end of this century, may be such as to embarrass or discomfort not only the Western world but its own Russian ally as well.

Europe west of the Iron Curtain has written the chapter of its history which was concerned with its leadership of the world. It now seeks, burdened as it is by defense costs, to maintain its still relatively high standard of living, by careful forethought and by wise adjustments to changing circumstances. No longer able to supplement its own food resources by the importation of cheap food from overseas, it concerns itself attentively with its own fields and farms, so as to increase their productivity. Aware that economic stability and progress are not a narrow local problem, it attempts, within its means, to promote economic developments in underdeveloped countries. Faced by changed demands for its manufactures in the world market, it strives, by specialization, to produce what is really wanted and, above all, to keep ahead in new productions (e.g., of nuclear-power plants) and in the provision of more elaborate manufactures such as aircraft, automobiles, and ships. Clearly, to attain these ends, much depends on the maintenance of its high level of scientific and technological research and on the increasing skill of more and more workers.

A marked characteristic of Western Europe is its political fragmentation, the survival of many relatively small national states into an age of fast and easy transportation and communication. West of the Iron Curtain, there are, excluding microstates, no less than 20 national states, which occupy only about a third of Europe as conventionally defined, an area equivalent to that of the United States, Australia, or Brazil. In this relatively small area, which coincides with the westerly peninsular protrusion of the continent, are concentrated 320 million people (one-tenth of mankind), the largest components being found in West Germany, the United Kingdom, Italy, and France. While it is being increasingly recognized that political fragmentation weakens the economy of Western Europe, as it also weakens its defensive strength, there are no short cuts either to effective political integration or to the creation of the community spirit which this necessitates. Only as education and thought bring the conviction that economic advantages and greater security can so accrue, and external political, economic, and military pressures, too, urge the relaxation of state sovereignties, can measures be taken, by stages, to produce larger functional units which make for a more rational economic use of available resources. The effects of these measures in creating new intergovernmental organizations are, we have seen, in no sense dramatic, and they point to no sudden creation of a federal political structure for Western Europe such as the U.S.S.R. achieved in its vast Eurasian territories or such as characterize many nations of North and South America. But the reaction against political and economic separatism in Western Europe is in full swing, and so, in so far as specific multinational associations prove their value in specific fields of common interest, the ultimate goal of federation begins to loom on the horizon.

BIBLIOGRAPHY

Books and Articles

Britain and Europe. London: Economist Intelligence Unit, 1957.

DEWAR, MARGARET. "Economic Cooperation in the Soviet Orbit," *The Yearbook of World Affairs*. London: Stevens & Sons, Ltd., 1939, 45–67.

DIEBOLD, WILLIAM, JR. *The Schuman Plan: A Study in Economic Cooperation 1950–1959*. New York: Frederick A. Praeger, Inc., 1959.

FAWCETT, CHARLES B. *The Bases of a World Commonwealth*. London: C. A. Watts & Co., Ltd., 1944.

HOFFMAN, M. L. *The Problems of East-West Trade*. No. 511. New York: International Conciliation, 1957.

Lister, Louis. *Europe's Coal and Steel Community.* New York: Twentieth Century Fund, 1960.

Quin, Marc. *The OEEC and the Common Market.* Paris: Organization for European Economic Cooperation, 1958.

The Commonwealth and Europe. London: Economist Intelligence Unit, 1960.

"The New Europe," *The Financial Times* (London: May 1, 1958).

"The Six and the Seven," *The Financial Times Supplement* (London: November 7, 1960).

Official Publications
(Including Statistics and Statistical Compilations)

Communauté Européene du Charbon et de l'Acier:
Bulletin Statistique (bimonthly).
Informations Statistiques (quarterly).

Economic Commission for Europe:
Economic Survey for Europe (annual).
Economic Bulletin for Europe (three times a year).

Organization for European Economic Cooperation:
Statistical Bulletin (bimonthly).

United Nations:
Statistical Yearbook (annual).
Demographic Yearbook (annual).

APPENDIX

Chart of Geologic Time

ERA	DURATION (millions of years)	TIME PERIODS (Geologic Formations)		AREAS AFFECTED BY	
				Fenno-Scandia	Northwest Europe
CENOZOIC	1	QUATERNARY	RECENT	⇒ Vistula ⇒ Warthe → Saale ⇒ Elster	⇒ "Newer ⇒ Drift" → "Older ⇒ Drift"
			PLEISTO-CENE		
	70	TERTIARY	PLIOCENE MIOCENE OLIGOCENE EOCENE PALEOCENE	(A)	(A)
MESO-ZOIC	160	CRETACEOUS			
		JURASSIC			
		TRIASSIC			
PALEOZOIC		PERMIAN			
		CARBONIFEROUS		(H)	(H)
	370	DEVONIAN			
		SILURIAN		(C)	CALEDONIAN
		ORDOVICIAN			
		CAMBRIAN			
PROTEROZOIC	1,000	PRE-CAMBRIAN		BALTIC	⇒

The shaded boxes indicate the location in geologic time and in space of the major mountain-building periods (orogenies). Letters in parentheses stand for the orogeny which occurred at the same time and is of secondary importance as compared to the major orogeny in the respective area. Wavy lines mark the prevalence of marine conditions (transgressions). Advances of ice sheets are indicated by arrows (length proportional to intensity of glaciation) and labeled *and Tectonic Evolution*

OROGENIES (■■■), MARINE CONDITIONS (▨▨), GLACIERS (⟹)			
Central Europe	Alpine Europe	European Russia	Asiatic Russia
⟹⟹ ?	⟹ Würm ⟹ Riss ⟹ Mindel ⟹ Günz	⟹ Valdai ⟹ Dnieper ⟹ Oka	⟹ ? ⟹
(A)	**ALPINE**	(A)	(A)
			CIMMERIAN
HERCYNIAN	(H)	**URALIAN**	**ALTAI**
(C)			(C)
			⟹
			ANGARA

according to regional terminology (the four glaciations of Fenno-Scandia and Alpine Europe probably correspond to those usually recognized on the American continent: Wisconsin, Illinoian, Kansan, and Nebraskan, in order of recency). Note that the widths of the boxes in the "Duration" column do not correspond to the actual lengths of the eras.

Appendix II
Climatic Data of Selected Stations in Europe *

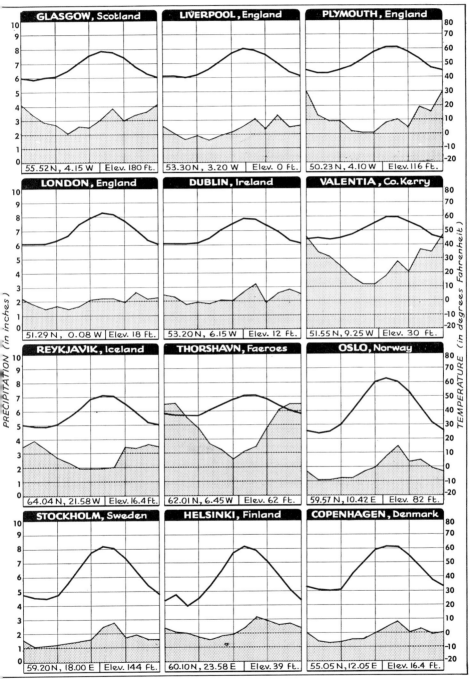

GLASGOW, Scotland	LIVERPOOL, England	PLYMOUTH, England
55.52 N, 4.15 W | Elev. 180 Ft.	53.30 N, 3.20 W | Elev. 0 Ft.	50.23 N, 4.10 W | Elev. 116 Ft.
LONDON, England	DUBLIN, Ireland	VALENTIA, Co. Kerry
51.29 N, 0.08 W | Elev. 18 Ft.	53.20 N, 6.15 W | Elev. 12 Ft.	51.55 N, 9.25 W | Elev. 30 Ft.
REYKJAVIK, Iceland	THORSHAVN, Faeroes	OSLO, Norway
64.04 N, 21.58 W | Elev. 16.4 Ft.	62.01 N, 6.45 W | Elev. 62 Ft.	59.57 N, 10.42 E | Elev. 82 Ft.
STOCKHOLM, Sweden	HELSINKI, Finland	COPENHAGEN, Denmark
59.20 N, 18.00 E | Elev. 144 Ft.	60.10 N, 23.58 E | Elev. 39 Ft.	55.05 N, 12.05 E | Elev. 16.4 Ft.

PRECIPITATION (in inches)

TEMPERATURE (in degrees Fahrenheit)

* Data from W. G. Kendrew, *Climates of the Continents* (3d ed.; New York: Oxford University Press, 1942).

765

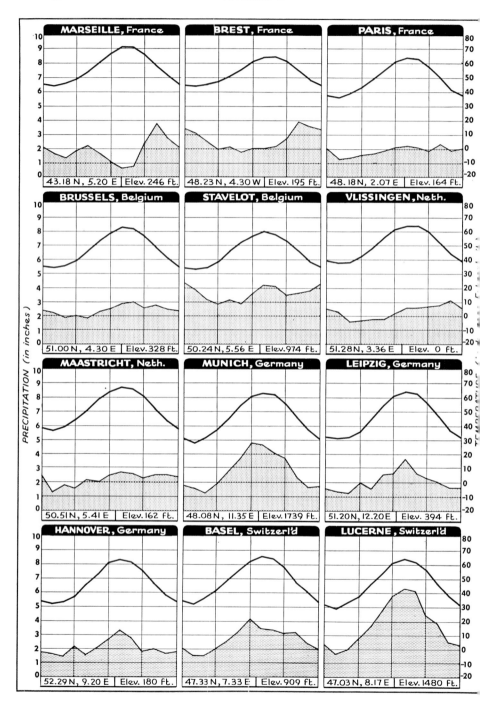

PRECIPITATION (in inches)

MARSEILLE, France — 43.18 N, 5.20 E | Elev. 246 ft.

BREST, France — 48.23 N, 4.30 W | Elev. 195 ft.

PARIS, France — 48.18 N, 2.07 E | Elev. 164 ft.

BRUSSELS, Belgium — 51.00 N, 4.30 E | Elev. 328 ft.

STAVELOT, Belgium — 50.24 N, 5.56 E | Elev. 974 ft.

VLISSINGEN, Neth. — 51.28 N, 3.36 E | Elev. 0 ft.

MAASTRICHT, Neth. — 50.51 N, 5.41 E | Elev. 162 ft.

MUNICH, Germany — 48.08 N, 11.35 E | Elev. 1739 ft.

LEIPZIG, Germany — 51.20 N, 12.20 E | Elev. 394 ft.

HANNOVER, Germany — 52.29 N, 9.20 E | Elev. 180 ft.

BASEL, Switzerl'd — 47.33 N, 7.33 E | Elev. 909 ft.

LUCERNE, Switzerl'd — 47.03 N, 8.17 E | Elev. 1480 ft.

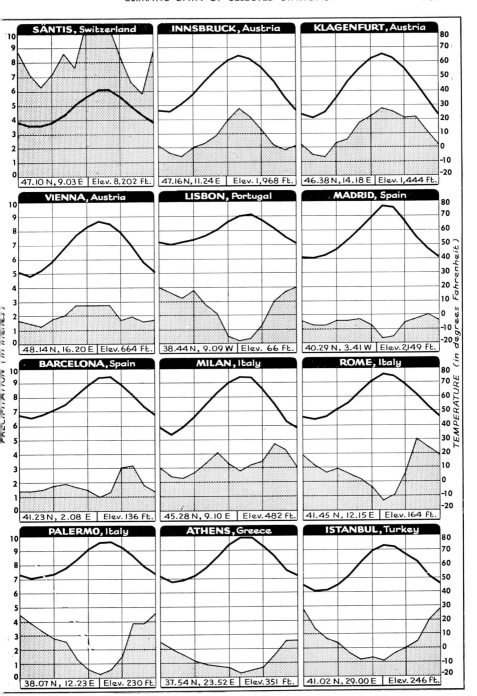

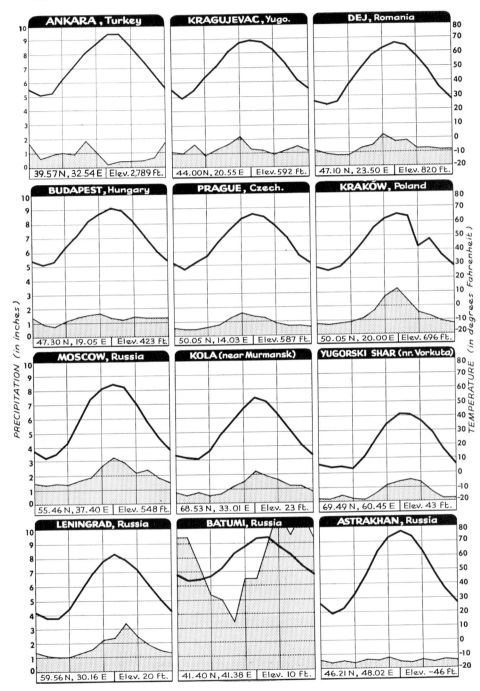

Appendix III

Statistical Tables

The following statistical tables have been compiled from various sources. The reader should be warned about the difficulty of making international comparisons, especially if the statistics are prepared by different agencies, and he is reminded of the fact that the reliability of the data varies greatly. Even for those countries where reasonably reliable statistics are available the figures obtained by different collecting agencies vary in quality.

Precise definitions of commodities, areas, and other classifications vary from country to country and from source to source. For details the reader should consult the sources cited in each table. In most cases, more recent data will be found in later issues of the sources given. In many cases data are available only for a limited number of countries. In the cases of the U.S.S.R. and Turkey, statistics generally include both the Asiatic and the European parts and separate figures for the European part are usually not available. In the case of the U.S.S.R., a series of special tables has been compiled, giving the reader an up-to-date picture of the growth of the Soviet economy.

An effort has been made to present the data in the most comparable form. This has meant that data frequently had to be converted from one unit of measurement into another (e.g., kilometers into miles) and that many of the figures were rounded off. The tables of measures and weights on the following page will be found useful.

It should also be explained that the figures in the statistical summary are not necessarily always the same as those in the text. This is because a certain comparability was desired in the Appendix, and compilations are based on a select and small number of sources. The text, on the other hand, contains figures based on national statistics, official announcements, and preliminary reports published by the United Nations. These are usually the latest available figures.

MEASURES AND WEIGHTS

UNITS OF LENGTH

1 millimeter (mm) = 0.0394 inch
1 centimeter (cm) = 0.3937 inch

1 meter (m)   = 3.2808 feet
1 kilometer (km) = 0.62137 mile

1 inch   = 2.540 centimeters
1 foot   = 0.3048 meter
1 yard   = 0.9144 meter
1 statute mile = 1.609 kilometers
                = 5,280 feet
1 nautical mile = 1.853 kilometers
                = 6,080 feet

UNITS OF AREA

1 square meter   = 10.7639 square feet
1 hectare (ha)   = 2.471 acres
1 square kilometer = 0.3861 square mile

1 square yard = 0.8361 square meter
1 acre   = 0.4047 hectare
1 square mile = 2.590 square kilometers

UNITS OF WEIGHT

1 metric ton   = 1.1023 short tons

               = 0.9842 long ton

1 quintal   = 220 pounds

1 short ton = 2,000 pounds
            = 0.9072 metric ton
1 long ton = 2,240 pounds
            = 1.0160 metric tons
1 U.S. hundredweight
   (cwt)   = 100 pounds
1 U.K. hundredweight
   (cwt)   = 112 pounds
1 gross registered ton = 100 cubic feet

UNITS OF DRY MEASURE

1 liter (l) = 0.9081 quart
             = 0.02837 bushel

1 quart = 1.1012 liters
1 bushel = 35.2383 liters

UNITS OF LIQUID MEASURE

1 liter = 1.0567 quarts
         = 0.264 gallon

1 quart   = 0.9463 liter
1 gallon (U.S.)   = 3.785 liters
1 gallon (imperial) = 1.2 gallons (U.S.)

1 metric ton (petroleum) = 264.4175 U.S. barrels

MISCELLANEOUS

1 board foot (fbm) = 144 cubic inches
1 barrel (42 gallons) crude petroleum   = 306.6 pounds = 139.07 kilograms
                                         = 158.984 liters

LIST OF STATISTICAL TABLES

TABLE 1

Population, Area, and Density of the World

(1957)

	Estimated Population (millions)	Area (sq. mi.) (thousands)	Population (per sq. mi.)
Europe........................	414.0	1,903	217
Africa	225.0	11,696	19
North America	250.0	9,357	27
South America	131.0	6,868	19
Asia (except U.S.S.R.)..........	1,556.0	10,477	148
U.S.S.R.	208.8[1]	8,647	24
Oceania.......................	15.4	3,303	4
Total........................	2,800.2	52,251	54

[1] 1959.

Source: United Nations, Demographic Yearbook: 1958, New York, 1959.

TABLE 2

Production of Electricity

(billion kwh)

World Area	1937	1950	1957
World total.............................	449	951	2,210
Europe without U.S.S.R..................	172	299	534
Western Europe	143	250	443
U.S.S.R.	36	90	209
Canada and U.S.A.	178	444	806
Africa	6	14	30
Asia without U.S.S.R..................	42	68	126
Latin America	10	22	36
Oceania..............................	5	14	26

Source: United Nations, Supplement to World Economic Report: 1950-51; United Nations, Statistical Yearbook: 1958, New York, 1959, p. 265.

TABLE 3
Production of Coal, Petroleum, and Steel
(million metric tons)

	Coal[1]		Crude Petroleum		Crude Steel	
	1937	1957	1937	1957	1937	1957
World total	1,264.0	1,604.5	285.2	884.0	135.8	286.3
Europe[2]	577.0	617.0	8.3	24.0	56.3	105.8
Eastern	55.0	125.1	7.7	12.5	4.7	16.8
Western[9]	522.0	491.9	0.6	11.5	51.6	89.0
Asia	79.0[5]	227.6[5]	9.7[6]	18.0[6]	8.2[7,8]	19.6[7]
Middle East	1.6[4]	3.9[4]	15.8	180.0	*	0.2
Latin America	4.4	7.9	44.4	182.0	0.2[8]	2.9
U.S.S.R.	109.9	328.5	29.0	113.0[3]	17.8	51.0
Canada and U.S.A. ..	461.7	478.0	178.0	378.0	52.8	106.8

*Data not available.
[1]Hard coal only.
[2]Excluding the U.S.S.R.
[3]1958.
[4]Turkey only; very small amounts are produced in Iran and Afghanistan.
[5]Excluding the Middle East and the Soviet Union.
[6]Including the Far East, but excluding the U.S.S.R.
[7]Far East.
[8]1935–9 average.
[9]Including Yugoslavia.

Sources: United Nations, *Steel Production and Consumption Trends in Europe and the World*, Geneva, 1952 (mimeo); United Nations, *European Steel Trends in the Setting of the World Market*, Geneva, 1949, p. 121; United Nations, *Statistical Yearbook: 1958*.

TABLE 4
Percentage Distribution of Foreign Trade, Population, and Area
(All figures are approximations.)

	Trade		Population		Area
	1938	1957	1938	1957	
Europe, excl. U.S.S.R.	51	46.0	19.0	14.7	3.6
U.S.S.R.	1	4.0	8.0	7.4	16.5
Asia, excl. U.S.S.R.	15	11.0	53.0	55.7	20.0
Africa	7	6.0	7.0	8.0	22.4
North America	14	22.0	7.0	6.7	15.9
South America	9	8.5	6.0	6.9	15.2
Oceania	3	2.5	0.5	0.6	6.4

Sources: League of Nations, *Europe's Trade*, Geneva, 1941, p. 9; International Monetary Fund, *International Financial Statistics*, Vol. IV, No. 8, Washington, D.C., 1951, pp. XXIV–XXVII; United Nations, *Demographic Yearbook: 1949–50*, New York, 1950, pp. 79–83; *Yearbook of International Trade Statistics: 1957*, Vol. II, New York, 1958.

TABLE 5
Economically Active Population
(per cent)

Country	Data Year	Agricult., Forestry, Hunting, & Fishing	Mining and Quarrying	Manufacturing	Construction	Transport and Communication	Commerce, Banking, & Insurance	Others
Albania	1955	70.0	15.0					15.0
Austria	1951	32.3	1.2	28.0	7.3	5.2	7.0	19.0
Belgium	1958	10.0	5.0	35.0	6.0	19.5	13.0	11.5
Bulgaria	1956	70.0	12.0		4.0	2.0	4.0	8.0
Czechoslovakia	1956	33.0	33.0		7.5	6.0	8.5	12.0
Denmark	1955	22.9	0.0	25.6	6.7	6.7	14.1	24.0
Finland	1950	46.0	0.3	20.7	6.2	5.4	8.1	13.3
France	1958	29.0	0.6	35.0	5.0	5.0	14.0	11.4
West Germany	1957	16.8	47.2				19.4	16.5
West Berlin	1950	2.1	42.0			7.2	21.9	26.8
East Germany	1957	7.0	55.0			20.0		18.0
Greece	1956	49.0	1.0	14.4	3.5	4.2	8.6	19.3
Hungary	1955	44.0	25.0		5.0	6.0	6.0	14.0
Iceland	1950	40.0	0.0	20.0	9.3	8.0	9.3	13.4
Ireland	1957	38.1	1.1	16.1	6.7	4.8	13.2	20.0
Italy	1951	43.2	1.0	23.6	7.7	4.2	14.1	6.2
Luxembourg	1947	26.0	2.8	29.3	6.8	6.3	8.7	20.1
Netherlands	1947	19.3	1.3	29.0	1.0	6.2	19.1	28.1
Norway	1950	25.9	0.6	25.7	9.3	10.1	10.8	17.6
Poland	1956	52.0	27.0			4.0	5.0	12.0
Portugal	1950	48.5	0.8	18.9	5.1	3.5	7.0	16.2
Rumania	1955	69.0	13.0		4.0	3.0	4.0	7.0
Saar	1951	14.9	17.3	29.1	7.9	5.6	10.5	14.7
Spain	1950	48.8	1.6	17.6	5.3	3.9	6.5	16.3
Sweden	1950	20.4	0.5	31.5	7.9	8.1	13.0	18.6
Switzerland	1950	22.0		39.0	8.0	5.0	10.0	16.0
Turkey (Eur. and Asia)	1955	87.8						12.2
United Kingdom	1958	4.3	3.7	39.5	6.5	7.4	38.6	
U.S.S.R.	1958	42.0	25.0		6.0	7.0	5.0	15.0
Yugoslavia	1953	66.0	14.0	12.0	2.5	2.0	3.0	13.1

Sources: United Nations, *Statistical Yearbook: 1957;* and national statistics.

TABLE 6
Population

Country	Date of Latest Census or Other Enumeration	Population in 1,000's on Census Date	Estimates of Population (1957) (thousands)	Area (1957) (sq. mi.)	Density per Square Mile, Based on Census Date
Albania........	1955	1,391	1,462	11,097	125
Andorra........	1954	5.6	6	175	32
Austria	1951	6,934	6,998	32,366	214
Belgium	1947	8,512	8,989	11,776	723
Bulgaria	1956	7,600	7,667	43,036	177
Czechoslovakia.	1950	12,338	13,353	49,353	250
Denmark	1955	4,448	4,500	16,614	268
Faroes	1950	32	35	540	59
Finland........	1950	4,030	4,336	130,085	31
France	1954	42,844	44,091	212,766	201
West Germany ..	1956	50,975	51,469	95,713	533
East Germany ..	1950	17,199	16,401	41,468	414
West Berlin	1956	2,224	2,223	186	11,957
East Berlin	1950	1,189	1,117	156	7,621
Greece	1951	7,633	8,096	51,169	149
Hungary	1949	9,205	9,815	35,910	256
Iceland	1950	144	165	39,758	4
Ireland	1956	2,898	2,885	27,129	107
Italy	1951	47,159	48,483	116,273	406
Liechtenstein ..	1955	14	15	61	230
Luxembourg	1947	291	316	999	291
Monaco	1956	20	21	0.4	50,000
Netherlands	1947	9,625	11,021	12,529	768
Norway	1950	3,279	3,494	125,032	26
Spitsbergen ..	1950	3.5	3.5	25,000	0.1
Poland	1950	25,008	28,300	120,328	208
Portugal	1950	8,441	8,909	35,589	237
Rumania	1956	17,489	17,829	91,675	191
Saar..........	1951	955	992 [1]	991	964
San Marino			14	24	583
Spain..........	1950	27,977	29,431	194,346	144
Sweden	1950	7,042	7,367	173,577	41
Switzerland	1950	4,715	5,117	15,937	296
Turkey	1955	24,122	25,500	299,914	80
United Kingdom.	1951	50,225	51,657	94,205	533
England and Wales	1951	43,758	45,043	58,343	750
N. Ireland....	1951	1,371	1,399	5,451	252
Scotland	1951	5,096	5,211	30,411	168
U.S.S.R.	1959	208,826		8,647,558	24
Vatican City ...	1948	0.9	1	0.2	5,294
Yugoslavia.....	1953	16,990	18,005	98,740	172

[1] 1955. Since January 1, 1958, part of German Federal Republic.

Sources: United Nations, Demographic Yearbook: 1958, New York, 1958; and national statistics for certain countries.

TABLE 7

Population: Natural Increase

Country	Natural Increase	
	1931–5	1957
Albania....................................	*	27.3
Austria....................................	0.9	4.2
Belgium	3.9	5.1
Bulgaria	13.8	10.1[1]
Czechoslovakia.............................	5.8	8.9
Denmark	6.8	7.4
Finland....................................	6.1	10.6
France	0.8	6.5
Germany	5.4	—
East Germany	—	3.3
West Germany	—	5.7
Greece	13.0	11.7
Hungary	6.5	6.4
Iceland....................................	12.4	21.7
Ireland	5.4	9.3
Italy	9.7	8.2
Luxembourg	4.5	3.6
Netherlands	12.3	13.7
Norway	4.8	9.6
Poland	13.0	18.0
Portugal	12.1	12.3
Rumania	12.2	12.7
Spain.....................................	10.7	11.9
Sweden	2.5	4.7
Switzerland	4.6	7.7
United Kingdom............................	3.3	5.0
U.S.S.R.	11.0	17.5
Yugoslavia.................................	13.9	13.1

*Not available.
[1]1956.

Source: United Nations, Demographic Yearbook: 1958, New York, 1958.

TABLE 8
Cities with Over 1,000,000 Inhabitants

City and Country	Date of Latest Census or Enumeration	Total Population* (thousand)
London, U.K.	1957	8,251
Moscow, U.S.S.R.	1959	5,032
Paris, France................	1954	4,823
Leningrad, U.S.S.R.	1959	3,300
Manchester, U.K..............	1956	2,412
West Berlin..................	1956	2,224†
Rome, Italy..................	1951	1,788
Madrid, Spain	1954	1,768
Vienna, Austria	1957	1,636
Liverpool, U.K.	1956	1,386
Milan, Italy.................	1951	1,370
Barcelona, Spain	1954	1,361
Bucharest, Rumania	1956	1,237
Copenhagen, Denmark..........	1955	1,227
Istanbul, Turkey	1956	1,215
Naples, Italy	1951	1,202
East Berlin..................	1950	1,189†
Birmingham, U.K.	1957	1,103
Lisbon, Portugal	1950	1,103
Kiev, U.S.S.R.	1959	1,102
Glasgow, U.K.	1957	1,079
Stockholm, Sweden	1956	1,062
Budapest, Hungary	1949	1,058†
Warsaw, Poland	1957	1,031
Brussels, Belgium............	1958 (est.)	1,000

*Metropolis—includes city and contiguous suburban areas.
†City proper only.

TABLE 9
Land Use

Country	Year	Total Area (million acres)	Percentage of Total Area			
			Arable Land	Meadows and Pastures	Forests	Other
Albania	1958	2.9	16.0	28.6	46.0	9.4
Austria	1957	20.7	21.1	27.6	37.3	14.0
Belgium	1957	7.6	32.4	23.9	19.4	24.3
Bulgaria	1956	27.4	38.4	2.3	33.0	26.3
Czechoslovakia	1957	31.6	42.2	15.2	34.0	8.6
Denmark	1957	10.6	64.2	8.6	10.2	17.0
Finland	1957	83.2	7.7	0.8	64.3	27.2
France	1957	136.1	38.7	24.0	20.9	16.4
East Germany	1957	26.6	48.0	11.9	27.2	12.9
West Germany	1957	61.2	35.1	22.9	28.6	13.4
Greece	1956	32.7	26.6	39.1	14.8	19.5
Hungary	1957	23.0	61.9	15.5	13.7	8.9
Iceland	1956	25.4	0.001	19.9	1.0	79.1
Ireland	1957	17.4	20.2	47.5	2.1	30.2
Italy	1957	74.4	52.4	17.0	19.2	11.4
Luxembourg	1957	0.6	30.1	23.9	33.2	12.8
Netherlands	1957	8.0	32.4	38.6	8.0	21.0
Norway	1957	80.0	2.6	0.6	23.2	73.6
Poland	1957	77.0	52.0	13.5	23.9	10.6
Portugal	1957	21.9	46.5	–	28.1	25.4
Rumania	1957	58.7	42.6	17.5	27.1	12.8
Spain	1957	124.6	40.8	2.6	47.2	9.4
Sweden	1957	111.1	8.2	1.5	50.0	40.3
Switzerland	1956	10.2	10.8	41.8	23.8	23.6
Turkey	1957	191.9	31.0	38.3	13.4	17.3
United Kingdom	1957	60.3	29.1	50.3	6.7	13.9
U.S.S.R.	1956	5,532.9	9.9	16.5	39.3	34.3
Yugoslavia	1957	63.2	32.4	25.9	34.9	6.8

Source: *Production Yearbook: 1958*, FAO, Rome, Italy, 1959, p. 3; and national statistics.

TABLE 10

Acreage, Production, and Yields of Major Crops

	ACREAGE (million acres)						
	Wheat	Rye	Barley	Oats	Maize	Potatoes	Sugar Beets
Eastern Europe							
1934–8	26.2	22.5	10.6	13.1	26.5	12.11	1.73
1957	20.1	18.9	7.9	9.4	21.3	12.4	2.9
Western Europe							
1934–8	20.3	8.6	6.9	19.0	1.0	9.9	2.0
1957	25.3	6.5	13.3	13.4	1.5	8.3	2.7
Mediterr. Europe							
1934–8	26.9	2.2	5.9	3.9	6.4	2.2	0.5
1957	27.7	2.3	5.2	3.6	5.7	2.2	0.8
	PRODUCTION (thousand metric tons)						
Eastern Europe							
1934–8	14.1	12.2	5.9	7.5	12.3	66.1	18.1
1957	16.3	11.7	5.9	5.8	17.2	67.7	28.3
Western Europe							
1934–8	15.2	6.1	5.6	14.0	0.7	58.1	24.3
1957	21.5	6.1	14.4	11.3	1.6	66.5	38.0
Mediterr. Europe							
1934–8	12.9	0.9	2.8	1.4	4.3	8.3	5.0
1957	15.9	0.8	2.5	1.4	4.9	8.9	8.3
	YIELDS (metric tons per acre)						
Eastern Europe							
1934–8	0.54	0.54	0.56	0.57	0.46	5.5	10.6
1957	0.81	0.62	0.75	0.62	0.81	5.5	9.8
Western Europe							
1934–8	0.75	0.71	0.81	0.74	0.71	5.9	12.2
1957	0.85	0.94	1.1	0.84	1.1	8.0	14.1
Mediterr. Europe							
1934–8	0.48	0.41	0.47	0.36	0.67	3.8	10.0
1957	0.57	0.35	0.48	0.39	0.86	4.0	10.4

Eastern Europe: Albania, Bulgaria, Hungary, Rumania, Yugoslavia, Czechoslovakia, Poland, East Germany.

Western Europe: Austria, Belgium, Denmark, France, West Germany, Ireland, Luxembourg, Netherlands, Norway, Sweden, Switzerland, United Kingdom, Finland.

Mediterranean Europe: Greece, Italy, Portugal, Spain.

Due to rounding, totals do not necessarily add.

Sources: Adapted from United Nations, Economic Bulletin for Europe, Vol. III, No. 2, 1951, p. 27. Based on: International Yearbook of Agricultural Statistics, IIA, Rome, Italy, and FAO Yearbook: 1958, Vol. XII; and national statistics.

TABLE 11

Eastern Europe: Cooperative Farming*

(per cent of total area)

Country	Total		Cooperatives‡		State Farms	
	1956	1959	1956	1959	1956	1959
Albania[†]	34	80	31	75[1]	3	5[1]
Bulgaria	77	96	77	93[2]	–	3[2]
Czechoslovakia	47	83[3]	30	63[3]	17	19[3]
East Germany..........	30	48[3]	23	40[3]	7	8[3]
Hungary...............	30	46[3]	20	40[3]	10	6[3]
Poland................	22	14[4]	9	1[4]	13	13[4]
Rumania	38	70[5]	13	NA	25	NA
Yugoslavia	9	9[6]	3	3[6]	6	6

NA—Not available.
*Yugoslavia included.
[†]Area related to arable land.
‡Includes collectives, special cooperatives, etc.
If not otherwise stated all figures are as of December of the respective year.
[1]October, 1958.   [4]June, 1958.
[2]August, 1958.   [5]June, 1959.
[3]June, 1959.   [6]December, 1958.

Sources: United Nations, *Economic Bulletin for Europe*, Vol. X, No. 3, 1958, p. 32;
United Nations, *Economic Bulletin for Europe*, Vol. XI, No. 3, 1959, p. 41; and *Statisticki Godisnjak FNRJ: 1959.*

TABLE 12

Production of Industrial Raw Materials (Selected Countries)

(All figures in thousand metric tons unless otherwise indicated.)

Country	Bauxite 1937	Bauxite 1957	Coal[1,6] 1937	Coal[1,6] 1957	Copper Ore 1937	Copper Ore 1957	Electric Energy[2] 1937	Electric Energy[2] 1957	Iron Ore 1937	Iron Ore 1957	Lead Ore 1937	Lead Ore 1957	Crude Petroleum[6] 1937	Crude Petroleum[6] 1957
Austria		22.3	0.2	0.2		2.4	2.9	12.5	0.6	1.1	8.7	6.0		3.2
Belgium			29.9	29.1			5.6	12.6	0.1	0.04		78.0		
Bulgaria	3[5]		0.1	0.4		7.0	0.2	2.7		0.2				0.3
Czechoslovakia			16.7	24.2	0.7		4.1	17.7	0.6	0.8	3.9	3.1	0.1	0.28
Finland					14.3	27.9	2.8	7.7			0.4			
France	691	1,684	44.4	56.8	0.6		20.1	57.4	11.5	18.7	4.6	10.8		1.4
Germany	93	5	171.1	153.6	30.4	26.9	49.0		2.5	4.7	78.9	71.1	0.5	
East Germany				2.7				32.7		0.4				
West Germany		5		134.4		25.8		91.8		4.3		71.1		3.9
Greece	137	833	0.9	2.3		1.1	0.2	1.7	0.1	0.2	8.5	3.0		
Hungary	533	917					1.1	5.5	0.1	0.1	0.5	2.0		0.7
Iceland								0.4						
Ireland			0.1	0.2			0.3	1.8						
Italy	387	261	1.3	1.02	1.0	0.4	15.4	42.7	0.5	0.8	35.0	54.7		1.3
Luxembourg							0.6	1.2	2.3	2.03				
Netherlands			14.3	11.4			3.5	13.4						1.5
Norway			0.8	0.4	20.7	15.3	9.0	25.8	0.6	1.0		0.9		
Poland			36.2	94.1		7.2	3.6	21.2		0.7	0.4	30.0	0.5	0.2
Portugal			0.3	0.5			0.4	2.4		0.03		1.5		
Rumania	11	61	0.3	0.2			1.1	5.4	0.1	0.2	7.4[4]	12.0	7.2	11.2
Saar[9]			13.4	16.5			3.3[3]							
Spain		8	6.9[3]	13.9	7.2	4.1	8.0	14.5		2.5	61.7[3]	65.2		
Sweden			0.5	0.3		18.0	6.8	29.0	6.9	11.9	9.3	36.5		
Switzerland								15.9		0.1				
Turkey			2.3	3.9	0.7[4]	24.4		2.1		0.7	7.6	2.9		0.3
United Kingdom			244.3	227.2	92.5		24.2	105.5	4.3	4.6	41.9[3]	7.1		0.2
U.S.S.R.	250	600[7]	100.0	496.0[10]	41.9	488.0	36.4	209.5	*	48.8		*	28.5	113.0[10]
Yugoslavia	354	888	0.4	1.2	33.5	33.5	0.9	6.3	0.3	0.9	65.9	90.1		0.4

*Not available.

[1] Anthracite and bituminous. Coal figures exclude lignite, the three major producers of which were:
East Germany .... 212,595,000 tons in 1957
West Germany .... 97,152,000 tons in 1957
Czechoslovakia .... 51,015,000 tons in 1957

[2] Figures in billion kwh.   [3] 1935.   [4] Smelter production.   [5] 1938.   [6] Million metric tons.   [7] 1950.   [8] 1954.   [9] Included in German Federal Republic since 1/1/1960.   [10] 1958.

Sources: United Nations, Statistical Yearbook: 1951, New York, 1952; United Nations, Monthly Bulletin of Statistics; Organization for European Economic Cooperation, General Statistics, July, 1952; United Nations, Quarterly Bulletin of Steel Statistics, No. 8, September, 1952; and national statistics.

TABLE 13

Industrial Production (Selected Commodities and Countries)

Country	Cotton Fabrics (thousand metric tons)		Nitrogen (not incl. industrial) (thousand metric tons)		Cement (million metric tons)		Crude Steel (million metric tons)		Aluminum (thousand metric tons)		Lumber (million cubic meters)	
	1937	1957	1938–9	1957–8	1937	1957	1937	1957	1937	1957	1937	1957
Austria	13	16.8	1.5[3]	157.1	0.4	2.120	0.7	2.509	4	72.8	1.9	4.098
Belgium	53	84.6	93.0[7]	260.4	3.0	4.700	3.9	6.276	1	2.2	0.5	0.625
Czechoslovakia	56	386.0[2]	24.5[1,8]	74.0	1.3	3.670	2.3	5.166		16.7	2.4	4.361
Denmark	5	5.4			0.7	1.160		0.262			0.8	0.605
Finland	9	14.0		21.9	0.4	0.940		0.204			6.4	3.924
France	159[1]	214.0	196.0	486.0	4.3	12.700	7.9	14.098	35	196.8	3.4	7.000
Germany	204[3]				14.0[1]		19.8		146		14.0	
East Germany	26[2]	205.0[5]	478.0			3.460		2.894	49[3]	30.0[10]		
West Germany	148[1,2]	287.0	354.0	1,060.0		19.250		24.507		243.5		6.944
Greece		83.0			0.3	1.250					0.4	0.303[1]
Hungary		208.0[5]			0.4	0.989	0.7	1.375	1	26.0	0.2	0.255
Ireland		13.6[5]			0.1[1]	0.452						0.035
Italy	90	117.0	109.0	425.0	4.3	11.860	2.1	6.787	23	90.0	2.1	1.676
Luxembourg					0.1	0.190	3.5	3.493			*	0.056
Netherlands			99.0	380.0	0.4	1.320	0.1	1.185			0.2	0.210
Norway	4	4.4	90.0	217.7	0.3	0.989		0.345	23	95.7	2.7	1.892
Poland	51	580.0[2]	51.0	200.6	1.3	4.496	1.5	5.304		20.8	4.6	7.043
Portugal	16[1]	33.0			0.3	0.979				10.0[10]	1.4	0.620
Rumania		188.0[5]			0.5	2.421	0.2	0.864			3.3	3.533
Saar						0.359	2.4	3.466				
Spain	20	48.7	4.0	54.1	0.6[1]	4.483	0.6[4]	1.345	1[4]	14.9	0.4	1.221
Sweden		24.2	8.0	36.2	0.9	2.450	1.1	2.511	2	13.6	6.6	7.325
Switzerland			10.0	12.0	0.6	2.511			25	31.0	0.6	1.035
Turkey	15	157.0[2]	1.0	1.2	0.2	1.260		0.176			*	0.492
United Kingdom	3,328	1,489.0[2]	123.0	346.0	7.4	12.154	13.2	22.047	19	128.4	0.5	1.104
U.S.S.R.[11]	2,612[2,4]	5,600.0[2]	*	2,100.0[9]	5.8[3]	28.908	17.7	51.200	45	440.0[10]	176.0	79.000
Yugoslavia	115[5,6]	207.0[5]	8.0	5.5	0.6	1.983	0.2	1.049	2[6]	18.1	2.8	1.745

*Data not available. [1]1938. [2]Millions of meters. [3]1936. [4]1935. [5]Millions of square meters. [6]1939. [7]Belgium and Luxembourg. [8]1937. [9]1955. [10]1956. [11]Estimate.

TABLE 14
Exports and Imports

Country	Exports (million dollars)			Imports (million dollars)		
	1938	1957	Per Capita 1957	1938	1957	Per Capita 1957
Austria............	171	979	141	263	1,128	163
Belgium-Luxembourg .	721	3,186	362	702	3,432	390
Bulgaria............	62	339[1]	44[1]	46	248[1]	33[1]
Czechoslovakia	338	1,356	110	262	1,385	113
Denmark............	335	1,174	261	307	1,359	302
Finland	181	822	205	163	889	222
France	863	5,065	118	1,198	6,110	143
Germany............	2,023	–	–	1,863	–	–
East Germany	–	1,811	105	–	1,615	94
West Germany	–	8,575	168	–	7,499	147
Greece	90	220	29	120	525	69
Hungary	147	497	53	116	665	72
Iceland.............	17	61	424	10	84	583
Ireland	118	368	127	183	517	178
Italy	549	2,540	54	519	3,626	77
Netherlands.........	579	3,097	282	732	4,105	373
Norway.............	193	822	242	262	1,274	375
Poland	223	982	35	231	1,251	45
Portugal............	59	288	32	95	502	56
Rumania............	160	395[1]	23[1]	125	352[1]	20[1]
Spain	101	476	16	130	862	29
Sweden.............	463	2,143	294	472	2,424	332
Switzerland	301	1,560	306	340	1,964	385
Turkey	122	345	14	121	397	16
United Kingdom	2,291	9,310	180	3,732	11,038	214
U.S.S.R.	365	4,381	21	328	3,938	19
Yugoslavia	130	395	22	124	661	37

[1]1956.

Source: United Nations, *Statistical Yearbook: 1958*, New York, 1958.

TABLE 15

Imports of Grains by Western European Countries

(million metric tons)

Exporting Area	Bread Grains[2]		Coarse Grains[3]		Total	
	1934–8	1957	1934–8	1957	1934–8	1957
U.S.S.R.	0.8	0.5	0.5	0.6	1.3	1.1
Other Eastern European Countries[1]	1.6	0.2	1.5	0.1	3.1	0.2
Total from Eastern Europe ..	2.4	0.5	2.0	0.7	4.4	1.2
Imports from all countries ...	12.1	12.8	11.1	9.4	23.2	22.3
Percentage share of Eastern Europe in total imports of Western Europe	20.0	4.0	18.0	7.7	19.0	5.6

[1] Including Yugoslavia, excluding Czechoslovakia.
[2] Wheat and rye, including flour in grain equivalent.
[3] Maize, barley, and oats.

Sources: United Nations, Economic Bulletin for Europe, Vol. III, No. 2, Geneva, 1951, p. 55; United Nations, Economic Bulletin for Europe, Vol. X, No. 2 (1958), p. 46.

TABLE 16
Imports of Selected Commodities from Eastern Europe into
10 Western European* Countries
(thousand metric tons)

Commodity	1938	1957
Coal	11,825	9,500
Of which: Sweden.............................	2,715	†
Austria..............................	1,864	1,700
Denmark.............................	295	542
Italy	2,198	339
France	1,724	1,813
Norway..............................	456	32
Timber (thousand cubic meters)....................	6,117	1,704
Of which: United Kingdom	2,786	522
West Germany	1,838	661
Belgium	343	165
Netherlands.........................	949	55
France	183	98
Steel..	214	–
Sugar	221	32
Meat	160	12 [1]
Of which: United Kingdom	41	0.99
West Germany	102	8.50
Eggs..	72	8.30
Of which: United Kingdom	42	1.70
West Germany	20	5.00

*Belgium, Luxembourg, France, the three western zones of Germany (for 1938, whole of prewar Germany), Italy, Netherlands, Norway, Sweden, Turkey, the United Kingdom.
†Not available.
[1]1955.

Sources: United Nations, Economic Bulletin for Europe, Vol. III, No. 2, Geneva, 1951, p. 54; United Nations, Economic Bulletin for Europe, Vol. X, No. 2, 1958; FAO, Trade Yearbook, 1958; OEEC, Statistical Bulletin, Individual Countries on Foreign Trade, Series IV, Paris, 1958.

TABLE 17
Railways

Country	Railway Lines (thousand miles) 1950	1957	Railway Tracks (thousand miles) 1950	1957	Line Miles per Square Mile 1950	1957	Passenger Miles (billion miles) 1950	1957	Freight Ton-Miles (billion miles) 1950	1957
Austria	3.8	4.1		7.1	0.12	0.12	2.7	3.7	3.4	5.0
Belgium	3.1	3.0	8.2	7.9	0.27	0.26	1.9	5.1	3.4	4.1
Bulgaria	2.0[7]	3.4[9]				0.08	1.6[2]	1.7[9]	0.8[2]	2.8[9]
Czechoslovakia	8.7[8]	8.3[9]			0.05	0.17	11.6[3]	14.9[9]	8.1[3]	24.5
Denmark		2.8	3.0	4.3	0.18[1]	0.17	2.1[3]	1.9[7]	0.7[3]	0.8
Finland		3.2		4.8		0.02	1.3	1.4[9]	2.1	2.7[9]
France	25.7	24.6	52.2	51.3	0.12	0.12	16.4	20.1	24.2	33.3
Germany										
West Germany	18.9	22.6[9]	43.8	47.1[9]	0.20	0.24	18.2	25.0	29.9	32.4[9]
East Germany		10.0	1.8			0.24		14.1		17.7
Greece	1.5	1.7[9]		1.9[9]	0.03	0.03	0.2[4]	0.6	0.1[3]	0.2[9]
Hungary	3.5	5.5[9]		8.2[9]	0.10	0.15	3.3[4]	5.6	2.0[4]	5.9
Ireland		2.2		3.4	0.08	0.08	0.3	*	0.3	0.3
Italy	9.8	13.7	17.1	21.7	0.24	0.12	13.8[3,4]	17.5	6.2	8.7
Luxembourg	0.2	0.2	0.6	0.5	0.16	0.24	0.1	0.2	1.9	0.4
Netherlands	2.0	2.0	4.3	4.4	0.02	0.16	3.8	4.7	0.9	2.1
Norway	2.8	2.7	3.1	3.4	0.12	0.02	0.9	1.0		0.6
Poland	14.5	17.3				0.14	16.4	23.7	19.9	34.3
Portugal		2.2[9]		2.9[9]	0.07[7]	0.06	0.9[3]	1.1[9]	0.4[3]	0.5[9]
Rumania	6.0						3.4[5]	8.3	2.4[5]	10.0
Spain		11.2[9]		14.4[9]	0.06	0.06	4.4	6.1	4.0	5.6
Sweden	10.3	10.0[9]	12.8	13.6[9]	0.11		4.1	3.9[9]	5.4	6.8[9]
Switzerland	1.8	3.2[9]	3.9	5.6[9]	0.02	0.20	4.0	4.5[9]	1.1[3]	2.2[9]
Turkey	4.5	4.8	5.1	5.6	0.21	0.02	1.3	3.1	1.6	3.1
United Kingdom	19.5	19.8	52.0	52.7	0.21	0.21	24.0	22.6	22.5	20.9
U.S.S.R.	75.1	75.1	70.0		0.01[1]	0.01		95.1	373.4	751.9
Yugoslavia	5.0[7]	7.3		10.0		0.07	5.0	5.0	6.2	7.3

*Not available.
[1] Track miles per square mile. [2] 1947. [3] 1949. [4] 1948. [5] 1946. [6] 1935. [7] 1938. [8] 1936. [9] 1956.

Sources: United Nations, *Annual Bulletin of Transport Statistics: 1947*, Geneva, 1958; United Nations, *Statistical Yearbook: 1958*, New York, 1958.

TABLE 18
Automobiles (Selected Countries)

Country	Passenger Automobiles (thousand)		Commercial Vehicles (thousand)		Miles of Road Network per Sq. Mi of Area, 1950
	1937	1957	1937	1957	
Austria	32.4	233.2	16.2	69.9	0.59
Belgium.................	144.0	539.0[1]	274.0	150.0[1]	4.89
Bulgaria	90.9	*	31.5	*	0.36
Czechoslovakia	90.9	*	31.5	*	1.52
Denmark	101.1	279.8	41.4	117.5	2.18
Finland.................	24.4	126.9	18.8	55.8	0.32
France.................	2,020.0[2]	3.9	285.0[2]	1,371.0	3.37
Germany	1,108.0		381.0		
West Germany	–	2,682.0	–	687.0	1.68
East Germany..........	–	*	–	*	0.67
Greece	8.7[2]	24.7[1]	8.6[2]	28.1[1]	0.36
Hungary................	25.9	*	36.4	*	0.50
Iceland................	0.8	11.9	1.1	5.9	0.14
Ireland................	48.8	140.2	11.1	45.3	1.89
Italy...................	271.0	1,238.0	82.1	405.0	1.06
Luxembourg	7.5	27.6	4.3	7.3	1.89
Netherlands	90.8	375.7	50.7	131.0	1.90
Norway	47.3	153.0	32.4	94.5	0.26
Poland[3]................	20.3	61.9	7.1	99.3	1.38
Portugal	30.7	105.8[1]	11.2	42.8[1]	0.52
Spain..................	*	152.6[1]	*	110.5[1]	0.39
Sweden	134.0	863.0	57.7	111.0	0.53
Switzerland.............	71.5	347.0	21.2	65.2	1.96
Turkey.................	3.8	33.4[1]	3.7	42.0[1]	0.11
United Kingdom.........	1,833.0	4,205.0	526.0	1,296.0	2.01
Yugoslavia..............	11.3	21.6	3.9	29.2	0.52

*Not available. [1]1956. [2]1939.

Sources: United Nations, *Statistical Yearbook: 1958*, New York, 1958; United Nations, *Annual Bulletin of Transport Statistics: 1957*, Geneva, 1958; and national statistics.

TABLE 19

Merchant Marine

Country	Merchant Marine (million gross tons)		International Sea-borne Shipping (million metric tons)			
			Loaded		Unloaded	
	1938	1957	1938	1957	1938	1957
Belgium............	0.4	0.579	11.3	15.50	15.0	25.40
Denmark	1.1	1.857	2.0	3.30	10.6	13.50
Finland	0.5	0.755	6.7	7.43	3.8	7.06
France.............	2.9	4.010	12.6	14.91	35.9	52.91
Germany	4.2		15.0		28.8	
East Germany.......				1.20		2.10
West Germany.......		3.887		14.14		44.34
Greece.............	1.9	1.472	0.7	1.96	2.6	4.50
Iceland		0.089				
Italy and Trieste	3.3	4.552	3.8[2]	9.79	20.1[2]	47.53
Netherlands	2.9	4.335	19.5	21.57	33.1	71.98
Norway	4.6	8.488				
Poland.............	0.1	0.324	13.2[2]	13.722*	3.1[2]	
Portugal	0.3	0.547	0.2[3]	2.37	0.7[3]	4.33
Spain..............	0.9	1.505	2.1	7.88[1]	2.4	8.30[1]
Sweden	1.6	3.048	12.0	17.41	12.2	20.48
Turkey.............	0.2	0.594		2.03		3.12
United Kingdom	17.7	19.857		33.60		104.10
U.S.S.R.	1.6	2.709				
Yugoslavia	0.4	0.374	1.5	1.70	0.6	3.69

*Figure indicates both loaded and unloaded.
[1]1956.
[2]Prewar boundaries.
[3]1940.

Sources: United Nations, *Statistical Yearbook: 1958*, New York, 1958; United Nations, *Annual Bulletin of Transport: 1957*, New York, 1958.

TABLE 20
Population of the Soviet Republics
(thousand)

	1939	1959
Russian S.F.S.R.	108,379	117,494
Western republics		
Ukrainian S.S.R......................	40,469	41,893
Belorussian S.S.R....................	8,910	8,060
Moldavian S.S.R.	2,452	2,880
Lithuanian S.S.R....................	2,880	2,713
Latvian S.S.R.	1,885	2,094
Estonian S.S.R.	1,052	1,196
Transcaucasia		
Georgian S.S.R.	3,540	4,049
Azerbaidzhan S.S.R.	3,205	3,700
Armenian S.S.R.....................	1,282	1,768
Central Asia		
Kazakh S.S.R.......................	6,094	9,301
Uzbek S.S.R........................	6,336	8,113
Kirghiz S.S.R.......................	1,458	2,063
Tadzhik S.S.R.	1,484	1,982
Turkmen S.S.R......................	1,252	1,520
U.S.S.R. total	190,678	208,826

TABLE 21
Population of Largest Soviet Cities
(thousand)

City	1939	1959
Moscow	4,183	5,032
Leningrad	3,105	2,888
With suburbs	3,385	3,300
Kiev	847	1,102
Baku	571	636
With suburbs	775	968
Gorky	644	942
Kharkov	833	930
Tashkent	550	911
Novosibirsk	404	887
Kuibyshev	390	806
Sverdlovsk	423	777
Stalino	466	701
Tbilisi	519	694
Chelyabinsk	273	688
Odessa	602	667
Dnepropetrovsk	527	658
Kazan	398	643
Perm	306	628
Riga	355	605
Rostov-on-Don	510	597
Stalingrad	445	591
Saratov	372	581
Omsk	289	579
Ufa	258	546
Minsk	237	509
Yerevan	204	509

TABLE 22
Soviet Grain Production (Barn Crop)

Year	Million Metric Tons
1950	82
1951	79
1952	92
1953	82
1954	86
1955	107
1956	128
1957	105
1958	139

TABLE 23
Soviet Livestock Holdings
(million head)

Year	Census Date	All Cattle	Cows Only	Hogs	Sheep
1928	Jan. 1	66.8	33.2	27.7	104.2
1933	Jan. 1	33.5	19.0 (1934)	9.9	36.5* (1934)
1950	Jan. 1	58.1	24.6	22.2	93.6*
1951	Jan. 1	57.1	24.3	24.4	82.6
1952	Jan. 1	58.8	24.9	27.1	107.6*
1953	Jan. 1	56.6	24.3	28.5	94.3
1953	*Oct. 1*	*63.0*	*26.0*	*47.6*	*114.9*
1954	Jan. 1	55.8	25.2	33.3	99.8
1954	*Oct. 1*	*64.9*	*27.5*	*51.1*	*117.5*
1955	*Oct. 1*	*67.1*	*29.2*	*52.2*	*125.0*
1956	*Oct. 1*	*70.4*	*30.9*	*56.5*	*129.9*
1957	Jan. 1	61.5	29.0	40.8	108.0
1958	Jan. 1	66.8	31.4	44.3	120.2
1959	Jan. 1	70.8	33.3	48.5	129.6

Notes: The year 1928 marked the precollectivization peak in livestock holdings, and the years 1933 and 1934 the postcollectivization low after peasants had slaughtered animals rather than give them up to collective ownership.

During the period 1953–6, the livestock census was taken on Oct. 1, before the heavy slaughtering season in the fall. The Oct. 1 figures (in italics) for these years are therefore considerably higher than those of Jan. 1 following the slaughter season. In 1957, the Jan. 1 census date was resumed.

In the sheep column, figures marked (*) refer to both sheep and goats. Goats make up about 10 per cent of the total.

TABLE 24

Soviet Production of Animal Products

Product	1950	1951	1952	1953	1954	1955	1956	1957	1958	1965 Plan
Meat and animal fats (million metric tons)										
Live weight...................	8.1			9.4			10.7			
Carcass weight................	4.9	4.7	5.2	5.8	6.3	6.4	6.6	7.4	7.9	16
Commercial meat (excl. farm slaughter) (million metric tons).........	1.56	1.72	1.97	2.21	2.46	2.52	2.66	3.1	3.4	
Milk (million metric tons)......	35.3	36.0	35.7	36.5	38.1	43.1	49.1	54.7	57.8	100–105
Wool (thousand metric tons)....	180	193	220	235	230	256	261	289	321	548
Eggs (billion).................	11.7	13.2	14.4	16.1	17.2	18.5	19.5	22.3	23.5	37

TABLE 25

Soviet Coal Production, by Major Fields

(million metric tons)

	1913	1928	1940	1950	1955	1958
Donets Basin..........	25.3	27.3	94.3	94.6	140.9	180
Kuznetsk Basin........	0.8	2.6	22.5	38.5	58.5	72
Karaganda............	–	–	6.3	16.4	24.7	25
Moscow Basin.........	0.3	1.1	10.1	30.9	39.5	40
Vorkuta..............	–	–	0.3	8.7	14.2	17
Urals................	1.2	2.0	12.0	32.5	47.1	60
U.S.S.R. total........	29.1	35.5	165.9	261.1	391.3	496

TABLE 26
Soviet Crude-Oil Production, by Major Fields
(million metric tons)

	1940	1950	1955	1958	1965 Plan
Tatar......................	–	0.9	13	28	65
Bashkir....................	1.5	5.8	15	23	50
Kuibyshev..................	0.2	3.5	7	16	40
Baku	22.2	14.8	15	16	22
U.S.S.R. total..............	31.1	37.9	71	113	230–240

TABLE 27
Soviet Thermal-Power-Station Fuels
(per cent of standard fuel)

	1958	1965 Plan
Coal	69.9	61.3
Fuel oil	5.9	12.3
Gas..................................	10.7	17.2
Peat	8.1	5.7
Oil shale	0.9	1.2
Others	4.5	2.3
Total	100.0	100.0

TABLE 28
Soviet Electric-Power Capacity and Output

	1940		1950		1958		1965 Plan	
	Cap.	Out.	Cap.	Out.	Cap.	Out.	Cap.	Out.
Thermal	9.6	43	16.4	78	40	183	90	410
Hydroelectric	1.6	5	3.2	13	12	50	22	90
Total	11.2	48	19.6	91	52	233	112	500

Cap.: Installed capacity in million kw.
Out.: Power output in billion kwh.

TABLE 29
Soviet Dressed (Concentrated) Iron-Ore Production
(million metric tons)

Region	1940	1955	1957	1965 Plan
Ukraine	20	40	47	80
Kursk Anomaly	–	–	0.3	11
Urals	8	25	28	40
Kazakhstan	–	0.2	1	8
Siberia	0.5	4	4	14
Others	1	3	4	7
U.S.S.R. total	30	72	84	160

TABLE 30
Soviet Steel Production
(million metric tons)

Region	1940	1955	1957	1965 Plan
European U.S.S.R.	12.5	24.0	27.5	48
Of which:				
Ukraine	8.9	16.9	19.6	32
Rustavi (Georgia)	–	0.6	0.8	1.2
Urals	3.9	16.4⎫	23.7	42
Asian U.S.S.R.	1.9	4.9⎭		
Of which:				
Siberia	1.9	4.5		
Kazakhstan	–	0.2	0.3	3
U.S.S.R. total	18.3	45.3	51.2	90

TABLE 31
Soviet Trade

By Major Commodity Categories

Category	1938		1958	
	Imports (%)	Exports (%)	Imports (%)	Exports (%)
Machinery	34.5	5.0	24.5	18.5
Metals	25.4	1.6	8.7	16.4
Ores............................	2.7	2.2	9.3	4.4
Fuels	1.2	8.8	4.8	15.2
Wood products....................	*	20.3	2.4	5.6
Textile fibers	9.7	4.2	7.1	6.8
Furs	–	9.4	–	1.1
Grain exports and food imports	12.7	21.3	14.9	8.3
Consumer goods	1.0	7.9	14.4	3.6
Others	12.8	19.3	14.9	20.1

By Major Countries

Country	1950 (per cent of total)		1958 (per cent of total)	
Communist bloc	80.8		74.0	
China		17.7		17.3
Poland		13.9		7.3
Czechoslovakia		13.0		11.0
East Germany		10.6		18.4
Rumania...........		7.8		5.5
Hungary		6.5		4.1
Bulgaria...........		5.1		4.6
Others		6.2		5.8
Non-Communist.......	19.2		26.0	
Britain		4.4		2.5
Finland		1.7		2.9
United States		1.7		0.3
Egypt		1.5		2.2
India..............		0.2		2.1
France		0.2		1.9
West Germany		0.0		1.6
Others		9.5		12.5

*Not available.
Note: Among commodities, contrast between 1938 and 1958 is most meaningful. Among trade partners, however, prewar and postwar countries cannot be compared, because of political shifts. Therefore, 1950 and 1958 have been selected for the country table. Because there is no significant difference between exports and imports in the country breakdown, they have been combined.

Index